NOBEL PRIZE LIBRARY

MAURIAC

F. MISTRAL

MOMMSEN

Nobel Prize Library

PUBLISHED UNDER THE SPONSORSHIP OF THE
NOBEL FOUNDATION & THE SWEDISH ACADEMY

François Mauriac

Frédéric Mistral

Theodor Mommsen

ALEXIS GREGORY, *New York*, AND
CRM PUBLISHING, *Del Mar, California*

CONTENTS

———

François Mauriac

1952

"For the deep spiritual insight and

the artistic intensity with which

he has in his novels penetrated

the drama of human life"

Illustrated by M. A. RACK-WILSER

PRESENTATION ADDRESS

By ANDERS ÖSTERLING

PERMANENT SECRETARY
OF THE SWEDISH ACADEMY

———————

THE STUDENT of François Mauriac's works will be struck from the very
first by the insistence with which Mauriac devotes himself to describing
a precise milieu, a corner of land one can point to on a map of France.
The action of his novels nearly always unfolds in the Gironde, the Bordeaux region, that old vine-growing country where chateaux and small
farms have taken possession of the earth, or in the Landes, the country
of pine trees and sheep pastures where the song of the cicadas vibrates in
the lonely spaces, and where the Atlantic sounds its far-off thunder. This
is Mauriac's native country. He considers it his calling to describe this
singular region and its people, especially those who own the land; and it
can be said that his personal style partakes of the restrained energy which
twists the branches of the grape vines and of the pitiless clarity of the
light which falls from a torrid sky. In that sense, this writer, who is read
the world over, is undeniably and markedly a man of the province, but
his provincialism does not exclude the great human problems of universal
scope. If one wants to dig deep one must first and always have a ground
to thrust one's pick into.

Mauriac had a more than usually restricted childhood: he grew up in
the shelter of a milieu in which the maternal influence made itself strongly
felt, an influence which did not cease to act on his adolescent sensitivity.
There is reason to believe that he had painful surprises later when he
made contact with the outside world. Guided until then by pious advice,
he had not suspected that evil dominated reality to such an extent as it
appears in all the monotony and indifference of everyday life. Catholic
by birth, brought up in a Catholic atmosphere which became his spiritual
country, he has, in short, never had to decide for or against the Church.

[3]

But he has on several occasions re-examined and publicly specified his Christian position, above all in order to question whether the demands a realist's position made on the writer could be reconciled with the commandments and prohibitions of the Church. Apart from these inevitable and insoluble antinomies, Mauriac, as a writer, uses the novel to expound a particular aspect of human life in which Catholic thought and sensitivity are at the same time background and keystone. Hence his non-Catholic readers may to a certain extent feel that they are looking at a world foreign to them; but to understand Mauriac, one must remember the one fact without which no account of him can be complete: he does not belong to the group of writers who are converts. He himself is conscious of the force that gives him those roots which permit him to cite a great and stern tradition when he probes souls overwhelmed by the weight of their faults and scrutinizes their secret intentions.

Mauriac has been assured a central position in modern literature for so long and so unquestionably that the denominational barriers have almost lost all importance. Whereas many writers of his generation who had a fleeting glory are almost forgotten today, his profile stands out more and more distinctly with the years. In his case it is not a question of fame achieved at the price of compromise, for his somber and austere vision of the world is scarcely made to please his contemporaries. He has always aimed high. With all the power and all the consistency of which he is capable, he has tried to continue in his realistic novels the tradition of such great French moralists as Pascal, La Bruyère, and Bossuet. To this let us add that he represents a tendency toward religious inspiration which, particularly in France, has always been an extremely important element of spiritual formation. If I may in this context say a few words about Mauriac as a distinguished journalist, we must not forget, in the interest of European thought, his work in that field, his commentaries on daily events, the entire side of his literary activity which deserves public esteem.

But if he is today the laureate of the Nobel Prize for Literature, it is obviously above all because of his admirable novels. Suffice it to name a few masterpieces—such as *Le Désert de l'amour* (*The Desert of Love*, 1925), *Thérèse Desqueyroux* (*Thérèse*, 1927), and its sequel *La Fin de la nuit* (*The End of the Night*, 1935), *La Pharisienne* (*A Woman of the Pharisees*, 1941), and *Le Noeud de vipères* (*The Knot of Vipers*, 1932) —without intending to say how far the artistic qualities of these works place them in a class apart. For everywhere, in the whole series of Mauriac's novels, are found unforgettable scenes, dialogues, and situations, so mysteriously and so cruelly revealing. The repetition of the same themes could create a certain monotony, but his acute analyses and sure touch awaken the same admiration with each new encounter. Mauriac remains unequaled in conciseness and expressive force of language; his prose can in a few suggestive lines shed light on the most complex and difficult things. His most remarkable works are characterized by a purity of logic and classic economy of expression that recall the tragedies of Racine.

The voiceless anxiety of youth, the abysses of evil and the perpetual menace of their presence, the deceitful temptations of the flesh, the ascendancy of avarice in the life of material goods, the havoc of self-satisfaction and pharisaism—these are the motifs that constantly reappear under Mauriac's pen. Small wonder that in his wielding of such a palette, he has been accused of blackening his subjects without cause, of writing as a misanthrope. But the response he gives is that, on the contrary, a writer who bases his whole concept of the world on grace and sees man's supreme recourse in God's love has the feeling of working in a spirit of hope and confidence. We have no right to doubt the sincerity of this declaration, but it is evident that in practice sin attracts him more than innocence. He detests what is edifying, and while he never grows tired of portraying the soul that persists in evil and is on its way to damnation, he generally prefers to bring down the curtain at the moment when the consciousness of its misery is about to push the soul toward repentance and salvation. This writer limits himself to the role of witness to the negative phase of this evolution, leaving all the positive side to the priest, who does not have to write a novel.

Mauriac himself once said that everyone is free to seek satisfaction in a literature that beautifies life and permits us to escape from reality, but the predilection which most people have for this kind of literature should not make us unjust toward the writers whose vocation is to know man. It is not we who hate life. Those alone hate life who, not being able to bear the sight of it, falsify it. The true lovers of life love it as it is. They have stripped it of its masks, one by one, and have given their hearts to this monster at last laid bare. In one of his controversies with André Gide, he returned to the cardinal point of his thought in affirming that the most complete sincerity is the form of honor which is linked to the writer's craft. Most often Tartuffe is made to appear under the ecclesiastical costume, but Mauriac assures us that this personage is found much more frequently in the midst of those supporting the theory of materialistic progress. It is easy to deride the principles of morality, but Mauriac objects to such derision; as he has stated quite simply, "Each of us knows he could become less evil than he is."

This simple phrase is perhaps the key that opens the secret of good in the chapters of Mauriac's work, the secret of their somber ardor and their subtle disharmony. His plunges into the midst of man's weaknesses and vices are more than the effect of a mania pushed to virtuosity. Even when he analyzes reality without pity, Mauriac preserves a last certainty that there is a charity which passes understanding. He does not lay claim to the absolute; he knows that it does not exist with virtue in the pure state, and he views without indulgence those who call themselves pious. Faithful to the truth which he has made his, he strives to describe his characters in such a way that, seeing themselves as they are, they would be stricken with repentance and the desire to become, if not better, at least a little less evil. His novels can be compared to narrow but deep wells at the bottom of which a mysterious water is seen glistening in the darkness.

Dear Sir and colleague—In the few moments at my disposal I could speak about your work only in a sketchy manner. I know how much it deserves admiration; I also know how difficult it is to do it justice, to make general statements without ignoring the specific characteristics of your work. The Swedish Academy has awarded you this year's Nobel Prize for Literature "for the deep spiritual insight and the artistic intensity with which you have in your novels penetrated the drama of human life."

There remains for me to extend to you the most heartfelt congratulations of the Swedish Academy, this younger sister of your venerable *Académie Française,* and to ask you to receive the Prize from the hands of His Majesty the King.

ACCEPTANCE SPEECH

By FRANÇOIS MAURIAC

THE LAST SUBJECT to be touched upon by the man of letters whom you are honoring, I think, is himself and his work. But how could I turn my thoughts away from that work and that man, from those poor stories and that simple French writer, who by the grace of the Swedish Academy finds himself all of a sudden burdened and almost overwhelmed by such an excess of honor? No, I do not think that it is vanity which makes me review the long road that has led me from an obscure childhood to the place I occupy tonight in your midst.

When I began to describe it, I never imagined that this little world of the past which survives in my books, this corner of provincial France hardly known by the French themselves, where I spent my school holidays, could capture the interest of foreign readers. We always believe in our uniqueness; we forget that the books which enchanted us, the novels of George Eliot or Dickens, of Tolstoy or Dostoevsky, or of Selma Lagerlöf, described countries very different from ours, human beings of another race and another religion. But nonetheless we loved them only because we recognized ourselves in them. The whole of mankind is revealed in the peasant of our birthplace, every countryside of the world in the horizon seen through the eyes of our childhood. The novelist's gift consists precisely in his ability to reveal the universality of this narrow world into which we are born, where we have learned to love and to suffer. To many of my readers in France and abroad my world has appeared somber. Shall I say that this has always surprised me? Mortals, because they are mortal, fear the very name of death; and those who have never loved or been loved, or have been abandoned and betrayed or have vainly pursued a being inaccessible to them without as much as a look for the creature that pursued them and which they did not love—all these are astonished and scandalized when a work of fiction describes the loneliness in the very heart of love. "Tell us pleasant things," said the Jews to the prophet Isaiah. "Deceive us by agreeable falsehoods."

[7]

Yes, the reader demands that we deceive him by agreeable falsehoods. Nonetheless, those works that have survived in the memory of mankind are those that have embraced the human drama in its entirety and have not shied away from the evidence of the incurable solitude in which each of us must face his destiny until death, that final solitude, because finally we must die alone.

This is the world of a novelist without hope. This is the world into which we are led by your great Strindberg. This would have been my world were it not for that immense hope by which I have been possessed practically since I awoke to conscious life. It pierces with a ray of light the darkness that I have described. My color is black and I am judged by that black rather than by the light that penetrates it and secretly burns there. Whenever a woman in France tries to poison her husband or to strangle her lover, people tell me: "Here is a subject for you." They think that I keep some sort of museum of horrors, that I specialize in monsters. And yet, my characters differ in an essential point from almost any others that live in the novels of our time: they feel that they have a soul. In this post-Nietzschean Europe where the echo of Zarathustra's cry "God is dead" is still heard and has not yet exhausted its terrifying consequences, my characters do not perhaps all believe that God is alive, but all of them have a conscience which knows that part of their being recognizes evil and could not commit it. They know evil. They all feel dimly that they are the creatures of their deeds and have echoes in other destinies.

For my heroes, wretched as they may be, life is the experience of infinite motion, of an indefinite transcendence of themselves. A humanity which does not doubt that life has a direction and a goal cannot be a humanity in despair. The despair of modern man is born out of the absurdity of the world; out of his despair as well as his submission to surrogate myths: the absurd delivers man to the inhuman. When Nietzsche announced the death of God, he also announced the times we have lived through and those we shall still have to live through, in which man, emptied of his soul and hence deprived of a personal destiny, becomes a beast of burden more maltreated than a mere animal by the Nazis and by all those who today use Nazi methods. A horse, a mule, a cow has a market value, but from the human animal, procured without cost thanks to a well-organized and systematic purge, one gains nothing but profit until it perishes. No writer who keeps in the center of his work the human creature made in the image of the Father, redeemed by the Son, and illuminated by the

Spirit, can in my opinion be considered a master of despair, be his picture ever so somber.

For his picture does remain somber, since for him the nature of man is wounded, if not corrupted. It goes without saying that human history as told by a Christian novelist cannot be based on the idyll because he must not shy away from the mystery of evil.

But to be obsessed by evil is also to be obsessed by purity and childhood. It makes me sad that the too hasty critics and readers have not realized the place which the child occupies in my stories. A child dreams at the heart of all my books; they contain the loves of children, first kisses and first solitude, all the things that I have cherished in the music of Mozart. The serpents in my books have been noticed, but not the doves that have made their nests in more than one chapter; for in my books childhood is the lost paradise, and it introduces the mystery of evil.

The mystery of evil—there are no two ways of approaching it. We must either deny evil or we must accept it as it appears both within ourselves and without—in our individual lives, that of our passions, as well as in the history written with the blood of men by power-hungry empires. I have always believed that there is a close correspondence between individual and collective crimes, and, journalist that I am, I do nothing but decipher from day to day in the horror of political history the visible consequences of that invisible history which takes place in the obscurity of the heart. We pay dearly for the evidence that evil is evil, we who live under a sky where the smoke of crematories is still drifting. We have seen them devour under our own eyes millions of innocents, even children. And history continues in the same manner. The system of concentration camps has struck deep roots in old countries where Christ has been loved, adored, and served for centuries. We are watching with horror how that part of the world in which man is still enjoying his human rights, where the human mind remains free, is shrinking under our eyes like the *peau de chagrin* of Balzac's novel.

Do not for a moment imagine that as a believer I pretend not to see the objections raised to belief by the presence of evil on earth. For a Christian, evil remains the most anguishing of mysteries. The man who amidst the crimes of history perseveres in his faith will stumble over the permanent scandal: the apparent uselessness of the Redemption. The well-reasoned explanations of the theologians regarding the presence of evil have never convinced me, reasonable as they may be, and precisely because they are reasonable. The answer that eludes us presupposes an order not of reason but of charity. It is an answer that is fully found in the affirmation of St. John: God is Love. Nothing is impossible to the living love, not even drawing everything to itself; and that, too, is written.

Forgive me for raising a problem that for generations has caused many commentaries, disputes, heresies, persecutions, and martyrdoms. But it is after all a novelist who is talking to you, and one whom you have preferred to all others; thus you must attach some value to what has been his inspiration. He bears witness that what he has written about in the light of his faith and hope has not contradicted the experience of those of his readers who share neither his hope nor his faith. To take another example, we see that the agnostic admirers of Graham Greene are not put off by his Christian vision. Chesterton has said that whenever something extraordinary happens in Christianity ultimately something extraordinary corresponds to it in reality. If we ponder this thought, we shall perhaps discover the reason for the mysterious accord between works of Catholic inspiration, like those of my friend Graham Greene, and the vast dechristianized public that devours his books and loves his films.

Yes, a vast dechristianized public! According to André Malraux, "the revolution today plays the role that belonged formerly to the eternal life." But what if the myth were, precisely, the revolution? And if the eternal life were the only reality?

Whatever the answer, we shall agree on one point: that dechristianized humanity remains a crucified humanity. What worldly power will ever destroy the correlation of the cross with human suffering? Even your Strindberg, who descended into the extreme depths of the abyss from which the psalmist uttered his cry, even Strindberg himself wished that a single word be engraved upon his tomb, the word that by itself would suffice to shake and force the gates of eternity: *"o crux ave spes unica."* After so much suffering even he is resting in the protection of that hope, in the shadow of that love. And it is in his name that your laureate asks you to forgive these all too personal words which perhaps have struck too grave a note. But could he do better, in exchange for the honors with which you have overwhelmed him, than to open to you not only his heart, but his soul? And because he has told you through his characters the secret of his torment, he should also introduce you tonight to the secret of his peace.

THE DESERT OF LOVE

By FRANÇOIS MAURIAC

Translated by Gerard Hopkins

❖ I ❖

For years Raymond Courrèges had been cherishing the hope that one day he might run across Maria Cross, the woman on whom he had so ardently longed to be revenged. Often in the street he would follow some chance passer-by, thinking to have found her. But in the course of time the edge of his resentment had become blunted, so that when, at length, they did come face to face, he felt, at first, none of that joy shot with fury which such a meeting should have stirred in him.

It was only ten o'clock when he entered the bar in the rue Duphot. The coloured jazz-band was playing softly for the delectation of a solitary waiter. Over the tiny floor which, when midnight came, would be crammed with dancing couples, a ventilating fan was making a noise like a gigantic bluebottle. To the doorman, who said, with a look of surprise, "Don't often see you here as early as this, sir," he replied with no more than a wave of the hand, which conveyed a wish that something should be done to stop this intrusive bumbling. The man did his best to explain, confidentially, but without success, that the new system "absorbed the smoke without causing a draft." Courrèges gave him such a look that he beat a hasty retreat to the cloak-room. Up in the ceiling the ventilator

droned to silence, as though a bee had suddenly alighted.

The young man sat down at one of the tables, thus breaking the immaculate vista of white cloths. A glance in a mirror showed him that he was not looking his best. What's the matter with me? he wondered. God! How he hated a wasted evening—and all because of that swine Eddy H——. He had had to dig the fellow out and almost drag him to a restaurant. During dinner Eddy had scarcely listened to what he was saying, and had excused his inattention on the ground of a sick headache. He had sat perched on the very edge of his chair, impatience in every line of his body, obviously preoccupied with the thought of some happiness to come. No sooner had he finished his coffee than he had taken eagerly to his heels—eyes shining, ears flushed, and nostrils flaring. Raymond had spent the day in delighted anticipation of their dinner and of the evening that was to follow it. But, no doubt, Eddy had in prospect pleasures more stimulating than any offered by a mere exchange of confidences.

Courrèges was amazed to find that he felt not only disappointed and humiliated, but also sad. The discovery that the companionship of a friend to whom he attached no particular importance could show as thus precious to him came as a shock. It was something entirely new in his life. Up to the age of thirty, being quite incapable of the selflessness demanded by true friendship, and devoting much of his attention to women, he had disregarded everything that was not an object to be possessed, and, like a greedy child, would have said, had he put the feeling into words, "I like only what I can eat." At that period of his life he made use of his cronies either as witnesses of his conquests or as recipients of his confidences. He looked on a friend as, first and foremost, a pair of ears. He liked, too, the feeling that he could dominate them and control their actions. Influencing others had become a passion with him. He flattered himself that he had reduced the demoralizing of his companions to a fine art.

Raymond Courrèges could have built up a big career for himself, as his grandfather the surgeon had done; his uncle, the Jesuit, and his father, the doctor, if only he had been capable of harnessing his appetites to work, if only his natural tastes had not led him to concentrate all his energies on the achievement of immediate satisfaction. But by now he was reaching the age at which only those who address themselves to the soul can set their dominance on a firm foundation. The best that Courrèges could do for his disciples was to assure them a quick yield in terms of pleasure. But the younger men of his acquaintance preferred to share their adventures with others of their own age, and his circle was growing thin. In the preserves of love there is no shortage of game, but we soon find that the little group of those in whose company we set out grows smaller year by year. Those who had survived the dark violence of the war had either dwindled into husbands or had their natures distorted by the pursuit of a calling. He noted their graying hair, their protuberant bellies, their bald pates, and hated them because

they were the same age as himself. He accused them of having murdered their youth, of having betrayed it even before it had fled from them.

It was a matter of pride with him to be taken for a "post-war product"; and this evening, in the still empty bar, where the only sound was the muted thrumming of a mandolin (the flame of the melody rising, falling, flickering), he studied with fierce attention the image thrown back at him from the mirrors, the image of a face with a thatch of vigorous hair on which his thirty-five years had not yet set their mark. It came to him, as he pondered, that age would lay hands upon his life long before it touched his body. If it bolstered up his self-esteem to hear women say among themselves—"Who's that tall young man?"—he knew that the keener eyed twenty-year-olds no longer thought of him as forming one in their ephemeral group. Maybe Eddy had had something better to do than talk about himself to an accompaniment of wailing saxophones; on the other hand, he might be doing just that at this very moment in some other bar, laying bare his heart to some youth born in 1904, who would constantly interrupt the flow of his talk with "me, too," and "that's just what I feel. . . ."

A number of young men began to drift in. They had assumed expressions of self-conscious arrogance preparatory to crossing the floor, and were now, at sight of the empty room, visibly embarrassed. They gathered in a little cluster round the bar. But Courrèges had made it a rule never to let himself suffer because of the behaviour of others—whether mistresses or friends. True, therefore, to this principle, he set himself to stress the lack of proportion existing between the insignificance of Eddy H—— and the feeling of uneasy restlessness which was the legacy left behind after that young man's defection. . . . He was pleased to find that this weed of sentiment, when he tried to pull it out, came away without any diffi-culty. He wound himself up to the pitch of thinking how little it would mean to him, next day, to show his friend the door. He even contemplated without con-cern the possibility that he might never set eyes on him again. It was almost with a sense of gaiety that he thought, I'll wash my hands of him once and for all. He sighed with relief, only to find that a sense of unease remained which had nothing whatever to do with Eddy. . . . Ah, yes, of course, that letter! He could feel it in the pocket of his evening-jacket. No point in reading it again. Dr. Cour-règes, in communicating with his son, made use of a telegraphic brevity of ex-pression which was easily remembered:

Staying at Grand Hotel duration Medi-cal Congress. Available mornings before nine, evenings after eleven.

> Your father,
> PAUL COURRÈGES

"Not if I know it!" he murmured, un-aware that his face had taken on an ex-pression of defiance. He held it against this father of his that it was less easy to despise him than the other members of the family. On reaching the age of thirty, Raymond had demanded a lump sum down comparable to what his sister had received on her marriage. But in vain. Faced by the parental refusal, he had burned his bridges and taken himself off. But it was Madame Courrèges who held the purse-strings, and he knew perfectly well that his father would have acted gen-erously by him had he been in a legal po-sition to do so, and that money meant nothing to the old man. "Not if I know it!" he said to himself once more, but could not, for all that, help catching the note of appeal which sounded in the dry little message. He was far less blind than was Madame Courrèges, who felt only irritation at her husband's undemonstra-tive nature and brusque manner. "He may be a good man, and he may have a heart of gold," she was fond of saying, "but what good is that to me if I never get a glimpse of it? Just think what he would be like if he was *bad!*"

Just because it was so difficult to hate his father, Raymond found these claims upon his affection hard to endure. He wasn't going to answer the letter. All the same. . . . Later, when he thought back to the circumstances of this evening, he remembered the bitterness of his mood when he entered the deserted little bar, but forgot what had caused it—the defec-tion of a friend called Eddy, and his fa-ther's presence in Paris. He believed that his sour ill-temper had been born of a presentiment, and that a connexion ex-isted between the state of his emotions, on that occasion, and the event which was fast approaching. He always later maintained that neither Eddy nor the doctor was, in himself, capable of getting him worked up like that, but that, from the very moment he had settled down with a cocktail, some inner voice, some clamour of the flesh, had warned him of the imminent appearance of the woman who, at that same moment, in a taxi which had already reached the corner of the rue Duphot, was rummaging in her little bag, and saying to her companion:

"What a bore! I've forgotten my lip-stick!"

To which the man replied, "There'll probably be one in the ladies' room."

"What a mad idea! one might catch . . ."

"Well then, get Gladys to lend you hers."

She came into the bar. A cloche hat completely obliterated the top part of her face, leaving visible only her chin, that feature on which time sets the sign-manual of age. Forty years had, here and there, touched this lower segment of her countenance, drawing the skin tight and sketching a hint of sagging flesh. Her body beneath its furs must, one felt, be shrunken. As blind as a bull brought suddenly from its dark pen into the glare of the arena, she stopped short on the threshold of the glittering room. When her companion, who had been delayed by a dispute over the fare, rejoined her, Courrèges, though not at once recognizing him, said to himself: "I've seen that fellow somewhere—bet he comes from Bordeaux"; and then, suddenly, as he looked at the face of the man of fifty, swollen, as it were, by the sense of its own identity, a name formed itself on his lips: Victor Larousselle. . . . With beating heart he resumed his examination of the woman who, quickly realizing that no one else was wearing a hat, had taken off hers, and was shaking out her freshly cropped hair in front of a mirror. He saw, first of all, a pair of eyes that were large and calm: next, a wide forehead, its limits sharply marked by the seven youthful points of her dark hair. All that remained of the legacy of youth seemed concentrated in the upper part of her face. Raymond recognized her in spite of the short hair, the middle-aged "spread," and nature's slow work of destruction, which, beginning at the neck, was busy invading the areas of mouth and cheeks. He recognized her as he would have a road familiar to him in childhood, even though the oaks once shading it had been cut down. He calculated the lapse of time. The sum took him a bare two seconds. She's forty-four, he thought; I was eighteen and she was twenty-seven. Like all those who confound the ideas of happiness and youth, he had a consciousness of the passage of time which was ever active, strive though he might to keep it muffled. His eye was forever measuring the sundering gulf of the dead years. He at once inserted in life's chronology every human being who had played a part in his exist-

ence. No sooner did he see a face than he could supply a date.

Will she recognize me? he wondered. But would she have so sharply turned away if she had not already done so? She went up to her companion and seemed to be begging him not to stay, for he replied very loudly, and in the tone of a man who craves an admiring audience, "What nonsense! it's not a bit gloomy. In a quarter of an hour it'll be as tight-packed as an egg with meat!" He pushed out a table not far from the one at which Raymond was leaning on his elbow, and sat down heavily. The blood had rushed to his face, sure sign of hardening arteries. But apart from that its expression was one of unruffled satisfaction. The woman was still standing motionless. "What are you waiting for?" he asked. Gone, suddenly, from the eyes, from the coarse and purplish lips, was all look of pleasure. In what he thought was a low voice, he said: "It's enough for me to like being here for you to start sulking—of course!" She must have told him to be careful, have warned him that he could be overheard, for his next words were almost shouted: "So I don't know how to behave, don't I? What does it matter if they *do* hear?"

Seated not far from Raymond, the woman seemed to have recovered her composure. In order to see her the young man would have had to lean forward. It was for her now to avoid his eyes. He realized her renewed sense of security, and was made suddenly aware, with a quick feeling of terror, that the opportunity which, for the last seventeen years, he had so eagerly desired might slip through his fingers. He thought that he was still, after all that time, determined to humiliate the woman who had so deeply humiliated him, to show her what manner of man he was—the sort that doesn't let a bitch get the better of him without hitting back. For years he had found pleasure in thinking what would happen when fate at last should bring them face to face, how he would skilfully contrive matters so as to ride rough-shod over, and reduce to tears, the woman in whose presence he had once cut so ridiculous a figure. . . . Doubtless, if to-night he had recognized not this woman, but some other trivial familiar of his eighteenth year—the boon companion of that distant time, the miserable usher whom he had loathed—he would, at sight of them, have found in himself no trace either of the affection or of the hatred, now outgrown, which the callow schoolboy had then felt. But, faced by this woman, did he not feel now just as he had felt on that Thursday evening of 19—, when he had walked in the fading light along a dusty suburban road smelling of lilies, and stopped before a gate whose bell would never again ring to the pressure of his finger?

Maria! Maria Cross! Of the shy and grubby youth he had been then she had made a new man, the man he was to be for ever after. How little she had changed! The same questioning eyes, the same radiant forehead. Courrèges reminded himself that his favourite school friend of 19— would, by this time, be heavy, prematurely bald, and bearded. But the faces of a certain type of woman remain steeped in childhood until well on into maturity, and it is that quality of childhood, perhaps, that produces in us a fixation of love kept inviolate from the weapons of time. There she was, as she had always been, after seventeen years of passions about which he knew nothing, like one of those black Virgins whose smile the flaming fanaticisms of Reform and Revolution have been powerless to change. She was still being "kept" by this same man of substance who was noisily venting his ill-humour and impatience because the people for whom he was waiting had not yet turned up.

"I expect it's Gladys as usual who's making them late. . . . I'm always on the dot myself . . . can't stand unpunctuality in others. I suppose I'm odd in that way. I just can't bear the thought of keeping other people waiting—some sort of an instinct, I suppose—no use fighting against it. But good manners are a thing of the past. . . ."

Maria Cross laid a hand on his shoulder, and must have said again: "Everyone can hear what you're saying," because he growled out that he wasn't saying anything he minded people hearing, and that it really was a bit too much *her* teaching *him* how to behave.

Her mere presence had the effect of delivering Courrèges bound hand and foot to the vanished past. Though he had always had a keen sense of days long gone, he had a hatred of reviving the memory of their details, and feared nothing so much as the shuffle of ghosts. But he could do nothing this evening to disperse the crowding procession of faces brought by Maria's presence to the surface of his consciousness. He could hear again, in memory, the clock striking six, and the banging of desk lids in Upper School. Not enough rain had fallen to lay the dust: the light in the trolley was too bad for him to finish reading *Aphrodite*—in the trolley filled with work-people to whose faces the exhaustion of another day had imparted a look of gentleness.

II

He was a grubby brat. Much of his time at school he spent being turned out of the classroom, wandering about the passages or leaning against old walls. When he left it in the evening, and before he got to his suburban home, there was a long interval of time, spent, most of it, in the trolley, which stood in his mind for freedom, for deliverance. At last he could feel himself alone, surrounded by indifferent faces and incurious eyes. This especially was so in winter, because then the darkness, shredded only at intervals by scattered street-lamps and the glare of occasional bars, shut him away from the world, isolated him in a universe that reeked of damp working-clothes. Dead cigarettes dangled from sagging lips; faces seamed with coal-dust lay tilted back in sleep; newspapers slipped from hands gone numb; a hatless woman held up her novelette to catch the light of the lamps, her lips moving as though in prayer. But the end of the journey came at last, and, just after they had passed the church at Talence, he had to get out.

The trolley—a moving Bengal candle —lit up for a few brief moments the yews and naked elm-branches of a private park. Then the boy heard the noise of the trolley-wheels diminish as he stood in the puddle-pocked road. His nose was filled with the scent of rotting wood and leaves. He turned up the lane that ran by the Courrèges garden wall and pushed open the half-closed gate leading to the backyard. The light from the dining-room window lay across a clump of bushes where, in spring, the fuchsias were planted, because they love the shade. At this point in the return journey his face took on the sullen look it wore at school; his eyebrows drew together till they showed as a single matted line above his eyes, and the right-hand corner of his mouth began to droop. Entering the drawing-room he threw a collective "Good evening" to the occupants, who sat grouped about a single niggardly lamp. His mother asked how often must he be told to wipe his feet on the scraper, and did he mean to sit down to dinner with his hands "like that"? Madame Courrèges, the elder, murmured to her daughter-in-law: "You know what Paul says: don't nag the boy unnecessarily." His very appearance seemed to start an exchange of bitter words.

He sat down where the light could not reach him.

Crouched over her embroidery, Madeleine Basque, his sister, had not so much as raised her head at his entrance. He was of less interest to her, he thought, than the dog. In her opinion, Raymond was the family's "running sore." "I don't like to think what *he'll* grow up into," she was for ever saying, to which her husband, Gaston Basque, would contribute his mite by adding: "It's all because his father's so weak."

She would look up from her work, sit for a moment with her ears pricked, say suddenly, "There's Gaston," and lay aside her task. "*I* don't hear a thing," Madame Courrèges would reamark. But—"Yes, it's him," the young woman would repeat, and then, though no sound had reached any ear but her own, would run out onto the terrace and disappear into the garden, guided by an infallible instinct, as though she belonged to a species of animal different from all others, where it was the male, and not the female, who exhaled the odor that would draw his partner to him through the darkness. In a moment or two the Courrèges would hear a man's voice followed by Madeleine's gratified and submissive laughter. They knew that the couple would not come back through the drawing-room, but would use a side door and go straight upstairs to the bedroom floor, from which they would not descend until the gong had been sounded twice.

The company round the dining-room table, beneath the hanging lamp, consisted of the elder Madame Courrèges, her daughter-in-law, Lucie Courrèges, the young couple, and their four little girls, all with their father's reddish hair, all dressed alike, all with the same complexion and the same patches of freckles. They sat huddled together like tame birds on a perch. "No one's to say a word to them," ordered Lieutenant Basque. "If anyone addresses them, it's they who will be punished. Now don't say I didn't warn you."

The doctor's chair remained empty for some considerable time, even when he happened to be at home. He would come in half-way through the meal, carrying a bundle of learned journals. His wife said, Hadn't he heard the gong? and complained that with everything in the house at sixes and sevens, it was quite impossible to keep any servant for long. Shaking his head, as though to chase away a fly, he proceeded to bury himself in one of his journals. This was not affectation on his part, but merely a way of saving time devised by a man who was in a constant condition of overwork, never free from worries, and fully aware that every minute was precious. At the other end of the table, the Basques sat isolated and aloof, supremely indifferent to everything that did not directly concern either them or their little ones. Gaston would be explaining how he was pulling strings to avoid being moved from Bordeaux, how the Colonel had written to the Ministry . . . his attentive wife all the while keeping a watchful eye on the children and maintaining an uninterrupted flow of educative comment: "Don't you know how to use a knife?" "Don't sprawl." "Keep your hands on the table—hands, I said, not elbows." "Now mind what I say, you won't get any more bread." "You've had quite enough to drink already."

The Basques formed an island of secrecy and suspicion. "They never tell me anything"—all Madame Courrèges' grievances against her daughter could be summed up in that phrase—"they never tell me anything." She suspected that Madeleine was pregnant, kept a careful eye on her figure, and drew her own conclusions when the girl complained of not feeling well. The servants, she maintained, always knew everything before she did. She believed that Gaston had

taken out an insurance policy on his life, but for how much? She had no idea what money they had come into on old Basque's death.

In the drawing-room, after dinner, when she grumblingly inquired whether Raymond hadn't any homework to do, any essay to write, he made no answer. He would take hold of one of the little girls, look as though he were about to crush her in his great hands, toss her up over his head so that she could touch the ceiling, and swing the lithe little body round and round, while Madeleine Basque, like a ruffled and uneasy hen— though disarmed by the child's excitement, would exclaim: *"Do* be careful; I'm sure you'll do her some injury"; and then, turning to the company in general, would remark: "He's so *rough,*" at which Grandmamma Courrèges, laying down her knitting and pushing up her spectacles, while her whole face crinkled into a smile, would at once embark on a brisk defence of Raymond: "Why, he *adores* children," she would say. "You can't deny that children are all he cares about . . ." for it was one of the old lady's convictions that he wouldn't be so devoted to them if he hadn't a heart of gold. "You've only got to see him with his nieces to realize that there's nothing really to worry about."

But did he really care so very much about children? The truth was he made use of anything that came his way, provided it was warm and living, as a weapon against those whom he called the "corpses." Depositing the young body on the sofa, he would, on these occasions, make for the door, rush from the house, and stride along the leaf-encumbered paths.

Between the branches a lighter patch of sky guided his steps. Doctor Courrèges' lamp glowed from behind a window on the first floor. Should he go to bed without looking in on his father to say good-night? The three-quarters of an hour of hostile silence each morning were all that he could stand. Every day, early, the brougham set out, carrying father and son. Raymond got out at the Barrière de Saint-Genès, from which he walked, by way of the boulevards, to school, while the doctor continued on to the hospital. For three-quarters of an hour they sat side by side in a smell of ancient leather, between streaming windows. The doctor, who a few moments later would be speaking eloquently, authoritatively, to his helpers and his students, had been vainly seeking for months some word that would provoke a response from this being of his own flesh and blood. How was he ever to succeed in blazing a path to this heart which was always bristling with defences? Each time he congratulated himself on finding a joint in the young man's armour, and began speaking to Raymond in phrases planned long in advance, his words seemed suddenly like the words of a stranger: his very voice, dry and mocking, had, he felt, turned traitor—no matter how hard he tried to make it sound natural. This powerlessness to give expression to his feelings was his habitual martyrdom.

It was only through his actions that Dr. Courrèges' kindness of heart was widely recognized, for they alone bore witness to the good that lay so deeply embedded in him that it was like a man entombed. He could never hear a word of gratitude without a growl and a shrug. Bumping along through rainy dawns beside his son, he was for ever addressing silent questions to the withdrawn and sullen face there at his elbow. In spite of himself he could not help interpreting the signs that showed upon that face as those of some dark angel—the deceptive sweetness, for instance, that he caught in eyes that were more deeply shadowed than they should have been. The poor boy regards me as his enemy, thought the

father, and the fault is mine, not his. But he was reckoning without the sure instinct for those who love him which is for ever active in the adolescent. Raymond heard the unvoiced appeal, and never confused his father with the others. But he deliberately turned a deaf ear to what never found release in words. Nor could he, on his side, have thought of anything to say to the victim of shyness at his side, for the effect of his presence was to numb the older man with timidity, and so turn him to ice. Nevertheless, the doctor could not refrain, now and again, from remonstrating with him, though he always did so as gently as possible, and in terms of a friendship between equals.

"I've had another letter about you from the headmaster. Poor Abbé Farge, you'll really send him out of his mind! It seems to be proved without a shadow of doubt that it was you who passed round that treatise on obstetrics—I suppose you sneaked it off my shelves. I must confess that his air of outraged virtue seems to me somewhat excessive. After all, you're old enough now to know about the facts of life, and it's a good deal better that you should get them from solid, scientific books. That's the line I took in my reply. . . . But I gather, too, that a number of *La Gaudriole* was found in the newspaper-rack in Upper School, and, very naturally, you are under suspicion. All the sins of Israel are laid to your charge. Better look out, my boy, or you'll find yourself expelled with the final exams still a good six months off."

"No."

"What do you mean—no?"

"Because I'm working extra hard and stand a good chance of not being flunked a second time. I know their sort! They're not going to get rid of the only fellow who's likely to pass. Besides, if they showed me the door, the Jesuits would snap me up in a jiffy! They'd far rather let me go on contaminating the others, as they put it, than run the risk of losing a good item in the school records. Think how triumphant old Farge will look on Speech Day: thirty candidates—twenty-three 'Honors' and two 'Passes.' . . . Thunderous applause. . . . What a lot of swine they are!"

"No, my boy, that's where you're wrong." The doctor stressed those words, "my boy." Now, perhaps, was his opportunity to penetrate the lad's stubborn heart. For a long time his son had obstinately refused to show the slightest sign of weakening. The glow of a trusting confidence showed through the cynical words. What should he say that might have the effect, without putting the boy on the defensive, of proving to him that there *are* men who don't resort to tricks and calculations, that sometimes the cleverest are those Machiavellis of high causes who wound us when they wish us well? . . . He felt about in his mind for the most suitable formula, and even while he pondered the problem, the suburban road had turned into a city street filled with the bright and melancholy radiance of morning and the jostle of milk-carts. A few moments more and they would reach the city limits, that Croix de Saint-Genès where once the pilgrims to St. James of Compostella had knelt in momentary adoration, and where now only bus inspectors leaned against the walls. Unable to find any suitable words, he took the other's warm hand in his, said in a low voice, "My boy" . . . and then noticed that Raymond, his head pressed to the window, was asleep, or pretending to be asleep. The young man had closed his eyes, perhaps for fear that they might, for all his efforts to the contrary, betray a weakening, a desire to yield. He sat there, his face fast shut to all approaches, a bony face that looked as though carved in granite, in which the only sign of sensitiveness was the vulnerable line of the eyelids.

Very gradually the doctor withdrew his hand.

Was it before that scene in the brougham, or later, that the woman sitting over there on the settee, separated from him by no more than a single table, so that he could have spoken to her without raising his voice, had come into his life? She seemed calmer now, and was sipping her drink with no fear, it seemed, that Raymond might have recognized her. Every now and again she looked at him, only to look away almost at once. Suddenly her voice—and how well he remembered it!—rose above the babble of noise: "There's Gladys!"

The newly arrived couple came over at once and sat down between her and her companion. They all started talking at once. "We were waiting for our cloak-room tickets." "We're always the first to arrive—well, anyhow you've come, that's the main thing."

No, it must have been more than a year before the scene between father and son in the brougham that one day at dinner (it would have been in the late spring, because the lamp in the dining-room had not been lit) Madame Courrèges the elder had said to her daughter-in-law: "I know whom the white hangings in the church were for, Lucie."

Raymond had thought that one of those endless conversations was about to begin, full of trivial phrases that dropped dead about the doctor's chair. As a rule, they had to do with household matters, each of the women present rushing to do battle for her own particular member of the staff, so that the encounter became a squalid Iliad in which the quarrels of the servants' quarters set the various patron Goddesses at one another's throat in the Olympus of the dining-room. Often the two families would sit about disputing the favours of the daily sewing-woman. "I've arranged with Travaillotte to come to me next week," Madame Courrèges would say to Madeleine Basque, and then the younger woman would at once protest that the children's underwear needed mending.

"You always grab Travaillotte."

"Well, then, why don't you get old broken-nose Mary?"

"Broken-nose Mary is a much slower worker. Besides, she always insists on my paying her car-fare."

But on this particular evening, the mention of the white hangings in church had given rise to a more serious discussion. Madame Courrèges the elder had more to say.

"They're for that poor little boy of Maria Cross's, the one who died of meningitis. I gather she ordered an extremely expensive funeral."

"How very tactless!"

At his wife's exclamation, the doctor, who sat reading a journal while he drank his soup, raised his eyes. She, as usual when that happened, lowered hers, angrily remarking that it was a pity, all the same, that the curé hadn't managed to instill some sense of guilt into a woman who, as everyone knew, was a kept creature, who flaunted her shame all over the place, with her horses and carriages and all the rest.

The doctor made a gesture with his hand indicative of protest.

"It's not for us to judge: she's done *us* no harm."

"What about the scandal? I suppose that doesn't count?"

From his face she could see that he was saying to himself how vulgar she was. She made an effort to moderate her tone, though a few seconds later she exclaimed as loudly as before that women like that gave her the horrors. . . . The house that for so long had been the home of her old friend, Madame Bouffard, Victor Larouselle's mother-in-law, was now occupied by a slut. . . . Every time she

passed the door it cut her to the heart. . . .

The doctor, speaking very calmly, and in an almost hushed voice, interrupted the flow to point out that the only person in that house to-night was a mother sitting by her dead child. At this, Madame Courrèges, with one finger raised, announced solemnly:

"It is God's judgment!"

The children heard the scraping sound made by the doctor's chair as he pushed it sharply back from the table. He thrust his journals into his pocket, and, without another word, walked across to the door. He forced himself to move slowly, but the family, all attention now, could hear him running upstairs four steps at a time.

"Did I say anything so very extraordinary?" Madame Courrèges addressed a questioning look at her mother-in-law, at the young couple, at the children, at the servant. The only sounds in the room were the scraping of knives and forks and Madeleine's voice: "Don't nibble your bread—stop playing with that bone. . . ."

Madame Courrèges, her eyes fixed on her mother-in-law, said: "I really think he must be ill."

But the old lady, her nose buried in her plate, seemed not to have heard. It was at this point that Raymond burst out laughing.

"If you must laugh you'd better go outside! And don't come back till you can control yourself!"

Raymond threw his napkin on the floor. How peaceful it was in the garden. Yes, it must have been late spring because he remembered the bumbling noise made by the cockchafers, and that they had had strawberries for dinner. He had sat down in the middle of the paddock on the still warm stone rim of a fountain which no human eye had ever seen spouting water. He noticed his father's shadow passing and re-passing the windows of the first floor. In the twilight that poured dusty and heavy over this stretch of country not far from Bordeaux, a bell was tolling at long intervals because death had come for the child of this same woman who now sat drinking so close to him that he could have stretched out his hand and touched her. Since starting on the champagne, Maria Cross had been gazing more boldly at the young man, as though she were no longer afraid that she might be recognized. To say that she had not aged was an understatement. In spite of the fact that she had cut her hair, and that she was wearing nothing that trespassed beyond the winter's fashion, her whole body had somehow kept the lines that had been in vogue about 19—. She looked young, but it was as though her youth had come to flower fifteen years ago and remained unchanged. She was young in the way that no one is young today. Her eyelids looked no wearier than they had when she had said to Raymond: "Our eyes have a fellow feeling."

Raymond remembered how, on the morning following the evening on which his father had suddenly left the table, he had sat very early in the dining-room drinking his chocolate. The windows were open on the dawn mist, and he shivered a little. There was a smell of freshly-ground coffee. The gravel of the drive crackled under the wheels of the ancient brougham. The doctor was late. Madame Courrèges, in a purple dressing-gown, her hair plaited and twisted in the way she always wore it when she went to bed, kissed him on the forehead. He went on with his breakfast without pausing.

"Isn't your father down yet?"

She said that she had some letter to give him to mail. But he could guess the reason for her early appearance. When the members of a family live cheek by jowl, they get into the habit of never giving away their own secrets but of ever being on the alert to probe the secrets of others. The mother said of her daughter-in-law: "She never tells me anything, but there's little I don't know about her." Each person in the group claimed to know all about the others, while remaining inscrutable himself. Raymond thought he knew why his mother was there: "She wants to make it up." After a scene like that of the previous evening, she would dog her husband's footsteps, seeking to be taken back into favour. The poor woman was always discovering too late that she had the fatal gift of habitually saying what would most get on the doctor's nerves. As in certain forms of nightmare, the more she tried to approach him, the farther away she seemed to get. She could do nothing, say nothing, that was not hateful to him. Tangled in her clumsy efforts at tenderness, she was, as it were, always groping her way forward with outstretched hands. But whenever she touched him it was to bruise.

As soon as she heard the sound of his bedroom-door closing, she poured out a cup of steaming coffee. A smile lit up her face, which was marked by the traces of a sleepless night and worn by the slow dripping of laborious and identical days. But the smile vanished as soon as the doctor appeared. She was already on her guard, trying to read the expression in his eyes.

"Why, you've got your top hat and overcoat on!"

"That is quite obvious."

"Are you going to a wedding?" . . . "A funeral, then?"

"Yes."

"Who has died?"

"Someone you don't know, Lucie."

"Tell me who it is."

"The little Cross boy."

"Maria Cross's son? Do you know her? You never told me you did. You never tell me anything. Considering that we were talking at dinner of that hussy . . ."

The doctor was drinking his coffee,

standing. He answered in his quietest tones, which was always a sign with him that he was exasperated almost beyond bearing, though well under control.

"Haven't you learned, even after twenty-five years, that I prefer to discuss my patients as little as possible?"

No, she hadn't, and insisted that it always amazed her to find out, quite by chance, in the course of a social call, that this or that friend of hers had been attended by Dr. Courrèges.

"It's so awkward for me when people look surprised. 'What,' they say, 'do you really mean to tell me that you didn't *know?*' and then I have to admit that you don't trust me, that you never tell me anything. Were you treating the child? What did he die of? I can't see why you won't tell me. I never repeat things. Besides, with people like that, what can it matter? . . ."

For any sign the doctor gave, he might not have heard or seen her. He put on his overcoat, calling to Raymond: "Get a move on; seven o'clock struck ages ago."

Madame Courrèges pattered along behind them.

"What have I said now? You suddenly put all your prickles out. . . ."

The door slammed. A clump of shrubs hid the brougham from view. The sun began to shred the mist. Madame Courrèges, talking disjointedly to herself, turned back towards the house.

Seated in the carriage, the schoolboy looked at his father with eager curiosity, anxious for confidences. Now, if ever, father and son might have drawn closer together. But the doctor's thoughts were far from the boy with whom, so often, he had longed to come to grips. Here was the young prey ready to his hand, and he did not realize it. He sat there, muttering into his beard, as though he had been alone: "I ought to have called in a surgeon. One can always try trepanning as a last resort." He pushed back his top hat with its nap all brushed the wrong way, lowered one of the windows, and thrust out his hirsute countenance above the traffic-encumbered road. At the city limits he said absent-mindedly: "See you this evening," but he did not gaze after Raymond's retreating form.

III

In the course of the following summer Raymond Courrèges had his seventeenth birthday. He remembered it as a season of torrid heat and shortage of water. Never since then had the city of stone lain prostrate under so intolerable a glare, cluttered though his memory was with many summers spent in Bordeaux, a city protected by hills from the north winds, and close invested by pines and sand which concentrated and accumulated the heat—Bordeaux, so poor in trees, except for its Public Gardens, where, to the eyes of children parched with thirst, it seemed as though the last vestiges of green in all the world were being burned to cinders behind the tall and solemn railings.

But perhaps, in retrospect, he was confusing the sun's heat of that particular summer with the inner flame that was burning him up, him and sixty others of his age, who had their being within the limits of a yard separated from other yards by the back walls of a row of latrines. It needed the constant presence of two monitors to control this herd of boys who were dying into life, of men on the verge of being born. Responsive to the thrust of painful growth, the forest of young lives put forth, in a few short months, spindly and ailing shoots. The world and its ways had the effect of pruning the rank growth of these young scions of good families, but in Raymond Courrèges the action of the rising sap was fierce and uninhibited. He was an object of fear and horror to his teachers, who

kept him with his scarred face (because his tender skin could not endure the razor) as far as possible from associating with his fellows. The good boys of the school looked on him as a "dirty beast" who carried photographs of women in his note-case and read *Aphrodite* (disguised as a prayer-book) in chapel. He had "lost his faith." This phrase caused as much terror in the school as would, in an asylum, the rumour that one of the most dangerous lunatics had broken out of his strait-jacket and was wandering stark naked through the grounds. It was matter of general knowledge that on those rare Sundays when he was not being "kept in," Raymond Courrèges hid his school uniform and his cap, with the monogram of the Virgin, in a bed of nettles, put on an overcoat bought ready-made at Thierry and Sigrand, clapped on his head an absurd bowler which made him look like a plain-clothes policeman, and hung about the more disreputable booths at the fair. He had been seen on the merry-go-round hugging a slut of indeterminate age.

When, in the pompous setting of Commencement day, an attendant multitude of parents sat stupefied by the heat in the shade of leaves already shrivelled by the sun, and heard the headmaster announce that Courrèges had "passed with distinction," he alone knew what an effort he had made, in spite of the apparent lawlessness of his days, not to be expelled. A single fixed idea had filled his mind to the exclusion even of the sense of persecution, so that the hours of detention, spent standing against the rough-cast walls of the playground, had actually seemed short—the idea of departure, of flight, in the first glow of a summer morning, along the highroad to Spain which ran past the Courrèges' garden, a road that looked as though it were weighed down by the bulk of its great flagstones, a relic of the Emperor, of his guns and of his

convoys. He savoured in anticipation the heady delight of every step that should put a little more distance between him, the school, and his depressing family. It was an understood thing that on the day he passed his examination his father and his grandmother would each give him a hundred francs. Since he had already saved up eight hundred, he would thus be owner of the thousand which, so he thought, would enable him to travel through the world, miles and miles from his own "people." That was why he had spent the hours of detention working, untroubled by the sight of others at play. Sometimes he would shut his book and chew the cud of day-dreams. In imagination he could hear the scrape of cicadas in the pine-trees along the roads which soon he would be travelling, could see the cool shade of the inn before which, tired out with travelling, he would sit in some unidentified village. The rising moon would wake the cocks, and off he would start again in the freshness of the dawn, with the taste of bread in his mouth. And sometimes he would sleep beneath a mill, a single corn-stook blotting out the stars: and the damp fingers of the early day would rouse him. . . .

But, though teachers and parents had agreed in thinking him capable of anything, he had not, after all, taken to flight. His enemies, though they did not know it, had been too strong for him. Defeat comes to the young because they let themselves be so easily convinced of their own wretched inadequacy. At seventeen the most undisciplined of boys is only too ready to accept the image of himself imposed by others. Raymond Courrèges was blessed with good looks, but thought himself a monster of ugliness and squalor. He was blind to the fine contours of his face, and convinced that he could rouse in others only feelings of disgust. He was filled with a horror of his own person, and felt assured that he could never pay back in kind the emotion of hostility which he caused in those about him. That was why, stronger even than the longing to escape, he felt the desire to hide, to veil his face, to be compelled no more to wipe away the hatred of future enemies yet unknown. This youthful debauchee, whose hand the pupils of the Church School were afraid to touch, was no less ignorant than they of women, and could not conceive that he might be capable of giving pleasure if only to a slattern in the gutter. He was ashamed of his body. It never occurred either to his parents or to his teachers that all his glorying in wildness and dirt was but the miserable bravado of the young which he assumed because he wanted to make them believe that he revelled in his own uncomeliness. His attitude was no more than the threadbare pride of adolescence, a sort of despairing humility.

The holidays that followed his examination, far from opening a way of escape, were a period of secret cowardice. Paralysed by timidity, he thought he could read contempt in the eyes of the servant-girl who did his room, and quailed before the brooding look which, at times, his father turned on him. Since the Basques were spending August at Arcachon, he had not even the consolation of the children with whose young bodies, supple as growing plants, he loved to play so roughly.

As soon as the young family had gone, Madame Courrèges heaved a sigh of relief.

"It's nice to have the place to ourselves for a bit," she said, in this way taking her revenge on a remark of her daughter's to the effect that "Gaston and I really need a little course of solitude."

Actually, the poor woman lived for nothing but the daily letter, and could not hear the muttering of a storm without seeing in imagination the whole Basque family being dashed to destruction in an open boat. The house was only half full, and the empty rooms weighed heavily on her spirits. Of what comfort to her was a son who spent his time running wild about the roads, and came back sullen-tempered and dripping with sweat, to dash at his food like a ravenous animal?

"People say, 'Well, you've got your husband.' My husband!—I ask you!"

"You forget, darling, how busy Paul is."

"He doesn't have any rounds to make, mother. Most of his patients are on holiday."

"Not his poorer patients. Besides, he's got his laboratory work, the hospital, and all those articles he has to write. . . ."

The embittered wife shook her head. She knew that her husband's active temperament would never lack employment, that never, till the day of his death, would there be a moment's pause in which, for a few brief instants, she might count on his whole and undivided attention. It never occurred to her that such a thing could be possible. She did not know that in even the fullest lives love can hollow out its little nest; that the harassed statesman will stop the wheels of the world when the moment comes for his mistress to pay him a visit. This ignorance spared her much suffering. Though she was only too familiar with the kind of love that dogs the feet of someone beyond the power to touch, someone who will not so much as turn his head to take a moment's notice, the mere fact that she had always been powerless to hold his attention for no matter how brief a while made it impossible for her to imagine that for some other woman the doctor might be a totally different person. She would have hated to think that somewhere a woman might exist who was capable of charming him from that incomprehensible world in which he lived, made up of statistics and observations, of blood and pus imprisoned between glass slides; and it was many years before she discovered that there were evenings when the laboratory remained deserted, when the sick had to wait in vain for the man who, when he might have eased their pain, preferred to stand motionless in a dark and stuffy drawing-room gazing down at a woman stretched upon a sofa.

In order to contrive such secret oases in his days of toil the doctor had to work with twice his normal intensity; had to hack his way through every kind of obstacle that he might win as his reward those few moments filled with concentrated watching and impassioned silence, when to look was all the satisfaction he desired. Sometimes, just when the long-expected hour had almost sounded, a message would reach him from Maria Cross saying that she was no longer free, that the man on whom she was dependent had arranged a party in some restaurant on the outskirts of the city. When that happened he would have found the thought of life intolerable had she not added a postscript to her note suggesting another day. Then, in a flash, the miracle occurred, and at once his whole existence centred about the thought of the new meeting promised by her words. Though every hour of every day was filled with duties, he included in a single sweeping act of vision, like a skilful chess-player, all the possible combinations that might enable him so to arrange matters that, when the time and date arrived, he could be there, motionless and disengaged, in the stuffy and encumbered room, gazing at the figure stretched upon its sofa. And when the moment came and went at which, had she not put him off, he might have been with her, he was filled with happiness, thinking: "It would have been over by now, but, as things are, I still have that happiness in front of me. . . ." There was something then with which he could fill the empty days that lay between. At such times the laboratory in particular took on the quality of a haven. Within its walls he lost all sense of the passing hours, even of love itself. Absorbed in research, he felt freed from time, filling with work the moments that must be lived till, suddenly, the longed-for hour would come when he could push open the gate of that small house where Maria Cross lived behind the church at Talence.

Devoured by his obsession, he gave, that summer, less and less attention to his son. He who had been made party to so many shameful secrets often said to himself: We always think that the happenings tucked away in newspaper paragraphs don't concern us, that murders, suicides, and scandals are what come to other people, while, all the time . . . And yet, all the time, he did not know that there had been moments in the course of that devastating August when his son had been within an ace of taking an irreparable step. Raymond longed to run away, but longed, too, to hide, to become invisible. He could not pluck up courage to go into a café or a shop. He would walk up and down a dozen times before a door before he could bring himself to open it. This mania made all flight impossible, though he felt stifled in his home. There were many evenings when death seemed to him to be the simplest of all solutions. He would open the drawer in which his father kept an old-fashioned revolver, but it was not God's will that he should find the cartridges. One afternoon he walked between the drooping vines down to the pond that lay beyond the sun-baked paddock. He hoped that the weeds, the growing water-plants, might knot a tangle round his feet, that he might be unable to extricate himself from the muddy liquid, that his eyes and mouth might be filled with slime, that no one might ever see him again, nor he see others watching him. Mosquitoes were skimming the surface, frogs were popping in the eddying shadows like so many stones. Caught in the weeds a dead animal showed white. What saved Raymond then was not fear but disgust.

Fortunately, he was not often alone. The Courrèges' tennis court was a focus of attraction for all the young people of the neighbourhood. It was one of Madame Courrèges' grievances that the Basques should have involved her in the expense of having it made, and then, when they might have played on it, had gone away. Only strangers got the benefit of it. Young men in white, with rackets in their hands, moving inaudibly on sandalled feet, appeared in the drawing-room at the hour of siesta, greeted the ladies, barely bothered to ask after Raymond, and went out again into the glare which echoed soon to their cries of "Play" and "Out," to the sound of their laughter. "They don't even trouble to shut the door," grumbled Grandmother Courrèges, who thought of nothing but keeping out the heat. Raymond might have been willing to play, but the presence of the young women frightened him—especially of the Cosserouge girls, Marie-Thérèse, Marie-Louise, and Marguerite-Marie, all three fat and fair and suffering from headache because of the weight of their hair, for they were condemned to wear upon their heads enormous structures of yellow tresses imperfectly secured with combs and always on the point of falling down. He hated them. Why must they always laugh so much? They were in a constant state of wriggling convulsions, convinced that everybody else was a "scream." They didn't, as it happened, laugh more at Raymond than at anybody else, but it was his particular curse to feel himself the centre of a universal derision. But there was one reason, in particular, why he hated them. The day before the Basques went away, he had found it impossible any longer to refuse to keep a promise he had made to his brother-in-law that he would ride a monstrous great horse that the lieutenant was leaving behind in the stables. He was at the age when no sooner was he in the saddle than he was seized with giddiness. Consequently, he cut a poor figure as a horseman. One morning the Cosserouge girls had come on him suddenly in a forest ride, clinging desperately to the pommel of his saddle. A moment later and he was sprawling on the sandy ground. He could never see them after that without hearing again the giggling screams in which, at that moment, they had indulged. Each time they met him they took delight in reminding him of every circumstance of that humiliating fall. What storms does teasing, however harmless in intention, raise in a young man's heart in the spring-time of life! Raymond was incapable of distinguishing one Cosserouge from another, but lumped them collectively within the orbit of his hatred, regarding them as a sort of fat, three-headed monster, always sweating and clucking beneath the motionless trees of that August afternoon of 19—.

Sometimes he took the trolley, crossed the blazing inferno of Bordeaux, and reached the docks, where human bodies, devoured by poverty and scrofula, were splashing about in the stagnant water with its iridescent scum of oil. Their owners laughed, chasing one another, and leaving on the flags the faint, damp outline of their feet.

October returned. The perilous passage had been accomplished. Raymond had passed the dangerous crisis of his life. It was written that he should be saved, and indeed he was already saved when, at the beginning of term, the new school-books (he had always loved the smell of them) brought to him a sort of concentrated vision as he stood upon the threshold of the year which was to initiate him into the study of philosophy, of all the dreams and systems that have beguiled the hu-

man mind. Yes, he was to be saved,
though not by his own unaided efforts.
The time was near when a woman would
come into his life—that same woman
who, this evening, was watching him
through the smoky haze and crowding
couples of the tiny bar, whose wide and
tranquil brow no passage of time had had
the power to change.

During the winter months through
which he had lived before they met, his
spirit had lain in a profound torpor. A
sort of dull passivity had left him weap-
onless. Stripped of his old aggressiveness,
he was no longer the eternal whipping-
boy of fate. Once the holidays had passed
that had tormented him with the twin obsession of escape and death, he found
himself acquiescing in the expected conduct of his days. Discipline came to his
assistance by making life a good deal
easier. But he savoured even more in-
tensely his daily journey home, the evening passage from one suburb to another.
The College gate once left behind, he
plunged into the secret darkness of the
damp little lane which was sometimes
filled with the smell of fog, sometimes
with the hard, dry breath of frost. With
the sky, too, in its many aspects, he became familiar—overcast, swept clear and
corroded with stars, veiled with a covering of cloud that seemed to be lit from
within by a moon he could not see. And
then, in a short while, would come the
city limits, with the same crowd of tired,
dirty, submissive men and women waiting
to lay siege to the trolley. The great glowing rectangle plunged ahead into a land,
half town, half country, rumbling on between pathetic little gardens that lay sub-
merged beneath the fathoms of the winter
night.

At home he no longer felt himself to be
the object of a never-ceasing curiosity.
General attention was now concentrated
upon the doctor.

"I'm worried about him," said Madame Courrèges to her mother-in-law.
"You're lucky to be able to take things so
calmly. I envy temperaments like yours."

"Paul is rather overworked. He does
too much, there's no doubt about that.
But he has a magnificent constitution, so
I'm not really concerned."

The younger woman shrugged her
shoulders, making no effort to hear what
the other muttered half to herself: "He's
not ill, I'm sure of that. All the same, he
is suffering."

Madame Courrèges said, not for the
first time, "Trust a doctor never to take
care of himself."

During dinner she kept a watchful eye
on him. How emaciated his face looked,
she thought, when he raised his eyes from
his plate.

"It's Friday, why cutlets?"

"You need a good body-building diet."

"What do you know about it?"

"Why won't you go and see Duluc? No
doctor can ever prescribe for himself."

"My poor Lucie, why have you made
up your mind that I am ill?"

"You can't see yourself. Why, the mere
look of you is enough to frighten one.
Everybody says the same thing. Only yesterday, someone—I forget who—said:
'What is the matter with your husband?'
You ought to take choline. I'm sure it's
your liver."

"Why my liver rather than some other
organ?"

Her reply was peremptory: "My impression is that it must be your liver."

Lucie's impression to that effect was
very definite, and nothing would induce
her to give it up. Her comments buzzed
round the doctor like so many flies, only
far more irritating: "You've already had
two cups of coffee—I must tell the cook
to see that the pot isn't filled. That's your
third cigarette since lunch. It's no good
your denying it. There are three stubs in
the ash-tray."

"What proves that he knows he's ill," she said one day to her mother-in-law, "is that I caught him yesterday looking at himself in the glass. As a rule, he never bothers about his appearance, but there he was, peering at his face and running his fingers over it. It was as though he wanted to smooth out the wrinkles on his forehead and round his eyes. He even opened his mouth and examined his teeth."

Madame Courrèges the elder looked at her daughter-in-law over the top of her spectacles, as though fearful of detecting upon that puzzled countenance something more than mere anxiety, something more in the nature of suspicion. The old lady had a feeling that her son's good-night kiss had recently been less perfunctory than usual. Perhaps she knew what that momentary surrender to emotion meant. Ever since he was a young man she had got into the way of guessing the precise nature of those wounds which one person alone, the owner of the hand that deals them, can cure. But the wife, though for many years frustrated in her instinct of tenderness, had thoughts only for physical ailments. Each time the doctor sat down opposite her and raised his clasped hands to his face with its look of suffering, she said:

"You really *ought* to see Duluc: we *all* think so."

"Duluc could tell me nothing I don't already know."

"Can you listen to your own heart?"

To this question the doctor made no reply. His whole attention was concentrated upon the pain at his heart. It was as though a hand were holding and just faintly squeezing it. Ah! who better than he could count its beats, for were they not the evidence of what he had just been through with Maria Cross? How difficult it was to slip a more than usually tender word, a hinted declaration, into a conversation with a woman who showed herself always so submissive, who insisted on regarding her doctor as an almost god-like creature, and forced upon him the dignity of a spiritual fatherhood!

He went over in his mind the circumstances of his most recent visit. He had got out of the carriage on the main road, opposite the church at Talence, and had walked up the puddled lane. So swift had been the progress of the dusk that it was almost dark before he reached the gate. At the far end of an untidy path a lamp threw a ruddy glow from the ground-floor windows of a low-built house. He did not ring. No servant preceded him through the dining-room. He entered the drawing-room without knocking. Maria Cross was lying on a sofa and did not get up. Indeed, for a second or two she went on reading. Finally:

"So there you are, doctor; I'm quite ready for you," she said, holding out both hands, and moving her feet so as to make room for him on the end of the sofa. "Don't take that chair, it's broken. I live, you know, in a jumble of luxury and squalor. . . ."

Monsieur Larousselle had set her up in this suburban villa where the visitor was liable to trip over tears in the carpet, and only the folds of the curtains concealed the holes in the fabric. Sometimes when he went to see her she said nothing. He was prevented from starting a conversation fitted to his role of suppliant lover— a conversation which he had made up his mind *must* take place—by the presence, over the sofa, of a mirror which reflected the image of a face eaten away by a mass of beard, of two bloodshot eyes dimmed as the result of constant application to a microscope, of a forehead from which the hair had already begun to recede when he was still a house physician. Nevertheless, he was determined to try his luck. One of her small hands was trailing over the edge of the sofa, almost touching the floor. He took it, and said in

a low voice: "Maria . . ." Such was her
confidence in him that she did not withdraw it. "I'm not feverish, doctor; really
I'm not." As always, she spoke of herself.
"Dear friend," she said: "I've done something of which you'll thoroughly approve.
I've told Monsieur Larousselle that I no
longer need the car, that he'd better sell it
and get rid of Firmin. You know how it
is with him, how incapable he is of
understanding any delicacy of feeling. He
just laughed, and said what was the point
of upsetting everything merely because of
a moment's whim? But I mean it, and I
never use anything but the trolley now,
whatever the weather. I came back in it
today from the cemetery. I thought you'd
be pleased. I feel less unworthy of our
poor dead darling . . . less . . . less
like a kept woman."

The last two words were barely au-
dible. The eyes which she raised to the
doctor's face were brimming with tears,
and seemed humbly to implore his approval. He gave it to her at once, gravely,
coldly. She was forever invoking him.
"You're so *big* . . . you're the noblest
human being I have ever known . . .
the mere fact that you exist makes me
believe in the reality of goodness." How
he longed to protest, to say: "I'm not the
man you think me, Maria; only a poor, a
very poor creature, eaten up by desire
just like other men. . . ."

"You wouldn't be such a saint," she replied, when he tried to put these thoughts
into words, "if you didn't despise yourself."

"No, no, Maria: not a saint at all; you
don't, you can't know . . ."

She gazed at him with a fixed stare of
admiration, but it never occurred to her
to worry about him, as Lucie worried, to
notice how ill he looked. The concentrated worship which was her tribute to
him made of his love a despair. His desire
was walled up within this admiration. He
told himself in his misery, when he was

far from her, that his love could sur-
mount all obstacles; but as soon as she
was there before him, deferential, hanging on his words, he could no longer deny
the evidence of a wretchedness that was
beyond all cure. Nothing in the world
could change the nature of their relation.
She was not his mistress but his disciple.
He was not her lover but her spiritual
director. To have stretched his arms towards her supine body, to have pressed it
to his own, would have been as mad an
act as to break the mirror hanging above
her head. He knew, too, with horrible
clarity, that she was waiting for him to
go. The realization that she was an object
of interest to the doctor was, for her, a
matter of pride. Surrounded by the
wreckage of her life, she prized very
highly the intimacy of so eminent a man.
But how he bored her! He, without having the slightest idea that his visits were a
burden to her, felt increasingly that his
secret was becoming more and more obvious, so obvious, indeed, that only her
complete indifference could explain her
inability to guess it. Had Maria felt even
a vestige of affection for him, his love
must have stared her in the face. Alas!
how utterly insensitive a woman can be
when confronted by a man whom, otherwise, she may esteem and even venerate,
whose friendship fills her with pride, but
who bores her! Of this truth the doctor
had some faint realization only, but it
was enough to crush him.

He got up, cutting her short in the
middle of something she was saying.

"I must say, you *are* a bit abrupt in
your manner of taking leave," she remarked; "but there are so many other
sufferers waiting for you. . . . I mustn't
be selfish and keep you all to myself."

Once again he crossed the empty dining-room and the hall. Once again he
breathed in the smell of the frost-bound
garden, and in the carriage on his way
home, thinking of Lucie's attentive, wor-

ried face—no doubt she was already getting anxious, and would be straining her ears for the sound of his return—said to himself: The great thing is not to *cause* suffering. It's quite enough that *I* suffer: I mustn't create suffering in others.

"You're looking much worse this evening. Why *will* you put off seeing Duluc? If you won't do it for your own sake, you might at least do it for ours. You're not the only person concerned. It affects all of us."

Madame Courrèges called the Basques to witness the truth of her pronouncement. They emerged from the low-voiced conversation which they were carrying on, and obediently backed her up.

"It's quite true, Papa, we all want to have you with us as long as possible."

At the mere sound of the hated voice the doctor felt ashamed of the strength of his dislike for his son-in-law. He's really quite a decent fellow . . . it's unforgivable on my part . . . But how was he to forget the reasons he had for hating him? For long years one thing only in his marriage had seemed to be precisely as he had always dreamed it would be—the narrow cot standing beside the vast conjugal bed, and he and his wife each evening watching the slumber of Madeleine, their first-born. Her breathing was scarcely perceptible. One innocent foot had kicked off the coverlet. A small hand, soft and marvellous, hung down between the bars. She was such a sweet-natured child that they could afford to spoil her without fear of consequences, and such advantage did she take of her father's infatuation that she would play for hours in his study without making a sound. "You say she's not very intelligent," he would say; "she's much *more* than intelligent." Later, though he hated going out with Madame Courrèges, he loved to be seen in the company of the young girl. "People think you're my wife!" It was about then

that he had made up his mind that the right man for her would be Fred Robinson, the only one, he felt, of all his pupils who really understood him. He already called him "My son," and was just waiting until Madeleine should turn eighteen to conclude the marriage, when, at the end of the first winter after she had "come out," she told him she was engaged to Lieutenant Basque. The doctor's furious opposition had lasted for months. No one could see any sense in it, neither his family nor the world at large. Why should he prefer a penniless young student, who came from heaven knew where, to a well-off officer of good ancestry with a brilliant future before him?

His reasons were too personal to himself to make it possible for him to discuss them. From the first moment that he had started to raise objections he felt that in the eyes of this dearly loved daughter he had become an enemy. He told himself that his death would have been a matter to her of rejoicing, that she looked on him now merely as an old wall that must be battered down so that she could join the male who was calling to her. Because he wanted to see precisely where he stood, because he wanted to be sure to what extent this child, on whom he had lavished all his affection, hated him, he had intensified his stubbornness. Even his old mother was against him and joined forces with the young people. Plots were hatched under his own roof to enable the lovers to meet without his knowledge. When, finally, he had given in, his daughter had kissed him on the cheek. He had pushed away her hair, as he used to do, so as to touch her forehead with his lips. Everyone said: "Madeleine adores her father. She has always been his favourite." Until the day of his death, no doubt, he would hear her calling him "Darling Papa." Meanwhile he must put up with this Basque fellow. But no matter how hard he tried, he could not help betraying the fact of his antipathy. "It really is extraordinary," said Madame Courrèges. "Here he is with a son-in-law who shares his views about everything, and yet he doesn't like him!" It was just this that the doctor could not forgive, this seeing all his most cherished ideas turning to caricature in the distorting mirror of the young man's mind. The lieutenant was one of those persons whose approval flattens us out, and makes us doubt the very truths for which, previously, we would have shed our blood.

"Really, Papa, I mean it. You must take care of yourself for your children's sake. You must allow them to take sides with you against yourself."

The doctor left the room without answering. Later, when the Basques had sought the refuge of their bedroom (so sacred was it held to be that Madame Courrèges was wont to say, "I never set foot in it. Madeleine has made it perfectly plain that she doesn't want me there. There are some things that don't have to be said twice; I can take a hint"), they undressed in silence. The lieutenant, on his knees, his head buried in the bed, turned round suddenly and put a question to his wife:

"Was this house part of your parents' marriage settlement? . . . What I mean is, did they buy it after they were married?"

Madeleine thought so, but was not certain. "It would be interesting to know, because in that case, should anything happen to your poor father, we should have legal right to one-half of it."

He said no more for a few moments, and then, after a pause, asked how old Raymond was, and seemed annoyed to learn that he was only seventeen.

"What difference does that make? Why do you ask?"

"Oh, nothing. . . ."

He may have been thinking that a minor always complicates an inheritance, because, getting to his feet, he said:

"Naturally, I hope that your poor father will be with us for a long time yet. . . ."

In the darkness of the room the huge bed yawned to receive them. They went to it, just as twice a day, at noon and at eight o'clock, they sat down to table—when they were hungry.

About this same time Raymond woke in the night. Something that had a flat taste was trickling over his face and down his throat. His hand felt for the matches. He lit one, and, by its light, saw that blood was spurting from his left nostril and staining his nightshirt and the sheets. He got up and stood, petrified with fear, in front of the mirror, staring at his long thin body all speckled with scarlet. He wiped his fingers, which were sticky with blood, on his chest, and thought how funny his smeared face looked. He began to play a game in which he was both murderer and murdered.

IV

The evening was just like any other evening at the end of January, when, in those latitudes, winter is already on the wane. Raymond, seated in his workmen's trolley, was jarred by the sight of the woman opposite. Far from being distressed at the thought that he formed but one anonymous unit of this human freight, he enjoyed pretending that he was an emigrant in the steerage while the ship drove ahead through the darkness. The trees were coral reefs, the people and the traffic on the road outside, denizens of the vasty deep. The journey, which while it lasted kept from him all sense of humiliation, was all too short. Every one of the bodies round him was as much neglected as his own, as badly dressed. When, as occasionally happened, his eyes met other eyes, he saw in the answering look no hint of mockery. All the same, his linen was cleaner than the unbuttoned shirt, say, of the man with as much hair on his chest as a wild animal. He felt at ease among these people. It never occurred to him that one spoken word would have been enough to conjure up the desert that separates classes as surely from one another as it does individuals. But such communion as might be possible was, no doubt, achieved by this contact, this shared immersion of a trolley-car driving through the suburban night. Rough though he was at school, here he made no effort to shake himself free of the head that was bumping up and down on his shoulder, the head of an exhausted urchin of his own age whose body sagged in sleep, as loosely articulated as a bunch of flowers too lightly bound.

But on this particular evening he noticed, opposite, a woman, a lady. She was dressed in black, and was wedged between two men in greasy overalls. There was no veil over her face. He was to wonder, later, how it was that beneath her gaze he had not, at first, been conscious of that shy awkwardness which the humblest servant-girl could usually produce in him. He was troubled by no feeling of shame, no embarrassment—perhaps because in this trolley-car he felt himself to be without identity, and could imagine no circumstances which might establish a relation between himself and this particular stranger. But the chief reason was that her expression was entirely devoid of anything that might have been taken for curiosity, mockery, or contempt. But, Lord, how she stared! It was as though, absorbed in that concentration, she was saying to herself: The sight of this face brings consolation for all the tedium to which one is exposed in a public vehicle. Confronted by what might well be a sullen angel, I can forget the whole miserable scene. Nothing now

has any longer the power to rasp my nerves. Merely to look brings me deliverance. He is like some unknown country. The lids of his eyes are a barren stretch of sea-sand. Two troubled lakes lie drowsing between their bordering lashes. The ink on his fingers, his grimy collar and cuffs, that missing button—all these things are no more than the earth that dirties a ripe fruit ready to fall from the tree, and only waiting the touch of a careful hand to gather it. . . .

He, too, feeling safe because he had nothing to fear from this stranger, not even a word, since nothing had built a bridge between them, stared back with that tranquil intensity with which we gaze upon a distant planet. . . . (What innocence still clung about her brow. Courrèges, this evening, cast a furtive look at it. The radiance which bathed it owed nothing to the glare of the tiny bar, all to that intelligence which is so rarely found in a woman's face, though, when it is, how deeply it moves us, how convincingly persuades us that Thought, Idea, Intelligence are words of the feminine gender!)

In front of the church at Talence the young woman got up, leaving with the men she was deserting only the fragrance of her presence, and even that had vanished by the time Raymond reached the end of his journey. It was scarcely cold at all on this January evening. He was not even tempted to run. Already there was a promise in the foggy air of the secret sweetness of the coming season. The earth was stripped but not asleep.

Raymond, intent on his own thoughts, noticed nothing that evening as he sat at table with his family, though his father had never looked so ill. Madame Courrèges made no reference to the fact. He mustn't be "pestered," as she said to the Basques as soon as he had gone upstairs with his mother. All the same, she had made up her mind to talk to Duluc without his knowledge. The room reeked of the lieutenant's cigar. Leaning against the mantelpiece, Gaston said: "There's no doubt about it, mother: something's the matter with him." There was a military quality of command about the jerky brevity of his speech, and when Madeleine, taking an opposite line to her mother, remarked: "It may be only some temporary upset . . ." he interrupted her.

"No, Madeleine, it's serious. Your mother is quite right."

The young woman had the temerity to argue. He raised his voice:

"I say that your mother is right, and that should be enough for you!"

Up on the first floor Madame Courrèges the elder knocked gently at her son's door. She found him seated with a number of books open before him. She asked no questions, but sat knitting, saying nothing. If her silence, her reticence, became more than he could bear, if he felt the sudden need to speak, she was ready to listen. But a sure instinct kept her from forcing his confidence. For a moment he was tempted to choke back no longer the cry which was stifling him. But to speak now would mean going so terribly far back in thought, would mean telling over one by one the beads of his misery up to the moment of to-night's discomfiture. . . . How could he explain the disproportion between his suffering and its cause? What had happened would seem so trivial. It was merely that when he had called on Maria Cross at the time they had arranged, the servant told him that she had not come in. The news had inflicted the first stab of pain. He had agreed to wait in the empty drawing-room where a clock was ticking—though less quickly than his heart. A lamp shone on the pretentious beams of the ceiling. On a low table beside the sofa he noticed an ash-tray filled with cigarette ends. She

smokes too much . . . she's poisoning herself, he thought. What a lot of books there were, but in none were the last pages cut. His eye took in the torn folds of the great curtains of faded silk. To himself he repeated: "Luxury and squalor, squalor and luxury" . . . looked at the clock, then at his watch, and decided that he would wait only another fifteen minutes. How quickly, then, did time begin to fly. That it might not seem too short, he refused to let his thoughts dwell on his laboratory, on his interrupted experiment. He got up, went over to the sofa, knelt down, and, after first glancing nervously towards the door, buried his face in the cushions. When he got up his left knee made its usual cracking sound. He planted himself in front of the mirror, touched with his finger the swollen artery at his temple, and thought to himself that if anyone had come in and seen him, he would have been thought mad. With the characteristic aridity of the intellectual worker who reduces everything to the terms of a formula, he said, "All men are mad when they are alone. Yes, self-control is active only when it is backed by the control imposed upon us by the presence of others." Alas! that one little piece of reasoning had sufficed to exhaust the fifteen minutes' grace he had allowed himself. . . .

How could he explain to his mother sitting there, eager for confidences, the misery of that moment, the degree of renunciation it had demanded, the fact that it had had the effect of tearing him up by the roots from the melancholy satisfaction of his daily conversation with Maria Cross? What matters is not the willingness to confide even when we have a sympathetic listener, even when that listener is a mother. Which of us is skilled enough to compress a whole inner world into a few words? How is it possible to detach from the moving flow of consciousness one particular sensation rather than another? One can tell nothing unless one tells all. How could he expect this old lady to understand the music that sounded so deep down in her son's heart, with its lacerating discords? He was of another race than hers, being of another sex. They were separated more surely than people living on two different planets. . . . There, in his mother's presence, the doctor recalled his misery but did not put it into words. He remembered how, tired of waiting, he had just picked up his hat, when he heard the sound of steps in the hall. It was as though his whole life hung suspended. The door opened, but instead of the woman he expected he saw Victor Larousselle.

"You know, doctor, you're spoiling Maria."

Not a hint of suspicion in the voice. The doctor smiled at the sight of the impeccable figure with its full-blooded face and light-coloured suit, bursting with self-satisfaction and contentment.

"What a windfall for you doctors these neurasthenics are, these *malades imaginaires.* No, no, I'm only joking. Everyone knows what a selfless fellow you are. . . . Still, it's a bit of damn good luck for Maria that she should have happened on so rare a bird of the species as you. Do you know why she isn't back? Just because she's given up the car—that's her latest fancy. Between ourselves, I really think she's a bit touched—but that's only an added charm in a pretty woman, eh? What do you think, doctor? I must say I'm very glad to see you. Look here, stay to dinner: Maria will be delighted: she adores you. You won't? Well, at least wait until she gets back. You're the only person I can talk to about her."

"You're the only person I can talk to about her." . . . That sudden outburst of tormented words from this fat, resplendent man! This passion of his, said the doctor to himself, as he drove home, is the scandal of the place. All the same,

it is the one noble sentiment of which the fool is capable. At fifty he has suddenly discovered that he is vulnerable; that he can suffer because of a woman whose body he has almost certainly conquered. But that is not enough for him. Somewhere, outside his world of business and horses, there will henceforward be a finer principle of suffering. . . . The romantic conception of passion is not, perhaps, as silly as we think it. Maria Cross! Maria! What misery not to have seen her! But even worse than that is the knowledge that she didn't even think of sending me word. How small a place I must occupy in her life! She can break an appointment without so much as a thought . . . I cram infinity into a few short minutes that for her mean nothing. . . .

The sound of spoken words roused him from his reverie. His mother could bear the silence no longer. She, too, had been following the drift of her secret preoccupations, and was no longer dwelling upon her son's load of mysterious sorrow. She was back once more with what so constantly obsessed her—her relation with her daughter-in-law.

"I let her trample on me; I never say anything but 'Have your own way, my dear, do just as you want.' Nobody could say I provoke her, but she's for ever throwing her money in my teeth. Money! as though you didn't make enough! I know, of course, that when you married you had nothing but your future to offer her, and that she was a Voulassier of Elbeuf—though their mills in those days weren't anything like what they have become since. All the same, she could have made a better match, I realize that. . . . 'When one's got something, one always wants more'—as she said to me one day about Madeleine. But let's not complain. If it wasn't for the servants, everything would be all right."

"There are few worse things in life, my poor, dear mother, than having servants of different masters all living together in the same kitchen."

He touched her forehead with his lips, left the door ajar so that she could see her way, and repeated mechanically, "There are few worse things in life."

The next day Maria's whim about the car must still have been in the ascendant, because, coming home in the trolley, Raymond saw the unknown woman seated in her usual place. Once more her tranquil gaze took possession of the childish face opposite, making the circuit of the eyelids, tracing the line where the dark hair met the forehead, pausing at the glint of teeth between the lips. He remembered that he had not shaved for two days, touched his skinny jaw, and then, in an access of shyness, hid his hands beneath his cape. She lowered her eyes, and he did not at first notice that, since he wore no garters, one of his socks had slipped down, revealing a patch of bare leg. Too nervous to pull it up, he changed his position. He was not, however, conscious of mental discomfort. What he had always hated in other people was their laughter, their smiles—even when suppressed. He could catch the faintest sign of a trembling at the corners of a mouth, knew only too well what it meant when somebody started to bite his lower lip. But the expression on this woman's face as she looked at him was something he had never met before, something at once intelligent yet animal. Yes, it was the face of some marvellous, impassive *beast,* incapable of laughter. He did not know that his father often teased Maria Cross about the way she had of adjusting laughter to her face like a mask, and then letting it fall again without the slightest hint of alteration in the imperturbable melancholy of her gaze.

When she got out of the trolley by the church at Talence, and there was nothing left for him to see except the faint dent in the leather of the seat which she had occupied, he felt absolutely certain that they would meet again next day. He could give no good reason for his hope, but just had faith in the event. That evening, as soon as dinner was over, he carried two jugs of boiling water to his room, and took down his hip-bath from where it hung on the wall. Next morning he got up a good half-hour earlier than usual, because he had made up his mind that henceforth he would shave every day.

The Courrèges might have spent hours watching the slow unfolding of a chestnut-bud without even beginning to understand the mystery of the rising sap. Similarly, they were blissfully unaware of the miracle that was happening in their midst. As the first strokes of a spade may bring to light the fragments of a perfect statue, so the first glance from Maria Cross had revealed a new being in the grubby schoolboy. Beneath the warmth of her contemplative gaze a body, lovely, though ill cared for, had on a sudden stirred as might, in the rough bark of some forest tree, a spell-bound goddess. The Courrèges had no eyes for the wonder, because the members of a family too closely united lose the power to see one another properly. In the course of a few weeks Raymond had become a young man careful of his appearance, converted to the use of soap and water, secure in the knowledge that he could be pleasing to others, eager to attract. But to his mother he was still an unwashed schoolboy. A woman, without uttering a single word, merely by the intensity of her watching eyes, had transformed their child, moulding him afresh, though they were incapable of detecting so much as a trace of this strange magic.

In the trolley-car, which was no longer lit now that the days were lengthening, Raymond, at each encounter, ventured on some new gesture. He crossed his legs,

[35]

displayed his clean and uncreased socks, his shoes shining like mirrors (there was a shoe-shine boy at the Croix de Saint-Genès). He had no longer any reason to conceal his cuffs. He wore gloves. There came a day when he took one of them off, and the young woman could not suppress a smile at sight of the overpink nails on which a manicurist had been working hard, though, because for years he had been in the habit of biting them, it would have been better had they not as yet been allowed to draw attention to themselves. All this was but the outward sign of an inner, an invisible, resurrection. The fog that for so long had been collecting in the boy's most secret heart was thinning by degrees under the influence of that serious and still wordless gaze to which custom had already given a certain intimacy. Maybe he wasn't a monster after all; perhaps, like other young men, he could hold the attention of a woman—and, perhaps, more than her attention! In spite of their silence, the mere passage of time was weaving between them a web of contacts which no word or gesture could have strengthened. They felt that the moment was coming when, for the first time, they would speak, but Raymond did nothing to hasten its approach. Shy galley-slave that he was, he found it enough that he no longer felt his chains. For the moment, all the happiness he needed lay in this feeling of his that he had become someone entirely different. Was it really true that until this unknown woman had begun to look at him he had been nothing but a dirty little brat? We are, all of us, moulded and remoulded by those who have loved us, and though that love may pass, we remain none the less *their* work —a work that very likely they do not recognize, and which is never exactly what they intended. No love, no friendship can ever cross the path of our destiny without leaving some mark upon it for ever. The Raymond Courrèges who sat this evening

in a small bar in the rue Duphot, the man of thirty-five, would have been someone quite different if, in 19— when he was just embarking on his philosophy course, he had not seen, sitting opposite him in a trolley on his way home from school, Maria Cross.

V

It was his father who first noticed the new man in Raymond. One Sunday, towards the end of that same spring, he was seated at the family table, more deeply buried in his own thoughts even than usual, so far buried, in fact, that he scarcely heard the noise which had started as the result of a dispute between his son and his son-in-law. The subject of the argument was bull-fighting, a sport of which Raymond was a passionate devotee. He had come away that afternoon after seeing four bulls killed, so as not to miss the six-o'clock trolley. But the sacrifice had gone unrewarded, because the unknown woman was not in her seat. He might have guessed as much, it being Sunday. And now she had made him miss two bulls. Thus was he busy with his thoughts while Lieutenant Basque was holding forth.

"I can't understand how your father comes to let you watch such an exhibition of slaughter."

Raymond's reply, "That's a bit comic, I must say: an army officer who can't stand the sight of blood!" started a real row.

The doctor suddenly became aware of what was going on.

"And what, may I ask, do you mean by that?"

"That you're just yellow."

"Yellow?—say that again!"

They were both on their feet. Every member of the family was now taking sides. Madeleine Basque cried to her husband:

"Don't answer him! He's not worth it! What does it matter what *he* says!"

The doctor begged Raymond to sit down.

"Get on with your meal, and let us have no more of this!"

The lieutenant shouted that he had been called a coward. Madame Courrèges maintained that Raymond had meant nothing of the sort. Meanwhile, they had all resumed their seats. As the result of a sort of secret connivance they one and all set about throwing water on the flames. Family feeling made them view with extreme repugnance anything that might upset the smooth running of their little circle. They were a crew embarked for life in the same ship, and an instinct of self-preservation made them careful to see to it that no one should start a fire. That was why silence now descended on the room. A light rain had been falling, but the sound of drops on the steps outside suddenly stopped, and the newly released fragrance of the garden drifted in to where they all sat saying nothing. Someone remarked hastily that it was already cooler, and another voice replied that the rain hadn't amounted to anything, and would barely lay the dust. The doctor, with a feeling of bewilderment, looked at the tall young man who was his son. He had hardly thought of him at all for some time, and now scarcely recognized him. He himself had just emerged from a long nightmare. He had been caught up in it ever since the day, now long past, when Maria Cross had failed to keep her appointment, and had left him closeted with Victor Larousselle. The Sunday now drawing to a close had been one of the most horrible days of his whole life, but at last it had given him back his freedom (or so he thought!). Salvation had come to him as the result of an overwhelming fatigue, an

indescribable lassitude. His sufferings had been too much for him. All he wanted now was to turn his back on the battle, to go to ground in old age. Almost two months had elapsed between the ordeal of his profitless vigil in the "luxury and squalor" of Maria Cross's drawing-room and this hideous afternoon which had witnessed his ultimate surrender. Seated at the now silent table, he once again forgot his son, letting his memory recall each separate circumstance of the hard road that he had travelled. In imagination he could see once more its every milestone.

The intolerable agony had started on the very morning after the broken appointment. Her letter of apology had struck the first note.

"It was to some extent *your* fault, my dear, good friend"—Maria had written in the missive which he had read and reread over and over again, in the course of those two months:

". . . because it was the thought of you that gave me the idea of turning my back on a hateful luxury which had begun to make me feel ashamed. Not having the car any longer, I couldn't get back by our usual time. Being without it meant that I reach the cemetery later, and that I stay there longer, because my conscience is clear. You've no idea how quiet it is there at the end of the afternoon, full of birds perched on the gravestones and singing. I felt that my baby-boy approved of what I had done, that he was satisfied with me. I feel already rewarded for my action by having been allowed to sit with all those working people in the trolley. You'll think I'm becoming too romantic, but indeed it is not so. It makes me feel happy to be there with all those poor people of whom I am so little worthy. I can't find words in which to

tell you what that coming home in the
trolley means to me. 'A certain person'
is ready to go down on his bended
knees, so anxious is he that I should
take back the car which 'a certain person' gave me. But I won't. Dear, dear
doctor, what does it really matter if we
don't see one another? Your example,
your teaching, is enough for me. We
are so closely united that mere physical
presence has no importance. As Mau-
rice Maeterlinck has so wonderfully
written—'A time will come, nor is it
far off, when human souls will be
aware of one another without the
intervention of any physical organ.'
Write to me. Your letters are all I
need, dear spiritual director!

M. C.

"Ought I to go on taking the pills and
the injections? I've only got three doses
left. Must I buy another box?"

Even had it not so cruelly wounded
him, this letter would have aroused the
doctor's displeasure, so eloquent was it of
self-satisfaction and the pleasure that
comes of sham humility. There was no
secret of the human heart to which he
had not been made privy, and, as a result,
his tolerance, where his fellow-men were
concerned, was almost unlimited. One
vice, and one vice only, irritated him beyond bearing: the effort of the morally
depraved to put a mask of beauty on their
depravity. For him the last infirmity of
the human creature lay in the ability to
be dazzled by its own filth as by a diamond. Not that this sort of lie in the soul
was habitual with Maria Cross. In fact,
what had first charmed the doctor had
been a power in her to see herself as she
was, a refusal to embellish what was naturally ugly. One of her favourite themes
had always been the noble example which
her mother, a poor schoolmistress in a
small country town, widowed while still
young, had given her.

"She worked like a slave to pay my
school fees, and had quite made up her
mind that I should go to a teachers' college. She had the great happiness, before
she died, of being present at my marriage,
a happiness for which she had never
dared to hope. Your son-in-law was well
acquainted with my husband, who was a
medical officer in his regiment. He adored
me, and I was very happy with him. Left,
as I was, with a child, I had scarcely
enough to live on which he died, but I
could have managed somehow. It wasn't
sheer necessity that was my undoing, but
something that is really much more hateful—the desire to cut a figure, the longing
for the security that marriage gives. . . .
What, now, keeps me from leaving 'him'
is the fact that I am too cowardly to take
up the struggle again, to work my fingers
to the bone for an inadequate salary."

Often, since the time of those first confidences, the doctor had heard her depre-
cate herself, mercilessly pass sentence on
her weaknesses. Why then had she suddenly fallen a victim to the detestable vice
of self-praise? But what most hurt him in
her letter was something quite different.
His grievance against her came from the
fact that he had lied to himself, that he
dared not probe a far deeper wound, the
only wound of which he could not endure
the pain. Maria showed no desire to see
him, could quite gaily envisage the possibility of their separation. Time and time
again, while he was listening to some patient endlessly elaborating the details of
his ailments, or to some floundering candidate hemming and hawing over the
definition of hemoptysis, he heard an
inner voice repeating that phrase of Maeterlinck's about human souls being aware
of one another without the intervention
of any physical organ. He must have
been mad ever to have believed for a
single moment that a young woman
could feel the need for his bodily presence. Mad, quite mad: but then, what re-

source of reasoning can save us from the unendurable pain of knowing that the adored creature whose "being there" is a necessary condition of our continued existence, even of our physical existence, can resign herself with complete indifference (perhaps, actually, with a certain sensation of relief) to the prospect of never seeing us again? At such times we realize that we mean nothing to the one person who means everything to us.

During all this period the doctor made an effort to get the better of himself. "I caught him again the other day looking at himself in the glass," said Madame Courrèges: "that means he's beginning to get worried." What sight better calculated to bring tranquillity and the apathy of complete despair than that of his own face, with all the telltale marks left upon it by fifty years of exhausting work? There was only one thing for him to do—to think of Maria only as he might have thought of someone dead and buried; to await the coming of death, and hasten it by doubling his daily dose of work—yes, to drive himself without mercy, to kill himself with work, to achieve deliverance through the opium of forced labour. But he who showed so little mercy to those of his fellow-men who lived a lie was still the dupe of his own thoughts: She needs me: I must give her what I would give any sick person. He answered her letter with one of his own, in which he said that he felt it necessary to continue his treatment. She was perfectly right, he told her, to travel by trolley, but was it necessary for her to go out every day? He begged her to let him know when he should find her at home. He would so arrange matters as to be free to come at the usual hour.

A whole week passed without a further word from her. Each morning he had only to glance at the pile of prospectuses and newspapers to see that she had not written. He gave himself up to a calcula-

tion of probabilities: I posted my letter on Saturday. There is only one delivery on Sundays. She can't have got it till Monday. Assuming that she has waited two or three days before replying, it would be very extraordinary if I heard from her to-day. If nothing happens tomorrow it will be time enough for me to start worrying.

And then, one evening, when he came in from a particularly hard day, he found a letter.

"I regard my daily visit to the cemetery as a sacred duty. I have quite decided to make my little pilgrimage no matter what the weather. It is just when evening is falling that I seem closest to my lost angel. I have a feeling that he knows when I shall come, that he lies there waiting for me. I know it is ridiculous, but the heart has its reasons, as Pascal says. I am happy and at peace when I get into the six-o'clock trolley. Have you any idea what a workers' trolley is like? But I feel no fear. I am not so very far removed from 'the people,' and though there may be an apparent gulf between us, am I not linked with them in another way? I look at all those men, and it seems to me that they are just as lonely as I am—how shall I put it?—no less uprooted, no less socially at sea. My house is more luxurious than their houses; still, it is nothing but a series of ready-furnished rooms. Nothing in it belongs to me any more than what is theirs belongs to them. That is true even of our bodies. Why not call one day, very late, on your way home? I know that you don't like meeting Monsieur Larousselle. I'll tell him that I want to see you alone. All you need do when our interview is over is just exchange a few polite words with him. . . . You forgot to say anything about the pills and the injections. . . ."

The doctor's first instinct had been to tear the letter up, and scatter the fragments. Then he went down on his knees, gathered them all together, and scrambled to his feet again with considerable difficulty. Didn't she realize that he couldn't bear even the proximity of Larousselle? Everything about the man was hateful to him. He belonged to just the same general type as Basque. The lips that showed beneath the dyed moustache, the heavy dewlaps, the stocky figure, all proclaimed a complacency that nothing could shake. The fat thighs below the covert coat were expressive of an infinite self-satisfaction. Because he deceived Maria Cross with the lowest of the low, it was said in Bordeaux that he "just kept her for show." Scarcely anybody but the doctor knew that she was still the one great passion of his life, the secret weakness which drove him almost beside himself. The man might be a fool, but the fact remained that he had bought her, that he alone possessed her. Now that he was a widower, he would probably have married her had it not been for the existence of his son, the sole heir to the Larousselle fortune, who was being prepared for his august destiny by an army of nurses, tutors, and priests. It was unthinkable that the boy should be exposed to contact with such a woman, unthinkable that he should inherit a name degraded by a *mésalliance*.

"There's no getting away from it," Basque was fond of saying—for he was deeply attached to all that made for the greatness of his native place—"there's no getting away from it, Larousselle's out of the top drawer all right, he's a gentleman through and through, and what more can one ask?"

Maria knew that the doctor loathed Larousselle. How, then, could she dare to make an appointment for the one time of the day when he would be sure to be brought face to face with the object of his execration? He went so far as to persuade himself that she had deliberately planned the meeting so as to get rid of him. After spending several weeks writing and tearing up a number of mad, furious letters, he finally sent her one that was both short and dry, in which he said that since she could arrange to be at home on only one afternoon, it must be because she was perfectly well and had no need of his ministrations. By return of post came four pages of excuse and protestation. She would, she said, be at home to him at whatever hour he might like to come on the next day but one, which happened to be a Sunday.

"Monsieur Larousselle is going to a bull-fight. He knows that I don't like that sort of thing. Come for tea. I shall wait for you until half-past five."

Never had the doctor received from her a letter in which the sublimities played so small a part, in which matters of health and treatment were not even mentioned. He re-read it more than once, and frequently touched it as it lay in his pocket. This meeting, he felt, would be different from all that had preceded it. At last he would be able to declare his passion. But, man of science that he was, and taught by repeated experiences that his presentiments had a way of never being realized, he kept on saying to himself: No, it's *not* a presentiment . . . my attitude of expectancy is wholly logical. I wrote her a churlish letter to which she has sent a friendly answer. Therefore, it is up to me to see to it that our first words shall give to our talk a tone of frankness and intimacy. . . .

As he drove from his laboratory to the hospital, he rehearsed the coming interview; again and again asked *her* questions, again and again framed the replies he would have her make. He was one of those imaginative persons who never read novels because for them no work of fic-

filled with joy each time that some more than usually hideous piece of "art" found its way into his hands. "Mind, nothing *old,*" his patients would say to one another when discussing how best they could please Doctor Courrèges.

But on the particular Sunday which was to enshrine his meeting with Maria Cross, the meeting that was to change the whole course of his life, he had agreed to see, at three o'clock in this same consulting-room, a business man suffering from neurasthenia who could not manage to visit the doctor on any other day of the week. He had resigned himself to the necessity. At least it would provide him with an excuse for going out immediately after luncheon, and would occupy the few last moments before that fatal meeting so eagerly awaited, so deeply dreaded. He did not use the carriage, nor did he attempt to get into any of the overcrowded trolleys. Groups of human beings were festooned about their platforms, for there was to be a big football match, and it was also the day of the first bull-fight of the season. The names of Albagene and Fuentes stared from great red-and-yellow bills. Though the spectacle was not due to begin until four o'clock, the gloomy Sunday streets, with their shuttered shop-fronts, were already filled with crowds making their way towards the arena. The young men wore straw hats with coloured bands, or hats of light gray felt which they fondly imagined had a Spanish look. They laughed in a thick cloud of cheap tobacco smoke. The cafés breathed into the street the clean smell of absinthe. He could not remember how long it was since he had last wandered aimlessly through the hurly-burly of the city with no other preoccupation than to kill time until a certain hour should strike. To be thus unemployed was a very strange experience for a man who was usually so overworked. He had lost the secret of doing nothing. He tried to think

of the experiment he had recently begun, but could see nothing with his inner eye but Maria Cross lying on a sofa with a book.

Suddenly the sun stopped shining, and the walking folk turned apprehensive eyes to where a heavy cloud was creeping across the sky. Someone said that he had felt a drop of rain, but after a few moments the sun once more came out. No, the storm would not break until the last bull had been put out of its agony.

Perhaps, reflected the doctor, things would not turn out precisely as he had imagined they would. But one thing was certain, mathematically certain: he would not leave Maria Cross without making her privy to his secret. This time he would put his question. . . . Half-past two: another hour to kill before he was due at his consulting-room. At the bottom of his pocket he could feel the key of his laboratory. No, if he went back there it would mean leaving again almost as soon as he had arrived. The crowd swayed as though in the grip of a blustering wind. A voice cried: "There they are!" In a procession of ancient victorias, driven by coach-men who had caught something of reflected glory for all their shabbiness, sat the glittering matadors with their *quadrillas.* It surprised the doctor that he could discern no baseness in the emaciated faces of this strange priesthood clad in red and gold, in violet and silver. Once again a cloud blotted out the sun, and they turned their thin profiles to the tarnished azure of the sky. He thrust a way through the crowd. He was walking now along narrow and deserted thoroughfares. His consulting-room, when he reached it, was as cool as a cellar. Women in terra cotta and alabaster smiled down on him from columns of malachite. The ticking of a sham antique timepiece was slower than that of an imitation Delft clock which stood in the middle of the table, where a "modern-style" female, seated on a block of crystal, did duty as a paperweight. All these various figures seemed to be singing in unison the title of a revue which had stared down on him from every corner of every street—*N'y a que ça de bon!*—including the bull in bogus bronze, his muzzle resting on the back of a companion cow. With a quick glance he took in the whole motley collection. Very quietly he said: "The human race could sink no lower!" He pushed open a shutter and set a dusty sunbeam dancing. Then he began to walk up and down the room, rubbing his hands. There must be no beating about the bush, he assured himself. With my very first words I must make her realize how terribly I suffered when I made up my mind that she no longer wanted to see me. She will express surprise. I shall tell her with all the earnestness I can command that it is impossible for me any longer to live without her . . . and then, perhaps . . . perhaps . . .

He heard the sound of the bell, went to the door, and admitted his visitor. No interruption to this day-dreaming would come from *him*. All *he* asked was to be allowed to talk and talk. Neurasthenics of that sort seem to demand nothing of their doctors beyond a patient hearing. This one must have endowed the members of the profession with a kind of priestly aura, so eloquent was he in pathological confession, so anxious to display the most secret wounds of his soul. The doctor was once more, in imagination, with Maria Cross: I am a man, Maria, a poor creature of flesh and blood like other men. No one can live without happiness. I have discovered that truth rather late in life, but not too late—say it is not too late—for you to throw in your lot with mine. . . . By this time his patient had stopped talking, and the doctor, with that air of noble dignity which had earned him such universal admiration, said:

"The essential thing is that you should believe in the power of your own will. If you refuse to regard yourself as a free agent, I can do nothing for you. Even the art of healing can be wrecked on the reef of a wrong mental attitude. If you persist in thinking of yourself as the helpless victim of heredity, how can you hope that I shall be able to do anything for you? Before going further I demand from you an act of faith. You must believe that it is in your power to control all those wild beasts in yourself that are not the real you at all."

The other kept on eagerly interrupting him, and all the time he was speaking, the doctor, who had risen and gone over to the window, pretended to be looking into the empty street through the half-closed shutters. It was with something amounting to horror that he noted in himself the survival of all these lying phrases which expressed nothing but a faith long dead. Just as we perceive the light given off by a star which has been cold for centuries, so those around him heard the echo of beliefs which he had ceased to hold. He came back to the table, saw that the sham Delft clock marked four o'clock, and hastily got rid of his patient.

I've got plenty of time, he told himself as he all but ran along the pavement. When he reached the Place de la Comédie he saw that the trolleys were being besieged by the crowds of people who were pouring out of the theatres. Not a cab was to be seen. He had to take his place in a queue, and kept consulting his watch. Accustomed as he was to driving everywhere, he had left himself too little time. He tried to calm his nervousness. Even putting things at their worst he would be no more than half an hour late —no unusual thing for a doctor. Maria always waited for him. Yes, but in her letter she had said "until half-past five," and it was already five! "Just you stop pushing!" exclaimed a fat and angry woman, the feather of whose hat was tickling his nose. Inside the trolley, which was packed to suffocation, he regretted that he was wearing an overcoat. He was sweating, and hated the thought of arriving with a dirty face and a strong smell.

Six o'clock had not yet struck when he got out in front of the church at Talence. At first he walked quickly, then, mad with anxiety, broke into a trot, though his heart was troubling him. A great storm-cloud had darkened the sky. In this ominous light the last bull must even now be bleeding. Between the railings of the little gardens branches of dusty lilac thrust out little begging hands, craving for rain. Under the warm slow drops he ran towards the woman whom he could see already, in imagination, stretched on her sofa. She would not immediately, on his entry, raise her eyes from her open book. . . . And then, just as he reached her front door, he saw her coming out. They both stopped. She was out of breath. Like him she had been running.

There was a hint of annoyance in her voice as she said:

"I *did* say half-past five in my letter."

He took in her appearance with an observant eye.

"You're not in mourning."

She glanced down at her summer frock and replied:

"Doesn't mauve count as half-mourning?"

How different, already, everything was from what he had been imagining! Oppressed by a great weight of cowardice, he said:

"Since you had given me up, and probably have an appointment somewhere else, we had better put off our meeting to another day."

She spoke eagerly, quickly:

"With whom *should* I have an appointment? What an odd creature you are, doctor!"

She turned back towards the house,

and he followed her. She let her skirt of mauve taffeta drag in the dust. When she bent her head he could see the back of her neck. She was thinking that if she had chosen Sunday for the doctor's call it was because she felt sure that the unknown boy would not be in the six-o'clock trolley. All the same, beside herself with joy and hope when he did not come at the hour named, she had run down the road, just on the off-chance, saying to herself:

There is just one possibility in a thousand that he has taken his usual trolley because of me. Whatever happens, I must not let such a chance of happiness slip.— But, alas! she would never know now whether the stranger had been struck with gloom when he saw that she was not in her usual seat. The heavy rain was splashing on the front steps as she hurried up them, and she could hear behind her the old man's laboured breathing. How importunate are those who do not touch our hearts, those whom we have not chosen! They are wholly external to ourselves. There is nothing about them that we want to know. Should they die, their death would mean no more to us than their lives . . . yet it is they who fill our whole existence.

They went through the dining-room. She opened the drawing-room shutters and took off her hat. Then she lay down and smiled up at the doctor, who was trying desperately to pick some shreds and tatters from the words he had so carefully prepared. She said to him: "You are out of breath. I made you walk too fast."

"I am not as old as all that."

He raised his eyes, as he always did, to the mirror that hung above the sofa. What! was he even now not familiar with his own appearance? Why was it that on each occasion he felt that stab at the heart, that sense of numb misery, as though he had expected to see his own youth smiling back at him? But already he was putting the usual question: "And how are we to-day?" in that tone of paternal concern, with that half-serious inflection, which he always adopted when he spoke to Maria Cross. Never had she felt so well, and in telling the doctor so she felt a pleasure which to some extent compensated her for the earlier disappointment. No, to-day, Sunday, the unknown boy would almost certainly not have been in the trolley. But to-morrow, yes, to-morrow he would be there: of that there could be no doubt, and already her whole being was turned towards the joy to come, the hope that, every day, was doomed to disappointment and rebirth, the hope that something fresh might occur, that the moment would come when he would speak to her.

"I see no reason why you shouldn't leave off the injections." (He saw reflected in the glass his skimpy beard and barren brow, and remembered the burning words he had prepared.)

"I'm sleeping well: I don't feel bored any longer—just think of that, doctor! And yet, somehow, I have no wish to read. I couldn't finish *Voyage de Sparte;* you'd better take it away with you."

"You still see nobody?"

"You don't really think that I should suddenly let myself get mixed up with all these men's mistresses, do you? I, who till now have always avoided them like the plague? In the whole of Bordeaux there is no one of my kind, as you must realize, nobody of whom I could make a friend."

Yes, she had said so often enough, but always, in the past, on a note of self-pity, never, as now, with peace and happiness in her voice. It was borne in on the doctor that her long and tapering flame would no longer point heavenward a flickering tongue, would no longer burn in a void, that somewhere, close to the earth, it had found, unknown to him, fuel on which to feed. He could not keep himself from saying with aggressive emphasis that though it might be true that she did

not frequent the women, she nevertheless occasionally saw the men. He felt himself blushing as he realized that the conversation might, even now, take the very tone he had so ardently desired. Indeed, Maria did actually say with a smile:

"Don't tell me you are jealous, doctor! I really do believe you're going to make a scene! No, no, don't be frightened, I was only joking," she added immediately. "I know you too well."

It was obvious that she had been within an ace of laughing outright, that it had never even occurred to her that the doctor might really be capable of such weakness. A worried look came into her eyes.

"I haven't said anything to hurt you, have I?"

"Yes, you have."

But she failed entirely to understand the nature of the hurt he spoke of. She said that her feeling for him was one of veneration and respect. Hadn't he lowered himself to her level? Hadn't he sometimes deigned to raise her to his? With a movement as insincere as her words had been, she seized his hand and drew it to her lips. He snatched it away. Annoyed by the action, she got up, went over to the window, and stared out at the drenched garden. He, too, had risen. Without turning her head, she spoke:

"Wait till the shower's over."

He made no move, but stood there in the dark room. In all things a man of method, he employed the agonizing moments in rooting from his heart all desire and all hope. Everything was over, really over. From now on, nothing that had to do with this woman would ever more concern him. He had withdrawn from the battle. With his hand he made in the empty air the gesture of a man sweeping some obstacle aside.

Maria turned her head.

"It has stopped raining," she said.

Seeing that he still did not move, she

hastened to add that it wasn't that she wanted to get rid of him, but wouldn't it be as well to take advantage of this momentary break? She offered him an umbrella which at first he accepted, only, a moment later, to refuse, because he had caught himself thinking, I shall have to bring it back: that will give me a chance to see her again.

He felt no pain, but only a sense of enjoyment in the tail-end of the storm. His thoughts ran on about himself, or rather one part of himself. He was like a man who finds consolation for the death of a friend in the certainty that he has ceased to suffer. He had played and lost. No use crying over spilled milk. Henceforward nothing would matter to him but his work. Yesterday they had phoned him from the laboratory to say that the dog had not survived the removal of its pancreas. Would Robinson manage to find another at the Lost Dogs' Home? The trolleys swept by, crammed with an exhausted, singing crowd. But he had no objection to walking along these suburban roads filled with lilac and smelling of the real country because of the rain and the effect of the failing light. He was done with suffering, with beating, like a prisoner, against the walls of his cell. The vital force which had been his since childhood, but which the pressure of so many human creatures had led him to dissipate, he now took back, thrusting it deep, deep into himself. Complete renunciation. In spite of staring posters and gleaming trolley-lines, in spite of cyclists bent double over handlebars adorned with bunches of faded lilac, the suburb merged gradually into open country, the bars gave place to inns full of muledrivers preparing to set off by moonlight. Onward through the darkness they would trundle, like so many corpses stretched out in the bottom of their wagons, their faces to the stars. On the doorsteps of houses children were playing with drowsy cockchafers. Never again would he kick against the pricks. For how long now had he been exhausting all his energies in this dreary battle? He saw himself by the light of memory sobbing (it must be almost half a century ago) beside his mother's bed on the last day of the holidays. "Aren't you ashamed of crying, you lazy little silly-billy?" she had exclaimed, not knowing that what had provoked the outburst had simply been despair at the thought of leaving her: and later . . . once more he made that sweeping gesture with his hand, as though he were clearing a space before him. Now, what have I got to do to-morrow morning? he thought, inoculating himself, as with an injection of morphine, with the thought of daily duties . . . of the dead dog, of the need to start the whole business over again from the beginning. Surely he had tabulated a sufficient number of observations already to enable him to confirm his hypothesis? What a lot of time he had wasted. Through what thickets of shame he had been wandering! Convinced that the whole human race must be hanging on his every movement as he worked away in his laboratory, he had yet been willing to see day after day go by spoiled and empty. Science must be served with an undivided passion. It brooks no rival. I shall never be more than an amateur scientist, he thought. He imagined he saw fire burning in the branches and realized that it was the rising moon. He caught sight of the trees that hid from view the house which harboured that group of beings whom he had the right to call "my people." So often already he had been false to his vow, only later to renew it in his heart: From this very evening I will make Lucie happy. He hastened his pace, impatient to prove that this time he would not weaken in his resolve. He thought of their first meeting, twenty-five years before, in a garden at Arcachon—a meeting engineered by one of his colleagues. But what he saw with his inward eye was not the betrothed of that distant time, not a pale and faded photograph, but a young woman in half-mourning, wild with joy because he was late, and hurrying to a meeting with someone else . . . but with whom? He felt a sharp stab of pain, stopped dead for a moment, and then broke into a run so as to put as great a distance as possible between himself and the man whom Maria Cross loved. The action brought comfort, ignorant though he was that each step he took was bringing him closer to the unknown rival. . . . And yet it was on this very evening that, scarcely across the threshold of the room where Raymond and his brother-in-law stood at odds, he became conscious of a sudden burgeoning, a sudden rising of the spring sap, in the stranger whom he had brought into the world.

Those present had risen from the table, the children offering their foreheads for their elders absent-mindedly to kiss. This done, they went off to their rooms under an escort provided by their mother, their grandmother, and their still more ancient ancestress. Raymond moved across to the French window. The doctor was struck by the way in which he took a cigarette from his case, tapped it, and lighted it. There was a rosebud in his buttonhole, an orthodox crease in his trousers. The doctor thought: How extraordinarily like my poor father he is! Indeed, he was the living image of the surgeon who, until he was seventy, had frittered away on women the fortune he had amassed by the practice of his art. He had been the first to introduce into Bordeaux the blessings of antiseptic treatment. He had never paid the slightest attention to his son, to whom he habitually referred as "the young 'un," as though he had forgotten

his name. One night a woman had brought him home. His mouth was twisted and dribbling. His watch, his note-case, and the diamond ring which he wore on his little finger were all missing. Paul thought: From him I have inherited a heart capable of passion, but not his gift of pleasing—that is a legacy reserved for his grandson.

He looked at Raymond, who was staring into the garden—at this grown man who was his son. After the day of feverish emotions just past he would have dearly loved to confide his troubles to a friendly ear, or, rather, to indulge in a burst of maudlin self-pity, to say to his child: "Why do we never have a good talk? Is it that you think I would not understand you? Is the gulf that separates father and son so unbridgeable? I have the same heart to-day as I had when I was twenty, and you are the flesh of my flesh. There is at least a good chance that we have in common the same set of tastes, antipathies, and temptations. . . . Which of us shall be the first to break this silence that divides us?" A man and a woman, no matter how completely estranged they may be, can at least come together in the ardour of an embrace. Even a mother may take between her hands the head of her grown-up son and kiss his hair. But a father can do no more than the doctor did when he laid his hand on Raymond's shoulder. The boy trembled and turned his head. His father averted his eyes and asked:

"Is it still raining?"

Raymond, upright upon the threshold, stretched his hand into the darkness.

"No, it's left off."

Then, without looking round, he added: "Good-night," and the sound of his footsteps died away.

About the same time, Madame Courrèges was feeling completely "bowled over" because her husband had just suggested that she should take a turn with him in the garden. She said she would go in and fetch a wrap. He heard her go upstairs and then come down again with unwonted speed.

"Take my arm, Lucie: there's a cloud in front of the moon, and it's difficult to see one's way."

"But the path shows white."

She leaned rather heavily on him, and he noticed that her body still smelled the same as it had in the old days of their engagement, when they sat together on a bench in the long June evenings. The mingled scent of human flesh and summer dusk was, as it were, the very essence of their betrothal.

He asked whether she, too, had not noticed the great change that had taken place in their son. No, she said, he was still as surly, as sullen, as pigheaded as he had always been. The doctor pressed his point. Raymond, according to him, was now far less undisciplined. He seemed to have more control over himself. It showed, if in nothing else, at least in the care he was giving to his personal appearance.

"That reminds me. Julie was complaining only yesterday that he wants her to press his trousers twice a week."

"Julie must be made to see reason. Don't forget that she has known him ever since he was a baby."

"Julie is devoted to us, but there are limits even to devotion. It's all very well for Madeleine to talk: *her* maids do nothing at all. I know that Julie is difficult, but I do understand why she should feel annoyed at having to sweep the back stairs as well as the front."

A skinflint nightingale uttered three short notes. Husband and wife caught the hawthorn's scent of bitter almonds as they sauntered on. In a low voice, the doctor continued:

"Our little Raymond . . ."

"We shan't find it easy to replace Julie, and the sooner we realize that, the better. I know you'll say that she drives every cook we have out of the house, but more often than not she is in the right. . . . For instance, Léonie . . ."

With weary resignation he asked:

"Which of them was Léonie?"

"Surely you remember?—the fat one, not the last, but the woman who only stayed with us for three months. She objected to doing the dining-room. But it isn't part of Julie's work."

He said: "Servants to-day are very different from what they used to be."

It was as though some tide in him were suddenly ebbing, and drawing back as it receded all desire in him to confide, to confess, to abandon pretence, to let his tears flow.

"We had better go in."

"Madeleine is for ever saying that the cook is stubborn, but that's not Julie's fault. The woman wants us to raise her wages. They don't make as much out here as they do in town, though things are cheaper. If it wasn't for that they wouldn't stay at all."

"I'm going in."

"Already?"

She had a feeling that she had disappointed him, that she ought to have waited, to have let him do the talking.

"We don't often get a chance to talk," she murmured.

From somewhere beyond the wretched fabric of words that she had built up, from somewhere beyond the wall that her vulgarity had erected, with ant-like patience, day by day, Lucie Courrèges could hear the stifled cry of a man who was buried alive, the shout of an imprisoned miner, and deep within herself, too, another voice replied to his, a sudden tenderness fluttered.

She made as though to lean her head upon her husband's shoulder, but guessed how his body would stiffen, his face take on an expression of hard remoteness.

Raising her eyes towards the house, she could not resist saying:

"You've left the light on in your room!"

She regretted the words as soon as she had uttered them. He hurried on so as to be free of her, ran up the steps, and sighed with relief at finding the drawing-room empty, because it meant that he could reach his study without meeting anybody. Safe there at last, he sat down at his table, kneaded his careworn face with both hands, and once more made that motion of sweeping something aside. . . . The dog's death was a nuisance. It wasn't easy to find animals for his experiments. With all the ridiculous nonsense that had been bothering him of late, he had lost something of his grip on things. I've been relying too much on Robinson, he thought. . . . He must have miscalculated the time of that last injection. . . . The only solution would be to begin again. From now on Robinson must confine his activities to taking the animals' temperature, to collecting and analysing their urine. . . .

VI

A failure of the current had brought the trolleys to a standstill. They stood all along the boulevards, looking like a procession of yellow caterpillars. It had needed this incident to establish, at long last, some sort of direct contact between Raymond Courrèges and Maria Cross; not but what, on the day following the Sunday when they had not seen one another, a terrified feeling that they might never meet again had laid hold on both, with the result that each had separately decided to take the first step. But to her he was a shy schoolboy whom the slightest thing might frighten; and how, he felt, would he ever summon up enough cour-

age to speak to a woman? Although for the first time she was wearing a light-coloured dress, he sensed rather than saw her presence in the crowd, while she, for all her shortsightedness, recognized him from afar. There had been some sort of ceremony, and he was dressed in his school uniform, with the cape unfastened and hanging loose about his shoulders (in imitation of the cadets of the Naval Medical School). A few intending passengers got into the trolley and settled down to wait until it started. Others wandered away in groups. Raymond and Maria found themselves side by side at the far end, close to the platform. Without looking at him, so that he might not think she was speaking for his benefit, she said in a low voice:

"After all, I haven't very far to go. . . ."

And he, with head averted and cheeks all flame:

"It might be rather nice to walk home for once."

It was then that she brought herself to look him full in the face. Never before had she been so close to him.

"We've been travelling back together for so long that we mustn't lose the habit."

They walked a short distance in silence. Furtively she looked at his hot and scarlet face, at the tender skin of youth scraped and sore from the razor. With a boyish gesture he was hugging to his body with both arms a well-worn portfolio crammed with books, and the idea that he was little more than a child became firmly fixed in her mind. This realisation produced in her a sense of uneasy shyness in which scruple, shame, and pure delight played an equal part. He, for his part, felt no less paralysed with nervousness than when, in earlier days, he had decided that only the exercise of superhuman will-power could induce him to enter a shop. Recognition of the fact that he was the taller of the two came as a staggering surprise. The lilac straw hat that she was wearing hid most of her face, but he could see her bare neck and one shoulder which had slipped free of her dress. The thought that he might not be able to find a word with which to break the silence, that he might ruin this precious moment, filled him with panic.

"You don't live very far away: I was forgetting."

"Not very far. The church at Talence is only about ten minutes' ride from the boulevards."

He took from his pocket an ink-stained handkerchief, mopped his forehead, noticed the ink, and put the handkerchief away again.

"But perhaps you've got farther to go?"

"Oh no I haven't: I get out just after passing the church—"

Then, very hurriedly, he added: "I'm young Courrèges."

"The doctor's son?"

There was an eager note in his voice as he asked:

"He's pretty well known, isn't he?"

She had raised her face, the better to see him, and he noticed that the colour had gone from her cheeks. But even as the fact was borne in on him, she said:

"It really is a very small world. But you mustn't talk to him about me."

"I never talk to him about anything. Anyhow, I don't know who you are."

"That's just as well."

Once more she fixed on him a long and brooding look. The doctor's son! In that case, he must surely be just a very innocent and very pious schoolboy who would turn from her in horror as soon as he heard her name. It was impossible that he should not know about her. Young Bertrand Larousselle had been at school with him until last year. The name of Maria Cross must be a by-word among the boys. Less from curiosity than sheer nervousness he pressed her to disclose it.

"You really *must* tell me your name. After all, I've told you mine."

The level light touched to flame a basket of oranges standing in the doorway of a shop. The gardens looked as though they had been daubed all over with dust. At this point a bridge crossed that very same railway line which once had been to Raymond an object of thrilling excitement because trains ran along it to Spain. Maria Cross was thinking: If I tell him who I am, I may lose him. . . . But isn't it my duty to scare him away? This inner debate was rich for her with pain and pleasure. She was quite genuinely suffering, but at the same time felt a vague satisfaction in murmuring to herself: "What a tragedy!"

"When you know who I am . . ." (she could not help thinking of the myth of Psyche, of *Lohengrin*).

His laugh was rather too boisterous. When he spoke, it was without restraint:

"Sooner or later we should have been bound to strike up an acquaintance in the trolley. You must have realized that I made a point of always taking the one that leaves at six. . . . You didn't? Oh, I say, come off it! I often get to the terminus early enough to catch the one before that leaves at a quarter to, but I always give it a miss, just so as to see you. Yesterday I actually came away from the fight after the fourth bull in order not to miss our meeting, and then you weren't there! They tell me that Fuentes was on top of his form in the last kill. But now we've broken the ice why should I care *what* your name is? There was a time when I didn't care about anything, but from the moment I realized you were trying to catch my eye . . ."

Had anyone else been speaking, Maria would have found such language atrociously vulgar, but in his mouth it had a delicious freshness, so that, later, each time she passed this particular spot on her journeys to and fro, she was to be reminded vividly of the sudden access of tenderness and joy that had been released in her by his schoolboy chatter.

"You can't get out of telling me your name. After all, I've only got to ask Papa. That'd be easy—the lady who always gets out of the trolley by the church at Talence."

"I'll tell it to you, but only on condition you swear never to talk about me to the doctor."

She no longer believed that the mention of her name would frighten him off, though she pretended to herself that the threat was real. Fate must decide, she thought—because, deep down, she was quite certain that she held the winning cards. Just before they reached the church she asked him to continue his journey alone—"because of the neighbours" who would recognize her and start gossiping.

"All right, but not until I know . . ."

Very hurriedly, and without looking at him, she said:

"Maria Cross."

"Maria Cross?"

She dug the point of her umbrella into the ground and added, precipitately:

"Wait until you know me . . ."

He was staring, as though dazzled by the sight of her:

"Maria Cross!"

So this was the woman whose name he had heard whispered one summer's day in the Allées de Tourny, when he and his companions were going back to school after the break. She had just passed them in a two-horse brougham. One of the other boys with whom he was walking had said: "Really, women like that! . . ." And suddenly another memory came back into his mind. There had been a time when he was taking a course of medicated baths, which meant that he had to leave school at four o'clock. On this particular occasion he had overtaken young Ber-

trand Larousselle. He was striding alone, his long legs encased in gaiters of undressed leather. Already, in spite of his tender years, he was a bullying and overbearing youth. The younger boy was, as a rule, accompanied by either a servant or a black-gloved priest with his coat-collar turned up. Among the "juniors" Raymond enjoyed the worst reputation of all the "uppers," and, whenever the two of them met, the pure and pious Bertrand would devour the notorious "dirty beast" with his eyes. It never even occurred to him that to this same dirty beast he was himself an object of mystery. At this time Madame Victor Larousselle was still alive, and many ridiculous rumours about her were rife in town and school. Maria Cross, it was said, had set her heart on marriage, and was demanding that her lover should turn his family out of doors. Others announced as a fact that she was waiting until Madame Larouselle should have died of cancer, so that she could then be married in church. More than once Raymond had caught sight of Bertrand behind the closed windows of a car, driving with his corpse-like mother. The women of the Courrèges and Basque families, speaking of her, used to say: "Poor thing! With what dignity she bears her martyrdom! If ever anybody had their purgatory here on earth, it's she! . . . If *my* husband behaved like that, I'd spit in his face and just clear out. *I* wouldn't stand it!"

On the day in question Bertrand Larousselle was quite alone. He heard behind him the whistling of the dirty beast and increased his pace. But Raymond kept on a level with him and never took his eyes off his short covert coat and cap of handsome English tweed. Everything that had to do with the younger boy fascinated him. Suddenly, Bertrand broke into a run, and a notebook slipped from his satchel. By the time he noticed his loss Raymond had already picked it up. Its owner turned back, his face pale with fear and anger. "Give it to me!" he cried: but Raymond read out in a low voice the title on the cover—"My Diary"—and sniggered.

"Young Larousselle's diary—that ought to be pretty juicy!"

"Give it to me!"

Raymond sprinted ahead, turned into the Parc Bordelais, and ran down one of the deserted paths. Behind him he could hear a miserable, breathless voice panting out, over and over again, "Give it to me! I'll tell them you took it!" But the dirty beast, hidden from view by a thick shrubbery, was engaged in mocking young Larousselle, who, by this time at the end of his tether, was lying full length on the grass and sobbing.

"Here's your lousy notebook, your precious diary. Take it, you little idiot!"

He pulled the boy to his feet, wiped his eyes, and brushed down the overcoat of English tweed. Whoever would have thought that the great bully could be so kind! The brat smiled his gratitude at Raymond, who, suddenly, could not resist putting into words a vulgar whim of curiosity:

"I say, have you ever seen her—this Maria Cross woman?"

Bertrand, scarlet to the tips of his ears, picked up his satchel and took to his heels. It never even occurred to Raymond to run after him.

Maria Cross . . . it was she now who was devouring *him* with her eyes. He had expected her to look taller, more mysterious. So this small woman in the lilac dress was actually Maria Cross. Noticing his confusion she mistook the cause.

"Please don't think . . ." she stammered. "You mustn't, really . . ."

She trembled in the presence of this judge whom she had viewed in the light of an angelic messenger. She saw no sign of the grubby thoughts of youth, did not know that spring is often the season of mud, and that this growing lad might be mostly composed of filth. She could not endure the contempt which she imagined him to be feeling, and, with a few hurried murmurs of farewell, was already beating her retreat. But he ran after her.

"To-morrow, same time, same trolley?"

"Are you sure that's what you want?"

She made off then, but twice turned her head. He was standing where she had left him, thinking: Maria Cross's got a crush on me!—As though he could not believe his good luck, he spoke the words aloud: "Maria Cross's got a crush on me!"

He breathed in the dusk as though it contained the very essence of the universe, as though he could savour it in every nerve and fibre of his exultant body. Maria Cross had got a crush on him! Should he tell his pals? Not one of them would believe it. He could already see before him the leafy prison where the members of one single family dwelt side by side, yet no less cut off from one another than the worlds which make up the Milky Way. How inadequate, this evening, was that cage to house the stature of his pride! He skirted it, and plunged into a plantation of pines—the only one that was not fenced in. It was called the Bois de Berge. The earth on which he flung himself was warmer than a human body. The pine-needles left deep imprints on the palms of his hands.

When he entered the dining-room his father was cutting the pages of a journal, and saying something in reply to an observation of his wife's.

"I'm *not* reading—just looking at the titles of the articles."

No one but his grandmother seemed to have heard his "good-evening."

"So it's you, you young rascal!"

As he passed her chair, she put out her hand and drew him to her:

"You smell of resin."

"I've been in the pine-woods."

She looked him up and down with an air of knowing tolerance, murmuring an abusive epithet as though it had been an endearment:

"You little horror!"

He lapped up his soup noisily, like a dog. How insignificant all these people seemed to him! He was way up above them, soaring in the sunlight. Only with his father did he feel that he had some connection, because *he* knew Maria Cross, had been in her house, had attended her professionally, had seen her in bed, had pressed his ear to her chest, her back . . . Maria Cross! . . . Maria Cross! . . . the name choked him like a clot of blood. He could taste its warm saltiness in his mouth. The hot tide of it flooded his cheeks, broke from his control.

"I saw Maria Cross this evening."

The doctor fixed him with a stare.

"How did you recognize her?"

"I was with Papillon—he knows her by sight."

"Hullo!" exclaimed Basque; "Raymond's blushing!"

One of the little girls took up the phrase:

"Oo! Uncle Raymond's blushing!"

He made an ill-tempered movement of the shoulders. His father questioned him again, this time averting his eyes:

"Was she alone?"

At his son's reply—"Quite alone"—he returned to his occupation of cutting pages. Madame Courrèges said:

"It really is extraordinary how much more interested you are in that woman than in any other. What's so very odd, after all, in his having seen that creature in the street? In days gone by, when she was a domestic servant, you wouldn't

have paid the slightest attention to her."

There was an interruption from the doctor: "My dear, she never *was* a domestic servant."

"Well, even if she had been," put in Madeleine, and there was a sharp edge to her voice, "that's nothing to be ashamed of—very much to the contrary, I should have thought!"

The maid having left the room with one of the dishes, she turned angrily on her mother:

"It almost looks as though you were deliberately trying to upset the servants and hurt their feelings! Irma has an extremely sensitive nature!"

"So I've got to handle the staff with kid gloves, now, have I? Really, no one would believe the things that go on in this house!"

"You can behave exactly as you like with your own servants: all I ask is that you shouldn't drive other people's away . . . especially when you expect them to wait at table!"

"You're not exactly tactful yourself where Julie is concerned, and you've got the reputation of never being able to keep a maid when you do get one. . . . Everyone knows that the only reason *my* servants ever give notice is because they can't get on with yours!"

At this point the maid came back and the altercation was interrupted. But as soon as she had once again returned to the pantry it was resumed in a series of whispers. Raymond studied his father with amusement. Had Maria Cross been a domestic servant, would *he* have so much as noticed her existence? Suddenly, the doctor raised his head, and, without looking at any of those present, announced:

"Maria Cross is the daughter of the woman who was principal of the St. Clair school when your beloved Monsieur Labrousse was curé there, Lucie."

"What? The harpy who used to plague

the life out of him? Who preferred to stay away from Mass unless she and her girls could have the front seats in the nave? Well, I can't say I'm surprised: like mother, like daughter."

"Don't you remember," said Madame Courrèges the elder, "that story of poor Monsieur Labrousse's about how, when the Marquis de Lur-Saluces was beaten in the elections by a wretched little attorney from Bazas, she came round in the evening attended by the whole school, and stood under the presbytery windows jeering at him, and how her hands were quite black with letting off fireworks in honour of the new Deputy? . . ."

"A nice lot they were, I must say."

But the doctor did not wait to hear more. Instead of going upstairs as usual to his study, he followed Raymond into the garden.

Both father and son wanted to talk. Unknown to themselves some strong influence was forming a bond between them. It was as though they were harbouring the same secret. In just such a way do initiates and conspirators recognize and seek one another. Each found in the other the one being in the world to whom he could unburden himself of his precious obsession. As two butterflies, separated by miles and miles, meet at the spot that houses the odorous female, so had they followed the convergent tracks of their desires, and alighted side by side on the invisible body of Maria Cross.

"Have you got a cigarette, Raymond? I've forgotten what tobacco tastes like. . . . Thank you. . . . What about taking a turn?"

He heard his own words with amazement. He was like a man who, having been cured by a miracle, sees the wound that he had thought healed suddenly open again. No longer ago than that morning, in his laboratory, he had been conscious of the lightness of spirit that comes to the devout penitent when he has received ab-

solution. Seeking in his heart some trace of his recent passion, he had found none. How solemnly, and rather priggishly, he had lectured Robinson, who, ever since the spring, had been somewhat neglecting his work for a lady of the chorus.

"My dear chap, the scientist who really loves his work and is consumed with the desire to make a reputation will always regard the hours and minutes given over to sexual passion as so much time wasted."

Robinson had swept back his tousled hair, rubbed his spectacles on his acid-stained overalls, and ventured a protest: "All the same, sir—love . . ."

"No, my boy, for the real scientist, except in brief moments of purely temporary surrender, his work must always take precedence of love. He will, if he sacrifices it, always be haunted by bitter thoughts of the noble satisfaction he might have known if only he had been faithful to his vocation."

"It certainly is true," Robinson had replied, "that most great scientists do occasionally indulge their sexual impulses, but I know scarcely any whom you would call men of really strong passions."

The doctor understood now why it was that this acquiescent attitude on the part of his disciple had brought the colour to his cheeks.

Raymond had only to say, "I saw Maria Cross," for the passion he had thought dead to stir again. Alas! it was merely in a state of torpor . . . a single word could bring it back to life, provide it with the food it craved. It was already stretching its limbs, yawning and getting to its feet. If it couldn't embrace in flesh-and-blood reality the woman of its choice, it would find relief in speech. No matter what the cost, he *must* talk about Maria Cross.

Though they had been drawn together by a mutual desire to sing Maria Cross's praises, their very first words set father and son at odds. Raymond maintained that a woman of her emotional scope could not but outrage the anemic susceptibilities of the devout. What he admired in her was her boldness, her limitless ambition, the dissolute life which he imagined her to have led. The doctor, on the contrary, insisted that there was nothing of the courtesan about her, that one must not believe what people said:

"I *know* Maria Cross! I was her best friend during all that time when her little François was so desperately ill, and I still am. . . . She unburdened herself to me. . . ."

"My poor dear father, what you mean is that she pulled the wool over your eyes. . . ."

The doctor controlled himself with an effort. His reply, when it came, was given with considerable warmth:

"You're quite wrong, my boy. She confided in me with quite extraordinary humility. If it is true to say of anybody that their actions bear no resemblance to themselves, it is certainly true to say it of Maria Cross. Incurable laziness has been her undoing. Her mother, the St. Clair principal, got her to work for the entrance examination for the Sèvres Training College, but when she married an army doctor of the 144th regiment all that went by the board. The three years she spent as his wife were uneventful, and if he had lived she would have led an ordinary decent and humdrum existence. The only cause of complaint he had against her was that temperamental indolence to which I have already referred, because it meant that she didn't run his house well. He used to grumble a bit, she told me, when he came home of an evening, at finding that there was nothing for dinner but a dish of noodles heated up over a spirit-lamp. Her favourite occupation was to lie in a torn dressing-gown and slippers, reading all day long. People call her a courtesan, but you'd be sur-

prised if you knew how little mere luxury means to her. Why, only a short time ago she decided to give up using the car which was Larousselle's present to her, and now she travels by trolley like anybody else. . . . What are you laughing at? I don't see anything particularly amusing about that. . . . Stop it! it's getting on my nerves. . . . When she found herself a widow with a child, you may imagine how ill-equipped for work an intellectual woman like that would feel. . . . Unfortunately, a friend of her husband's got her the post of secretary to Larousselle. She was completely innocent of any sort of scheming, but—well, though Larousselle had the reputation of being a harsh employer, he never said a word to her, though she was always late at the office and was hardly ever up to time with her work. That alone was enough to compromise her, and by the time she realized the situation it was too late to do anything about it. The others treated her as the boss's little bit, and their hostility made her position impossible. She spoke to Larousselle about it, which was just what he had been waiting for. He had a small property close to Bordeaux for which, just then, he had failed, or perhaps not wanted, to find a tenant. He suggested that she should act as caretaker until she could land another job. . . ."

"And I suppose she found the suggestion all innocent and above board?"

"Not at all. Obviously, she realized perfectly well what he was after: but the poor woman was saddled with an establishment far too expensive for her straitened circumstances, and, to crown it all, the child was struck down with enteritis, and the doctor thought it essential that he should have country air. Finally, in view of the fact that she was already so deeply compromised, she just hadn't the courage to refuse such a windfall. She let herself be over-persuaded. . . ."

"You're telling *me!* . . ."

"Don't talk like that! You know nothing whatever about her. She stood out for a long time. But what was there for her to do? She couldn't prevent Larousselle from bringing his friends out to dinner. I realize that she was weak and irresponsible, that she ought to have refused to act as his hostess; but I can assure you that those famous Tuesday evenings were very far from being the hideous orgies of popular imagination. The only thing at all scandalous about them was that they occurred at a time when Madame Larousselle's health had taken a turn for the worse. I can swear that Maria had no idea that her employer's wife was in danger. 'My conscience was clear,' she told me. 'At that time I had not permitted Monsieur Larousselle so much as a kiss. There was nothing between us, absolutely nothing. What harm was there in my presiding over a tableful of fools? . . . I admit that the idea of dazzling them did go to my head. I enjoyed playing the bluestocking. I knew that my employer was proud of me. He had promised to do something for the boy.' "

"And you really swallowed all that? . . ."

What a simpleton his poor father was! But the thing that Raymond really resented was that the doctor should have diminished Maria Cross to the stature of a respectable, weak-willed little schoolteacher—and thereby reduced his sense of conquest to nothing.

"She didn't yield to Larousselle's suggestions until after his wife's death, and then only from lassitude, from a sort of despairing apathy—yes, that exactly describes it. She used the phrase herself when describing the situation—a *despairing apathy*. She had no illusions, was perfectly clearheaded. She was not taken in by his assumption of the role of inconsolable widower any more than she was by his promise of eventual marriage. She

knew too much about men of his type, she told me, to be deluded. As his mistress she was a distinct asset, but things would be very different if she were his wife! I suppose you know that he sent young Bertrand to the Collège de Normandie so that he wouldn't be exposed to contact with her? In his heart of hearts he thought her no different from the common-or-garden drabs with whom he was for ever deceiving her. Besides, I happen to know that their physical intimacy doesn't amount to much. I am convinced of that; you can take my word for it. He, of course, is mad about her, and he's not the sort of man to be content with having her just for show purposes, as is generally supposed in Bordeaux: but she is adamant. . . ."

"You're not going to tell me that Maria Cross is a saint?"

They could not see one another, but each could sense hostility in the other, though they kept their voices low. They had been brought together for a moment by the name of Maria Cross, and it was her name that separated them now. The man walked with head high: the youth kept his eyes fixed upon the ground and vented his ill-humour by kicking at a pine-cone.

"You think me a fool, but of us two, it is you who are the innocent. If you think only ill of people, you'll never get to know them. You have stumbled on precisely the right word. I know what Maria Cross has been through, and I know that somewhere in her there are the makings of a saint . . . yes, really, a saint. . . . But you could never understand that."

"Don't make me laugh!"

"What do you know about her? You've merely been listening to gossip. I *do* know about her."

"I know what I know."

"And how much may that be?"

The doctor stopped dead in the middle of the path where the chestnut-trees

FRANÇOIS MAURIAC

threw a deep shade. He gripped Raymond by the arm.

"Oh, let me alone! It's all one to me whether Maria Cross does, or does not, go to bed with Larousselle—but he's not the only pebble on her beach!"

"Liar!"

Raymond was brought up with a shock. "Oh, look here . . ." he muttered. A suspicion had dawned in his mind, only to die out again almost at once, or rather to withdraw from his immediate consciousness. Exasperating his father might be, but he found it no more possible than did Maria to connect the idea of love with the rather neutral image of him which had been his since childhood. He had always seemed to him to be a man without passions and without sin, a man impervious to evil, incorruptible, living in a world far above the rather earthy concerns of other men. He heard the sound of his rather heavy breathing in the darkness.

The doctor made a violent effort to control his feelings. In a tone that was half mocking and almost cheerful, he repeated:

"Yes, liar and humbug. All you want to do is to destroy my illusions. . . ."

And, since Raymond remained obstinately silent, he added:

"Go on, out with it. . . ."

"I don't know anything. . . ."

"You said just now—'I know what I know.'"

The boy replied that he had spoken without thinking. His manner was that of someone who has made up his mind to say nothing. The doctor did not press him. This son of his, so close that he could feel the warmth of his body and catch the smell he exuded as of some young and untamed animal, would never understand him.

"I shall stay out here a bit. Won't you sit down a moment, Raymond? There's a breeze getting up at last."

But his son said that he would rather go to bed. For a moment or two longer the doctor heard the sound he made as he kicked at the pine-cones, then he was alone under the dense and drooping leaves —alive to all the passionate melancholy flung heavenward by the sleeping fields. With an immense effort he rose from his seat. The light was burning in his study. . . . I suppose Lucie thinks I'm still working. What a lot of time I've wasted! I'm fifty—no, fifty-three. What tittle-tattle has that Papillon boy been repeating? . . . He let his hands wander over the bark of a chestnut-tree where he remembered that Madeleine and Raymond had once carved their initials, and suddenly, flinging his arms about the trunk, closed his eyes and laid his cheek against the smooth surface of the wood. Then he stood back, dusted the sleeves of his jacket, straightened his tie, and walked towards the house.

Sauntering between the vines, Raymond was still amusing himself by kicking a pine-cone. With his hands stuck deep in his trouser pockets, he muttered to himself: "What a simple-minded old fool! there can't be many of his sort left!" Well, he at least would be equal to his opportunity; no one would lead *him* by the nose. He had no intention of prolonging his happiness through the dragging hours of this stifling night. The stars meant nothing to him, nor the scent of the pale acacia blooms. The assault of the summer darkness was powerless against this well-armed young male who was so sure of his strength in the splendid present, so sure of his young body, so utterly indifferent to all that it could not subdue and penetrate.

VII

Work, the one and only opium. Each morning the doctor woke, cured of his

[58]

obsession, as though what had been gnawing at his heart had been cut out by the surgeon's knife. He left the house unaccompanied (in fine weather Raymond did not use the brougham). But his mind raced ahead of him. Already, in imagination, he was at work on his experiments. His passion diminished to a dull throb which made itself felt as a threat rather than an actuality. Whether it would become more than that, would wake again into active life, depended upon him, and upon him alone. Let him but touch the sore spot, and the sudden pain would make him cry out. . . . But yesterday his pet hypothesis had been brought tumbling to the ground by one single fact—or so Robinson assured him. What a triumph for X, who had accused him before the Biological Society of using faulty methods.

One of women's curses is that they can never free themselves of the enemy who preys upon their vitals. And so it happened that while the doctor, intent on his microscope, was blissfully unaware of his own wretchedness and of the world outside the walls of his laboratory, a prisoner pent within the confines of his observations, Maria Cross, lying on a sofa behind closed shutters, could think of nothing but the moment when she would see Raymond again, of that brief flame which alone brought warmth and brightness into the dreary sequence of her days. But how disappointing the moment was when it came! Almost at once they had had to give up their plan of travelling together as far as Talence church. Maria Cross went on ahead and met him in the Park, not far from the school-buildings. He was less forthcoming now than he had been on the occasion of their first exchanges, and his attitude of shy mistrust did much to convince her that he really was only a callow boy, though an occasional snigger, a sudden furtive glance, should have put her on her guard. But she clung to her

darling theory of his angelic purity. With infinite precautions, as though she were dealing with an untamed and still unsullied bird, she, as it were, crept closer and closer, walking on tiptoe and holding her breath. Everything about him conspired to strengthen the outlines of that false image of him which she had constructed: the cheeks so prone to blush, the schoolboy slang, the still visible traces of childhood that hung like morning mist about the strong young body. She was terrified by what she thought she had discovered in Raymond, though it had no existence in fact. The candour of his glance set her trembling, and she felt guilty of having brought into that frank gaze a hint of trouble and unease. Nothing occurred to warn her that when they were together he wanted only to run away, the better to gloat on the thought of her and to decide what line he had better take. Should he hire a room? Papillon knew an address, but it was a bit too squalid for a woman of her type. Papillon had told him that one could get rooms by the day at the Terminus. He'd have to find out about that. He had already walked up and down outside the hotel without being able to summon up courage enough to make inquiries at the desk. There might be other difficulties, too, of a physical nature. Over these he brooded until he had made mountains out of molehills.

Maria Cross was playing with the idea of asking him to her house, but of this plan she had, so far, said nothing. She was resolved not to smirch, even in thought, this child of nature, this untamed bird. In the stiffness of her drawing-room, in the drowsy heat of the garden, their love would burgeon into words, and the storm within her breast would find relief in rain. Beyond this point she would not let imagination go. The extreme of her permitted indulgence was to fancy the feel of his head pressed to her body. He would be to her as a fawn domesticated by kindness . . . she would feel the warm, soft muzzle in her hand. . . . She seemed to see before her a long, long vista of caresses. They must be fond yet chaste. She would not let herself, even in imagination, dwell upon a fiercer pilgrimage of love, upon that ultimate bliss of tangled forest undergrowth into which they might plunge and be lost to all the world. . . . No, no—passion must never be allowed to sweep them to such extremes! Not for all the world would she destroy the childish innocence which filled her with such fear, such adoration. How to convey, without startling him into flight, that this very week he might take advantage of Monsieur Larousselle's absence on business in Belgium and venture into the stuffy and encumbered intimacies of her drawing-room? Surely, if she put such a thought into words, he would at once suspect some evil intention? What she did not know was that he took his pleasure of her with far greater satisfaction to himself when they were not together, that she was with him in fancy wherever he went, or that he possessed her, turned from her, and possessed her, again and again, like a famished puppy.

At dinner the doctor kept his eyes upon him. He watched him greedily lapping up his soup, and saw, not his son, but a man who had said, speaking of Maria Cross, "I know what I know. . . ." What could that Papillon possibly have told him? It was no use deceiving himself. Quite obviously, someone of whom he knew nothing was monopolizing Maria's thoughts. I go on expecting her to write, he thought, when it should be perfectly clear that she doesn't want to see me ever again. And if that is true, it means, further, that she has given herself to another . . . but to whom? Impossible to sound the boy any more than I have done. If I insist on his telling me what he knows I shall merely be betraying myself. . . . At that point in his ruminations his son got up and left the room, without deigning to answer his mother, who called after him: "Where are you off to?"

"He goes into Bordeaux almost every evening now," she said. "I know that he gets the key of the gate from the gardener, and comes in at 2 A.M. by the scullery-window. You ought to hear what he says when I question him. It's for *you* to do something about it, but you're so weak!"

The doctor could only stammer: "The wisest thing is to keep our eyes shut."

He heard Basque's voice: "If he was *my* son I'd bring him to heel soon enough. . . ."

The doctor got up from the table in his turn and went into the garden. He would have liked to cry aloud: "My torment is the only thing that has any reality for me!" No one realizes that it is a father's passions, more often than not, that alienate him from his son. He returned to the house, sat down at his worktable, opened a drawer, took out a packet of letters, and settled down to re-read what Maria had written to him six months earlier:

"Only the desire to become a better woman reconciles me to the necessity of living. . . . I care little what the world should know of my salvation, or that others should continue to point at me the finger of scorn. . . . Humbly I accept their censure."

He no longer remembered that, when he had read those words for the first time, such extravagance of virtue had filled him with despair, that the obligation to walk with her in so rarefied an air had been his martyrdom, that it was maddening to think that he was expected to show the way of salvation to the one woman with whom he would so gladly have gone to perdition. He thought how, reading this letter, Raymond would laugh; grew indignant at the fancy, and voiced a protest in a half whisper as though someone were walking at his side. "Bogus, you say? . . . bogus? . . . The trouble is that whenever she gets a pen in her hand she becomes too 'literary'. . . . But was that humility of tenderness when she sat by her dying child bogus, that acquiescence of hers in suffering, as though the mysterious heritage of faith had come down to her through all her mother's tedious rehash of Kantian principles? In the presence of that small bed beneath its load of lilies" (how isolated and alone the body of the dead child had looked, how silently it had seemed to be accusing her!) "she gave expression to her sense of guilt, beating her breast and groaning aloud that all was for the best, finding consolation in the thought that he had been too young to feel ashamed of her. . . ." But here the man of science intervened: The truth is rather more complicated. She *was* sincere in her grief, but, all the same, she got a certain amount of satisfaction out of her heroics—they gave her the excuse to strike an attitude. . . . Maria Cross had always had an appetite for situations of high romance. Hadn't she even gone so far as to play with the idea of having an interview with Madame Larousselle on her death-bed? It was only with the utmost difficulty that he had made her realize that scenes of that kind never "come off" except on the stage. She had given up the plan, but only on condition that he should undertake to plead her cause with the wife. Luckily, he had been able to assure her that she had been forgiven.

He went to the window, and, leaning out in the half darkness, occupied his mind with analysing the various night sounds—a continuous scraping of crickets and grasshoppers, the croaking of two frogs in a pond, the intermittent notes of a bird that probably wasn't a nightingale, the clanging of the last trolley. "I know

what I know," Raymond had said. Who could it be that had caught Maria's fancy? The doctor pronounced one or two names, but at once rejected them. She had a horror of those particular men. But of whom *hadn't* she a horror? He thought: Remember what Larousselle told you in confidence that time he came to have his blood-pressure tested—"Quite between ourselves, she doesn't really enjoy—you know what I mean. She puts up with it from me because, well, with me it's rather different. . . . It really was screamingly funny the first time I asked all these chaps to the house. They fluttered round her like moths. When a man introduces one to his mistress, one's first thought, isn't it? is whether one can cut him out. . . . Go ahead, my fine fellows, said I to myself . . . and, of course, nothing happened. They were all quite quietly kept in their place. No one knows less about love than Maria, and takes so little pleasure in it—and I'm speaking about what I know. She's as innocent as you make 'em, doctor, a great deal more innocent than most of the fine respectable ladies who turn up their noses at her." He had said, too: "It is because Maria is so completely unlike other women that I'm always terrified that, some time when I'm not there, she may make some absurd decision. She spends her whole day in a sort of dream, and only leaves the house to go to the cemetery. Do you think it's possible that she has been influenced by something she's read?"

It may be something she's read, thought the doctor: but, no; if it were I should have heard about it: books are my line of country. A book sometimes turns a *man's* life upside down, or so one's told, but does the same hold true of women? It's only life that really and truly affects them deeply, things of flesh and blood. A book?—he shook his head. The word book brought "buck" to his mind, and he had a sudden vision of some wild young animal rearing at Maria's approach.

Some cats in the grass set up a prolonged miaowing. A footstep sounded on the gravel: there was the noise as of a window being opened. It must be Raymond coming back. A moment later the doctor heard someone in the corridor. There was a knock at his door. It was Madeleine.

"Not in bed yet, Papa? I'm worried about Catherine. She suddenly started a nasty hacking cough. I was afraid it might be croup."

"Croup doesn't come on suddenly like that. I'll be along in a moment."

Some time later, as he was coming out of his daughter's room, he felt a pain in his left side, and stood leaning against the wall in the darkness, clutching at his heart. He did not call for help. His brain was perfectly clear, and he could catch from behind the door the sounds of a conversation that had just started between husband and wife.

"I know all about his being a good scientist, but science has made him skeptical. He no longer believes in medicines. But how can illness he cured without them?"

"He assured us it was nothing, not even a false croup."

"Don't kid yourself: if it had been one of his own patients he'd have prescribed something, but because it's one of the family he's not going to spend an unnecessary penny. There are times when it's an awful nuisance not being able to call in an outside man."

"But it's very convenient having him always on the spot, especially at night. When the poor old thing's no longer there, I shall never know what it is to sleep in peace, worrying about the children."

"You ought to have married a doctor, that's what *you* ought to have done!"

There was a sound of a laugh being quickly silenced by a kiss. The doctor felt the hand that was squeezing his heart loosen its grip. Very quietly he stole away. He turned in, found that he could not lie at full length without pain, and spent the night sitting upright on his bed. The whole world was asleep. The only sound was the fluttering of the leaves. . . . Has Maria ever known what it is to love? I know she's had crazes for people—for instance, there was that little Gaby Dubois girl, she tried to make her break with young Dupont-Gunther, but that was a romantic passion. She must have had some apostolic ancestor from whom she inherits that taste of hers for saving souls. Who was it, by the way, who told me a lot of ugly things about her, in connection with this same Gaby? . . . Can she be "one of them"? I remember other crazes of the same kind. . . . There may be a touch of it in her case. I've always noticed that an excess of romanticism . . . Dawn already!

He lowered his pillow, and with many precautions lay down in such a way that his wretched carcass suffered no hurt. In a few moments he had lost consciousness.

VIII

"But what am I going to say to the gardener?"

In one of the deserted paths of the Parc Bordelais Maria Cross was trying to persuade Raymond to pay her a visit at home. In her own house there would be no risk of their meeting people. She urged him to agree, and felt ashamed of doing so, felt that, in spite of herself, she was corrupting him. How was it possible not to see in the unreasoning terror of a boy who had once walked up and down in front of a shop because he didn't dare go in, the indisputable evidence of frightened innocence? With that thought in her mind she hastened to say:

"But, Raymond, you mustn't think I want . . . you mustn't start imagining. . . ."

"It'll be so awkward if I run into the gardener."

"But there *isn't* a gardener: I've told you so already. I'm living in an empty house which Monsieur Laroussselle had not succeeded in renting. He has installed me there as caretaker."

Raymond burst into a guffaw of laughter:

"A lady-gardener, eh?"

The young woman looked down so that he should not see her face, and stammered out:

"I *know* appearances are against me. After all, people can't be expected to know that I accepted the situation in perfect good faith. . . . François had to have country air. . . ."

Raymond was familiar with this particular refrain. Talk away, he said to himself, and broke in with:

"So I needn't worry about the gardener, but what about the servants?"

She reassured him on that point too. On Sundays she always let Justine, her only maid, go out. She was a married woman whose husband, a chauffeur, slept in the house so as to ensure there being a man about the place, which was none too well protected. The suburban road was not very safe. But on Sunday afternoons Justine and he always went out together. Raymond would merely have to enter by the front door and go through the dining-room on the left. He would find the drawing-room at the far end.

He dug his heel into the gravel with a thoughtful air. The creaking of a swing could be heard coming from behind a privet hedge. An old woman was hawking stale cakes and bars of chocolate done up in yellow paper. Remarking that he had had no lunch, he bought a crescent and a chocolate praline. As she watched him munching his meagre meal, Maria suddenly saw with perfect clarity the inexorable nature of her destiny. The desire that had come to birth in her heart had been pure and limpid, yet her every action had the appearance of a monstrous depravity. When, in the trolley, her eyes had first found rest and refreshment in the young face opposite, there had been no trace of evil intention in her mind. Why should she have fought against a temptation that was so little suspect? A thirsty traveller has no reason to beware of the stream he happens on. I *do* want him to come to my house, she thought, but only because in the streets, on the bench of a public garden, I shall never succeed in probing his secret self. . . . But that doesn't alter the fact that, so far as appearances go, here is a young kept woman of twenty-seven luring a young boy into her web— the son of the only man who has ever believed in me and has never cast a stone. . . . A little later, after they had parted, and just before reaching the Croix de Saint-Genès, her thoughts returned to the subject: I want him to come, but with no evil design, not the least in the world. The very idea of such a thing makes me feel sick. But he doesn't trust me, and why should he? Everything I do is double-faced: to me it looks innocent enough, but to the world, hateful, abominable. Perhaps the world sees more truly than I do. . . . She spoke first one name, then another. If it were true that she was held in contempt for actions in which she had become unintentionally involved, she could remember others that she had done in secret, others of which no one knew but herself.

She pushed open the gate which, next Sunday, Raymond would unlatch for the first time, and walked up the drive which was overgrown with grass (there was no gardener). So heavily did the sky seem to sag that it was hard to believe the overarching cloud would not burst with its own weight—it was as though the heavens had caught discouragement from a thirsty world. The leaves hung blighted from the trees. The maid had not closed the shutters, and great bluebottles were bumping against the bottom of the window-frames. She had only just energy enough to throw her hat onto the piano. Her shoes left dirty marks on the sofa. There was only one thing possible to do —light a cigarette. But she was aware, too, of something no less habitual, the physical apathy that accompanied the activity of her imagination, no matter how wrought-up that might be. What an endless number of afternoons she had wasted lying just here, feeling slightly sick as the result of over-smoking! How many plans of escape, of self-betterment, she had elaborated, only to see them fall in ruins! To bring them to fruition she would have had, first, to stop lying there supine, to do something positive, to see people. . . . But even if I abandon all attempts to improve the external conditions of my life, I can at least refuse to do anything of which my conscience would disapprove, which might cause it to feel uneasy. Take, for instance, this case of young Courrèges. . . . She had quite decided that if she were about to lure him into her house it was only because she wanted to indulge that sweet and harmless sentiment which had come to her, originally, in the six-o'clock trolley; that sense of comfort in another's presence, that melancholy pleasure of quite quietly letting her eyes take their fill—though here, in this room, she would taste it more intimately than had been possible in the trolley, and at greater leisure. But was that really all? When the presence of another person thrills us emotionally, our imagination leaps ahead, though we may not always realize it, opening up vistas the very vagueness of which has something about it that is not wholly innocent. She

thought: Very soon I should have grown tired merely of looking at him had it not been that I felt convinced that he would respond to my handling, that, sooner or later, we should speak to one another. . . . This room, so far as I can foresee, will witness nothing but motherly caresses and unimpassioned kisses, will hear nothing but spoken confidences. . . . Oh, come now, be honest with yourself! Admit that you *are* aware of the existence, beyond such innocuous happiness, of a whole region of the emotions, forbidden, it is true, yet open to exploration. There will be no barrier to break down. The field of action will lie open before you. You have only to work your way cautiously forward, to lose yourself in the misty distance as though by accident. . . . And afterwards? Who is there to forbid you the enjoyment of this delight. . . . Don't you know that you could make the boy happy? . . . Ah, that's where you begin to be the dupe of your own appetites. . . . He is the son of Dr. Courrèges, of the saintly Dr. Courrèges. . . . He wouldn't admit that the case was even open to argument. You once told him jokingly that the moral law within him was as bright and shining as the starry sky above his head. . . .

She could hear the raindrops on the leaves, the tentative rumble of the storm. She closed her eyes, tried to fix her thoughts, concentrated her mind on the beloved face of the young boy whose innocence was wholly unsmirched (or that was what she wanted to believe), the boy who, at that very moment, was hurrying along in an attempt to outstrip the coming storm, and thinking: Papillon says it's always best to take the bull by the horns. With women of that kind, he says, brutality's the only thing that counts, the only thing they really like. . . . With his thoughts in turmoil he looked up at the growling heavens. Suddenly he began to run, his cape flung over his head, took a short cut, and jumped over a patch of shrubbery as nimbly as a buck. The storm was moving away, but it was still there. The very silence betrayed its presence. Maria had a sudden inspiration which she felt certain could not be misunderstood. She got up, sat down at her desk, and wrote:

"Don't come Sunday—or any other day. It is for your sake, and for your sake only, that I agree to this sacrifice. . . ."

She should have left it at that, and just signed her name. But some devilish counsellor persuaded her to add a whole page more:

". . . You will have been the one and only happiness of a tormented and hopeless life. As we traveled home together all through this last winter, the sight of you brought me peace, though you did not know it. But the face that was your gift to me was but the outward and visible sign of a soul which I longed to possess. I wanted there to be nothing about you that I did not know. I wanted to provide the answer to your uncertainties, to smooth the path before your feet, to become for you someone who would be more than a mother, better than a friend. I live in my dream of that. But it is not in my power to be other than I am. In spite of yourself, in spite of me, you would breathe the corruption with which the world has choked me."

On and on she wrote. The rain had settled in for good, and the only sound to be heard was that of falling water. The windows of all the rooms were shut. Hailstones rattled in the hearth. Maria Cross took up a book, but it was too dark to read, and, because of the storm, the electricity was not working. She sat down at the piano, and leaned forward as she played. It was as though her head were drawn by some attraction to her hands.

The next day, which was Friday, she felt vaguely pleased that the storm had broken the spell of heat, and spent the whole day in a dressing-gown, reading, making music, idling. She tried to recall every word of her letter, to imagine the effect it would have on young Courrèges. On Saturday, after a close and heavy morning, the rain began again. She realized then the reason for her pleasure. The bad weather would prevent her from going out on Sunday, as she had meant to do, so that should the boy after all keep their appointment in spite of her letter, she would be there to receive him. Stepping back from the window through which she had been watching the rain splashing on the garden path, she said aloud in a firm, strong voice as though she were taking a solemn oath: "Whatever the weather, I shall go out."

But where would she go? If François were alive she would take him to the circus. It was her habit, sometimes, to go to a concert, where she would sit alone in a private box, or—and this she preferred—would take a seat in a public one. But on these occasions the audience always quickly recognized her. She could guess, from the movement of their lips, that people were talking about her. Levelled opera-glasses delivered her up, at close range and utterly defenceless, to a world of enemies. A voice would say: "When all's said, women like that *do* know how to dress—but then, of course, with all that money it's not difficult; besides, they've nothing to think about *except* their bodies." Occasionally one of Monsieur Larousselle's friends would leave the Club Box and pay her a visit. Half turned towards the audience he would laugh loudly, proud of being seen in conversation with Maria Cross.

Except for the Saint-Cecelia concert

she had, even during François' lifetime, given up going anywhere. This change in her habits had occurred after several women had insulted her at a music-hall. The mistresses of all these various men hated her because she had never shown herself willing to be on terms of familiarity with them. The only one of them who, for a short while, had found favour in her eyes was Gaby Dubois. The girl, she had decided on the strength of a brief exchange of talk one evening at the Lion Rouge, where Larousselle had dragged her, was a "sweet creature." The champagne had had a good deal to do with Gaby's spiritual effervescence on that occasion. For a whole fortnight the two had met daily. With dogged determination Maria Cross had vainly tried to break the links that bound her new friend to her various other acquaintances. Then they had begun to see less and less of one another, and a little while later, during a matinée at the Apollo into which Maria had drifted from sheer boredom, alone as usual, and, as usual, drawing all eyes, she had heard, coming from a row of stalls just beneath the box where she was sitting, Gaby's shrill laughter. Other laughs had mingled with it, and odds and ends of insulting comment had reached her ears, though the voices had been kept low. "That tart who gives herself the airs of an Empress . . . who's always putting on a virtue act. . . ." It had seemed to Maria that all the faces in the theatre were turned towards her—and the faces were the faces of wild beasts. Then the lights had gone down, all eyes had been riveted on a naked dancer, and she had slipped away.

After that she would never leave the house without her little boy François. And now, even though a year had passed since he had vanished, it was still he alone who could tempt her out, or rather, that gravestone, no longer than a child's body, though to reach it she had to walk

along the special avenue in the cemetery marked "Adults." But Fate had ordained that on the way leading to the dead boy another, living boy should cross her path.

On Sunday morning there was a great wind—not one of those winds that serves to dandle the piled clouds, but a roarer from the south with the smell of the sea, and driving before it a sweep of muffled sky. The note of a solitary tit only emphasized the silence of a million other birds. There could be no question of going out in such weather, which was a nuisance: but by this time young Courrèges would have had her letter. Aware of the extent of his shyness, she felt sure that he would obey her injunction. Even had she not written he would probably never have dared to cross her threshold. She smiled to herself as she conjured up a vision of him digging his heel into the gravel of the drive, and saying to himself, with that mulish expression which she knew so well: "What about the gardener?" While she ate her solitary luncheon she could hear the storm raging round the house. The flying horses of the wind galloped madly on, and now, their task accomplished, were whinnying and snorting among the trees. No doubt from the cloven turmoil of the deep Atlantic they had brought flights of gulls seeking the sanctuary of the river, and kittiwakes that hold the air and do not settle. A livid colouring of seaweed seemed to tint the clouds of this suburban sky, a salty scud to splash the inland foliage. Leaning from her window that looked on the garden, Maria had the taste of it upon her lips. No, he would not come: how could he in such weather, even if she had not sent her letter? Had she not been sure of that she would have known an agony of apprehension that he might suddenly appear. Far, far better to feel that she was safe, to know for certain that he would not come. And yet, if expectation was wholly absent, why should she open the sideboard cupboard just to make sure that there was some port left?

At last the rain began to fall in a solid curtain shot with vagrant sunlight. She opened a book, but her eyes would not take in the sense of what she read. Patiently she went back to the top of the page, but in vain. Then, seated at the piano, she began to play, but not so loudly that she could not hear the sound made by the opening of the front door. She was overcome by dizziness, and just had time to say to herself: It's the wind, it must be the wind, and, a moment later, though the shuffle of hesitating footsteps reached her from the dining-room—It's just the wind. She had not strength enough to get up from her chair. He was already in the room, awkward, embarrassed, not knowing what to do with his streaming hat. He did not dare to take a step forward, nor did she call to him, so powerless was she in the tumult of a passion that had burst its banks and was sweeping all before it, vengeful and frantic. In a moment it engulfed her, leaving no inch of body or soul unfilled, topping the peaks, drowning the roots, of her being. Nevertheless, when she did at last manage to speak, her expression was stern, her words no more than ordinary.

"Didn't you get my letter?"

He stood there dumbfounded. ("She wants to lead you up the garden," Papillon had said. "Don't let her put you where she wants you. Just stroll in on her with your hands in your pockets.") But, faced by what he took to be her anger, he hung his head like a schoolboy in disgrace. And she, tense and trembling with emotion, as though what she had caught in this stuffy trap of her over-furnished interior were a frightened fawn, could venture on no movement. He had come, though she had done everything in her power to keep him away. Therefore no remorse could poison this, her happiness. She could surrender to it wholly. To that

destiny which had precipitated the boy into this room as food for her hunger, she swore that she would be worthy of the gift. Of what had she been afraid? There was nothing in her mind at this moment but love at its noblest. If that truth needed to be proved, proof lay in the tears which she checked, thinking of François. In a very few years he would have grown to be just such a boy as this. . . . She could not know that Raymond had interpreted the face she made in her effort not to cry as a sign of ill-humour, perhaps of anger.

She said: "After all, why not? You did well to come. Put your hat down on one of the chairs. It doesn't matter if it's damp; it's not the first wet hat their Genoa velvet has seen. . . . I'm sure you'd like a glass of port now, wouldn't you? Yes, of course you would."

While he was drinking she went on: "Why did I write that letter? Honestly, I don't know. . . . Women do funny things . . . and then, of course, I knew you'd come in any case."

Raymond wiped his lips with the back of his hand.

"All the same, I nearly didn't come. I said to myself—she'll probably be out, and I shall look an awful fool."

"I hardly ever go out—since I've been in mourning. I've never talked to you about my little François, have I?"

François had come tiptoeing as though he were in very truth alive. Just so might his mother have kept him by her to break a dangerous tête-à-tête. But Raymond saw no more in her words than a trick designed to make him keep his distance, though Maria's only thought was to put him at his ease. Far from fearing him, she thought that she was an object of fear. Besides, this intrusion of the dead child was not of her contriving. The little boy had forced his presence on them. He had come as children do, when, hearing their mother's voice in the drawing-room, they enter without knocking. The mere fact that he is there, she thought, proves, you poor dear, the purity of your intentions. What's worrying you? François is standing by your chair, not blushing but smiling.

"It's rather more than a year since he died, isn't it? I very well remember the day of the funeral. Mother made a scene . . ."

He broke off. He would have unsaid the words if he could have done so.

"A scene, why? Ah, yes, I understand. Even on that day there was no pity in people's hearts."

She rose, fetched an album, and laid it on Raymond's knees.

"I should like to show you his photographs. No one but your father has seen them. That's him at a month old, in my husband's arms. When they're as young as that they look like nothing on earth—except to their mothers. Look at this one, with a ball in his arms—laughing. That was taken when he was two. *This* was when we were at Salies. He was already ailing. I had to sell out some of my tiny capital to pay for our trip. But the doctor there was kindness and generosity itself. He was called Casamajor . . . that's him, holding the donkey's bridle. . . ."

As she leaned over Raymond to turn the pages, she was quite innocently pouring oil on the flames, stoking the blaze. Her breath fanned the fire within him. She could not see the look of fury on his face. There he sat, the heavy album weighing down his knees. He was breathing heavily and trembling with frustrated violence.

"Here he is at six and a half, just two months before he died. He looks much better, doesn't he? But I can't help wondering whether I didn't make him work too hard. When he was six he read everything that came his way, even books he couldn't understand. Living as he did, all the time with grown-ups.

"You see," she said, "he was my companion, my friend"—because, at this moment, she could make no distinction between what François had been for her in actuality and what she had hoped he might become.

"Even then he used to ask me questions. What nights of torment I went through thinking that one day I should have to explain. The only thing that consoles me now is the realization that he went without knowing . . . that he never knew . . . that now he never will know . . ."

She was standing upright, her arms hanging at her sides. Raymond dared not raise his eyes, but he could hear the rustling of her movements. Struck though he was by her words, he had an uneasy suspicion that her grief was not altogether genuine. Later, when he was walking home, he said to himself: She was playing a game, and taking herself in with it. . . . She was running the dead-child business for all it was worth. Still, there's no getting away from it, she *was* crying. . . . He was shaken in the idea he had formed of her. In his youth and inexperience he had painted for himself a picture of "bad women" that was entirely theological in character and modelled on what his masters had told him, convinced though he was that he had successfully resisted their influence. Maria Cross hemmed him in like an army ordered for battle. On her ankles tinkled the bangles of Delilah and of Judith. There was no treachery, no trickery that he would have put beyond one whose glance the saints had dreaded like the glance of death.

Maria Cross said to him: "Come and see me whenever you like: I am always here." With tears in her eyes and peace in her heart, she went with him to the door, without even fixing another day for their next meeting. When he had gone, she sat down by François' bed, carrying her sorrow like a sleeping child in her arms. The

tranquillity she felt may have been the result of disappointment. She did not know
that she would not always be safe. The
dead cannot help the living. In vain do we
invoke them from the edge of the abyss.
Their silence, their absence, seem to take
sides against us.

IX

It would have been far better for Maria
Cross if this, Raymond's first visit, had
not left her with an impression of security
and innocence. She was amazed that
everything had gone so smoothly. I
worked myself up unnecessarily, she
thought. She believed her predominant
feeling to be one of relief, but already she
felt unhappy in the knowledge that she
had let Raymond go without arranging
for another meeting. She was careful now
never to go out at the times he might be
likely to come. So simple is the squalid
game of passion that a youth can master
it on his very first adventuring into love.
It needed no worldly-wise counsellor to
persuade this one to "let her cook in her
own juice."

After waiting for four days, she was in
a fit state to lay all the blame for his silence on herself, thinking: I talked to him
about nothing but my own troubles, and
about François. It must have been terribly depressing for him. What possible interest could he take in my album? I ought
to have asked him about his life. . . . I
ought to have laid myself out to win his
confidence. . . . He is bored with me
. . . thinks me just a tedious woman.
. . . What if he never comes back?

What if he never came back? To such
an extent did she worry over the possibility that it was well on the way to becoming a torment: I may wait as long as I
like, he won't come. I have lost my hold
on him. He's at the age when young men
don't suffer bores gladly. Better face it,

the whole thing is over and done with.
. . . The evidence was too shattering,
too terrible. He would never come back.
Maria Cross had filled up the last well to
be found in her desert. Nothing now but
sand. The most dangerous of all things in
love is the flight of one of the parties to
the plot. The presence of the adored is,
more often than not, an obstacle to passion. When she was with Raymond Courrèges she saw, in the first place, a young
creature whose innocent heart it would be
a crime to disturb. She remembered
whose son he was. The last traces of
childhood in his face reminded her of her
own lost boy. Even in thought she could
not draw near that young body save with
a sense of ardent modesty. But now that
he was no longer there, now that she
feared she might never see him again, of
what use was it any longer to mistrust the
muddied waters of her heart, the dark
confusion of her feelings? Now that this
fruit was to be dashed from her thirsty
lips, why deprive herself of the satisfaction of imagining the flavour she would
never know in fact? Whom would she
wrong by so doing? What reproach need
she fear at sight of the headstone on
which the name of François was engraved? Who was there to see her shut
away in this house, without a husband,
without a child, without servants? Madame Courrèges' endless lamentations
about the quarrels of her domestic staff
might be trivial enough, but how glad
would Maria Cross have been to occupy
her mind with such things? Where was
there for her to go? Beyond the drowsing
garden stretched the suburban roads, and
further still the stone-built city where,
when a storm bursts, one knows for certain that nine days of stifling heat will
follow. A fierce and torpid beast seems to
prowl, to growl, to crouch in a sky
drained of all colour. She too, pacing like
a beast the garden or the empty rooms,
yielded (how else could her misery find

an issue?) little by little to the fascination of a hopeless love, a love that could offer nothing but the wretched happiness of a self-consuming anguish. She gave up all attempt to put out the fire—no longer suffered from aimlessness and lassitude, since she had no thoughts now for anything but the blaze. A nameless devil whispered in her ear: "You may be dying, but at least you are not bored!"

What is strange about a storm is not its tumult but the silence, the torpor which it imposes upon the world. Maria could see the leaves lying motionless against the panes of the window, almost as though painted on them. There was something human about the drooping melancholy of the trees. It was as though they were conscious of their lifelessness, their numbed and sleeping state. Her mood was one in which passion takes on the semblance of a physical presence. She scratched at the sore place in her soul: she kept the fire in her heart alive. Her love was becoming a choking contraction which, had she so wished, she could have localized in her throat, in her chest. A mere letter from Monsieur Larousselle had the power to make her shudder with disgust. As to the idea of his making approaches to her, *that* from now on would be no longer possible for her to endure. He would not be back for another fortnight—time enough in which to die. She gorged her imagination on thoughts of Raymond, on certain memories that formerly would have overwhelmed her with a sense of shame: I looked at the leather lining of his hat, where it presses against his forehead . . . seeking in it the very smell of his hair. . . . She yearned for his face, for his neck, for his hands, for all and each of them had become the incomparable signs and symbols of a secret reality which was filled to overflowing with delight. . . . How inconceivable was this new tranquillity at the heart of her despair. Sometimes the thought came to her

that so long as he was alive nothing was lost; that maybe he would return. But as though there were something terrifying in the hope which such dreaming implied, she hastened to immure herself once more in an absolute renunciation, in the peace of mind that refuses to expect. There was for her a horrible pleasure in digging still deeper the gulf which separated her from the being whom she forced herself to see as pure. The inaccessible youth blazed in her firmament bright as the hunter Orion, and no less remote from her passion. I am already a woman burned up by life, she thought, a woman lost, while he has about him still the magic of childhood. His purity has set great spaces of sky between us, across which my longing refuses even to blaze a trail.

All through these days winds from the west and south drew after them great tumbled ranks of cloud, legions of grumbling vapour which, just as they were about to burst in a torrential downpour, suddenly hesitated, turned round about the charmed and toppling peaks of ether, and disappeared, leaving behind them that sudden sense of freshness which comes when somewhere rain has fallen.

In the night hours between Friday and Saturday the rain at last set in with an unbroken sound of murmuring waters. Thanks to the chloral that she had taken, Maria, at peace with all the world, breathed in the scented air which the garden wafted through the blinds to her tumbled bed. Then she fell into a dreamless sleep.

Lying there relaxed under the early morning sun, she thought with amazement of all the suffering she had been through. She must have been mad. Why had she seen everything in such gloomy colours? The boy was alive: he was merely waiting for a sign from her. The crisis past, she felt once more clearheaded, balanced, perhaps even slightly disappointed. Is that all it was? she thought. He'll come, and just to make doubly sure, I'll write. . . . I'm going to see him again. . . . At all costs she must confront her misery and the youth that caused it. She forced herself to contemplate in memory only a simple, inoffensive child, and was surprised to find that she no longer trembled at the thought of his head upon her knees. She thought: I'll write to the doctor telling him that I have made the acquaintance of his son (but she knew that she would not). Why shouldn't I? What harm are we doing? . . . In the afternoon she went into the garden with its waste of puddles. She felt really at peace, too wholly at peace, so much at peace that she was vaguely frightened. The less she felt her passion, the more she felt the threat of nothingness. Reduced in stature, her love no longer obliterated her inner emptiness. Already she was regretting that her round of the garden had lasted only a bare five minutes, and made the circuit once again, following the same paths. Then she hurried back because the grass had made her feet wet. . . . She would change into slipers, would lie down, smoke, read . . . but what? She had no book on hand that really interested her. As she approached the house she raised her eyes to the windows, and there, behind the drawing-room panes, saw Raymond. He was pressing his face to the glass, amusing himself by squashing his nose flat. Was this rising tide of feeling in her, joy? She walked up the front steps, thinking of the feet that, but a moment before, had pressed them. She pushed open the door, her eyes fixed on the latch because of the hand that had rested on it, crossed the dining-room at a slower pace, composed her features.

It was Raymond's misfortune that he should have come immediately after the long train of days during which she had dreamed so exclusively of him, and suffered so much on his account. Seeing him there in the flesh, she could not fill the void between the endless agitation of her heart and the being who had caused it. She did not know that she was disappointed. That she was, her first remark soon proved:

"Have you just been to the barber?" She had never seen him look like this before, with his hair cut far too short, and shining. She touched the faint scar left above his temple by some blow.

"I got that falling off a swing when I was eight."

She looked at him, trying to bring into focus her desire, her pain, her hunger, her renunciation, and this long, lean youth who looked so like an overgrown puppy. A thousand feelings, all to do with him, surged up within her, and those of them she could retain grouped themselves, for good or ill, about the taut, congested face. But she failed to recognize the peculiar expression in his eyes that betokened the blind fury of the timid man who has decided to try his luck, of the coward who has screwed himself to the sticking point. Never to her had he looked so much like a child, and she said with an air of kindly authority what, so often, in the old days, she had said to François:

"Are you thirsty? I'll give you some red currant syrup in a moment: but you must cool down first."

She directed him to an armchair, but he chose to sit on the sofa where she had already lain down. He protested that he wasn't a bit thirsty:

". . . and if I were, it wouldn't be for syrup."

Her legs were rather too much exposed, and she pulled down her skirt. The action provoked a compliment:

"What a pity!"

She changed her position and sat down beside him. He asked her why:

"It couldn't be that you're afraid?"

His words made Maria realize that that was precisely what she was. But afraid of what? This was Raymond Courrèges, young Courrèges, the doctor's son.

"How is your dear father?"

He shrugged his shoulders and stuck out his lower lip. She offered him a cigarette which he refused, lit one herself, and leaned forward, her elbows on her knees:

"You told me once before that you aren't on very intimate terms with your father. That's natural enough. . . . Relations between parents and children are never easy. . . . When François used to hide his face against my knees, I always thought to myself—make the most of it, it won't always be like this."

She had misinterpreted the movement of his shoulders, the pouting of his lips. Just now he wanted to push the memory of his father into the background—not from any feeling of indifference, but, on the contrary, because the thought of the elder man had become an obsession with him since something odd that had happened two evenings before. After dinner the doctor had joined him on the path that ran between the vines, where he was smoking a solitary cigarette, and had walked beside him in silence, like a man who has something to say but does not say it. What's he after? Raymond had wondered, indulging to the full the cruel pleasure of silence—that same pleasure which he gave himself on early autumn mornings in the carriage, with the rain streaming down the windows. Mechanically, he had quickened his pace, because he saw that his father had difficulty in keeping up with him, and was lagging a little behind. Realizing suddenly that he could no longer hear the sound of his breathing, he had turned his head. He could see the vague outline of the doctor standing there motionless on the path between the vine-shoots. His two hands were clutching at his chest, and he was swaying on his feet like a drunken man. He took a few paces forward, and then sat down heavily between two of the rows. Raymond dropped to his knees and raised the seemingly dead face to rest on his shoulder. Only a few inches separated them. He had looked at the closed eyes, at the cheeks that had taken on the colour of dough.

"What's the matter, Papa, Papa, *dear?*"

The sound of his voice, at once beseeching and authoritative, roused the sick man as though it possessed some peculiar virtue. He tried to smile, but looked bewildered, and his words, when they came, were breathless.

"It's nothing. . . . I shall be all right. . . ."

He fixed his eyes on his son's worried face, heard in his voice the same note of tenderness that it had had when he was a boy of eight.

"Rest your head against me: haven't you got a clean handkerchief? Mine's dirty."

Very gently Raymond wiped the face in which, now, there were signs of returning life. The eyes were open, gazing at the boy's hair which the wind was lightly fluttering. Behind him was the dense foliage of a vine-plant, and, further still, a yellowish sky full of growls and grumblings. It sounded as though it were emptying cartloads of stones. Leaning on his son's arm, the doctor returned to the house. The warm rain splashed their shoulders and their cheeks, but it was impossible to walk any faster. He had said to Raymond:

"It's this false angina—just as painful as the real thing. I'm suffering from a form of auto-intoxication. . . . I'll stay in bed for forty-eight hours on a diet of water . . . and remember, not a word about this to your granny or your mother."

But Raymond broke in on him with words of his own:

"You're not kidding me? You're *sure* it's nothing? Swear to me that it's nothing."

In a low voice, the doctor said:

"Would you mind so much, then, if I . . ."

But Raymond would not let him finish. He put his arm about the body that was shaking with its gasping efforts to draw breath, and his protest came in a sudden cry:

"What an old *idiot* you are!"

The doctor was to remember later the sweet insolence of the words, to remember it in the bad times when once again his child had turned into a stranger and an enemy . . . into someone whose heart was deaf to all appeals, who was incapable of responding. . . .

They went together into the drawing-room, but the father dared not venture an embrace.

"Let's talk about something else: I didn't come here to chat about Papa . . . we've got better things to do than that . . . haven't we?"

He thrust forward a large and awkward paw, but she caught hold of it before it had attained its goal, restraining it with gentle insistence.

"No, Raymond, no. You live too close to him really to understand. Those closest to us are always the ones we know least about. . . . We reach a point at which we can't even see what lies beneath our eyes. Do you know, my relations always thought of me as ugly, because when I was a child I had a slight squint. I was amazed, when I went to school, to find that the other girls regarded me as pretty."

"That's right, tell me nice little stories about when you were at school!"

His fixed obsession made him look prematurely old. Maria dared not let go

of the great hand. She could feel it growing damp, and a feeling that was almost disgust took hold of her. This was the same hand whose touch, ten minutes ago, had made her turn pale. There had been a time when merely to hold it in hers had compelled her to shut her eyes and turn away her head; and now, it was just a flabby, clammy object.

"I want to show you what the doctor's really like, and when I've made up my mind I can be as obstinate as a mule."

He stopped her by saying that he, too, could be obstinate.

"Look here, I swore that to-day I wouldn't be played with. . . ."

He spoke in a low voice, stumbling over his words; so low, indeed, that it was not difficult for her to pretend that she had not heard. But she increased the space between them. Then, after a moment, she got up and opened one of the windows: "It's stifling in here—just as though it hadn't rained at all! But I can still hear the storm, unless it's gunfire from Saint-Médard."

She pointed to where, above the trees, a dense, dark cloud showed a wind-tossed summit edged with sunlight. But he seized her forearm in both his hands and pushed her towards the sofa. She forced a laugh—"Let go!"—and the more she struggled, the more she laughed, to prove that this wrestling match was just a game, and that she regarded it as such. "Let me alone, you nasty little creature! . . ." The lines of laughter about her lips became a grimace. She stumbled against the divan, and saw, only a few inches away, the myriad drops of sweat on his low forehead, the blackheads on his nose. She could smell his sour breath. But the young faun strove to hold both her wrists in one hand so as to have the other free for what he wanted to do, and with one convulsive wriggle she freed herself. There was now between them the sofa, a table, and an armchair. She was rather breathless, but again forced herself to laugh.

"So you really think, my child, that you can take a woman by force?"

He did not laugh, the young male humiliated and infuriated by defeat, touched in the most sensitive part of that pride of body which was already abnormally developed in him, so that it bled. All his life he was to remember this particular moment when a woman had found him not only repellent but grotesque. No matter how often he might be victorious in days to come, no matter how many victims he might subdue and make miserable, nothing could assuage the burning smart of this first humiliation. For many years, remembering this moment, he would bite his lips till the blood came, would tear his pillow with his teeth in the watches of the night. . . .

He fought back the tears which sheer frustrated anger had brought to his eyes—never for an instant imagining that the smile on Maria's face might be no more than a mask, never for an instant understanding that she was seeking, not to hurt an oversensitive boy, but rather to keep herself from betraying by any sign the sense of the disaster and the ruin in which she found herself involved. . . . If only he would go away! If only she could be left alone!

It was only such a short while ago that he had been struck with amazement to feel that the famous Maria Cross was actually within his reach. Again and again he had said to himself, This simple little creature is Maria Cross! He had only to stretch out his hand, and there she would be, inert, submissive to his will. He could take her when and how he chose, let her fall and then pull her to her feet again—and now, the movement of his outspread arms had sufficed to send her dizzily spinning out of reach. She was still there in the flesh, but he knew with a sure knowledge that from now on he could no

more touch her than he could have touched a star. It was then that he realized how beautiful she was. Entirely occupied in thinking how to pluck and eat the fruit, without for a moment doubting that it was meant for him, he had never really looked at her. And now, all he could do was to devour her with his eyes.

She said, gently, for fear of irritating him, but with a terrible fixity of purpose: "I want to be alone. . . . Please listen to me, Raymond . . . you *must* leave me to myself. . . ." The doctor had suffered because he felt that Maria did not want to have him with her. Raymond knew an anguish still keener—the certainty which comes to us that the beloved object can no longer pretend, no longer hide the fact that it is the imperative need of her being not to see us any more, that she has rejected us and spewed us up. We realize, then, that our absence is necessary to her life, that she is on fire to forget us. She would hustle us from the room were it not that she is afraid we might resist.

She held out his hat, opened the door, flattened herself against the wall, while he, once more the adolescent youth, filled with horror of himself, wanted only to vanish, babbled idiotic excuses, was paralysed with shame. But no sooner was he out on the road again, no sooner had the door closed behind him, than he found the words he should have thrown in the trollop's teeth. But it was too late! For years to come he was tortured by the thought that he had turned tail without so much as telling her what he thought of her.

While the boy, as he walked home, was voiding his heart of all the abuse with which he had been unable to smother Maria Cross, that young woman, having first closed the door and then the window, lay down. Somewhere beyond the trees a bird was uttering a fragmentary song that sounded like the broken mutter-

ings of a man asleep. The suburban air echoed to the noise of trolleys and factory-whistles. Drunken singing reached her from the Saturday streets. Yet, for all that, Maria Cross lay swaddled and stifled in silence—a silence that came not from without but from within, from the depths of her being, filling the empty room, invading the house, the garden, the city, the whole world. She lived at its airless centre, her eyes fixed on that inner flame which, though suddenly all fuel was lacking, burned inextinguishably. Whence, then, did it derive its sustenance? She was reminded how, sometimes, at the fag-end of her lonely evenings, a last flicker would sometimes start from the blackened ashes in the hearth where she had thought all life was dead. Eagerly she sought the loved face of the boy whom so often she had seen in the six-o'clock trolley, and could not find it. All that had reality for her was a little tousled hooligan, driven beside himself with shyness, forcing himself to overcome his own timidity—a vision as different from the real Raymond Courrèges as had ever been that idealized portrait which had given beauty to her love. Against him on whom she had bestowed the transfigured features of divinity she raged and fumed: Did I suffer the torments of hell and the ecstasies of heaven for a grubby little urchin like that? . . . What she did not know was that it had been sufficient for her glance to fall upon this unformed boy for him to become a man whose dishonesties many women were to know to their cost, submitting to him as lover and as bully. If it were true that she had created him by virtue of her love, it was no less true that by scorning him she had added the last finishing touch to her work. She had let loose upon the world a young man whose mania it would be to prove to himself that he was irresistible, even though a Maria Cross had successfully resisted him. From now on, in all the amorous intrigues of his future, there would always be an element of unexpressed antagonism, a longing to wound, to extract a cry of pain from the female lying helpless at his mercy. He was to cause many tears to flow on many nameless faces, and always they would be *her* tears. Doubtless he had been born with the instincts of a beast of prey, but, had it not been for Maria Cross, their violence might have been softened by some touch of weakness.

How fathomless her disgust for this "hooligan"! Yes, the inextinguishable flame burned on within her though there was nothing now for it to feed upon. No human being would ever have the benefit of all this light, all this warmth. Where should she go? To the cemetery where François' body lay? No, no; far better to admit at once that the dead body of her son was nothing now to her but an alibi. She had been content in her visits to the child's grave only for the sake of the sweet homeward way which she had trodden with another, a living, child at her side. Hypocrite! What could she do, what could she say, before that tomb? She could but cast herself upon it as upon some doors she could not open, a woman damned to all eternity. As well might she fall upon her knees in the dusty street. . . . Little François was no more than a handful of ashes, he who once had been so full of laughter and of tears. . . . Whom did she wish to have near her? The doctor?—*that* bore?—no, not a bore. But what availed all her striving to attain perfection since it was her destiny to set her hand to nothing that did not turn awry, no matter how excellent her intentions? Many had been the glorious goals on which she had set her heart, yet in each of them only the worst part of herself had found its satisfaction. She wanted no one with her, nor yearned to find herself elsewhere than in this room with its torn curtains. Perhaps at St.

Clair? St. Clair had seen her childhood. . . . She remembered the park into which she had crept as soon as the church-going family, so antagonistic to her mother, had gone away. Nature, it had seemed, was only waiting for their departure after the Easter holidays to break the coverings of all its shoots. The bracken grew high and rank, touching with formless, frothy green the lowest branches of the oaks. Only the pines swayed, unchanged, the same gray tops that seemed indifferent to the spring, and even for them a moment came when they, too, saw torn from their entrails the cloudy plenty of their pollen, the yellow immensity of their passion. At a turn in the path she would find, in those days, a broken doll, a handkerchief caught on a furze-bush. But to-day she was a stranger to that world. Nothing would greet her there but the sand on which so often she had lain face downward. . . .

When Justine came to tell her that dinner was ready, she tidied her hair and sat down before her steaming plate of soup. But because nothing must stand in the way of her maid's visit to the movies with her husband, she was once again, half an hour later, alone at the drawing-room window. The fragrant lime had as yet no fragrance. Below her the rhododendrons already showed dark with coming colour. The fear of nothingness, the longing for a breathing space, led her to seek some piece of wreckage to which she might cling. I yielded, she thought, to that instinct for flight which comes over all of us when confronted by a human face made ugly by exigence and hunger. I convinced myself that the young brute and the young creature whom I once adored were different persons—but they were the same, the same child, only wearing a mask. As pregnant women wear a mask of fretfulness, so men, obsessed by love, have, too, close-moulded on their faces that look, so often hideous and al-

ways terrible, of the beast of prey that stirs within them. Galatea fled from what frightened her, yet lured her on. . . . I had dreamed of a long pilgrimage of kisses along which, making scarce noticeable progress, we should have passed from the regions of temperate warmth to those of enervating heat. But the young buck was too headstrong. Why did I not surrender to his fumbling urgency! In my raped and ravished body I might have found peace beyond imagining, something, perhaps, even better than peace. . . . Maybe, where human beings are concerned, there is no severing gulf that kisses will not bridge. . . . But kisses of what sort? Remembering the rictus of his grin, she gave vent to an "Ugh!" of disgust. A whole gallery of pictures forced themselves into her mind. She saw Larousselle turning from her with a muttered growl, his face suffused: "What *is* it you want? . . . You're just a lump of wood, not flesh and blood at all!"

What, if it came to that, did she want? She wandered about the deserted room, sat for a while by the window, looking out, elbow on sill and head on hand, dreamed of some mysterious, unvisited land of silence where she might have felt her love, yet not demand of it speech or sound, though the beloved would have heard it, would have understood the nature of her desire even before desire was born. The touch of hands and lips implies between two persons a physical separation. But so deeply interfused would they have been one with the other, that no grip and clasp of limbs would have been necessary, that brief encounter so quickly loosed again by shame. Shame? She seemed to hear the laugh of Gaby Dubois, the light o' love, the words that once she had spoken: "Speak for yourself, my dear . . . *that's* the only consolation I've got in the bloody awful life I lead. . . ."

Whence came this feeling of disgust? Did it really mean anything at all? Was it something positive and personal? A thousand formless thoughts woke in her mind and disappeared again, like, in the empty sky above her head, the shooting stars and falling, burned-out meteors.

Is not my lot, thought Maria, the common lot of all womankind? Without husband, without children, no one, indeed, could be more lonely than herself. But was this solitude more actual or more intense than the sense of isolation from which no family life, however happy, could have saved her—the sense of being alone which comes to all of us as soon as we learn to recognize in ourselves the distinguishing marks of that accursed species, the race of lost souls whose instincts, needs, and mysterious ends we alone can interpret? A truce to such exhausting analysis! Pale though the sky might be with traces of the lingering day, with the promise of a rising moon, beneath the still leaves darkness was massing. Leaning out into the night air, drawn, almost physically absorbed, by the quietness of the vegetable world, Maria Cross yielded not so much to a desire to drink deep of the branch-encumbered air as to a temptation to lose herself in it, to feel herself dissolved and atomised, till the inner desert of her heart should become one with the emptiness of space, till the silence within her should in no way differ from the silence of the spheres.

X

Meanwhile, Raymond Courrèges, having, as he walked the road, emptied his mind of all its foul abuse, and inwardly raging that he had not turned the flood on Maria Cross, felt an urgent need to spatter her with still more mud. Obsessed by that craving, he longed, as soon as he got home, to see his father. The doctor, true to his expressed intention, had decided to spend the next forty-eight hours in bed, eating nothing and drinking only water— to the great satisfaction of his wife and mother. The onset of his false angina was not alone in determining him to act in this manner. He was curious to observe the effect upon his own constitution of such a regimen. Robinson had already looked in to see him on the previous evening.

"I'd rather it had been Duluc," said Madame Courrèges, "but Robinson's better than nothing: after all he *is* a doctor, and knows all about testing the heart."

Robinson crept cautiously through the house, keeping close to the wall, and furtively climbed the stairs, dreading lest he find himself suddenly face to face with Madeleine, though they had never been actually engaged. The doctor, his eyes closed, his head feeling empty but his mind curiously lucid, his body free from pain beneath the light encumbrance of the sheets, and screened from the blaze of the sun, found no difficulty in following the tracks made by his thoughts. Here for a moment lost, there recovered, tangled and confused, they stretched before him, and his mind nosed its way along them as a dog might beat the bushes while his master walked, but did not shoot, amid the undergrowth. Without the slightest sense of fatigue he composed whole articles, to the last word, so that all that was left for him to do was to set them down on paper. Point by point he answered all the criticisms that had been provoked by the paper he had recently read to the Biological Society. His mother's presence was sweet to him—but so, also, was his wife's, and that was a matter to give him pause. Brought to a standstill at last, after an exhausting chase, he was ready to acquiesce now in Lucie's company. He noticed with appreciative wonder how careful his mother was to efface herself, and so avoid all risk of conflict. Without a shadow of mutual recrimination, the two women seemed content to share the prey, now that he had been torn for a few brief moments from his professional duties, from his private research, and from a passion which, for them, remained anonymous. He did not put up a struggle, but appeared to take an interest in all that they said, however trivial. His world had suddenly contracted to the dimensions of their own. He actually wanted to know whether Julie was really leaving, or whether there was a chance that she might come to terms with Madeleine's maid. The feel of a woman's hand upon his forehead, his mother's or his wife's, gave him back the sense of security which he had known in the days of his childhood ailments. It rejoiced him to know that if he was to die, he would not die in solitude. It seemed to him that death in that room, with its familiar mahogany furniture, with his wife and his mother forcing themselves to smile, would be the most normal, the simplest, occurrence in all the world; for would not the bitter taste of his last moments be disguised by them as always, in the past, had been the nasty taste of medicine? . . . Just to slip away, wrapped in the warm folds of a lie, knowing himself a dupe. . . .

A flood of light invaded the room. Raymond came in, grumbling that he couldn't see a thing. He approached the man lying in the bed. In his presence alone he could relieve himself of all the vicious hatred that he felt for Maria Cross. Already he could taste in his mouth the sour flavour of what he was about to vomit forth. The sick man said: "Give me a kiss." A great warmth of feeling was in the eyes which he turned upon his son who, two evenings ago, among the vines, had wiped his face. But the young man, coming straight from the daylight into the darkened room, could not make out his father's features very

distinctly. There was a harsh note in his voice as he put a question:

"Do you remember our talk about Maria Cross?"

"Yes, what of it?"

Raymond, leaning above the supine body, as though for an embrace or a murderous blow, saw beneath him two tormented eyes fixed upon his lips. He realized that someone else, besides himself, was suffering. I have known it, he thought, ever since that evening when he called me a liar. . . . But he felt no jealousy. He was incapable of imagining his father in the role of lover: no, not jealousy, but a strange desire to cry, with which was mingled a sense of irritation and of mockery. The poor cheeks looked gray under the thinning beard, and there was a tightness in the voice that begged him to go on:

"Well, what is it you know? Don't keep me on tenterhooks: tell me!"

"I was misled, Papa; you are the only person who really knows Maria Cross. I just wanted to tell you that. Now try and get some sleep. How pale you look. Are you sure this diet is agreeing with you?"

It was with amazement that he heard his own voice saying the very reverse of what he had meant to say. He laid a hand upon the sad and arid brow—the same hand which Maria Cross had held such a short while before. The doctor found it cool, was afraid that it might be taken away.

"My opinion of Maria dates from far back. . . ."

At that moment, Madame Courrèges came back into the room. He put his finger to his lips, and Raymond noiselessly withdrew.

His mother was carrying a paraffin-lamp (because in the doctor's weak state the electric light would have hurt his eyes). She put it on the table and lowered the shade. The restricted circle of illumination, the old-fashioned nature of its source, brought suddenly to light the mysterious world of rooms now vanished for ever, where a night light had been wont to struggle with a thick darkness full of furniture half drowned in obscurity. The doctor loved Maria, but he could see her with detachment. He loved her as the dead must love the living. She made one with all the other loves of his life, from boyhood on. . . . Feeling his way along the pathway of this thought, he now saw that one and the same sentiment had always held him in thrall down the years. It had always been like the one that had caused him the torment from which he had only just been released. He could feel his way back along the dreary sameness of that eternal pilgrimage, could have put a name to each one of all the passionate adventures, most of which, like this one, had ended only in frustration. Yet, in those days he had been young. It wasn't, then, age alone that stood between him and Maria Cross. No more successfully at twenty-five than now could he have crossed the desert separating this woman and himself. He remembered how, just after he had left college, when he was the same age as Raymond, he had loved, yet never known a moment's hope. . . . It was the law of his nature that he could never make contact with those he loved. He had never been more conscious of that truth than in those moments of partial success when he had held in his arms the object so long desired, and found it suddenly poor and dwarfed and utterly different from what it had been in the agonies of his desire. No reason to seek in the mirror the reasons for that solitude in which he was fated to remain until his death. Other men—his father had been one such, Raymond would be another—can follow the law of their being into old age, obedient to the demands of their vocation of love. But he, even in his youth, had been obedient

only to the call of his predestined solitude.

The ladies having gone downstairs to dinner, he heard a sound that came straight out of his childhood, the tinkle of spoons on china. But closer to his ears and to his heart were the noises made by rustling leaves, by the crickets, by a frog pleased at the coming of the rain. Then the ladies returned. They said:

"You must be feeling very weak."

"I certainly couldn't stand upright."

But because this diet of his was a form of "treatment" they were pleased that he felt weak.

"Wouldn't you like a little . . . ?"

The sense of weakness helped him on his way of exploration into the distant past. The two ladies were carrying on a conversation in undertones. The doctor heard a name mentioned, and questioned them:

"Wasn't that a certain Mademoiselle Malichecq?"

"So you heard what we were saying? I thought you were asleep. No, it's her sister-in-law who's a Malichecq. . . . She's a Martin."

The doctor had gone to sleep by the time the Basques put in an appearance, and did not open his eyes until he heard the doors of their rooms shut. Then his mother rolled up her knitting, rose heavily from her chair, and kissed him on the forehead, the eyes, and the neck.

"Your skin's quite cool," she said.

He was alone with Madame Courrèges, who at once embarked upon a grievance:

"Raymond took the last trolley into Bordeaux again. God knows what time he'll come in. He looked terrible this evening; I felt quite frightened. When he's spent the money you gave him, he'll run into debt, if he hasn't started already!"

In a low voice the doctor said: "Our

little Raymond . . . nineteen already," and shuddered, thinking of certain streets in Bordeaux that were always deserted after dark. He remembered the sailor over whose body he had tripped one evening. The man's face and chest had been blotched with stains of wine and blood. . . . Somebody was still moving about upstairs. A dog in the stable-yard started to bark furiously. Madame Courrèges listened intently:

"I can hear somebody moving about. It can't be Raymond as early as this. Besides, if it were, the dog wouldn't be making all that noise."

Somebody was coming towards the house. There was nothing furtive about his movement, indeed, he seemed to be going out of his way to avoid concealment. The shutters of the French window were shaken. Madame Courrèges leaned forward.

"Who's there?"

"An urgent message for the doctor."

"The doctor doesn't go out at night: you ought to know that by this time. Try Doctor Larue in the village."

The man, who was holding a lantern in his hand, was insistent. The doctor, who was still half asleep, cried out to his wife:

"Tell him it's useless. I didn't come to live in the country just in order to be pulled out of bed by night-calls."

"It's out of the question. My husband only sees patients by appointment. He has an arrangement with Doctor Larue . . ."

"But, Madame, it's about one of his patients that I've come, a neighbour of his. . . . He'll come soon enough when he hears the name. It's Madame Cross, Madame Maria Cross. She's had a fall— on her head."

"Maria Cross? Why should you think he'd put himself out for her more than for anybody else?"

But at the sound of the name the doctor had got out of bed. He elbowed his wife aside and leaned out of the window.

"Is that you, Maraud? I didn't recognize your voice. What has happened to your mistress?"

"She's had a fall, sir, on her head. She's delirious and asking for the doctor."

"I'll be with you in five minutes; just give me time to get something on."

He shut the window and started looking for his clothes.

"You're not really going?"

He made no reply but muttered to himself: "Where are my socks?" His wife protested. Hadn't he just said he wouldn't be disturbed at night for anybody? Why this sudden change of mind? He could scarcely stand up: he would faint from sheer weakness.

"It's one of my patients. Surely you see that I can't *not* go?"

There was sarcasm in her voice as she answered:

"Oh yes, I see right enough. . . . It has taken me some time, but I see now."

She did not yet actually suspect her husband. For the moment she was intent only on wounding him. He, confident in his detachment, in the fact of his renunciation, had no qualms on her account. After the long torment of his passion, nothing, he felt, could be less blameworthy, less guilty than his feeling now of friendly alarm. It never occurred to him that though he might, his wife could not draw a comparison between the past and present states of his love for Maria Cross. Two months earlier he would not have dared to show his anxiety so openly. When passion is a flaming fire we instinctively dissimulate. But once we have given up all hope of happiness, once we have accepted an eternal hunger, an eternal thirst, the least we can do—or so we think—is not to wear ourselves out with pretending.

"My poor Lucie, you're quite wrong. All that is very far away now . . . quite, quite finished. Yes, I *am* deeply attached to the poor creature . . . but that has nothing to do . . ."

He leaned against the bed, murmuring: "She's right; I've eaten nothing," and proceeded to ask his wife to make him some chocolate on the spirit-lamp.

"Where do you think I'm going to find milk at this time of night? I don't suppose there's a scrap of bread in the kitchen, either. But no doubt, when you've seen to this—this woman, she'll make you a nice little supper. It will be well worth while having been disturbed for that!"

"What a fool you are, my dear. If only you knew . . ."

She took his hand and came close: "You said—all that's quite finished . . . all that's very far away—then there *was* something between you? What was it? I have a right to know. I won't reproach you, but I want to know."

The doctor felt so breathless that he had to make two attempts before he could get his boots on. He muttered:

"I was speaking generally: what I said had nothing to do with Maria Cross. Look at me, Lucie . . ."

But she was busy going over in her mind the events of the past months. She had the key to it all now! Everything hung together: everything was as clear as clear. . . .

"Paul, don't go to that woman. I've never bothered you with questions . . . you must do me the justice to admit that."

He answered gently that it was not in his power to do what she asked. His duty was to his patient—she might be dying: a fall on the head might well prove fatal.

"If you keep me from going out, you will be responsible for her death!"

She loosed him, finding no more to say. As he moved away from her she began speaking to herself, stumbling over her words: "It may be all a trick . . . they may have fixed it up between them." Then she remembered that the doctor had had nothing to eat since the previous evening. Seated on a chair, she listened to the murmur of voices in the garden.

"Yes, she fell out of the window . . . it must have been an accident. She wouldn't have chosen the drawing-room one, which is on the ground floor, if she had meant to throw herself out. Quite delirious . . . complaining about her head . . . doesn't remember a thing."

Madame Courrèges heard her husband tell the man to get some ice in the village: he would find some at the inn or at the butcher's. He must get some bromide, too, at the chemist's.

"I'll go by the Bois de Berge: it'll be quicker that way than if I had the horse put in."

"You won't want the lantern, sir: it's as bright as day with this moon."

The doctor had only just passed through the small gate leading to the stable-yard when he heard someone running after him. A voice panted out his Christian name. He saw that it was his wife, in her dressing-gown, with her hair in plaits, ready for bed. She was too breathless to say more, but held out to him a piece of stale bread and a large bar of chocolate.

He went through the Bois de Berge. The clearings were stained with moonlight, though the full strength of the white radiance could not penetrate the leaves. But the great planet sat in throned majesty above the road, shining as though in a river-bed cut for its brightness. The bread and chocolate recalled the taste of all his schoolboy snacks—the taste of happiness—at dawn, when he used to go out shooting, in the days when his feet were soaked with dew and he was seventeen. Numbed by the shock of the news, he only now began to feel the pain. Suppose Maria Cross was going to die? Who was it that had made her want to die? But had she wanted it? She could remember nothing. How completely knocked out are those victims of shock who never remember anything, who smother up in darkness the essential moment of their destiny! But he mustn't question her. The important thing for the time being was that she should work her brain as little as possible. Remember, he thought, you are only a doctor attending his patient. There can be no question of suicide. When people have made up their minds to die, they don't choose a ground-floor window. She doesn't take drugs, or not as far as I know, though it's true that there was a smell of ether in her room one evening when I was there; but she'd been suffering from headache. . . .

Beyond the area of his stifling torment, on the very edge of his consciousness, another storm was growling. When the appointed moment came, it would burst: Poor Lucie—jealous! what a wretched business . . . but time enough to think about that later. . . . Here I am. The moon makes the garden look like a stage scene. It's as puerile as a setting for *Werther*. . . . No sound of raised voices. . . . The main door was ajar. From sheer habit he went straight to the empty drawing-room, then turned and climbed the stairs. Justine opened the door of the bedroom. He went across to the bed, on which Maria was lying, moaning to herself, and trying to push away the compress from her forehead. He had no eyes for her body beneath the close-clinging sheet, the body which so often he had undressed in imagination. He had no eyes for her disordered hair, nor for her arm, naked to the armpit. All that mattered was that she recognized him, that her delirium was only intermittent. She kept on saying: "What happened, doctor?—what was it?" He made a mental note: amnesia. Leaning over the naked breast whose veiled loveliness had once made him tremble, he listened to her

heart, then, very gently touching her injured forehead with his finger, he traced the extent of the wound. "Does it hurt you here . . . or here . . . or here?" She complained, too, of pain in her hip. Very carefully he drew down the sheet so as to expose no more than the small bruised surface; then covered it up again. With his eyes on his watch, he felt her pulse. This body had been delivered to him for cure, not for possession. His eyes knew that they were there to observe, not to be enchanted. He gazed intently at her flesh, bringing all his intelligence to bear. The clearness of his mind barred all roads of approach to his melancholy passion.

"I'm in pain," she moaned; "I'm in such dreadful pain."

She pushed away the compress, then asked for a fresh one, which the maid proceeded to soak in the kettle. The chauffeur came in with a bucket of ice, but when the doctor tried to apply it to her head, she pushed away the rubber skull-cap and, in commanding tones, insisted on a *hot* compress. To the doctor she exclaimed: "Don't be so slow: it takes you an hour to carry out my orders!"

He was extremely interested in these symptoms, which were similar to others he had noticed in cases of shock. The body lying there before him, which once had been the carnal source of all his dreams and reveries and delight, roused in him nothing but an intense curiosity, a concentrated and enhanced attention. The patient's mind was no longer wandering, but she poured forth a spate of words. He noticed with surprise that she, whose powers of speech were normally so defective that she had to make an effort, and not always a successful effort, to find the right words for what she wanted to express, had suddenly become almost eloquent. She had complete command of her vocabulary, and seemed capable of calling on technical terms at will. What a mysterious organ, he reflected, is the human brain. How extraordinary it is that it can develop its scope in this amazing way merely as the result of shock.

"I never meant to kill myself—you must believe that, doctor. I absolutely forbid you to think that such an idea ever came into my mind. I can remember nothing. The only certain thing is that what I wanted was not to die but to sleep. I've never truly longed for anything in my life but peace and quiet. If ever you hear anybody boasting that he dragged me down to the point of making me want to kill myself, I tell you you mustn't believe it. Do you understand me? I prohibit anything of the sort."

"Yes, dear lady. I swear to you that nobody has ever uttered such a boast in my hearing. . . . Now, just sit up and drink this. It's only bromide: it will soothe your nerves."

"I don't need soothing. I am in a good deal of pain, but I am perfectly calm. Move the lamp farther away. There now, I've messed the sheets. But I don't care—I'll empty the drug all over the bed if I want to. . . ."

When he asked whether the pain was less acute, she replied that it was excruciating, but that it didn't come only from her injury. In an access of talkativeness she once more raised her voice and spoke in such an unbroken flow that Justine observed that Madame was talking like a book. The doctor told the woman to go and get some sleep. He would sit up with the patient, he said, until daybreak.

"What other way out is there, doctor, except sleep? I see everything so clearly now. I understand what I never understood before . . . the people we think we love . . . the passions that end so miserably . . . now, at last, I know the truth. . . ." (The compress had grown cold and she pushed it away with her hand. The damp hair clung to her forehead as though she were sweating.) "No,

not passions, but one single passion. It goes on inside us, and from a casual meeting, from the eyes and lips of some perfect stranger, we build up something that we think corresponds with it. . . . Only by physical contact, by the embraces of the flesh, by, in short, the sexual act, can two persons ever really communicate. . . . But we know only too well where that road leads, and why it was traced—for the sole purpose of continuing the species, as you would put it, doctor. We choose the one path open to us, but it was never designed to lead us to our hearts' desire."

At first he had lent but half an ear to this outburst. He made no attempt to understand what she was saying. What interested him was her irrelevant talkativeness. It was, he noticed, as though the physical disturbance she had suffered had sufficed partially to bring into the open ideas that had been lying repressed in her mind.

"One's got to love the pleasure of the body, doctor. Gaby used to say—it's the only thing in the world, darling, that has never disappointed me—but, unfortunately we can't, all of us, do that. And yet it *is* the only thing that makes us forget the object of our search, forget so far that it actually becomes that object. Stupefy yourself . . . that's easier said than done."

How curious it was, thought the doctor, that she should speak of sexual pleasure precisely as Pascal had spoken of faith. In order to quiet her at all costs so that she might get some sleep, he held out some syrup in a spoon. But she pushed it away, and once again made a stain upon the sheets.

"No, I don't *want* any bromide. I shall empty it all over the bed if I like: *you* can't prevent me!"

Without the slightest subtlety of transition she went on: "Always between me and those I have longed to possess there has stretched this fetid region of swamp and mud. But they didn't understand. . . . They always thought I was calling to them because I wanted to wallow in the dirt."

Her lips moved, and the doctor thought that she was muttering names, Christian names. He leaned over her eagerly, but did not hear the one name which would have utterly destroyed his peace of mind. For a few moments he forgot that she was his patient and saw only a woman who was lying to him. In an agony of misery he murmured:

"You're just like all the others. You want one thing, and one thing only, pleasure. . . . It's the same with all of us. It's the only thing we want."

She raised her lovely arms, hid her face, uttered a long-drawn moan. In a low voice he said: "What's the matter with me? I must be mad!" He renewed the compress, poured some more syrup into a spoon, and supported the sufferer's head. Maria at last consented to drink: then, after a moment's silence:

"Yes, I too, I too. You know, doctor, how sometimes one sees the lightning and hears the thunder simultaneously—well, with me pleasure and disgust are all confused, just like the lightning and the thunder: they strike me at the same moment. There is no interval between the pleasure and the disgust."

She grew calmer and stopped speaking. The doctor sat down in an armchair and watched beside her, his mind a confusion of thoughts. He believed that she was asleep, but suddenly her voice, dreamy now and at peace, rose again:

"Someone with whom we might make contact, someone we might possess—but not in the flesh—by whom we might be possessed. . . ."

Fumblingly she pushed the damp cloth from her brow. The room was filled with the silence of the dying night. It was the hour of the deepest sleep, the hour at which the constellations change their pattern in the sky so that we no longer recognize them.

Her pulse was calm. She was sleeping like a child whose breathing is so light that one gets up to make sure that it is still alive. The blood had once more mounted to her cheeks and gave them colour. Her body was no longer that of a sufferer: not now did pain divorce her from desire. How long must his poor tormented flesh keep watch beside this other flesh deadened at last to suffering? The body has its agony, thought the doctor: To the simple, Paradise lies wide open. . . . Who was it said that love was the pleasure of the poor? I might have been the man who, his day's work ended, lay down each night beside this woman. But then, she would not have been *this* woman. . . . She would have been a mother more than once. All her body would bear signs of the purpose it had served, the traces of a life spent in degrading tasks. . . . Desire would be dead: nothing would remain but a few grubby habits. . . . Dawn already! How long the servant is in coming!

He was afraid that he would never be able to walk as far as his house. He told himself it was hunger that made him weak, but he dreaded the treachery of his heart whose beats he could so clearly hear. Physical anguish had freed him from love's sickness. But already, though no sign came to warn him, the destiny of Maria Cross was imperceptibly drifting away from his own. . . . The mooring-ropes are loosed, the anchor raised: the vessel moves, but as yet one does not realize that it is moving, though in another hour it will be no more than a dark stain upon the sea. He had often observed that life takes no heed of preparations. Ever since the days of his youth, the objects of his affection had, almost all of them, disappeared with dramatic suddenness, carried away by some other passion, or, with less fuss and bother, had just packed up and left town. Nothing more was ever heard of them. It is not death that tears from us those we love; rather, it keeps them safe, preserving them in all the adorable *ambiance* of youth. Death is the salt of love: it is life that brings corruption. To-morrow the doctor would be stretched upon a sick-bed, with his wife sitting beside him. Robinson would be keeping a watchful eye on Maria Cross's convalescence, and would send her to Luchon to take the waters, because his best friend had set up in practice there, and he wanted to help him with a few patients. In the autumn, Monsieur Larousselle, whose business often took him to Paris, would decide to rent a flat close to the Bois, and would suggest to Maria that she move there, because, by that time, she would have said that she would rather die than go back to the house at Talence, with its worn carpets and torn curtains, or put up any longer with the insults of the Bordeaux folk.

When the maid came into the room, even had the doctor not felt so weak that he seemed to be conscious of nothing but his weakness—even had he been full of life and vigour, no inner voice would have warned him to take his last long look at the sleeping Maria Cross. He was fated never to enter this house again, yet all he said to the maid was: "I'll look in again this evening. . . . Give her another spoonful of bromide if she seems restless." He stumbled from the room, holding to the furniture to keep himself from falling. It was the only time in his life that he had left Maria Cross without turning his head.

He hoped that the early morning air would sting his blood to activity, but he had to stop at the bottom of the steps. His teeth were chattering. So often in the past, when hastening to his love, he had crossed the garden in a few seconds, but now, as he looked at the distant gate,

he wondered whether he would have strength enough to reach it. He dragged himself through the mist and was tempted to turn back. He would never be able to walk as far as the church, where, perhaps, he might find somebody to help him. Here was the gate at last, and, beyond the railings, a carriage—his carriage. Through the window he could see the face of Lucie Courrèges. She was sitting there quite motionless and as though dead. He opened the door, collapsed against his wife, leaned his head on her shoulder, and lost consciousness.

"Don't agitate yourself. Robinson has everything under control in the laboratory, and is looking after your patients. At this very moment he is at Talence, you know where. . . . Now don't talk."

From the depths of his lassitude he noticed the ladies' anxiety, heard their whispering outside his door. He believed that he was seriously ill, and attached no importance to what they said: "Just a touch of influenza, but in your anemic state that's quite bad enough." He asked to see Raymond, but Raymond was always out. "He came in while you were asleep, but didn't want to wake you." As a matter of fact, for the last three days Lieutenant Basque had been in Bordeaux hunting everywhere for the boy. They had taken no one into their confidence but a private investigator. "Whatever happens, he must never know. . . ."

At the end of six days Raymond suddenly appeared in the dining-room while they were at dinner. His face looked thin and tanned by exposure. There was a bruise under his right eye where somebody had hit him. He ate as though he were famished, and even the little girls did not dare to question him. He asked his grandmother where his father was.

"He's got a touch of influenza . . . it's nothing, but we were rather worried because of the state of his heart. Robinson says that he mustn't be left alone. Your mother and I take turns at sitting with him."

Raymond said that to-night he would relieve them, and when Basque ventured to remark, "You'd much better go to bed: if you could only see what you look like! . . ." he declared that he wasn't the slightest bit tired, and that he had been sleeping very well all the time he was away:

"There's no shortage of beds in Bordeaux."

The tone in which he made the remark made Basque lower his eyes. Later, when the doctor opened his, he saw Raymond standing beside him. He made a sign for him to come closer, and, when he did so, murmured: "You reek of cheap scent . . . I don't need anything: go to bed." But towards midnight he was roused by the sound of Raymond walking up and down. The boy had opened the window and was leaning out into the darkness. "It's stifling to-night," he grumbled. Some moths flew in. Raymond took off his jacket, waistcoat, and collar. Then he sat down in an armchair. A few seconds later the doctor heard his regular breathing. When day came, the sick man woke before his watcher and gazed in amazement at the child sitting there, his head drooping, seemingly without life, as though sleep had killed him. The sleeve of his shirt was torn, and revealed a muscular arm that was the colour of a cigar. It was tattooed with the sort of obscene design favoured by sailors. The congested patch beneath his eye had obviously been caused by a fist. But there were other scars on his neck, on his shoulder, and on his chest, scars that had the form of a human mouth.

XI

The revolving door of the little bar never remained still for a moment. The circle of tables pressed closer and closer on the dancing couples, beneath whose feet the leather floor covering, like the wild ass's skin, continually shrank. In the contracted space the dances were no more than vertical jerkings. The women sat jammed together on the settees and laughed when they noticed on bare arms the mark of an involuntary caress. The one called Gladys and her companion put on their fur-coats.

"You staying?"

Larousselle protested that they were leaving just as things might get amusing. With his hands thrust into his pockets, unsteady on his feet, and his paunch sticking out provocatively, he went across and perched himself on a high stool. The barman burst out laughing, as did the young men to whom he was explaining with considerable pride the ingredients of a special aphrodisiac cocktail of his own invention. Maria, alone at her table, took another sip of champagne and put down her glass. She smiled vaguely, utterly indifferent to Raymond's proximity. What passion might occupy her mind he could not know. She was armed against him, separated from him, by the accumulated experiences of seventeen years. Like a dazed and blinded diver he fought his way to the surface, up from the dead past. But the only thing in the unclear backwash of time that really belonged wholly to him was a narrow path, quickly traversed, between walls of clotted darkness. With his nose to the ground he had followed the scent, oblivious to all others that might cross it. But this was no place for dreaming. Across the smoky room and the crowd of dancing couples Maria gave him a hasty glance, then turned away. Why had he not even smiled at her? He dreaded to think that after all these years the youth that once he had been might again take visionary form in this woman's eyes, that image of the shy young boy in the grip of an impotent and furtive desire. Courrèges, notorious for his audacities, trembled with anxiety this evening lest, at any moment now, Maria might get up and disappear. Wasn't there anything he could try? He was the victim of that fatality which condemns us to play the role of a man in whom a woman makes exclusive, unalterable choice of certain elements, for ever ignoring those others that may, too, be part of him. There is nothing to be done against this particular chemical law. Every human being with whom we come in contact isolates in us a single property, always the same, which as a rule we should prefer to keep concealed. Our misery, on these occasions, consists in our seeing the loved one build up, beneath our very eyes, the portrait of us that she has made, reduce to nothing our most precious virtues, and turn the light full on our one weakness, absurdity, or vice. And not only that. We are forced to share in the vision, to conform to it, for just so long as those appraising eyes, with their single, fixed idea, are bent on us. Only to others, whose affection is of no value to us, will our virtues glow, our talents shine, our strength seem superhuman, our face become as the face of a god.

Now that he had become, under Maria Cross's gaze, once more an abashed and foolish youth, Courrèges no longer wanted to revenge himself. His humble desire went no further than that this woman might learn the details of his amorous career, of all the victories he had won from that moment when, shortly after he had been thrown out of the house at Talence, he had been taken up, almost kidnapped, by an American woman who had kept him for six months at the Ritz (his family believed that he was in Paris working for his exam). But it was just that, he told himself, that was so impossible—to show himself as someone totally different from what he had

been in that over-furnished drawing-room, all "luxury and squalor," when she had said, averting her face, "I want to be alone, Raymond—listen to me—you *must* leave me to myself."

It was the hour at which the tide begins to ebb. But those regular patrons of the little bar who left their troubles with their coats in the cloak-room stayed on. A young woman in red was whirling round ecstatically, her arms extended like wings, while her partner held her by the waist—two happy May flies united in full flight. An American showed the smooth face of a schoolboy above a pair of enormous shoulders. With ears only for the voice of some god within him, he danced alone, improvising steps which were probably obscene. To the applause which greeted his efforts he responded awkwardly with the grin of a happy child.

Victor Larousselle had resumed his seat opposite Maria. Now and again he turned his head and stared at Raymond. His large face, of a uniform alcoholic red (except under the eyes, where there were livid pouches), had the look of a man eager for a sign of recognition. In vain did Maria beg him to turn his attention elsewhere. If there was one thing above all others about Paris that Larousselle could not bear, it was seeing so many strange faces. At home there was scarcely one that did not immediately bring to mind some name, some married relationship, someone whom he could immediately "place"—whether publicly, as a person demanding social acknowledgment, or surreptitiously, as a member of the half-world whom he might know but could not openly greet. Nothing is commoner than that memory for faces which historians attribute only to the great. Larousselle remembered Raymond perfectly well from having seen him driving with his father in the old days, and from having occasionally patted his head. At Bordeaux, in the Cours de l'Intendance, he would have made no sign of recognition, but here, apart from the fact that he could never get used to the humiliation of passing for ever unnoticed, he was secretly anxious that Maria should not be left alone while he played the fool with the two Russian girls who were so obviously wearing nothing under their frocks. Raymond, acutely conscious of Maria's every gesture, concluded that she was doing her best to prevent Larousselle from speaking to him. He was convinced that, even after the lapse of seventeen years, she still saw him as an uncouth and furtive oaf. He heard the man from Bordeaux snarl: "Well, I *want* to, and that ought to be enough for you!" A smile lay like a mask on his unpleasant countenance as he picked his way towards Raymond with all the self-confidence of a man who believes his handshake to be a privilege. Surely, he *couldn't* be mistaken? he said. It was, wasn't it, the son of that excellent doctor Courrèges? His wife remembered quite clearly that she had known him at the time when the doctor was attending her. . . . He was completely master of the situation, took the young man's glass, and made him sit down beside Maria, who held out her hand, and then, almost immediately, withdrew it. Larousselle, after sitting down for a few moments, jumped up again and said without the slightest show of embarrassment:

"Forgive me, will you?—back in a minute."

He joined the two young Russian women at the bar. Though it might be only a matter of moments before he would be back again, and though nothing seemed to Raymond more important than to turn this short respite to the best advantage, he remained silent. Maria turned away her head. He could smell the fragrance of her short hair, and noticed with deep emotion that a few of the strands

were white. A few?—thousands perhaps! The strongly marked, rather thick lips seemed miraculously untouched by age, and still gave him the impression of fruit ripe for the picking. In them was concentrated all the sensuality of her body. The light in her eyes, under the wide, exposed brow, was astonishingly pure. What did it matter if the storms of time had beaten against, had slowly eaten away and relaxed, the lines of neck and throat?

Without looking at him, she said:

"My husband is really very indiscreet. . . ."

Raymond, as sheepish now as he could ever have been at eighteen, betrayed his amazement at the news that she was married.

"Do you mean to say you didn't know? It's common knowledge in Bordeaux."

She had made up her mind to maintain an icy silence, but seemed astounded to find that there was anybody in the world —least of all a man from Bordeaux— who was ignorant of the fact that she was now Madame Victor Larousselle. He explained that it had been many years since he'd lived in that city. At that she could no longer keep from breaking her vow of silence. Monsieur Larousselle, she said, had made up his mind the year after the war . . . he had waited until then because of his son.

"Actually, it was Bertrand who begged us, almost before he was out of the army, to get the whole thing settled. It didn't matter to me one way or the other. . . . I agreed from the highest motives only."

She added that she would have preferred to go on living in Bordeaux:

"But Bertrand is at the Polytechnic. Besides, Monsieur Larousselle has to be in Paris for a fortnight every month, so we thought it better to make a home there for the boy."

She seemed suddenly overcome by shyness at having spoken like this, at having confided in him. Once again remote, she said:

"And the dear doctor? Life has a way of separating us from our best friends. . . ."

How delightful it would be to see him again! But when Raymond, taking her at her word, replied: "As a matter of fact, my father is in Paris at this very moment, at the Grand Hotel. He would be more than pleased . . ." she stopped short, and appeared not to have heard him.

Eager to touch her on the raw, to rouse her to a show of anger, he took his courage in both hands and proceeded to voice his one burning preoccupation:

"You don't still hold my boorishness against me? I was only a clumsy child in those days, and really very innocent. Tell me you don't bear me a grudge . . ."

"Bear a grudge?"

She pretended not to understand. Then:

"Oh, you're referring to that ridiculous scene . . . really, there's nothing to forgive. I think I must have been slightly mad myself. Fancy taking a little boy like you seriously! It all seems to me so entirely unimportant now . . . so very, very far away."

He certainly had touched her on the raw, though not in the way he had expected. She had a horror of all that reminded her of the old Maria Cross, but the adventure in which Raymond had played a part she looked on as merely ridiculous. Suddenly grown cautious, she found herself wondering whether he had ever known that she had tried to kill herself. No, for if he had he would have been prouder, would have seemed less humble.

As for Raymond, he had discounted everything in advance—everything except this worst of all foreseeable possibilities, her complete indifference.

"In those days I lived in a world of my own, and read the infinite into all sorts of nonsensical trifles. It is as though you were talking to me of some perfectly strange woman."

He knew that anger and hatred are but extensions of love, that if he could have roused them in Maria Cross his cause would not have been entirely hopeless. But the only effect his words had had upon this woman was to irritate her, to make her feel ashamed at the thought that once she had been caught out with such a wretched trick and in such paltry company.

"So you actually thought," she went on, "that a piece of silliness like that could mean something to me?"

He muttered that it had certainly meant something to him—an admission that he had never before made to himself, but now, at last, scarcely knowing what he said, put into words. He had no idea that the whole pattern of his life had been changed by that one squalid incident of his youth. He was caught in an uprush of suffering. He heard Maria's calm, detached voice:

"How right Bertrand is to say that we don't really begin to live until we've reached twenty-five or thirty."

He had a confused feeling that the remark was not true; that by the time we are beginning to grow up the future is wholly formed in us. On the threshold of manhood the bets have already been placed; nothing more can be staked. Inclinations planted in our flesh even before birth are inextricably confused with the innocence of our early years, but only when we have reached man's estate do they suddenly put forth their monstrous flowers.

Completely at sea, fighting his losing battle against this inaccessible woman, he remembered now what it was that he had so longed to tell Maria, and even though he realized increasingly as he spoke that his words were about as ill-timed as they possibly could be, declared that "our little adventure certainly hasn't stood in the way of my learning about love." Oh, very far from it! He was quite sure that he had had more women than any young man of his age—and women who had something to them, not just your common-or-garden tarts. . . . In that respect she had brought him luck.

She leaned back and, through half-closed eyes, looked at him with an expression of disgust. What, then, she asked, was he complaining of?

"Since, I presume, that sort of filth is the only thing you care about."

She lit a cigarette, leaned her cropped neck against the wall, and watched, through the smoke, the gyrations of three couples. When the jazz-players paused for breath the men detached themselves from their partners, clapped their hands, and then stretched them towards the Negro instrumentalists in a g 'ture of supplication—as though their very lives depended upon a renewal of the din. The Negroes, moved by compassion, resumed their playing, and the May flies, borne aloft on the rhythm, clasped one another in a fresh embrace and once again took wing. But Raymond, with hatred in his heart, looked at this woman with the short hair and the cigarette, who was none other than Maria Cross. He searched for the one word that would shake her self-control, and at last he found it.

"Well, anyhow, you're—here."

She realized that what he meant was—we always return to our first loves. He had the satisfaction of seeing her cheeks flush to a deep red, her brows draw together in a harsh frown.

"I have always loathed places like this. To say that sort of thing shows how little you know me! Your father, I am sure, remembers the agonies I went through when Monsieur Larousselle used to drag

me off to the Lion Rouge. It wouldn't be of the slightest use my telling you that the only thing that brings me here is a sense of duty—yes, of duty. . . . But what can a man like you know of my scruples? It was Bertrand himself who advised me to yield—within reason—to my husband's tastes. If I am to retain any influence, I mustn't ride him on too tight a rein. Bertrand is very broad-minded. He begged me not to resist his father's wish that I should cut my hair. . . ."

She had mentioned Bertrand's name merely in order to lessen her nervous tension, to feel at peace and mollified. By the light of memory, Raymond saw once again a deserted path in the Public Park in Bordeaux. The time was four o'clock. He could hear the panting of a small boy running after him, the sound of a tear-thickened voice: "Give me back my notebook." What sort of a man had that delicate youth become? Intent on wounding, he said:

"So you've got a grown-up son now?"

But she wasn't wounded at all; she smiled happily:

"Of course, you knew him at school. . . ."

Raymond suddenly took on for her a real existence. He had been one of Bertrand's schoolfellows.

"Yes, a grown-up son, but a son who can be at once a friend and a master. You cannot imagine how much I owe to him. . . ."

"You told me—your marriage."

"Oh that! . . . my marriage is the least of my debts. You see, he has revealed—but it's no good, you wouldn't understand. It was only that I was thinking how you'd known him at school. I'd so much like to have some idea of what he was like as a little boy. I've often asked my husband about him, but it's extraordinary how little a man can tell one about his son's childhood: 'A nice little chap, just like all the others'—that's as

much as he can say. I've no reason to believe that you were any more observant.
In the first place, you were much older
than he was."

"Four years—that's nothing," Raymond muttered, and added: "I remember
that he had a face like a girl."

She showed no sign of anger, but answered with quiet contempt that of
course they could not have had much in
common. Raymond realized that in the
eyes of Maria Cross her stepson floated in
an airy world far above his head. She was
thinking of Bertrand: she had been drinking champagne; there was a rapturous
smile upon her lips. Like the disunited
May flies, she, too, clapped her hands,
eager for the music to renew its spell
about her. What remained in Raymond's
memory of the women he had possessed?
Some of them he would scarcely have
recognized. But hardly a day had passed
during the last seventeen years that he
had not conjured up in his mind, had not
insulted and caressed, the face which to-
night he could see in profile close beside
him. He could not endure that she should
be so far from him in spirit. At all costs
he must bridge the gap, and to that end
he took the conversation back to Bertrand.

"I suppose he'll be leaving college very
soon now?"

She replied with a show of polite interest that he was in his last year. He had
lost four years because of the war. She
hoped that he would graduate very high,
and when Raymond remarked that no
doubt Bertrand would follow in his father's footsteps, said, with some anima-
tion, that he must be given time in which
to make up his mind. She was quite sure,
she added, that he would make his influence felt no matter what profession he
adopted. Raymond could not make out in
what way he was so remarkable.

"The effect he has on his fellow-
students is quite extraordinary. . . . But

I don't know why I am telling you all
this. . . ."

She gave the impression that she was
coming down to earth, coming down a
long way, when she asked:

"And what about you. What do *you*
do?"

"Oh, I just potter about, in the business
world, you know."

It was suddenly borne in on him what
a wretched mess he had made of his life.
But she was barely listening. It wasn't
that she despised him—that, in its way,
would have been something definite—but
that for her he simply did not exist. She
half rose from her chair and made signs
to Larousselle who was still holding forth
from his stool. "Just a few more minutes!" he called back. In a low voice she
said, "How red he looks—he's drinking
too much."

The musicians were packing up their
instruments with as much care as though
they had been sleeping children. Only the
piano seemed incapable of stopping. A
single couple was revolving on the floor.
The other dancers, their arms still inter-
twined, had collapsed onto seats. This
was the moment of the evening which
Raymond Courrèges had so often sipped
and savoured, the moment when claws
are retracted, when eyes become veiled by
a sudden softness, when voices sink to a
whisper and hands become insidiously inviting. . . . There had been a time
when, at such moments, he had smiled to
himself, thinking of what was to come
later, of men walking homeward in the
early dawn, whistling to themselves and
leaving behind, in the secrecy of some
anonymous bedroom, a jaded body
sprawled across a bed, so still, so spent,
that it might have been that of a murdered woman. . . . Not thus would he
have left the body of Maria Cross! A
whole lifetime would have been all too
short to satisfy his ravenous hunger.

So completely indifferent was she to his

presence that she did not even notice how he had moved his leg closer to her own, did not even feel the contact. He had no power whatever over her. And yet in those distant years he had been hers for the taking. She had thought she loved him—and he had never known. He had been an inexperienced boy. She should have explained what it was she wanted of him. No whim, however extravagant, would have rebuffed him. He would have proceeded as slowly as she wished. He could, at need, make smooth and easy the voyage of pleasure . . . it would have brought her joy. But now it was too late. Centuries might pass before their ways should cross again in the six-o'clock trolley. . . . He looked up and saw in a mirror the wreckage of his youth, the first sure signs of creeping age. Gone were the days when women might have loved him. Now it was for him to take the initiative, if, indeed, he were still worthy of love.

He laid his hand on hers:

"Do you remember the trolley?"

She shrugged her shoulders, and, without so much as turning her head, had the effrontery to ask:

"What trolley?"

Then, before he could reply, she hurried on:

"I wonder whether you would be so very kind as to bring Monsieur Larousselle over here and get his coat for him from the cloak-room . . . otherwise we shall never make a move."

He seemed not to have heard her. She had asked that question, "What trolley?" quite deliberately. He would have liked to protest that nothing in his whole life had ever meant so much to him as those moments when they had sat facing one another in a crowd of poor work-people with coal-blackened faces and heads drooping with sleep. He could see the scene in imagination—a newspaper slipping to the floor from a hand gone numb; a bare-headed woman holding up her

novelette to catch the light of the lamps, her lips moving as though in prayer. He could hear again the great raindrops splashing in the dust of the lane behind the church of Talence, could watch the passing figure of a workman crouched over the handlebar of his bicycle, a canvas-sack, with a bottle protruding from it, slung over his shoulder. The trees behind the railings were stretching out their dusty leaves like hands begging for water.

"Do, please, go and fetch my husband. He's not used to drinking so much. I ought to have stopped him. Liquor is so bad for him."

Raymond, who had resumed his seat, got up again and, for the second time, shuddered at what he saw reflected in the mirror. He was still young, but what good would that do him? True, he might still awaken love, but no longer could he choose in whom. To a man who can still flaunt the passing glories of the body's spring-time, everything is possible. Had his age been five years less than it was, he might, he thought, have had a chance. Better than most he knew what mere youthfulness can achieve with a woman who has been drained dry, how magically it can overcome antipathies and preferences, shame and remorse, what pricking curiosity, what appetites it can wake. But now he was without a weapon. Looking at himself he felt as a man might who goes into battle with a broken sword.

"If you won't do what I ask, I suppose I must go myself. They're making him drink. . . . I don't know how I can manage to get him away. How disgusting it all is!"

"What would your Bertrand say if he could see you now, sitting here with me . . . and his father in that state?"

"He would understand everything: he *does* understand everything."

It was at that moment that the noise of a heavy body crashing to the ground

came from the bar. Raymond rushed across the room and, with the help of the barman, tried to lift Victor Larousselle, whose feet were caught in the overturned stool. His hand, streaming with blood, still convulsively clutched a broken bottle. Maria tremblingly threw a coat round the shoulders of Bertrand's father, and turned up the collar so as to hide his now purple face. The barman said to Raymond, who was settling the bill, that one could never be sure it wasn't a heart-attack, and half carried the great hulking body to a taxi, so terrified was he of seeing a customer die before he had got clear of the premises.

Maria and Raymond, perched on the bracket-seats, held the drunken creature in a sitting position. A bloodstain was slowly spreading over the handkerchief which they had wrapped round the injured hand. "This has never happened to him before," Maria moaned. "I ought to have remembered that he can't touch anything but wine. Swear you won't breathe a word of this to anyone." Raymond's mood was exultant. In an access of joy he greeted this unexpected turn in his affairs. No, nothing could have parted him from Maria Cross this evening. What a fool he had been to doubt his lucky star!

Although winter was on the wane, the night was cold. A powdering of sleet showed white on the Place de la Concorde under the moon. He continued to hold up on the back seat the vast mass of flesh from which came the sound of hiccups and a confused burble of speech. Maria had opened a bottle of smelling-salts. The young man adored their faint scent of vinegar. He warmed himself at the flame of the beloved body at his side, and took advantage of the brief flicker of each passing street-lamp to take his fill of the face that looked so lovely in its humiliation. At one moment, when she took the old man's heavy and revolting head

between her hands, she looked like Judith.

More than anything she dreaded that the porter might be a witness of the scene, and was only too glad of Raymond's offer to help her drag the sick man to the elevator. Scarcely had they got him on to his bed than they saw that his hand was bleeding freely, and that only the whites of his eyes were visible. Maria was worse than useless. She seemed quite incapable of doing the simplest things that would have come naturally to other women. . . . Must she wake the servants, who slept on the seventh floor? . . . What a scandal there would be! She decided to ring up her doctor. But he must have taken off the receiver, for she could get no answer. She burst into sobs. It was then that Raymond, remembering his father's presence in Paris, had the happy idea of ringing him, and suggested to Maria that he should do so. Without so much as a "Thank you," she started to hunt through the directory for the number of the Grand Hotel.

"He'll come as soon as he gets dressed and finds a taxi."

This time Maria did take his hand. She opened a door and switched on the light.

"Would you mind waiting in here: it's Bertrand's room." She said that the patient had been sick and felt better. But his hand was still giving him a good deal of pain.

As soon as she had left the room Raymond sat down and buttoned his overcoat. The radiator was not giving much heat. His father's sleepy voice was still in his ears. How far away it had sounded. They had not seen one another since old Grandmamma Courrèges had died three years before. At that time Raymond had been in pressing need of money. Perhaps there had been something rude and aggressive in the way he had demanded his share of the inheritance, but what had really got under his skin and precipitated a rupture had been the way in which his father lectured him on the subject of his choice of a profession. The mixture of cadging and pimping by which he had elected to earn a living had horrified the elder man, who regarded such an occupation as being unworthy of a Courrèges. He had gone so far as to try to extract a promise from Raymond that he would find some regular occupation. And now, in a few moments, he would be here, in this apartment. What ought his son to do—kiss him, or merely offer him his hand?

He tried to find an answer to the question, but all the time his attention was being drawn to, was being held by, one particular object in the room—Bertrand Larousselle's bed, a narrow iron bed, so unaccommodating, so demure beneath its flowered cotton coverlet that Raymond could not keep himself from bursting out laughing. It was the bed of an elderly spinster or a seminarist. Three of the walls were quite bare, the fourth was lined with books. The work-table was as neat as a good conscience. If Maria came to my place, she'd get a bit of a shock, he thought. She would see a divan so low that it seemed part of the floor. Every woman who ventured into that discreetly dimmed interior was at once conscious of a dangerous sense of being in some strange new world, of a temptation to indulge in activities which would no more commit her than if they had taken place in a different planet—or in the innocent privacy of sleep. . . . But in the room where Raymond was now waiting, no curtains hid the windows frosted by the winter night. Its owner wished, no doubt, that the light of dawn should wake him before the sounding of the earliest bell. Raymond was entirely insensitive to all the evidences of a life of purity. In this room designed for prayer he could see merely a cunning piece of trickery, a de-

liberate exploitation of refusal, of denial, designed to increase the delights of love by suppressing all obvious allurements. He looked at the titles of some of the books. "What an ass!" he murmured. These volumes that spoke of another world were quite outside his experience and gave him a feeling of disgust. . . . What a time his father was taking! He did not want to be alone much longer. The room seemed to mock at him. He opened the windows and looked out at the roofs beneath a late moon.

"Here's your father."

He closed the window, followed Maria into Victor Larousselle's room, saw a figure bending over the bed, and recognized his father's huge bowler-hat lying on a chair, and the ivory-knobbed stick (which had been his horse in the days when he had played at horses). When the doctor raised his head he hardly knew him. Yet he realized that this old man who smiled and put his arm about his shoulder was his father.

"No tobacco, no spirits, no coffee. Poultry at lunch and no butcher's meat at night. Do as I say, and you'll live to be a hundred. . . . That's all."

The doctor repeated the words. "That's all," in the drawling voice of a man whose thoughts are elsewhere. His eyes never left Maria's face. She, seeing him standing there motionless, took the initiative, opened the door, and said:

"I think what we all need is a good night's sleep."

The doctor followed her into the hall. Very shyly he said: "It was a bit of luck, our meeting like this." All the time he had been hurriedly dressing, and later, in the taxi, he had been quite convinced that as soon as he had said that Maria would break in with—"Now I've found you again, doctor, I'm not going to let you get away so easily." But that wasn't at all the answer she had made when, from the open door, he had eagerly remarked, "It was a bit of luck. . . ." Four times he repeated the phrase he had so carefully prepared, as though by stressing it he could force from her the hoped-for answer. But no; she just held up his overcoat and did not even show signs of impatience when he failed to find the sleeve. Quite unemotionally she said:

"It really is a very small world. This evening has brought us together after many years. It is more than likely that we shall meet again."

She pretended not to hear him when he said: "But don't you think it is up to us to put a spoke in fortune's wheel?"

He repeated the same remark more loudly: "Don't you think we might manage to put a spoke in fortune's wheel?"

If the dead could come back how embarrassing they would be! They do come back sometimes, treasuring an image of us which we long to destroy, their minds full of memories which we passionately desire to forget. These drowned bodies that are swept in by the flooding tide are a constant source of awkwardness to the living.

"I am very different from the lazy creature whom you once knew, doctor. I want to get to bed, because I've got to be up by seven."

She felt irritated by him for saying nothing. She had a sense of discomfort beneath the brooding stare of this old man who merely went on repeating: "Don't you think we might put a spoke in fortune's wheel?"

She replied with a good grace, though rather brusquely, that he had her address.

"I scarcely ever go to Bordeaux these days; but perhaps you . . ."

It had been so kind of him to take all this trouble.

"If the staircase light goes out, you'll find the switch *there*."

He made no movement, but stayed obstinately where he was. Did she never, he asked, feel any ill effects from her fall?

Raymond emerged from the shadows: "What fall was that?"

She made a gesture with her head expressive of utter exhaustion.

"What would really give me pleasure, doctor, would be to think that we could write to one another. I'm not the letter-writer I used to be . . . but for you . . ."

He replied: "Letters are worse than useless. What's the point of writing if we are never to see one another?"

"But that's precisely the reason."

"No, no. Do you think that if people knew they were never going to see one another again they would want to prolong their friendship artificially by corresponding, especially if one of the two realized that letter-writing imposed a dreary duty on the other? . . . One becomes a coward, Maria, as one grows older. One has had one's life and one dreads fresh disappointments."

He had never put his feelings so clearly into words. Surely she would understand now!

Her attention had strayed because Larousselle was calling for her, because it was five o'clock, because she wanted to get rid of the Courrèges.

"Well, *I* shall write to *you*, doctor, and you shall have the dreary duty of replying."

But a little later, when she had locked and bolted the door and gone back to the bedroom, her husband heard her laugh and asked what she was laughing at.

"The most extraordinary thing's just occurred to me . . . promise you won't mock. I really believe that the doctor was a bit in love with me in the old Bordeaux days . . . it wouldn't surprise me."

Victor Larousselle replied thickly through clammy lips that he wasn't jealous if that was what she meant, and followed up the remark with one of his hoariest jokes: "He's just ripe for the cold stone." He added that the poor fellow had obviously had a slight stroke. Many of his old patients, who didn't like to abandon him, secretly consulted other doctors.

"Not feeling sick any longer? Sure your hand doesn't hurt?"

No, he was quite comfortable.

"I only hope that the story of what happened to-night doesn't make the rounds in Bordeaux. . . . Young Courrèges is quite capable . . ."

"He never goes there nowadays. Try to get some sleep. I'm going to put out the light."

She sat in the darkness, motionless, until a sound of quiet snoring rose from the bed. Then she went to her room, passing, on the way, Bertrand's half-open door. She could not resist the temptation to push it wide. Standing on the threshold she sniffed. The mingled smell of tobacco and the human body filled her with a cold fury: I must have been mad to let him come in here! . . . She opened the windows to let in the cold air of dawn, and knelt down for a moment at the head of the bed. Her lips moved. She buried her face in the pillow.

XII

The doctor and Raymond drove away in a taxi. It was like the old days when they had sat together in the carriage with its streaming windows on a suburban road. At first they said no more to one another than they had used to do in that forgotten time. But there was a difference in the quality of their silence. The old man was sagging with weariness and leaned against his son. Raymond held his hand.

"I had no idea that she was married."

"They didn't tell anybody: at least, I believe and hope that they didn't. They certainly didn't tell me."

It was said that young Bertrand had insisted on the situation being regularised. The doctor quoted a remark made by Victor Larousselle: "I am making a morganatic marriage." Raymond muttered: "What dam' cheek!" He stole a glance in the half-light at the tormented face beside him, and saw that the bloodless lips were moving. The frozen expression, the features looking as though they were carved in stone, frightened him. He said the first thing that came into his head.

"How's everybody?"

Flourishing. Madeleine, in particular, said the doctor, was being splendid. She lived for nothing but her two girls, took them out to parties, and hid her sorrow from the world, showing herself worthy of the hero she had lost. (The doctor never neglected an opportunity of praising the son-in-law who had been killed at Guise, striving, in this way, to make honourable amends for the past. He blamed himself for having been wrong about him. So many men in the war had been surprisingly unlike themselves in death.) Catherine, Madeleine's eldest daughter, was engaged to the Michon boy, the youngest of three brothers, but there was to be no public announcement until she was twenty-two:

"You mustn't breathe a word about it."

The voice in which he uttered this injunction was his wife's, and Raymond caught back the words he had been about to say: "Why should anyone in Paris be interested?" The doctor broke off as though suddenly silenced by a stab of pain. The young man began silently to calculate: He must be sixty-nine or seventy. Is it possible to go on suffering at that age, and after all these years? . . . He became suddenly aware of his own hurt, and the consciousness of it frightened him. It wouldn't last . . . very soon it would pass into forgetfulness. He remembered something that one of his mistresses had said: "When I'm in love and going through hell, I just curl up and wait. I know that in a very short while the particular man in question will mean absolutely nothing to me, though at the moment I may be ready to die for him, that I shan't so much as spare a passing glance for the cause of so much suffering. It's terrible to love, and humiliating to stop loving. . . ." All the same, this old man had been bleeding from a mortal wound for seventeen long years. In lives like his, hedged about with routine, dominated by a sense of duty, passion becomes concentrated, is put away, as it were, in cold storage. There is no way of using it up, no breath of warm air can reach it and start the process of evaporation. It grows and grows, stagnates, corrupts, poisons, and corrodes the living flesh that holds it prisoner.

They swung round the Arc de Triomphe. Between the puny trees of the Champs Élysées the black road flowed on like Erebus.

"I think I've done with pottering around. I've been offered a job in a factory. They make chicory. At the end of a year I shall be managing director."

The doctor's reply was perfunctory: "I'm so glad, my boy." Suddenly he shot a question: "How did you first meet?"

"Meet whom?"

"You know perfectly well what I mean."

"The friend who offered me this job?"

"Of course not—Maria."

"It goes back a long way. When I was in my last term at school, we got to exchanging a few words in the trolley. I think that's how it all began."

"You never told me, though once, if I remember correctly, you did mention that some friend had pointed her out to you in the street."

"Perhaps I did . . . one's memory gets a bit hazy after seventeen years. Yes, it all comes back now: it was the day after that meeting that she first spoke to me—actually, it was to ask after you. She knew me by sight. I think that if her hus-band hadn't come over to me this evening she'd have cut me."

This brief interchange seemed to have set the doctor's mind at rest. He leaned back in his corner. He muttered: "Anyhow, what does it matter to me? What does it matter?" He made the old familiar gesture of sweeping away some obstacle, rubbed his cheeks, sat up and half turned towards Raymond in an effort to escape from his thoughts, to occupy his mind only with his son's concerns.

"As soon as you've got an assured position, my boy, hurry up and get married."

Raymond laughed, protested, and the old man was once more driven in upon himself:

"You can have no idea what a comfort it is to live in the middle of a large family. Yes, I mean it. One's all the time got to think about other people's troubles, and those thousands of little hypodermic pricks keep the blood flowing. Do you see what I mean? One has no time to think of one's own secret miseries, of the wounds that strike deep into the very roots of one's being. One gets to rely on all these family concerns. . . . For instance, I meant to stay in Paris until the end of the Conference, but I've suddenly decided to catch the eight-o'clock train this morning. I just can't help myself. The great thing in life is to make some sort of refuge for oneself. At the end of one's existence, as at the beginning, one's got to be borne by a woman."

Raymond mumbled something about rather seeing himself dead first. He looked at the shrunken, moth-eaten old figure at his side.

"You can have no idea how safe I've always felt with all of you round me. To have a wife, children, about one, pressing in on one, is a sort of protection against all the undesirable distractions of outside life. You never used to say much to me— I don't mean that as a reproach, dear boy —but I don't think you'll ever realize how often, just as I was on the point of yielding to some delicious, maybe criminal, temptation, I would feel your hand on my shoulder gently guiding me back into the right path."

"How ridiculous to think that there are such things as forbidden pleasures," Raymond muttered. "We're completely different, you and I; I'd have overturned the whole apple-cart in next to no time."

"You're not the only one who made your mother suffer. We're not really so different. Scores of times I've sent the apple-cart spinning—in imagination. You don't know. . . . No, you *don't*. A few casual infidelities would have brought me far less sorrow than the long-drawn-out disloyalty of desire of which I have been guilty for the last thirty years. It is essential that you should know all this, Raymond. You'd find it pretty difficult to be a worse husband than I have been. Oh, I know my orgies never went beyond daydreaming, but does that make it any better? The way your mother takes her revenge now is by being over-attentive. Her fussing has become a necessity of my existence. The endless trouble to which she goes. She never lets me out of her sight day or night. I shall die in the lap of comfort, never fear. We're not looked after now as we used to be. Servants, as she says, are no longer what they were. We've never replaced Julie—do you remember Julie? She's gone back to her native village. Your mother does everything. I have to scold her, often. There's nothing she won't turn her hand to—sweeping out the rooms, polishing the floors."

He stopped, then, with a note of supplication in his voice:

"Don't live alone," he said.

Raymond had no time to reply. The taxi stopped in front of the Grand Hotel. He had to get out, feel for his money. The doctor had only just enough time to do his packing.

These early hours of the morning, all given over to street-sweepers and market-gardeners, were familiar to Raymond Courrèges. He breathed in the dawn air, rejoicing in the well-known sights, remembering how he always felt as he walked home in the small hours, physically exhausted, his senses gorged and satisfied, happy as a young animal wanting nothing but to find its burrow, to curl up and sleep. What a blessing that his father had decided to say good-bye at the door of the Grand Hotel. How he had aged! How he had shrunk! There can never be too many miles for my liking, between me and the family, he thought: The farther away one's relations, the better. . . . It came over him that he was no longer thinking about Maria. He remembered that he had a whole lot of things to do to-day. He took out his engagement book, turned the pages, and was amazed to discover how vast the day had become—or was it that the things with which he had proposed to fill it had diminished in number? The morning?—an empty waste: the afternoon?—two appointments which he had no intention of keeping. He leaned over his day like a child over the rim of a well. Only a few pebbles to drop into it, and *they* wouldn't fill the yawning void. Only one thing could do that—going to see Maria, being announced, being welcomed, sitting in the same room with her, talking to her—it wouldn't matter about what. Even less than that would have sufficed to fill these empty hours and many, many more—even just to have known that he had arranged a meeting with her, no matter how far ahead it might be. With the patience of a marksman, he would have shot down the days separating him from that longed-for moment. Even if she had put him off, he would have found comfort somehow—provided she had suggested an alternative date, and the new hope thus started on its way would have been enough to fill the infinite emptiness of his life. For life now had become for him nothing but a feeling of absence which he had got to balance by a feeling of anticipation. "I must think the whole business out seriously," he told himself, "and begin only with what is possible. Why shouldn't I get in touch with Bertrand again and worm my way into his life?" But they had no single taste in common, did not even know the same people. Anyhow, where was he to find him?—in what sacristy run this sacristan to earth? In imagination he obliterated all the intervening stages which separated him from Maria, jumped the gap, and reached the point at which he was holding that mysterious head in the crook of his right arm. He could feel on his biceps the touch of her shaven neck, like the cheek of a young boy. Her face swam towards him, closer, closer, enormously enlarged as on a movie-screen, and no less intangible. . . . It struck him with amazement that the early wayfarers he met did not turn to look at him, did not notice his mania. How well our clothes conceal our real selves! He dropped on to a seat opposite the Madeleine. This seeing her again . . . that was the trouble. He ought never to have seen her again. All the passions in which he had indulged for seventeen years had, unknown to him, been lit to protect himself from her—as the peasants of the Landes start small fires to keep the greater fire from spreading. . . . But he *had* seen her, and the fire had got the better of him, had been increased by the flames with which he had thought to combat it. His sensual aberrations, his secret vices, the cold technique of self-indulgence, so patiently learned, so carefully cultivated, all had added fuel to the conflagration, so that it roared upward now, sweeping towards him on a vast front with a sound of crackling undergrowth.

"Lie low, curl yourself up into a ball,"

he kept on saying to himself. "It won't last, and until it's over, find some drug with which to stupefy yourself—float with the current." Yes, but—his father would know no lessening of *his* pain until the day of his death. What a dreary life he'd led! But would a course of debauchery have freed him from his passion?— that was the question. Everything serves as fuel for passion: abstinence sharpens it; repletion strengthens it; virtue keeps it awake and irritates it. It terrifies and it fascinates. But if we yield, our cowardice is never abject enough to satisfy its exigence. It is a frantic and a horrible obsession. He should have asked his father how on earth he had managed to live with that cancer gnawing at his vitals. . . . Of what use is a virtuous existence? What way of escape can it provide? What power has God over passion?

He concentrated his attention on the minute-hand of the great clock away to his left, trying to catch it in the act of moving. By this time, he thought, his father must already have left the hotel. He suddenly felt that he would like to give the old man one last kiss. There was more than paternity between them, there was another tie of blood. They were related in their common feeling for Maria Cross. . . .

Raymond hastened towards the river, though there was plenty of time before the train was due to leave. Perhaps he was yielding to that species of madness which compels those whose clothes have caught fire to run. He was oppressed by the intolerable conviction that he would never possess Maria Cross, that he would die without ever having her. Though he had had his will of many women, taken them, held them for a while, abandoned them, he felt himself to be in the grip of the same sort of wild despair which sometimes overwhelms men who have never known physical love, men condemned to a life of virginity, when they face the horror of dying without ever having known the delights of the flesh. What he had had in the past no longer counted. Nothing seemed worth the having save what he would never have.

Maria! He was appalled to think how heavily one human being may, without wishing it, weigh in the scales of another's destiny. He had never given a thought to those virtues which, radiating from ourselves, operate, often without our knowing it and often over great distances, on the hearts of others. All the way along the pavement that stretches between the Tuileries and the Seine he found himself, for the first time in his life, compelled to think about things to which, up till then, he had never given a moment's consideration. Probably because on the threshold of this new day he felt emptied of all ambitions, of all plans, of all possible amusements, he found that there was nothing now to keep his mind from the life that lay behind him. Because there was no longer any future to which he might look forward, the past swarmed into his mind. For how many living creatures had not his mere proximity meant death and destruction? Even now he did not know to what lives he had given purpose and direction, what lives he had cut adrift from their moorings; did not know that because of him some woman had killed the young life just stirring in her womb; that because of him a young girl had died, a friend had gone into a seminary; and that each of these single dramas had given birth to others in an endless succession. On the brink of this appalling emptiness, of this day without Maria, which was to be but the first of many other days without her, he was made aware, at one and the same moment, of his dependence and his solitude. He felt himself forced into the closest possible communion with a woman with whom he would never make contact. It

was enough that her eyes should see the light for Raymond to live for ever in the darkness. For how long? If he decided that, at no matter what cost, he must fight his way out of the dense blackness, must escape from this murderous law of gravity, what choices were there open to him but the alternatives of stupor or of sleep?—unless this star in the firmament of his heart should go suddenly dead, as all love goes dead. He carried within him a tearing, frantic capability of passion, inherited from his father—of a passion that was all-powerful, that would breed, until he died, still other planetary worlds, other Maria Crosses, of which, in succession, he would become the miserable satellite. . . . There could be no hope for either of them, for father or for son, unless, before they died, He should reveal Himself who, unknown to them, had drawn and summoned from the depths of their beings this burning, bitter tide.

He crossed the deserted Seine and looked at the station clock. By this time his father must be in the train. He went down on to the departure platform and walked along the row of waiting coaches. He did not have to search for long. Through the glass of one of the windows he saw the corpse-like face etched on the darkness of the interior. The eyes were closed, the clasped hands lay on a spread of newspaper, the head leaned slightly backward, the mouth was half open. Raymond tapped with his finger. The corpse opened its eyes, recognized the source of the sound, smiled, and, with uncertain steps, came out into the corridor. But all the doctor's happiness was ruined by his childish fear that the train might start before Raymond had had time to get out.

"Now that I've seen you, now that I know you wanted to see *me* again, my mind is at rest. Better go now, dear boy. They're closing the doors."

It was in vain that the young man as-

sured him that they had a good five minutes before the train would start, and
that, in any case, it stopped at the Auster-
litz station. The other continued to show
signs of nervousness until his son was
once more safely on the platform. Then,
lowering the window, he gazed long and
lovingly at him.

Raymond asked him whether he had
got everything he wanted. Would he like
another paper or a book? Had he reserved a seat in the restaurant-car? To all
these questions the doctor replied, "Yes,
yes." Hungrily he fixed his eyes on the
young man who had asked them; the man
who was so different from himself, and
yet so like him—the part of his own flesh
and blood that would survive him for a
few more years, but that he was fated
never to see again.

THE LIFE AND WORKS OF
FRANÇOIS MAURIAC

By HENRI PEYRE

IF THE FRENCH critics of 1930–1945 had been asked which novelist, in their estimation, was the most likely to outlive the wreckage of time and rank next to Proust in greatness, more votes would probably have been cast for Mauriac than for any other living French writer, his rivals being Malraux, Giono, and Bernanos, probably in that order. Mauriac's eminence remained comparatively unrecognized in English-speaking countries, long after his election to the French Academy in 1933 and even after the Nobel Prize had been bestowed upon him in 1952. Translations of his works have been coming out timidly. The utmost tribute, that of a paperback edition with a seductive or a sickening cover (as tastes may go), came to *Le Désert de l'amour* (*Desert of Love,* 1925) only in 1953. The brevity of Mauriac's *récits* may have appeared unorthodox to publishers who like a novel to conform to the supposed demands of readers who insist that they get their money's worth in weight. The poetic finish of his style may have frightened off translators. But the pessimism of Mauriac's novels and their Roman Catholic view of sin and of love must have proved the chief deterrent to Anglo-Saxon readers. Pessimism, to be sure, abounds in their own fiction, but it dons youthful violence, and evil is somehow depicted in glaring and alluring colors.

There were signs of a change in the tastes of many educated readers, at the very time (since 1945 or thereabout) when the compatriots of Mauriac tended to dismiss him as a classical writer who, afraid of spoiling his earlier successes through imitating himself, was driven to dramas and to journalism. Many students in American colleges were fascinated by Mauriac as a craftsman and also by the use he has made of the religious theme.

Religion once again has become fashionable in fiction. It has been found by reassured critics to permeate James Joyce's work, to explain William Faulkner's protrayal of an evil that was original and hence ennobling, and to give a Catholic hue to Eugene O'Neill's plays and James T. Farrell's saga. The adjective "Catholic" paired with the word "novelist," has, in the eyes of some readers, enhanced the stature of Graham Greene and Evelyn Waugh. Somerset Maugham made skillful use of the theme in *The Razor's Edge,* and Aldous Huxley wrote fondly of Machiavellian mystics like Father Joseph. But Mauriac's place in contemporary letters owes little to sectarianism or to tides of changing taste. Out of the score of novels he has published, four or five seem clearly destined for survival. Few are the novelists in any language of whom such a prophecy could be ventured.

[103]

If the factors at work at any time in life and in art may be grouped into the conflicting forces of tradition and of experiment, Mauriac seems to rank with those novelists who have shunned the loudly advertised paths of experimentation. At a time when the *roman-fleuve* appeared as the order of the day and when juggling with the old-fashioned structural unity and with the continuous flow of time had become the first gesture of a writer asserting his modernity, Mauriac chose to compose isolated novels, strictly organized, with few of those contradictions and violent plunges into the unconscious that other Frenchmen took as evidence that they lived in a post-Dostoevskian era. Once or twice, the same characters recur in two different books. But their creator had enough humility not to presume that his readers might, after several years, remember the earlier doings of certain women of ill repute or of angelic adolescents. He rightly feared the lack of freshness and the artificiality of novelists who have chained themselves, volume after volume, to the drawn-out career of a Forsyte or of a Jean-Christophe. Every one of Mauriac's novels is a fresh attempt and adventure into the unknown, though every one of them ends with the gift of grace that the novelist insists upon imparting to his sinners.

Mauriac's fiction has been charged with monotony. It moves in a world that, indeed, is, geographically and socially, narrowly limited. It revolves around the same perennial obsessions with money, property, the enticements of the flesh, and the wages of sin. Within these confines, however, it explores in depth. What is more, it conjures up that diseased and haunted world, and gains in vivid intensity what is sacrificed in diversity. In contrast with several experimenters among contemporary novelists, Mauriac stands as the upholder of the traditional virtues of the French novel. He is fully aware of the new complexity that Stendhal, Dostoevsky, and Proust have led us to expect from fiction. But his purpose is not to experiment with new fictional forms or to explore recesses of the unconscious with awe, or with the naiveté of one who has lately discovered the jargon of clinical psychology.

Mauriac writes because he must rid himself of the obsession of his characters and endow with shapes and sounds the desolate world that he carries within his imagination. The traditional form of the French novel, condensed, linear in its development, and strongly tempted to return to the unities of the classical tragedy, suited his talent as it did the themes he treated. Like Racine's plays, his novels are dramatic presentations of a psychological crisis. The plot permits very few incidents, and only those that help bring out new aspects of the characters. His novels move swiftly to a relentless denouement. Indeed, their tension is so feverish that they could hardly last longer without becoming painful to the reader. They are no more relieved by humor, by the restful oasis of pure description or of lyrical escape than is Racinian tragedy. Within the traditional mold of the French novel, classical in its economy, swift in its pace, written with elaborate care for stylistic values, Mauriac subtly casts the molten lead of dark motives and destructive passions, such as we have come to expect from modern fiction since Balzac, Melville, and the great Russians.

Mauriac's date of birth, 1885, makes him one of the group of gifted French novelists who were to reach full manhood on the eve of World War I and to stage, in the years 1910–1913, a literary renaissance in Paris. Martin du Gard, Giraudoux, Duhamel, Romains, Maurois, Alain-Fournier, Jouhandeau, and Bernanos belong to the same age group. Their ascendancy over French letters reached its height in 1925–1935, when, with the exception of Alain-Fournier who was killed in the war, they were to meet with an audience attuned to their music, and to produce their most accomplished work. Most of them belonged to the middle or lower strata of the bourgeoisie, whose creative vitality has remained astounding in France, despite savage attacks repeatedly launched against it by its own scions, from Flaubert to Mauriac himself. Most of them were provincials; and Mauriac's fiction, even after he had taken up residence in Paris, fed on the observations and memories accumulated in his provincial childhood.

The area of France to which he belongs with all his being had already given birth to many men of letters, most of them of a cheerful and humorous disposition, inclined to skeptical enjoyment of the varieties and inconsistencies of mankind. The power of literature is such that the Bordeaux region and its inhabitants will henceforth appear to many in the gloomy hues lent to them by Mauriac's fiction, as Georgia and Mississippi have been stamped as lands of oppressive tragedy by contemporary American novelists. The traditional Gascon, with his bravado or with the playful irony that Renan thought he owed to his Gascon mother, the smiling beauty of his vineyards, and his Epicurean delight in choice food, never appear in Mauriac's stories of frustration and of remorse.

Yet Mauriac loves his native city of Bordeaux, its wine merchants and its lawyers, its cafés and its public gardens, where his characters repair, pleasure-bound, when they leave their country estates to celebrate a rich crop or an advantageous sale of timber. Rather, he hates Bordeaux because he loves it too much, as he confessed at the conclusion of his unfinished autobiography, *Commencement d'une vie* (Beginnings of a Life). "We hate our city as we do the being whom we love, for all that is usurped by that being, for the limits which it imposes upon us; it sets irreparable bounds upon our existence, and defrauds us of a higher fate." His debt to his provincial childhood has been loudly and repeatedly proclaimed.

In fact, he confessed his inability to place any of his novels in a setting other than the one in which he grew up; he compared the fascination wrought over him by his province to the blinding of a mule doomed to grind corn in its circular prison. When his characters rush to Paris, eager to escape for a brief respite from the passions that hold them captive in their drab familiar surroundings, they appear suddenly less real. The dance halls or the cafés, where they attempt to drown their regret for their childhood and for their native village, are depicted as some devil's den in a modern Babylon. The characters who had hoped to escape from themselves remain provincials in exile. "The provinces are Pharisaic," said Mauriac in a small book of notes and maxims on that subject, *La Province* (The Province). "Only in the provinces do people know how to hate well. . . . The provinces condemn most women to chastity. How many of them lacked the vocation for it. . . . Every writer leaving his province for Paris is a fugitive Emma Bovary." But life is more intense because it is less subject to idle diversion than in Paris. The human heart can be more easily laid bare to one who, in his teens, had silently observed his elders, dreamed about women whom he would never approach, tamed his wild desires, and stifled his rebellious sobs.

The child, in Mauriac, is father of the man. He was molded by his early memories. Malagar, the country house in which he took refuge every summer, has been repeatedly transfigured by him into a setting for his stories. Langon, which has become a gloomy abode of the dying wife and of the domineering mother-in-law in *Genitrix* (*Genitrix*, 1923), situated near the railway line between Bordeaux and Sète, was his grandfather's property. That grandfather, stubborn and anticlerical, who was converted on his dying day, provided his grandson with a few features of the pathetic old man in *Le Noeud de vipères* (*The Knot of Vipers*, 1932).

Yet Mauriac's childhood was a happy one. He liked solitude and found it, even at school, where he seldom took part in games and sports. His faith was a source of deep inner joy to him. His meditative habits developed in him a precious sensitiveness to nature. He feared the beauty of the fields and the hills, yet drank it avidly. Unlike the psalmist, he could not read the glory of God's bounty in the starry nights and the fragrant orchards in springtime. "Cybele has more worshippers in France than has Christ," he wrote, denouncing the religion of the earth as the most potent religion among French peasants. He, too, was swayed by that pagan cult: the struggle between earthly and earthy attachments and a thirst for divine grace is an ever-recurring one in his characters. His early studies in a religious school near home developed religious sensibility in him and the other schoolboys but did little toward fostering religious intelligence, as he later remarked. Pascal was the favorite writer of his youth; although he later took him to task for his Jansenism, Mauriac remained his spiritual descendant.

Mauriac completed his secondary studies at the lycée in Bordeaux. He passed his baccalaureate and went to Paris to pursue his scholarly education. Paleography and medieval archeology then attracted him, and, after passing the required tests, he entered the Ecoles des Chartes, where curators of French archives and medievalists are trained. However, he soon resigned. His was not the scholar's patient and modest gift. He car-

ried an ardent world within him, made up of memories of his province, of human desires and temptations, and, even more, of an impossible conflict between human and divine love. His ambition was to translate that inner universe into words.

Along with Pascal and Racine, who were, among the French classics, the chief builders of his soul, the writers he admired were the more sincere and the more tormented of the romantics. He admired Alfred de Vigny, whose thoughtful poetry attracted him in spite of, or perhaps because of, its passionate revolt against God, which Mauriac tended to prefer to conservative religious complacency. He felt close to Mauriac de Guérin (1810–1839), who worshipped nature with a burning fervor that set him apart from other French romantics. Guérin was a pagan and a pantheist tempted by Christ, struggling to be a true Christian but engulfed by the worship of the elements celebrated in his famous prose poem, *Le Centaure*. A centaur himself, he aspired toward the serenity of the heavens but was held back by animal life and earthly beauty.

Jean Lacordaire and Félicité de Lamennais were also spiritual and literary intercessors, the first for his eloquent charity and because "he dares call human love by its name; the flesh and the blood are not silenced by him," the second because he rejected the placid comfort of orthodoxy and a religion unmoved by the sufferings of the poor. Baudelaire's fame was spreading among the French youth in 1905–1910, when Mauriac was himself courting the muse. One of his early essays vindicated *The Flowers of Evil* against the Catholic critics who tried to reject such poetry on account of the poet's life or his occasional blasphemies. Mauriac advanced the assertion that a sinner who half repents or who, like Baudelaire, with remorse and anguish damns himself is more truly Christian than many a virtuous man who has, like the philosopher Taine, led an impeccable life.

Among the writers then living, Mauriac, on the threshold of his literary career, was attracted by Barrès. At the age of sixteen, he drew comfort from a formula in *A Free Man,* one of Barrès's early novels, which described what the provincial adolescent was then practicing: "To feel as much as possible while analyzing oneself as much as possible." Mauriac rejoiced in his youthful sorrows, which made him a younger brother of those men of letters whose biographies he was devouring at that time. During his solitary years in Bordeaux and later among the temptations of the metropolis, the young Mauriac was followed by his familiar demon of self-knowledge. (The title of his most searching short story was "Le Démon de la connaissance"—The Demon of Knowledge.) Soon, however, he discovered, like all born novelists, that it is easier to know oneself by lending one's own feelings to imaginary creatures and developing them to the full than by remaining confined to complacent introspection. He cultivated in himself "the fondness for taking a voluptuous interest in souls" that he attributed to one of the characters in his earliest novel.

Mauriac's literary debut, with two volumes of verse, was hailed by Barrès in 1909 and 1911. Soon after, the young poet, having married, gave up formal poetry, in which he felt his style was always cramped, and adopted the form of the novel. He returned to poetry only after his fiftieth year, in *Atys.* His early attempts at fiction, *L'Enfant chargé de chaines* (*Young Man in Chains,* 1913) and *La Robe prétexte* (*The Stuff of Use,* 1914), are immature and overinclined to lyrical exuberance, which detracts from the convincingness that the plot and characters might have had.

The author, already the father of a child, served in the army during World War I. The war, as a theme, left little trace in his work; but, in its gloomiest year, while a member of the expeditionary force on the Macedonian front in 1917, he meditated on the French moralists of whom he knew himself to be the heir. He strengthened his resolve to follow in their footsteps. But his ambition was to be a Christian moralist because he considered the Christian as the truest of all humanists since, "to reach God, he must cross the whole of himself, and see the light dawn only through and beyond his own heart."

On his return to civilian life, Mauriac brought out two brief, ardent, but still unconvincing and youthful novels: *La Chair et le sang* (*Flesh and Blood,* 1920) and *Préséances* (*Questions of Precedence,* 1921). They, as well as a stronger work, *Le Fleuve de feu* (*The River of Fire,* 1923), are permeated with the obsession of the flesh. The delight of the senses is depicted as mysteriously entrancing, driving the characters to wild forsaking of all self-control and even to suicide. Yet those carnal pleasures are not merely the snares of the devil. The power of love is great because we are aware of its frailty, we desperately try to embrace a beautiful body and to discover a soul behind it because we dread soon to be deprived of such ephemeral loveliness. Fear of the passing of time and of our own hasty march toward old age and death, search for self-oblivion in the abysses of passion, dim realization that the sufferings of love and the disgust of our sins draw us nearer to religion—such are the feelings lurking in the frantic adolescents depicted in Mauriac's earlier novels.

With *Le Baiser au lepreux* (*A Kiss for the Leper,* 1922), Mauriac composed his first masterpiece. Weaker novels were still to alternate with others of rare finish and power. *Destins* (Destinies, 1928), *Ce qui était perdu* (*What Was Lost,* 1930), *Le*

Mystère Frontenac (The Frontenac Mystery, 1933), *Le Mal* (*Evil*, 1935), *Les Anges noirs* (Black Angels, 1936), *Les Chemins de la mer* (Ways of the Sea, 1939), are considered definitely feeble products of the novelist's pen. Even *La Fin de la nuit* (*The End of the Night*, 1935), "Insomnie" (Insomnia), and "Thérèse chez le docteur" (Therese at the Doctor's), two striking, long short stories published in 1938, and *La Pharisienne* (*A Woman of the Pharisees*, 1941), while far from negligible, suffer from blemishes that impair their effectiveness as a whole. The best of Mauriac lies, for us, in the next five works to be discussed in these pages.

In *A Kiss for the Leper*, all the greatness of Mauriac's art is already fully developed. The vision of nature is vividly suggested, contrasting in its magnificence with the cringing and self-ashamed hideousness of the hero. The characters are powerfully sketched in their physical personality with a few harsh touches. The stifling rites of bourgeois existence imprison in a strait jacket the latent paganism of those who dare not rebel against them. The tone of the novelist is one of satire blended with pity and enhanced by poetry.

Genitrix (1923) is laid in the same setting of a gloomy country house near Bordeaux. It is, in its condensed beauty, almost unbearably harsh; the theme of maternal love driven to tyrannical excesses, worthy of Greek tragedy, has seldom been approached by a novelist with such stark courage. The three characters are depicted with cruel truth, unrelieved by any touch of irony or tenderness. The beauty of the flesh and the fond transfiguration of the loved one by the lover have little place in such a novel. Only the changing seasons or the tragic grandeur of the night, with the whistle of express trains in the distance and the sounds of the owls or the nightingales in the garden, bring a momentary vision of external beauty, contrasting with the feverish emotions of the characters, bent on mutual torture.

The Desert of Love has more ample scope. Not only is the novel longer, with changes in place and time, but it offers a subtle orchestration of diverse themes and varies the novelist's focus by presenting four protagonists of almost equal importance. Dr. Courrèges who has led a life of incessant labor; his wife, absorbed by material worries of daily living, who has gradually lost all spiritual companionship with her husband; Maria Cross, a woman of doubtful reputation, kept by some rich merchant; and finally Raymond.

A technique of relating the events in retrospect, as they flash upon the memory of the chief actor reliving every gesture, every sensation or thought that once was his, is used to superb advantage in *Thérèse Desqueyroux* (*Thérèse*, 1927). The point of view of the protagonist is thus adopted without any artificiality, and the reader shares the sense of solitude that afflicted the heroine, to the point of excusing her criminal attempt. Of all his women characters, Mauriac has drawn Thérèse with the deepest sympathy and with the finest nuances of convincing verisimilitude. Twice he felt impelled to return to the same heroine and perhaps to bring her to God. He shrank, however, before the conversion that might have saved Thérèse in the religious sense but would have imperiled her complex humanity.

Thérèse, the sinner, the unbeliever, is the heroine of Mauriac. For she has suffered and revolted; and she is lamentably misunderstood by her middle-class family, who are aghast that one of them should insist upon thinking and acting in her own way. Mauriac delineated her with tender care, while apologizing for not creating characters "streaming with virtue and pure in heart." He presented her with the most precious gift a novelist can make to his heroes: he endowed her with mystery. She herself never knew what had impelled her to poison her husband. Shade plays with light, and half-shades with more glaring color in Thérèse, the most subtle and the most pitiful of Mauriac's oppressed women.

Mauriac's most successful novels eschew the confusing turbulence of the fiction in which life seems constantly to erupt with fresh incident and new characters. The novelist's most powerful stories are also the barest. Artistic unity is achieved through our perceiving every detail through the lens of one central character. But our vision remains impartial, for the protagonist who tells the tale is pitiless to his own failings. The form of reminiscences or of a diary occasionally interposes remoteness between the events remembered and the reader, keeping the reader at a distance and in a state of tranquility. In Mauriac's use of the form, on the contrary, the reader is carried away by the torrent overflowing from the tormented heart of the protagonist. The feverish, broken-up style of the interior monologue wins the reader's participation in sordid calculations and venomous hatreds.

The Knot of Vipers is an artistic masterpiece, as somber as a Shakespearean tragedy without comic relief and momentary escape into the ecstasy of lyric. The hero is a King Lear with no Cordelia at his side, a Balzacian miser without fierce passion for gold that transfigures Père Grandet. Everything in the middle-class family described by Mauriac is sordid. Jealousy, hatred, spying on one another, lying, and the sadistic infliction of wounds through words poison the family circle, which Mauriac, himself the happiest of family heads, refuses to see in rosy hues. In its final pages, the move toward divine charity appears too sudden and unexplained—a common feature of literary works in which supernatural grace invades a soul through an illumination, which can neither be prepared nor accounted for rationally. Apart from that, *The Knot of Vipers* ranks among the most masterly novels of the century. Within a brief compass and through a voluntarily restricted technical medium, Mauriac has explored depths of evil and potentialities for good in a human creature. He has given concrete form to a vision of life and of man that is dark but is lighted up by charity. Without any elaborate description or ideological digression, he has afforded his reader an insight into social problems proposed by a middle class gnawed by avarice, Pharisaism, conventionality, and relentless selfishness.

Only one other of Mauriac's novels, in my opinion, ranks among his best, and even in that one the flaws are more conspicuous than in the earlier masterpieces, and the emphasis on the Catholic psychology of the characters is overstressed for the non-Catholic reader. The novel is *A Woman of the Pharisees*. The leading character, Brigitte Pian, is a deeply religious woman who might be called an unconscious or a sincere hypocrite. She forces others to practice virtue and thus drives them to revolt or hatred. She ruins a priest whose faith she finds too weak, dooms a frail young woman who insists upon knowing love of the flesh, and turns her own religion into a caricature of Christian mercy. With his usual subtlety, Mauriac allows us to infer only that impure elements may enter into the making of such an imperious propagandist of enforced virtue, who may combine greed for power over souls, sexual unbalance perhaps, and sincere striving after saintliness. But he refrains from intrusive analysis and from the comments of a moralist. Several paths exist down which the reader may venture to seek an interpretation of the novel. The technique differs from the retrospection or from the diary device of most earlier stories. A narrator is introduced, who participates in the action yet abstracts herself from it at times to interpret it to the readers. Some of the stark unity of Mauriac's more vivid masterpieces is thus lost.

Much in Mauriac must be explained by his determination not to become another Bourget, who preached the validity of Christianity for political and social reasons and praised Catholicism as an adjunct of order and an instrument for discipline. The author of *A Woman of the Pharisees* is Catholic but not clerical. Faith is, to him, not a haven of security and serene joy. Good does not reign on earth, and the hearts of the faithful are far remote from the purity of little children. Indeed, St. Francis celebrating the naive beauty of birds and flowers, and Christ pointing to the lilies of the field are infrequent visitations in modern Catholic literature. Evil lurks behind every shape and perfume that is beautiful; the ultimate descent of grace into disturbed hearts takes place most surely once sin has paved the way to regeneration. Mauriac's Catholic novel insists upon remaining bold and powerful; it is Catholic and Christian because it respects the ugly truth of life and conforms to reality. Its characters are not docile believers bent at will by their creator; they resist him, rebel against being led to Paradise. In a little book written in memory of a friend of his youth who died during World War I, *La Vie et la mort d'un poète* (The Life and Death of a Poet, 1924), Mauriac clearly defined his purpose: "A certain literature of edification falsifies life. The transcendence of Christianity appears most manifest in its conformity with reality. Do not then fake reality. To depict man in all his misery is to unmask the abyss opened, in the modern world, by God's absence."

The advantages derived by Mauriac from his Catholic conception of the world are to perceive life as unceasingly torn between contrary forces and to picture man as restlessly preyed upon by the powers of evil. Christianity, says Mauriac, enters into souls in order to divide them. The world is an arena for the struggle in which the devil fights against God, vice against virtue, the animal part of ourselves against the call of the spirit. To the honest observer, virtue is not triumphant, as it may be in edifying novels; nor can vice win in the end, for that would be a denial of Providence. Thus a conflict is perpetually being waged. Man finds in his own ability to doom himself the very proof of his freedom. He revolts against God; but the life he makes for himself is, but for a few unreal moments of bodily and sensuous exaltation, afflicted with an oppressive sense of dereliction.

The Catholic novel rests on a sharp distinction between good and evil. Man surrenders to the call of his desires or to the violence of his passions voluntarily and, what is more, fully conscious that he is breaking a moral law. *"La conscience dans le mal"* gives added zest to his pleasures, but works for his remorse, and in some cases for his salvation. Mauriac goes much further. Sinning appears in his fiction as the prerequisite for entering through the strait gate and winning "more room in Heaven," after the sinner will have atoned for the sin by repentance. This concept reassures his disturbed characters that they were not born to the conventional existence of a timid Pharisee; they are not, therefore, incapable of the élan that plunges them into hell only to raise them all the more securely into the abode of the elect. "Those who seem vowed to evil were perhaps elect before all others, and the depths of their fall measure the extent to which they have betrayed the task to which they were destined. There would be no blessed in

Heaven if they had not received the power to damn themselves; it may be that they alone rush into perdition who might have become saints."

The doctrine is not without its dangers, which moralists could denounce. (Indeed, a moralist had denounced the doctrine in the second century A.D., for the view that sin gives the sinner a moral superiority and a prior claim to the Kingdom of Heaven is as ancient as Christianity.) But it offers unambiguous advantages to the Catholic novelist, who uncovers snares laid by demons in the beauty of an April morning, in the loveliness of a youthful face, in the encounter of a young man and a young woman in a restaurant or on a bathing beach. While Anatole France and many another novelist traditionally called Gallic accepted the pleasures of the flesh as the most valuable adornment of our brief life, Mauriac pictures them as unreal and followed by unspeakable misery. "Christianity makes no allowance for the flesh; it suppresses it," asserts the theologian-novelist. And, as he elsewhere adds, we cannot love both Cybele and Christ. Conflict waged against one half of ourselves and vigilance against all in outward nature that could seduce us into paganism give Mauriac's novels a tragic meaningfulness that Epicureans and skeptics seldom achieve in fiction.

Not all Catholic readers feel secure in the presence of such stories of temptation and subsequent remorse. Some openly regret that this Frenchman from the south should be relentlessly oppressed by the vision of sin. They would prefer the harmonious balance between the flesh and the spirit achieved by Hellenic culture and attempted by humanism after its discovery of antiquity. They contrast the hideousness of caresses exchanged between lepers in Mauriac's world with the splendor of the kiss bestowed by Cleopatra on Antony in Shakespeare's play,

when the Queen of Egypt, who had mastered the art of sinning with grace, proclaimed herself and her lover peerless before the world. Others, less nonchalant in their tolerance of the charming evils that flesh is heir to, have wondered which of the two phases often described alternately in Mauriac's novel was the more powerfully delineated and the more likely to remain engraved in the memory of young readers: the descent into the abysses of vice, or the ultimate dipping into holy water and the visitation of faith when sinners were no longer able to bear their strenuous life of sin?

Love hallowed by the sacrament of marriage and embellished by the devotion of the Christian couple to the service of God is hardly a theme for Catholic novelists. Happiness does not interest a creator. The radiating joy of lovers who might find an absolute in physical love is the foe Mauriac pursues relentlessly, either in the second act of *Tristan und Isolde,* where, to Mauriac's relief, the lovers' raptures can end only in death, or in *Lady Chatterley's Lover,* against which he has shot the arrows of his bitterest irony, in "Eros," *Journal I,* and "Une Gorgée de poison," *Journal II.* To him, desire is always hideous. "It transforms the person who draws near us into a monster that is no longer like him. Nothing then stands any longer between us and our accomplice." His married women have, of course, ceased to expect any pleasure or joy. No mutual esteem, no admiration ever precedes or prolongs physical love. Love is nothing but a delusion that makes us feel our loneliness more acutely, or a fleeting sadistic impulse to humiliate our partner. More often still, with Mauriac, love is the inordinate power to torment us with which we have suddenly invested another creature. "There's beggary in the love that can be reckoned," whispered Shakespeare's Antony. The French novelist, listening to Wagner's opera, mourns: "How can love ever be reckoned, except by the tears that we draw from our partner?"

Mauriac indicts the flesh because he fears its power. Like the ascetics, he brands its pleasures as lamentably brief and preposterously vain, since they rest on illusions about our partner and delusions about ourselves. Love cannot live on if the lovers renounce the martyrdom of separation. Let lovers understand their true role, which is that of being the executioner of one another, he exclaims in a very pregnant preface to *Trois Récits* (1929). Human love will fill its only true purpose if it serves as a tool to inflict suffering upon us, a hook to catch us unawares and lift us to the only love that disappoints not—divine love.

His partial view of passion, his denial of the mere possibility of happiness illustrates the limitations of Mauriac. He never aimed at universality and he did not claim objectivity. "The novel does not reproduce reality; it transposes it" is one of the many lucid remarks made by the novelist on his art. The novel falsifies life for many a technical reason: for example, it cannot render silences, and must resort to dialogues far more than we do in life; and no fictional device is perhaps more artificial than the much-vaunted interior monologue, in which the novelist conceals his intervention and blends confusedly the perception of a series of events and the consciousness of such a perception. Mauriac cannot hold the mirror up to nature because he starts from an a priori vision of the world. The word "metaphysician" recurs in critical essays devoted to Mauriac, who is nevertheless hardly a philosophical mind, and he has used it himself in the most fitting characterization that he has made of himself in *Journal II:* "I am a metaphysician working on the concrete. Owing to a certain gift of atmosphere, I try to make

the Catholic universe of evil perceptible, tangible, odorous. The theologians give us an abstract idea of the sinner; I give him flesh and blood."

Not only must he resort to exaggeration and distortion but he must (or so Mauriac thinks) focus his lens on the inner and on the isolated individual. Even the portrayal of a family is, with Mauriac, the portrayal of divergent members of one group, impatiently fretting at the prison where they must gather for meals or for the evening rest. They hardly ever communicate. Mauriac repeatedly contended that factory workers do not differ from duchesses in the quality or the manner of their feeling and that love and hatred are fundamentally the same in a farmer's daughter and in Racine's Hermione. He does not attempt to delineate groups or a whole society. He says of himself and of novelists in general, "we can only depict with some adequacy beings oppressed by a law. . . . The art of the novelist is a bankruptcy."

Brevity is another self-imposed limitation with him. It keeps him from gaining for his stories the slow collaboration of time. The effect of the corrosion of the years on his characters does not interest Mauriac any more than it did the French tragic writers of the classical age. His manner, to use the Jamesian terminology, is not panoramic (except when characters survey their remembered past) and it is seldom dramatic in the literal sense, for there is very little drama enacted in the presence of the reader. Several of the best novels begin after the climax of the action has been reached, after Raymond Courrèges has lived his life of futility, after Thérèse has been judged for her attempt at poisoning, and after Louis has undone some of the viper's coils oppressing his heart.

Sartre, in a scathing article, has pitilessly pointed out the truest weakness of Mauriac: the absence of freedom in his characters. Everything in them is pre-determined by heredity, by the curse of original sin, and by their creator or by God. Mauriac once defined the novelist as "the ape of God." Sartre concludes his article with the oft-quoted words: "God is no artist. Neither is Mauriac." He charges Mauriac with first identifying himself with his characters, then suddenly forsaking them in order to act as a stern judge. Like God, he decrees that his wretched creatures be such and such, but he does not show them in the process of becoming what they are to be. The reader is not uncertain enough about the fate that will ultimately be meted out to them. The element of indetermination, which Sartre, the philosopher and the novelist of freedom, boasts of having restored to fictional characters, is indeed woefully lacking in Mauriac.

But he has other gifts, which compensate those he may lack: that of the tragic writer, hasty, feverish, eager to integrate the discoveries made by Dostoevsky and Freud into the French mold of strict construction and swift, unrelenting ardor; that of the moralist, whose concern is to bring to light the still-unexplored or dark recesses of the human heart and to explore the perilous force of passions; above all others, that of the poet. In an interview with Frédéric Lefèvre, Mauriac indirectly hinted at his finest achievement when he declared: "There is little danger in the novel's invading the rest of literature. I believe that only poetry counts, and that only through the poetical elements enclosed in a work of art of any genre whatever does that work deserve to last. A great novelist is first of all a great poet. Both Proust and Tolstoi were great, because their power of suggestion was boundless."

François Mauriac died, at the age of eighty-four, at his home Malagar on September 1, 1970. He had never recovered from a fall in his home in April, 1969.

Henri Peyre is Sterling professor of French Literature at Yale University.

THE 1952 PRIZE

By KJELL STRÖMBERG

François Mauriac had already been proposed for the Nobel Prize several times in succession before he actually won it in 1952. That year, no less than forty nominees were proposed, at least a dozen of them French. Mauriac's candidacy had been submitted by Prince William of Sweden, the younger brother of King Adophe Gustav VI, in the name of the Swedish Pen Club, of which he was president. A few years before, Prince William had successfully advanced the candidacy of William Faulkner.

Since the end of World War II, a perennial French candidate had been the poet and dramatist Paul Claudel. In 1952, he was not nominated, and the Swedish Academy was thus freed from having to choose between France's two greatest Catholic writers. At the same time, Graham Greene—someone has dubbed him the "English Mauriac"—was a nominee, the official candidate of the British Pen Club. Also, one of the most representative writers of the United Kingdom, E. M. Forster, was nominated. The great novelist and essayist, author of *A Passage to India,* was unfortunately not well known outside the English-speaking world. However, neither Forster nor Greene was a serious threat to the leading French nominee. Mauriac indeed had only one dangerous rival—Sir Winston Churchill, the favorite of the Scandi-navian and English-language press since the first time his name had been mentioned as a possible winner of the Nobel Prize for Literature.

Sigfrid Siwertz, a talented novelist, whose books had been translated into a dozen languages, and a member of the Swedish Academy since 1932, was the first to propose Mauriac as a candidate. His colleagues at the Academy called upon him to prepare the customary report on the candidate's work.

Before World War II, nearly a dozen novels and several essays of Mauriac's had been translated into Swedish. They were warmly welcomed in Sweden by the intellectual public. Thus it was not an unknown writer whom Siwertz was introducing to his colleagues. Few writers, Siwertz observed, have been more alluring interpreters of the atmosphere and milieu of their childhood. He found in this narrow compass a particular power which had made Mauriac the Catholic writer *par excellence.*

We sometimes have the impression that the author is amusing himself in depicting sin, that he strays so far afield on the road to perdition that he gets lost. When he arrives at the bottom of the blackest abyss, he infuses divine grace with a gentle sparkle, and this device makes the miracle of redemption all the more striking when finally it comes to pass. However that may be, Mauriac is a writer of the greatest importance, in a word—let us say it frankly—a great writer. His analysis of the human soul, this deeply penetrating analysis which is never negative, has contributed something basic to literature, to a degree such that we can unhesitatingly consider him as a candidate for the Nobel prize.

From 1946, when he was a candidate for the first time, until he finally won in 1952, Mauriac's name appeared, like Claudel's, almost every year on the list of candidates rumored.

On November 6, when the Academy announced its choice, the great international Prize was awarded "to François Mauriac, for the deep spiritual insight and the artistic intensity with which he has in his novels penetrated the drama of human life." Note that no allusion is made to the profound religious commitment that always infused his work, or to his impressive activity as a brilliant, crusading journalist in the postwar years. This omission was in great part remedied by Anders Österling in his presentation address at the awards ceremony.

A few minutes after the Swedish Academy had cast its vote, but before the news was sent out from Stockholm, the Swedish ambassador in Paris had leaped into his car to be the first to inform Mauriac of the good news. The winner, mindful that he was himself a journalist, did something that scarcely any of his predecessors had ever done: he invited his press colleagues (they had rushed in droves to his home) to a sumptuous reception organized in his honor in the offices of *Le Figaro,* the newspaper for which he wrote his column of political and social comment.

The French press was generous in its praise, not only of the Prizewinner but of the Swedish Academy as well. By voting the award first to André Gide, a pagan and self-styled immoralist, and then, after so short an interval, to Mauriac, a Catholic and a moralist, the Academy had demonstrated its intellectual flexibility beyond any doubt, revealing a spirit shorn of all religious prejudice. And this doubtless was an agreeable surprise to many people.

When he arrived in Stockholm, Mauriac made a tremendous impression. His handsome face had in it something of the features of an El Greco knight; his manners were more those of a *grand seigneur* than of a monsignore; his "wounded" voice lent itself equally well to a pathetic declaration, a slashing bit of repartee, or a flashing epigram, and he employed it to telling effect in his very personal speech of acceptance.

Translated by Dale McAdoo.

Frédéric Mistral

1904

"In recognition of the fresh originality and

true inspiration of his poetic production,

which faithfully reflects the natural scenery

and native spirit of his people and,

in addition, his significant work

as a Provençal philologist"

Illustrated by **YVES BRAYER**

PRESENTATION ADDRESS

By C. D. AF WIRSÉN

PERMANENT SECRETARY

OF THE SWEDISH ACADEMY

ONE SOMETIMES HEARS it said that the Nobel Prizes should be awarded to authors still in the prime of life and consequently at the height of their development, in order to shelter them from material difficulties and assure them a wholly independent situation.

The institution charged with awarding these Prizes should like to bear such striking witness to the value of a young genius; but the statutes of the Nobel Foundation stipulate that the works eligible for such a reward must be of exceptional importance and confirmed by experience. Thus there cannot be any hesitation in choosing between a talent in process of formation and a proven genius at the end of his development. The jury does not have the right to ignore a still active author of European fame, merely because he is old. The works of an old writer are often proof of a unique and youthful energy. The Swedish Academy therefore was right to render homage to Mommsen and Bjørnson in awarding them Nobel Prizes even at a time when both were past their prime. In making its choice among the candidates proposed this year for the Nobel Prize, the Academy has again given its attention to several literary veterans of recognized fame, and it has wished to renew its pledge to genius held in high esteem in the literary world.

The Academy has thought particularly of two authors who would both have been worthy of the whole Nobel Prize. Both have attained the final limits not only of the poetic art, but even of human life; one is seventy-four years old, the other two years younger. Therefore the Academy believes it should not wait longer to confer on them a distinction they both equally merit, although from different points of view, and it has awarded half the annual Prize to each. If the material value of the award is thus diminished for each of the laureates, the Academy nonetheless wishes to state publicly that, in this particular case, it considers each of these two Prizes as the equivalent of the whole Prize.

The Academy has given one of the awards to the poet Frédéric Mistral. In the freshness of his poetic inspiration this venerable old man is younger than most of the poets of our time. One of his principal works, *Lou pouèmo dóu Rose* (*The Song of the Rose*), was published not long ago, in 1897, and when the Provençal poets celebrated their fiftieth anniversary on May 31, 1904, Mistral tuned his lyre for a poetry that in verve and vigor does not yield to any of his previous works.

Mistral was born on September 8, 1830, in the village of Maiano (in French, Maillane), which is situated midway between Avignon and Arles in the Rhône Valley. He grew up in this magnificent natural setting among the countryfolk and soon became familiar with their work. His father, François Mistral, was a well-to-do farmer, devoted to the customs of his faith and of his ancestors. His mother nursed the soul of the child with the songs and traditions of his birthplace.

During his studies at the College of Avignon, the young boy learned the works of Homer and Virgil, which made a profound impression on him, and one of his professors, the poet Roumanille, inspired in him a deep love for his maternal language, Provençal.

According to the wish of his father, Frédéric Mistral took a law degree at Aix-en-Provence; after that he was left free to choose his career as he pleased. His choice was soon made. He devoted himself to poetry and painted the beauties of Provence in the idiom of the country, an idiom which he was the first to raise to the rank of a literary language.

His first attempt was a long poem about rustic life; then he published poems in a collection entitled *Li Prouvençalo* (1852). After that he spent seven consecutive years on the work that established his universal fame, *Mirèio* (1859).

The action of this poem is very simple. A good and attractive peasant girl cannot marry a poor young man whom she loves because her father refuses his consent. In despair she flees from the paternal home and goes to seek succor at the church on the site of the pilgrimage of the Three Saint Marys on the island of Camargue in the Rhône delta. The author recounts in charming fashion the youthful love of the young people and retraces with masterly hand how Mirèio rushes across the rocky plains of the Crau. Smitten by a sunstroke in the torrid Camargue, the unfortunate young girl crawls to the chapel of the pilgrimage site to die. There, in a vision, the three Marys appear to her at the very instant in which she breathes her last.

The value of this work is not in the subject or in the imagination displayed in it, no matter how interesting the figure of Mirèio may be. It lies in the art of linking together the episodes of the story and of unreeling before our eyes all Provence with its scenery, its memories, its ancient customs, and the daily life of its inhabitants. Mistral says that he sings only for the shepherds and the country people; he does so with Homeric simplicity. He is, indeed, by his own admission, a student of the great Homer. But far from imitating him slavishly, he gives proof of a very personal originality in his descriptive technique. A breath of the Golden Age animates a number of his descriptions. How can one forget his paintings of the white horses of the Camargue? Galloping, with manes flying in the wind, they seem to have been touched by Neptune's trident and set free from the sea god's chariot. If you remove them from their beloved pastures at the edge of the sea, they always escape in the end. Even after long years of absence, they return to the well-known plains which they salute with their joyous neighing as they hear again the breaking of the waves on the shore.

The rhythm of this poem has beauty and harmony, and its artistic composition succeeds on all counts. The source from which Mistral has drawn is not psychology; it is nature. Man himself is treated purely as a child of nature. Let other poets sound the depths of the human soul! Mirèio is a half-opened rose, still all shining from the rosy light of dawn. This is the spontaneous work of an original spirit and not the fruit of purely reflective labor.

The poem was greeted with enthusiasm from its first appearance. Lamartine, worn out with personal cares but always smitten by beautiful poetic works, wrote "A great poet is born!" He compared Mistral's poem to one of the islands of an archipelago, to a floating Delos which must have detached itself from its group in order to join, in silence, the fragrant Provence. He applied to Mistral these words of Virgil: *"Tu Marcellus eris!"*

Seven years after the publication of *Mirèio,* Mistral published a second work of equal dimensions, *Calendau* (1867). It has been said that the action of this poem is too fantastic and improbable. But it matches its predecessor in the charm of its descriptions. How could one question the grandeur of its ideas about the ennoblement of man through trial? While *Mirèio* celebrates peasant life, *Calendau* presents a gripping picture of the sea and the forests. It is like a brilliant glistening of water in several remarkably precise scenes about the life of the fisherman.

Mistral is not only an epic poet; he is also a great lyricist. His collection, *Lis Isclo d'or* (*Islands of Gold,* 1876) contains some poems of an immortal beauty. Suffice it to recall the stanzas on the drum of Arcole, on the dying mower, on the chateau of Roumanin with its memories of the times of the troubadours that seem to evoke the splendor of the sunsets, or, again, the beautiful mystic chant that should be spoken in the veiled twilight of the evening.

In other lyric poems Mistral insists with fervor on the rights of neo-Provençal to an independent existence and seeks to protect it against all attempts to neglect or discredit it.

The poem in the form of a short story, "Nerto" (1884), offers many beautiful pages for the reader's admiration. But the epic narrative, *Lou pouèmo dóu Rose,* is more profound. Composed by a poet of sixty-seven years, it is still full of life, and its numerous vignettes of the regions washed by the Rhône are most engaging. What a superb type is that proud and devout captain of the ship *Aprau,* who thinks that one must be a sailor to know how to pray! Another ravishing little scene shows us the pilot's daughter, Anglora, whose imagination has been fed on old legends. One night she imagines that she has seen Lou Dra, the god of the river, in the moonlit waves of the Rhône and that she has been touched by him. The very verses here seem to stream and sparkle in the moonlight.

In short, Mistral's works are all lofty monuments to the glory of his beloved Provence.

This year is a year of celebration for him. Fifty years ago on St. Estelle's day he founded, together with six literary friends, the Association of Provençal Poets, whose goal was to purify and give a definitive form to the Provençal language. The language which is spoken from St. Rémy to Arles and, without significant differences, in all the Rhône Valley from Orange to Martigues, served as a basis for a new literary language, as earlier the Florentine dialect had served to form Italian. Experts such as Gaston Paris and Koschwitz tell us that this movement was not at all retrograde. It did not seek to restore to life the old Provençal, but on the basis of dialects in use among the people, it attempted to create a national language understood by all. The efforts of the Provençal poets have not been slow to be crowned with success. In his great neo-Provençal dictionary, *Tresor dou Félibrige* (1879–1886), a giant work on which he has worked for more than twenty years, Mistral has recorded the wealth of the Provençal dialects and built an imperishable monument to the *lengo d'O.*

It goes without saying that a man like Mistral has received all kinds of honors. The French Academy has awarded him a prize four times. The Institute of France gave him the Reynaud prize of 10,000 francs for his dictionary. The universities of Halle and Bonn have conferred honorary doctorates on him. Several of his poems have been translated into various foreign languages. *Mirèio* has been set to music by Gounod, and *Calendau* by the composer Maréchal.

One knows the motto given by Mistral to the Association of Provençal Poets: *"Lou soulèu me fai canta"* ("The sun makes me sing"). His poems have, in effect, spread the light of the Provençal sun in many countries, even in northern regions where they have made many hearts rejoice.

Alfred Nobel demanded idealism from an author to be judged worthy of the Prize he established. Is it not amply found in a poet whose work, like that of Mistral, is distinguished by a healthy and flourishing artistic idealism; in a man who has devoted his entire life to an ideal, the restoration and development of the spiritual interests of his native country, its language and its literature?

There was no formal Acceptance Speech by Mistral.

TO LAMARTINE

I OFFER THEE MIRÈIO: IT IS MY HEART AND SPIRIT,

THE BLOSSOM OF MY YEARS.

A CLUSTER OF CRAU GRAPES, WITH ALL THE GREEN LEAVES NEAR IT,

TO THEE A PEASANT BEARS.

MIRÈIO

A PROVENÇAL POEM

By FRÉDÉRIC MISTRAL

Translated by Harriet W. Preston

CANTO I.

LOTUS¹ FARM.

I sing the love of a Provençal maid;
How through the wheat-fields of La
    Crau² she strayed,
Following the fate that drew her to the
    sea.
Unknown beyond remote La Crau was
    she;
And I, who tell the rustic tale of her,
Would fain be Homer's humble follower.

What though youth's aureole was her
    only crown?
And never gold she wore nor damask
    gown?
I'll build her up a throne out of my song,
And hail her queen in our despisèd
    tongue.
Mine be the simple speech that ye all
    know,
Shepherds and farmer-folk of lone La
    Crau.

God of my country, who didst have Thy
    birth
Among poor shepherds when Thou wast
    on earth,
Breathe fire into my song! Thou knowest,
    my God,
How, when the lusty summer is abroad,

And figs turn ripe in sun and dew, comes
    he,—
Brute, greedy man,—and quite despoils
    the tree.

Yet on that ravaged tree thou savest oft
Some little branch inviolate aloft,
Tender and airy up against the blue,
Which the rude spoiler cannot win unto;
Only the birds shall come and banquet
    there,
When, at St. Magdalene's, the fruit is fair.

Methinks I see yon airy little bough:
It mocks me with its freshness even now;
The light breeze lifts it, and it waves on
    high
Fruitage and foliage that cannot die.
Help me, dear God, on our Provençal
    speech,
To soar until the birds' own home I
    reach!

Once, then, beside the poplar-bordered
    Rhone,
There lived a basket-weaver and his son,
In a poor hut set round with willow-trees
(For all their humble wares were made
    from these);
And sometimes they from farm to farm
    would wend,

[125]

And horses' cribs and broken baskets
    mend.

And so one evening, as they trudged their
    round
With osier bundles on their shoulders
    bound,
"Father," young Vincen said, "the clouds
    look wild
About Magalouno's[3] tower up-piled.
If that gray rampart fell, 'twould do us
    harm:
We should be drenched ere we had gained
    the farm."

"Nay, nay!" the old man said, "no rain
    to-night!
'Tis the sea-breeze that shakes the trees.
    All right!
A western gale were different." Vincen
    mused:
"Are many ploughs at Lotus farmstead
    used?"
"Six ploughs!" the basket-weaver an-
    swered slow:
"It is the finest freehold in La Crau.

"Look! There's their olive-orchard,
    intermixt
With rows of vines and almond-trees
    betwixt.
The beauty of it is, that vineyard hath
For every day in all the year a path!
There's ne'er another such the beauty is;
And in each path are just so many trees."

"O heavens! How many hands at harvest-
    tide
So many trees must need!" young Vincen
    cried.
"Nay: for 'tis almost Hallowmas, you
    know,
When all the girls come flocking in from
    Baux,[4]
And, singing, heap with olives green and
    dun
The sheets[5] and sacks, and call it only
    fun."

The sun was sinking, as old Ambroi said;
On high were little clouds a-flush with
    red;
Sideways upon their yokèd cattle rode
The laborers slowly home, each with his
    goad
Erect. Night darkened on the distant
    moor;
'Twas supper-time, the day of toil was
    o'er.

"And here we are!" the boy cried. "I can
    see
The straw-heaped threshing-floor, so
    hasten we!"
"But stay!" the other. "Now, as I'm alive,
The Lotus Farm's the place for sheep to
    thrive,—
The pine-woods all the summer, and the
    sweep
Of the great plain in winter. Lucky sheep!

"And look at the great trees that shade
    the dwelling,
And look at that delicious stream forth
    welling
Inside the vivary! And mark the bees!
Autumn makes havoc in their colonies;
But every year, when comes the bright
    May weather,
You lotus-grove a hundred swarms will
    gather."

"And one thing more!" cried Vincen,
    eagerly,
"The very best of all, it seems to me,—
I mean the maiden, father, who dwells
    here.
Thou canst not have forgotten how, last
    year,
She bade us bring her olive-baskets two,
And fit her little one with handles new."

So saying, they drew the farm-house door
    a-nigh,
And, in the dewy twilight, saw thereby
The maid herself. Distaff in hand she
    stood,

Watching her silk-worms at their leafy
food.
Then master Ambroi let his osiers fall,
And sang out cheerily, "Good-even, all!"

"Father, the same to you!" the damsel
said.
"I had come out my distaff-point to
thread,
It grows so dark. Whence come you now,
I pray?
From Valabrègo?" [6] Ambroi answered,
"Yea.
I said, when the fast coming dark I saw,
'We'll sleep at Lotus Farm, upon the
straw.' "

Whereat, with no more words, father and
son
Hard by upon a roller sat them down,
And fell to their own work right busily.
A half-made cradle chanced the same to
be.
Fast through the nimble fingers of the two
The supple osier bent and crossed and
flew.

Certes, our Vincen was a comely lad.
A bright face and a manly form he had,
Albeit that summer he was bare sixteen.
Swart were his cheeks; but the dark soil,
I ween,
Bears the fine wheat, and black grapes
make the wine
That sets our feet a-dance, our eyes
a-shine.

Full well he knew the osier to prepare,
And deftly wrought: but ofttimes to his
share
Fell coarser work; for he the panniers
made
Wherewith the farmers use their beasts to
lade,
And divers kinds of baskets, huge and
rough,
Handy and light. Ay, he had skill enough!

And likewise brooms of millet-grass, and
such,—
And baskets of split-cane. And still his
touch
Was sure and swift; and all his wares were
strong,
And found a ready sale the farms among.
But now, from fallow field and moorland
waste,
The laborers were trooping home at last.

Then hasted sweet Mirèio to prepare,
With her own hands and in the open air,
Their evening meal. There was a broad
flat stone
Served for a table, and she set thereon
One mighty dish, where each man
plunged his ladle.
Our weavers wrought meanwhile upon
their cradle.

Until Ramoun, the master of the farm,
Cried, "How is this?"—brusque was his
tone and warm.
"Come to your supper, Ambroi: no de-
clining!
Put up the crib, my man: the stars are
shining.
And thou, Mirèio, run and fetch a bowl:
The travellers must be weary, on my
soul!"

Wherefore the basket-weaver, well-
content,
Rose with his son and to the table went,
And sat him down and cut the bread for
both;
While bright Mirèio hasted, nothing loth,
Seasoned a dish of beans with olive oil,
And came and sat before them with a
smile.

Not quite fifteen was this same fair
Mirèio,
Ah, me! the purple coast of Font Vièio,[7]
The hills of Baux, the desolate Crau plain,
A shape like hers will hardly see again.
Child of the merry sun, her dimpled face

Bloomed into laughter with ingenuous
    grace.

Eyes had she limpid as the drops of dew;
And, when she fixed their tender gaze on
    you,
Sorrow was not. Stars in a summer night
Are not more softly, innocently bright:
And beauteous hair, all waves and rings
    of jet;
And breasts, a double peach, scarce
    ripened yet.

Shy, yet a joyous little sprite she was;
And, finding all her sweetness in a glass,
You would have drained it at a single
    breath.
But to our tale, which somewhat lin-
    gereth.
When every man his day's toil had re-
    hearsed
(So, at my father's farm, I heard them
    first),—

"Now, Ambroi, for a song!" they all
    began:
"Let us not sleep above our supper, man!"
But he, "Peace! peace! My friends, do ye
    not know
On every jester, God, they say, doth blow
And sets him spinning like a top along?
Sing ourselves, lads,—you who are young
    and strong."

"No jest, good father, none!" they an-
    swered him.
"But, since the wine o'erflows your gob-
    let's brim,
Drink with us, Ambroi, and then to your
    song!"
"Ay, ay, when I was young—but that was
    long
Ago—I'd sing to any man's desire;
But now my voice is but a broken lyre."

"But, Master Ambroi," urged Mirèio,
"Sing one song, please, because 'twill
    cheer us so."

"My pretty one," the weaver said again,
"Only the husks of my old voice remain;
But if these please you, I cannot say nay,"
And drained his goblet, and began
    straightway:—

I.

Our captain was Bailly Suffren;
    We had sailed from Toulon,
Five hundred sea-faring Provençaux,
    Stout-hearted and strong:

'Twas the sweet hope of meeting the Eng-
    lish that made our hearts burn,
And till we had thrashed them we vowed
    we would never return.

II.

But all the first month of our
    cruise
    We saw never a thing
From the shrouds, save hundreds
    and hundreds
    Of gulls on the wing;
And in the next dolorous month, we'd a
    tempest to fight,
And had to be bailing out water by day
    and by night.

III.

By the third, we were driven to
    madness
    At meeting no foe
For our thundering cannon to
    sweep
    From the ocean. When lo!
"Hands aloft!" Captain cried. At the
    maintop one heard the command
And the long Arab coast on the lee-bow
    intently he scanned.

IV.

Till, "God's thunder!" he cried.
    "Three big vessels
    Bear down on us strong;
Run the guns to the ports! Blaze
    away!"
    Shouted Bailly Suffren.

"Sharp, lads! Of our Antibes figs we will
    give them a taste.
And see how they like those," Captain
    said, "ere we offer the rest!"

V.

A crash fit to deafen! Before
    The words left his lips
We had sent forty balls through
    the hulls
Of the Englishers' ships!
One was done for already. And now the
    guns only heard we
The cracking of wood and perpetual
    groan of the sea.

VI.

And now we were closing. Oh,
    rapture!
    We lay alongside,
And our gallant commander stood
    cool
    On the deck, and he cried,
"Well done, my brave boys! But enough!
    Cease your firing, I say,
For the time has come now to anoint
    them with oil of Aix."

VII.

Then we sprang to our dirks and
    our hatchets,
    As they had been toys;
And, grapnel in hand, the
    Provençal
    Cried, "Board 'em, my boys!"
A shout and a leap, and we stood on the
    Englishers' deck;
And then, ah, 'twas then we were ready
    our vengeance to wreak!

VIII.

Then, oh, the great slaughter! The
    crash
    Of the mainmast ensuing!
And the blows and the turmoil of
    men
    Fighting on 'mid the ruin!

More than one wild Provençal I saw seize
    a foe in his place.
And hug till he strained his own life out
    in deadly embrace.

And then old Ambroi paused. "Ah, yes!"
    said he,
"You do not quite believe my tale, I see.
Nathless these things all happened, under-
    stand:
Did I not hold the tiller with this hand?
Were I to live a thousand years, I say,
I should remember what befell that day."

"What, father, you were there and saw the
    fun?"
The laborers cried in mischief. "Three to
    one,
They flattened you like scythes beneath
    the hammer!"
"Who, me? The English?" the old tar 'gan
    stammer.
Upspringing; then, with smile of fine dis-
    dain,
Took up the burden of his tale again:—

IX.

So with blood-dabbled feet fought
    we on
    Four hours, until dark.
    Then, our eyes being cleared of
    the powder,
    We missed from our bark
Fivescore men. But the king of the Eng-
    lish lost ships of renown:
Three good vessels with all hands on
    board to the bottom went down.

X.

And now, our sides riddled with
    shot,
    Once more homeward hie we,
    Yards splintered, masts shivered,
    sails tattered;
    But brave Captain Bailly
Spake us words of good cheer. "My com-
    rades, ye have done well!

*To the great king of Paris the tale of your
    valor I'll tell!"*

XI.
*"Well said, Captain dear!" we re-
        plied:
    "Sure the king will hear you
When you speak. But for us, his
        poor mariners,
    What will he do,—
Who left our all gladly, our homes and
    our firesides," we said,
"For his sake, and lo! now in those homes
    there is crying for bread?*

XII.
*"Ah, Admiral, never forget
    When all bow before you.
With a love like the love of your
        seamen
    None will adore you!
Why, say but the word, and, ere home-
    ward our footsteps we turn,
Aloft on the tips of our fingers a king you
    are borne!"*

XIII.
A Martigau,[8] *mending his nets
    One eve, made this ditty.
Our Admiral bade us farewell,
    And sought the great city.
Were they wroth with his glory up there
    at the court? Who can say?
But we saw our beloved commander no
    more from that day!*

A timely ending thus the minstrel made,
Else the fast-coming tears his tale had
        stayed;
But for the laborers,—they sat intent,
Mute all, with parted lips, and forward
        bent
As if enchanted. Even when he was done,
For a brief space they seemed to hearken
        on.

"And such were aye the songs," said the
    old man,

"Sung in the good old days when Martha
        span.[9]
Long-winded, maybe, and the tunes were
        queer.
But, youngsters, what of that? They suit
        my ear.
Your new French airs mayhap may finer
        be;
But no one understands the words, you
        see!"

Whereon the men, somewhat as in a
        dream,
From table rose, and to the running
        stream
They led their patient mules, six yoke in
        all.
The long vine-branches from a trellised
        wall
Waved o'er them waiting, and, from time
        to time,
Humming some fragment of the weaver's
        rhyme.

Mirèio tarried, but not quite alone.
A social spirit had the little one,
And she and Vincen chatted happily.
'Twas a fair sight, the two young heads to
        see
Meeting and parting, coming still and go-
        ing
Like aster-flowers[10] when merry winds
        are blowing.

"Now tell me, Vincen," thus Mirèio,
"If oftentimes as you and Ambroi go
Bearing your burdens the wild country
        over,
Some haunted castle you do not discover,
Or joyous fête, or shining palace meet,
While we in the home-nest for ever sit?"

" 'Tis even so, my lady, as you think.
Why, currants quench the thirst as well as
        drink!
What though we brave all weathers in our
        toil?

Sure, we have joys that rain-drops cannot
spoil
The sun of noon beats fiercely on the
head,
But there are wayside trees unnumberèd.

"And whensoe'er return the summer
hours,
And olive-trees are all bedecked with
flowers,
We hunt the whitening orchards curiously,
Still following the scent, till we descry
In the hot noontide, by its emerald flash,
The tiny cantharis upon the ash.

"The shops will buy the same. Or off we
tramp
And gather red-oak apples in the
swamp,[11]
Or beat the ponds for leeches. Ah, that's
grand!
You need nor bait nor hook, but only
stand
And strike the water, and then one by one
They come and seize your legs, and all is
done.

"And thou wert never at Li Santo[12] even!
Dear heart! The singing there must be like
heaven.
'Tis there they bring the sick from all
about
For healing; and the church is small, no
doubt:
But, ah, what cries they lift! what vows
they pay
To the great saints! We saw it one fête-
day.

"It was the year of the great miracle.
My God, that was a sight! I mind it well.
A feeble boy, beautiful as Saint John,
Lay on the pavement, sadly calling on
The saints to give sight to his poor blind
eyes,
And promising his pet lamb in sacrifice.

" 'My little lamb, with budding horns!"
he said.
'Dear saints!' How we all wept! Then
from o'erhead
The blessed reliquaries came down
slowly,
Above the throngèd people bending lowly,
And crying, 'Come, great saints, mighty
and good!
Come, save!' The church was like a wind-
swept wood.

"Then the godmother held the child aloft,
Who spread abroad his fingers pale and
soft,
And passionately grasped the reliquaries
That held the bones of the three blessed
Maries;
Just as a drowning man, who cannot
swim,
Will clutch a plank that the sea heaves to
him.

"And then, oh! then,—I saw it with these
eyes,—
By faith illumined, the blind boy outcries,
'I see the sacred relics, and I see
Grandmother all in tears! Now haste,'
said he,
'My lambkin with the budding horns to
bring
To the dear saints for a thank-offering!'

"But thou, my lady, God keep thee, I
pray,
Handsome and happy as thou art to-day!
Yet if a lizard, wolf, or horrid snake
Ever should wound thee with its fang,
betake
Thyself forthwith to the most holy saints,
Who cure all ills and hearken all com-
plaints."

So the hours of the summer evening
passed.
Hard-by the big-wheeled cart its shadow
cast

On the white yard. Afar arose and fell
The frequent tinkle of a little bell
In the dark marsh: a nightingale sang
    yonder;
An owl made dreamy, sorrowful re-
    joinder.

"Now, since the night is moonlit, so the
    mere
And trees are glorified, wilt thou not
    hear,"
The boy besought, "the story of a race
In which I hoped to win the prize?"—
    "Ah, yes!"
The little maiden sighed; and, more than
    glad,
Still gazed with parted lips upon the lad.

"Well, then, Mirèio, once at Nismes," he
    said,
"They had foot-races on the esplanade;
And on a certain day a crowd was there
Collected, thicker then a shock of hair.
Some shoeless, coatless, hatless, were to
    run:
The others only came to see the fun.

"When all at once upon the scene appears
One Lagalanto, prince of foot-races.
In all Provence, and even in Italy,
The fleetest-footed far behind left he.
Yes: Lagalanto, the great Marseillais,—
Thou wilt have heard his name before
    to-day.

"A leg, a thigh, he had would not look
    small
By John of Cossa's,[13] the great seneschal;
And in his dresser many a pewter plate,
With all his victories carved thereon in
    state;
And you'd have said, to see his scarfs, my
    lady,
A wainscot all festooned with rainbows
    had he.

"The other runners, of whate'er condition,
Threw on their clothes at this dread
    apparition:

The game was up when Lagalanto came.
Only one stout-limbed lad, Lou Cri by
    name,
Who into Nismes had driven cows that
    day,
Durst challenge the victorious Marseillais.

"Whereon, 'Oh, bah!' cried foolish little I
(Just think!—I only chanced to stand
    thereby),
'I can run too!' Forthwith they all sur-
    round me:
'Run, then!' Alas! my foolish words con-
    found me;
For I had run with partridges alone,
And only the old oaks for lookers-on.

"But now was no escape, 'My poor boy,
    hasten,'
Says Lagalanto, 'and your latchets fasten.'
Well, so I did. And the great man mean-
    while
Drew o'er his mighty muscles, with a
    smile,
A pair of silken hose, whereto were sewn
Ten tiny golden bells of sweetest tone.

"So 'twas we three. Each set between his
    teeth
A bit of willow, thus to save his breath;
Shook hands all round; then, one foot on
    the line,
Trembling and eager we await the sign
For starting. It is given. Off we fly;
We scour the plain like mad,—'tis you!
    'tis I!

"Wrapped in a cloud of dust, with smok-
    ing hair,
We strain each nerve. Ah, what a race was
    there!
They thought we should have won the
    goal abreast,
Till I, presumptuous, sprang before the
    rest:
And that was my undoing; for I dropped
Pale, dying as it seemed. But never
    stopped

"The others. On, on, on, with steady gait,
Just like the pasteboard horses[14] at Aix
  fête.
The famous Marseillais thought he must
  win
(They used to say of him he had no
  spleen);
But, ah! my lady, on that day of days,
He found his man,—Lou Cri of Mouriès.

"For now they pass beyond the gazing
  line,
And almost touch the goal. O beauty
  mine!
Could'st thou have seen Lou Cri leap for-
  ward then!
Never, I think, in mountain, park, or glen,
A stag, a hare, so fleet of foot you'd find.
Howled like a wolf the other, just behind.

"Lou Cri is victor!—hugs the post for joy.
Then all of Nismes comes flocking round
  the boy,
To learn the birthplace of this wondrous
  one.
The pewter plate is flashing in the sun,
The hautboys flourish, cymbals clang
  apace,
As he receives the guerdon of the race."

"And Lagalanto?" asks Mirèio.
"Why, he upon the ground was sitting
  low,
Amid the dust raised by the gathering
  throng,
Clasping his knees. With shame his soul
  was stung;
And, with the drops that from his fore-
  head fell,
Came tears of bitterness unspeakable.

"Lou Cri approached, and made a modest
  bow.
'Brother, let's to the ale-house arbor now,
Behind the amphitheatre. Why borrow,
Upon this festive day, tears for the mor-
  row?
The money left we'll drink together thus:

There's sunshine yet enough for both of
  us.'

"Then trembling rose the runner of
  Marseilles,
And from his limbs made haste to tear
  away
The silken hose, the golden bells. 'Here,
  lad!'
Raising his pallid face, 'take them!' he
  said.
'I am grown old: youth decks thee like a
  swan;
So put the strong man's gear with honor
  on.'

"He turned, stricken like an ash the storm
  bereaves
In summer-time of all its tower of leaves.
The king of runners vanished from the
  place;
And never more ran he in any race,
Nor even leaped on the inflated hide,
In games at Saint John's or Saint Peter's
  tide."

So Vincen told the story, waxing warm,
Of all he'd seen, before the Lotus Farm.
His cheeks grew red, his eyes were full of
  light;
He waved his hand to point his speech
  aright,—
Abundant was the same as showers in
  May
That fall upon a field of new-mown hay.

The crickets, chirruping amid the dew,
Paused more than once to listen. Often,
  too,
The bird of evening, the sweet nightingale,
Kept silence; thrilling so at Vincen's tale,
As still she harked her leafy perch upon,
She might have kept awake until the
  dawn.

"Oh, mother!" cried Mirèio, "surely
  never,
Was weaver-lad so marvellously clever!

I love to sleep, dear, on a winter night;
But now I cannot,—it is all too light.

Ah, just one story more before we go,
For I could pass a lifetime listening so!"

NOTES TO CANTO I.

[1] LOTUS FARM, or *Falabrego Mas.* The word *mas*, meaning a farm or homestead, is used in the *arrondissement* of Arles and in Languedoc. Every *mas* has a distinctive name,—*Mas de la Font,* Fountain Farm; *Mas de l'Oste,* Host Farm; &c. The *falabrego* is the fruit of a species of lotus, called in French *micoculier.* (It is the *Celtis australis* of Linnæus; and nearly related to, if not identical with, *Celtis occidentalis,* the sugar-berry of our Northern woods, remarkable for the delicate texture of its foliage and singularly rich crimson color of its fruit.—H.W.P.)

[2] La Crau, from the Greek κραῦρος, *arid,* is a vast stony plain, bounded on the north by the Alpines (Lower Alps), on the east by the meres of Martigue, west by the Rhone, and south by the sea. It is the Arabia Petræa of France.

[3] Magalouno. Of this city, formerly a Greek colony, nothing now remains but a single church in ruins.

[4] Li Baus, in French Les Baux, is a ruined town, formerly the capital of the princely house of Baux. It is three leagues from Arles, on the summit of the Alpines; and, as the name of this poetical locality occurs often in the poem, the following description from Jules Canonge's History of the town of Baux, in Provence, may interest the reader:—

"At length there opened out before me a narrow valley. I bowed to the remains of a stone cross that sanctify the way; and, when I raised my eyes, they were riveted in astonishment on a set of towers and walls on the top of a rock, the like of which I had never before seen, save in works in which the genius of painting had been inspired by the most fabulous imaginings of Ariosto. But, if my surprise was great at the first aspect, it was doubly so when I reached an eminence, whence the whole town was displayed to view. It was a spectacle of desolate grandeur, such as a perusal of the Prophets presents to the mind. It was something I had never suspected the existence of,—a town almost monolithite. Those who first had the idea of inhabiting the rock had hewn them a shelter out of its sides. This novel mode of architecture was plainly approved of by their successors; for soon from the vast compact mass a town issued, like a statue from a block

touched by the wand of Art. An imposing town, with fortifications, chapels, and hospitals,—a town in which man seemed to have eternalized his habitation. The dominion of the city was extensive, and brilliant feats of arms have secured for it a noble place in history; but it has proved no more enduring than many others less solidly constituted."

The action of the poem begins at the foot of these ruins.

[5] Sheet spread to catch the olives as they are shaken from the trees.

[6] Valabrègo, a village on the left bank of the Rhone, between Avignon and Tarascon.

[7] Font Vièio (the Old Woman's Well), a village in one of the valleys of the Alpines near Arles.

[8] Martigau, an inhabitant of Martigue, a curious Provençal town inhabited almost solely by fishermen, built on some narrow islands, intersected by salt lakes and channels of the sea, by way of streets, which has occasioned it to be surnamed La Venire Provençale. It was the birthplace of Gerard Tenque (Thom or Tung), the founder of the order of St. John of Jerusalem.

[9] "When Martha span," a proverbial expression signifying, "in the good old days," and alluding to Martha the hostess of Christ, who, after having, according to the legend, delivered Tarascon from a monster that ravaged its territory, ended her days in these parts. She is said to have inhabited a small house on the banks of the Rhone, at the door of which she used to sit, surrounded by her neophytes, and modestly ply her spinning-wheel.

[10] The *aster trifolium,* common on the marshes of the South.

[11] *Li garrigo,* swamps or barren lands where only the *agarrus,* or dwarf-oak, grows.

[12] Li Santo is the Provençal name of a small town of 543 inhabitants situated on the island of Camargue, between the mouths of the Rhone. In obedience to a poetical and very venerable tradition, an innumerable host of pilgrims from every part of Provence and lower Languedoc assemble at this place every 25th of May. The tradition—which will be found very fully detailed in the eleventh canto of the poem—is, briefly, as follows: After the crucifixion, the Jews compelled some of the most ardent disciples to enter a dismantled ship, and consigned them to the

mercy of the waves. The scene is thus described in an ancient French canticle:—

LES JUIFS.

Entrez, Sara, dans la nacelle,
Lazare, Marthe, et Maximin,
Cléon, Trophime, Saturnin,
Les trois Maries et Marcelle,
Eutrope et Martial, Sidoine avec Joseph
     (d'Arimathée)
Vous pierez dans cette nef.

Allez sans voile et sans cordage,
Sans mât, sans ancre, sans timon,
Sans aliment, sans aviron;
Allez, faire un triste naufrage!
Retirez-vous d'ici, laissez-nous en repoz,
Allez, crever parmi les flots.

Guided by Providence, the bark at length stranded on the isle of Camargue, in Provence; and the exiles, thus miraculously delivered from the perils of the sea, dispersed over Gaul, and became its first evangelists. Mary Magdalene retired to the desert of La Sainte Baume, to weep over her sins. The other two Maries,—the mother of St. James the Less, and Mary Salome, mother of St. John the Evangelist and St. James the Great, —accompanied by their maid Sara, converted to the new faith some of the neighboring people, and then returned to the place of their landing to die. (See Canto XI.)

"It is reported that a prince whose name is unknown, learning that the bodies of the holy Maries were interred on this spot, built a church over it in the form of a citadel, that it might be safe from piratical invasion. He also built houses round the church and ramparts, for the safety of the inhabitants. The buildings that remain bear out this tradition."

The choir of the church presents the peculiarity of being composed of three stories,—a crypt, which is pointed out as the very site of the ancient oratory of the saints; a sanctuary, raised higher than usual; and a chapel above, where the reliquaries are exposed. A chain is attached to the latter, so that, by the unwinding of a capstan, they may be let down into the church. The moment when they descend is the one propitious to miracles, like that which Vincen describes.

[13] John of Cossa, a Neapolitan noble who had followed King René. He was Grand Seneschal of Provence, and died in 1476. John of Cossa is very popular at Tarascon, where the people ascribe to him the building of St. Martha's steeple. He is interred in the crypt of that church; and his statue, in a recumbent attitude, surmounts the tomb.

[14] The *chivaus-frus,* or painted cardboard horses, used in Provence at public rejoicings, and particularly at Aix in the *Fête Dieu.* The seeming riders attach them to the waist, and prance the streets to the sound of the tambourine.

CANTO II.

THE LEAF-PICKING.

Sing, magnarello,[1] merrily,
     As the green leaves you gather!
In their third sleep[2] the silk-worms lie,
     And lovely is the weather
Like brown bees that in open glades
     From rosemary gather honey,
The mulberry-trees swarm full of
          maids,
     Glad as the air is sunny!

It chanced one morn—it was May's
          loveliest—
Mirèio gathered leaves among the rest.
It chanced, moreover, on that same May
          morning,

The little gypsy, for her own adorning,
Had cherries in her ears, for rings, suspended,
Just as our Vincen's footsteps thither
          tended.

Like Latin seaside people everywhere,
He wore a red cap on his raven hair,
With a cock's feather gayly set therein;
And, prancing onward, with a stick made
          spin
The flints from wayside stone-heaps, and
          set flying
The lazy adders in his pathway lying.

When suddenly, from the straight, leafy
          alley,

"Whither away so fast?" a voice comes
	gayly.
Mirèio's. Vincen darts beneath the trees,
Looks up, and soon the merry maiden
	sees.
Perched on a mulberry-tree, she eyed the
	lad
Like some gray-crested lark,[3] and he was
	glad.

"How then, Mirèio, comes the picking
	on?
Little by little, all will soon be done!
May I not help thee?"—"That were very
	meet,"
She said, and laughed upon her airy seat.
Sprang Vincen like a squirrel from the
	clover,
Ran nimbly up the tree, and said, more-
	over,—

"Now since old Master Ramoun hath but
	thee,
Come down, I pray, and strip the lower
	tree!
I'll to the top!" As busily the maiden
Wrought on, she murmured, "How the
	soul doth gladden
To have good company! There's little joy
In lonely work!"—"Ay is there!" said the
	boy:

"For when in our old hut we sit alone,
Father and I, and only hear the Rhone
Rush headlong o'er the shingle, 'tis most
	drear!
Not in the pleasant season of the year,
For then upon our travels we are bound,
And trudge from farm to farm the coun-
	try round.

"But when the holly-berries have turned
	red,
And winter comes, and nights are long,"
	he said,
"And sitting by the dying fire we catch
Whistle or mew of goblin at the latch;

And I must wait till bed-time there with
	him,
Speaking but seldom, and the room so
	dim,"—

Broke in the happy girl, unthinkingly,
"Ah! but your mother, Vincen, where is
	she?"
"Mother is dead." The two were still
	awhile:
Then he, "But Vinceneto could beguile
The time when she was there. A little
	thing,
But she could keep the hut."—"I'm won-
	dering—

"You have a sister, Vincen?"—"That have
	I!
A merry lass and good," was the reply:
"For down at Font-dou-Rèi, in Beaucaire
Whither she went to glean, she was so fair
And deft at work that all were smitten by
	her;
And there she stays as servant by desire."

"And you are like her?"—"Now that
	makes me merry.
Why, she is blonde, and I brown as a
	berry!
But wouldst thou know whom she is like,
	the elf?
Why, even like thee, Mirèio, thine own
	self!
Your two bright heads, with all their
	wealth of hair
Like myrtle-leaves, would make a perfect
	pair.

"But, ah! thou knowest better far to
	gather
The muslin of thy cap[4] than doth the
	other!
My little sister is not plain nor dull,
But thou,—thou art so much more beau-
	tiful!"
"Oh, what a Vincen!" cried Mirèio,
And suddenly the half-culled branch let
	go.

Sing, magnarello, merrily,
  As the green leaves you gather!
In their third sleep the silk-worms lie,
  And lovely is the weather.
Like brown bees that in open glades
  From rosemary gather honey,
The mulberry-trees swarm full of
    maids,
  Glad as the air is sunny!

"And so you think I have a pretty face,
More fair than hers?" Then sighed the lad,
  "Ah, yes!"
"But what more have I than this little
    wench?"
"Mother divine! What more hath the gold-
finch
Than hath the fragile wren,—unless it be
Beauty and grace and richer minstrelsy?"

"What more? Ah, my poor sister! Hear
    me speak,—
Thou wilt not get the white out of the
    leek:
Her eyes are like the water of the sea,
Blue, clear,—thine, black, and they flash
    gloriously.
And, O Mirèio! when on me they shine,
I seem to drain a bumper of cooked
    wine! 5

"My sister hath a silver voice and mel-
    low,—
I love to hear her sing the *Peirounello*,—
But, ah! my sweet young lady, every word
Thou 'st given me my spirit more hath
    stirred,
My ear more thrilled, my very heart-
    strings wrung,
More than a thousand songs divinely
    sung!

"With roaming all the pastures in the sun,
My little sister's face and neck are dun
As dates; but thou, most fair one, I think
    well,
Art fashioned like the flowers of Aspho-
del.

So the bold Summer with his tawny hand
Dare not caress thy forehead white and
    bland.

"Moreover, Vinceneto is more slim
Than dragon-flies that o'er the brooklet
    skim.
Poor child! In one year grew she up to
    this;
But verily in thy shape is naught amiss."
Again Mirèio, turning rosy red,
Let fall her branch, and "What a Vincen!"
    said.

Sing, magnarello, merrily,
  The green leaves ever piling!
Two comely children sit on high,
  Amid the foliage, smiling.
Sing, magnarello, loud and oft:
  Your merry labor hasten.
The guileless pair who laugh aloft
  Are learning love's first lesson.

Cleared from the hills meanwhile the
    mists of morn,
And o'er the ruined towers, whither re-
    turn
Nightly the grim old lords of Baux, they
    say;
And o'er the barren rocks 'gan take their
    way
Vultures,6 whose large, white wings are
    seen to gleam
Resplendent in the noontide's burning
    beam.

Then cried the maiden, pouting, "We have
    done
Naught! Oh, shame to idle so! *Some one*
Said he would help me; and that some one
    still
Doth naught but talk, and make me laugh
    at will.
Work now, lest mother say I am unwary
And idle, and too awkward yet to marry!

"Ah! my brave friend, I think, should one
    engage you

To pick leaves by the quintal, and for
    wage, you
Would all the same sit still and feast your
    eyes,
Handling the ready sprays in dreamy
    wise!"
Whereat the boy, a trifle disconcerted,
"And so thou takest me for a gawky!"
    blurted.

"We'll see, my fair young lady," added he,
"Which of us two the better picker be!"
They ply both hands now. With vast
    animation,
They bend and strip the branches. No
    occasion
For rest or idle chatter either uses,
(The bleating sheep, they say, her mouth-
    ful loses,)

Until the mulberry-tree is bare of leaves,
And these the ready sack at once receives,
At whose distended mouth—ah, youth is
    sweet!—
Mirèio's pretty taper hand will meet
In strange entanglement that somehow
    lingers
That Vincen's, with its brown and burning
    fingers.

Both started. In their cheeks the flush rose
    higher:
They felt the heat of some mysterious
    fire.
They dropped the mulberry-leaves as if
    afraid,
And, tremulous with passion, the boy
    said,—
"What aileth thee, my lady? answer me!
Did any hidden hornet dare sting thee?"

Well-nigh inaudible, with drooping brow,
"I know not, Vincen,"—thus Mirèio.
And so they turned a few more leaves to
    gather,
And neither spake again unto the other.
But their bright, sidelong glances seemed
    to seek

Which would be first to laugh, and the
    spell break.

Their hearts beat high, the green leaves
    fell like rain;
And, when the time for sacking came
    again,
Whether by chance or by contriving it
The white hand and the brown hand al-
    ways met.
Nor seemed there any lack of happiness
The while their labor failed not to pro-
    gress.

    Sing, magnarello, merrily,
       As the green leaves you gather!
    The sun of May is riding high,
       And ardent is the weather.

Now suddenly Mirèio whispered, "Hark!
What can that be?" and listened like a
    lark
Upon a vine, her small forefinger pressing
Against her lip, and eager eyes addressing
To a bird's nest upon a leafy bough,
Just opposite the one where she was now.

"Ah! wait a little while!" with bated
    breath,
So the young basket-weaver answereth,
And like a sparrow hopped from limb to
    limb
Toward the nest. Down in the tree-trunk
    dim,
Close peering through a crevice in the
    wood,
Full-fledged and lively saw he the young
    brood.

And, sitting firmly the rough bough
    astride,
Clung with one hand, and let the other
    glide
Into the hollow trunk. Above his head
Mirèio leaned with her cheeks rosy red.
"What sort?" she whispered from her
    covert shady.

"Beauties!"—"But what?"—"Blue tomtits,
      my young lady!"

Then laughed the maiden, and her laugh
      was gay:
"See, Vincen! Have you never heard them
      say
That when two find a nest in company,
On mulberry, or any other tree,
The Church within a year will join those
      two?
And proverbs, father says, are always
      true."

"Yea," quoth the lad; "but do not thou
      forget
That this, our happy hope, may perish yet,
If all the birdies be not caged forthwith."
"Jesu divine!" the maiden murmureth:
"Put them by quickly! It concerns us
      much
Our birdies should be safe from alien
      touch."

"Why, then, the very safest place," said
      he,
"Methinks, Mirèio, would thy bodice be!"
"Oh, surely!" So the lad explores the hol-
      low,
His hand withdrawing full of tomtits cal-
      low.
Four were they; and the maid in ecstasy
Cries, "Mon Dieu!" and lifts her hands on
      high.

"How many! What a pretty brood it is!
There! There, poor darlings, give me just
      one kiss!"
And, lavishing a thousand fond caresses,
Tenderly, carefully, the four she places
Inside her waist, obeying Vincen's will;
While he, "Hold out thy hands! there
      are more still!"

"Oh, sweet! The little eyes in each blue
      head
Are sharp as needles," as Mirèio said

Softly, three more of the wee brood she
      pressed
Into their smooth, white prison with the
      rest,
Who, when bestowed within that refuge
      warm,
Thought they were in their nest and safe
      from harm.

"Are there more, Vincen?"—"Ay!" he
      answered her.
"Then, Holy Virgin! you're a sorcerer!"
"Thou simple maid! About St. George's
      day,
Ten, twelve, and fourteen eggs, these tom-
      tits lay.
Ay, often. Now let these the others fol-
      low!
They are the last: so good-by, pretty hol-
      low!"

But ere the words were spoken, and the
      maid
In her flowered neckerchief had fairly
      laid
Her little charge, she gave a piercing wail:
"Oh me! oh me!" then murmured, and
      turned pale;
And, laying both her hands upon her
      breast,
Moaned, "I am dying!" and was sore
      distressed,

And could but weep: "Ah, they are
      scratching me!
They sting! Come quickly, Vincen, up
      the tree!"
For on the last arrival had ensued
Wondrous commotion in the hidden
      brood;
The fledglings latest taken from the nest
Had sore disorder wrought among the
      rest.

Because within so very small a valley
All could not lie at ease, so must they
      gayly

Scramble with claw and wing down either
    slope,
And up the gentle hills, thus to find
    scope:
A thousand tiny somersets they turn,
A thousand pretty rolls they seem to
    learn.

And "Ah, come quick!" is still the
    maiden's cry,
Trembling like vine-spray when the wind
    is high,
Or like a heifer stung with cattle-flies.
And, as she bends and writhes in piteous
    wise,
Leaps Vincen upward till he plants his
    feet
Once more beside her on her airy seat.

Sing, magnarello, heap your leaves,
    While sunny is the weather!
He comes to aid her where she grieves:
    The two are now together.

"Thou likest not this tickling?" kindly
    said he.
"What if thou wert like me, my gentle
    lady,
And hadst to wander barefoot through
    the nettles?"
So proffering his red sea-cap, there he
    settles
Fast as she draws them from her
    neckerchief
The birdies, to Mirèio's vast relief.

But still her eyes are downcast,—the
    poor dear!
Nor can she look at her deliverer
For a brief. But then a smile ensues,
And the tears vanish, as the morning dews
That drench the flowers and grass at
    break of day
Roll into little pearls and pass away.

And then there came a fresh catastrophe:
The branch whereon they sat so cosily

Snapped, broke asunder, and with ringing
    shriek
Mirèio flung her arms round Vincen's
    neck,
And he clasped hers, and they whirled
    suddenly
Down through the leaves upon the supple
    rye.

Listen, wind of the Greek,[7] wind of the
    sea,
And shake no more the verdant canopy!
Hush for one moment, O thou childish
    breeze!
Breathe soft and whisper low, beholding
    these!
Give them a little time to dream of
    bliss,—
To dream at least, in such a world as this!

Thou too, swift streamlet of the prattling
    voice,
Peace, prithee! In this hour, make little
    noise
Among the vocal pebbles of thy bed!
Ay, little noise! Because two souls have
    sped
To one bright region. Leave them there,
    to roam
Over the starry heights,—their proper
    home!

A moment, and she struggled to be free
From his embrace. The flower of the
    quince-tree
Is not so pale. Then backward the two
    sank,
And gazed at one another on the bank,
Until the weaver's son the silence brake,
And thus in seeming wrath arose and
    spake:

"Shame on thee, thou perfidious mul-
    berry!
A devil's tree! A Friday-planted tree!
Blight seize and wood-louse eat thee!
    May thy master
Hold thee in horror for this day's disaster!

Tell me thou are not hurt, Mirèio!"
Trembling from head to foot, she an-
    swered, "No:

"I am not hurt; but as a baby weeps
And knows not why,—there's something
    here that keeps
Perpetual tumult in my heart. A pain
Blinds me and deafens me, and fills my
    brain,
So that my blood in a tumultuous riot
Courses my body through, and won't be
    quiet."

"May it not be," the simple boy replied,
"Thou fearest to have thy mother come
    and chide
Thy tardy picking,—as when I come
    back
Late from the blackberry-field with face
    all black,
And tattered clothes?" Mirèio sighed
    again,
"Ah, no! This is another kind of pain!"

"Or possibly a sun-stroke may have
    lighted
Upon thee!" And the eager Vincen cited
An ancient crone among the hills of
    Baux,
Taven by name, "who on the forehead,—
    so,—
A glass of water sets: the ray malign
The dazed brain for the crystal will
    resign."

"Nay, nay!" impetuously the maiden
    cried,
"Floods of May sunshine never terrified
The girls of Crau. Why should I hold you
    waiting?
Vincen, in vain my heart is palpitating!
My secret cannot bide a home so small:
I love you, Vincen, love you!—That is
    all!"

The river-banks, the close-pruned willows
    hoary,

Green grass and ambient air, hearing
    this story,
Were full of glee. But the poor basket-
    weaver,
"Princess, that thou who are so fair and
    clever,
Shouldst have a tongue given to wicked
    lying!
Why, it confounds me! It is stupefying!

"What! thou in love with me? Mirèio,
My poor life is yet happy. Do not go
And make a jest thereof! I might believe
Just for one moment, and thereafter
    grieve
My soul to death. Ah, no! my pretty maid,
Laugh no more at me in this wise!" he
    said.

"Now may God shut me out of Paradise,
Vincen, if I have ever told you lies!
Go to! I love you! Will that kill you,
    friend?
But if you *will* be cruel, and so send
Me from your side, 'tis I who will fall ill,
And at your feet lie low till sorrow kill!"

"No more! no more!" cried Vincen, des-
    perately:
"There is a gulf 'twixt thee and me! The
    stately
Queen of the Lotus Farm art thou, and all
Bow at thy coming, hasten to thy call,
While I, a vagrant weaver, only wander,
Plying my trade from Valabrègo yonder."

"What care I?" cried the fiery girl at once.
Sharp as a sheaf-binder's came her re-
    sponse.
"May not my lover, then, a baron be,
Or eke a weaver, if he pleases me?
But if you will not have me pine away,
Why look so handsome, even in rags, I
    say?"

He turned and faced her. Ah, she was
    enchanting!

And as a charmèd bird falls dizzy, pant-
    ing,
So he. "Mirèio, thou 'rt a sorceress!
Else were I not so dazzled by thy face.
Thy voice, too, mounts into this head of
    mine,
And makes me like a man o'ercome with
    wine."

"Why, can't it be, Mirèio? Seest thou not
Even now with thy embrace my brain is
    hot.
I am a pack-bearer, and well may be
A laughing-stock for evermore to thee,
But thou shalt have the truth, dear, in this
    hour:
I love thee, with a love that could devour!

"Wert thou to ask,—lo, love I thee so
    much!—
The golden goat,[8] that ne'er felt mortal
    touch
Upon its udders, but doth only lick
Moss from the base of the precipitous
    peak
Of Baux,—I'd perish in the quarries there,
Or bring thee down the goat with golden
    hair!

"So much, that, if thou saidst, 'I want a
    star,'
There is no stream so wild, no sea so far,
But I would cross; no headsman, steel or
    fire,
That could withhold me. Yea, I would
    climb higher
Than peaks that kiss the sky, that star to
    seek;
And Sunday thou shouldst wear it on thy
    neck!

"O my Mirèio! Ever as I gaze,
Thy beauty fills me with a deep amaze.
Once, when by Vaucluse grotto I was
    going,
I saw a fig-tree in the bare rock growing;
So very spare it was, the lizards gray

Had found more shade beneath a jasmine
    spray.

"But, round about the roots, once every
    year
The neighboring stream comes gushing,
    as I hear
And the shrub drinks the water as it rises,
And that one drink for the whole year
    suffices.
Even as the gem is cut to fit the ring,
This parable to us is answering.

"I am the fig-tree on the barren mountain;
And thou, mine own, art the reviving
    fountain!
Surely it would suffice me, could I feel
That, once a year, I might before thee
    kneel,
And sun myself in thy sweet face, and
    lay
My lips unto thy fingers, as to-day!"

Trembling with love, Mirèio hears him
    speak,
And lets him wind his arms about her
    neck
And clasp her as bewildered. Suddenly,
Through the green walk, quavers an old
    wife's cry:
"How now, Mirèio? Are you coming
    soon?
What will the silk-worms have to eat at
    noon?"

As ofttimes, at the coming on of night,
A flock of sparrows on a pine alight
And fill the air with joyous chirruping,
Yet, if a passing gleaner pause and fling
A stone that way, they to the neighboring
    wood,
By terror winged, their instant flight
    make good;

So, with a tumult of emotion thrilled,
Fled the enamoured two across the field.

But when, her leaves upon her head, the
  maid
Turned silently toward the farm, he
  stayed,—

Vincen,—and breathless watched her in
  her flight
Over the fallow, till she passed from
  sight.

NOTES TO CANTO II.

[1] *Magnarello* are women silk-worm rear-ers. *Magnan* are silk-worms.

[2] Silk-worms live in the larva state about thirty-four days; and, in this interval, moult, or shed their skin, four times. At the ap-proach of each of these periods, they be-come, as it were, paralyzed, and cease eating, —*dormon*. They say in Provençal *dourmi de la proumiero, di doz, di tres, di quatre,* which means, literally, sleeping the first, second, third, fourth (moult).

[3] A gray-crested lark,—the *Alauda cristata.*

[4] "The muslin of thy cap." The Crau women wear their hair tightly enveloped in a kerchief of fine, transparent linen or mus-lin, around which is passed a band of velvet, usually of a blue-black, at a distance of about one-third from the top of the muslin, leav-ing, therefore, so much of it visible. Another turn is then passed immediately below the first, and then another, until two-thirds of the muslin are concealed. The black band is finally fastened at the back of the head with a large gold pin; while the other end, to the length of about a foot, is left pendant. On either side of the forehead, the hair is suffered to fall as low as the cheek-bone, where it is gracefully curved back, and gathered under the muslin.

[5] "Cooked wine." The grape-juice, on be-ing removed from the press, is boiled in a caldron, and, after one year's bottle, has the color and flavor of the best Spanish wines. The Provençaux drink it at feasts, galas, and always at Christmas.

[6] Vultures. The *Vultur percnoptus.*

[7] *Gregali, gregau,* and *gre* are all words used to signify the Greek, or north-east, wind.

[8] "The golden goat," *la cabro d'or,* is a phrase used to signify some treasure or talis-man, that the people imagine to have been buried by the Saracens, under some one or other of the antique monuments of Provence. Some allege that it lies under the Mausoleum of Saint Rémy; others, under the Baux rocks. "This tradition," says George Sand (in *Les Visions de la Nuit dans les Campagnes*), "is universal. There are few ruins, castles, or monasteries, few Celtic monuments, that have not their treasure hidden away some-where, and guarded by some diabolic animal. M. Jules Canonge, in a charming collection of Southern tales, has rendered graceful and beneficent the poetical apparition of the golden goat, the guardian of the riches hid-den in the bosom of the earth."

CANTO III.

THE COCOONING.[1]

When the crop is fair in the olive-yard,
  And the earthen jars are ready
For the golden oil from the barrels
  poured,
  And the big cart rocks unsteady
With its tower of gathered sheaves, and
  strains
And groans on its way through fields and
  lanes;

When brawny and bare as an old athlete
  Comes Bacchus the dance a-leading,
And the laborers all, with juice-dyed feet,
  The vintage of Crau are treading,

And the good wine pours from the brimful presses,
And the ruddy foam in the vats increases;

When under the leaves of the Spanish
  broom
  The clear silk-worms are holden,
An artist each, in a tiny loom,
  Weaving a web all golden,—
Fine, frail cells out of sunlight spun,
Where they creep and sleep by the mil-
  lion,—

Glad is Provence on a day like that,
  'Tis time of jest and laughter:
The Ferigoulet[2] and the Baume Muscat[3]
  They quaff, and they sing thereafter.

And lads and lasses, their toils between,
Dance to the tinkling tambourine.

"Methinks, good neighbors, I am For-
	tune's pet.
Ne'er in my trellised arbor saw I yet
A silkier bower, cocoons more worthy
	praise,
Or richer harvest, since the year of grace
When first I laid my hand on Ramoun's
	arm
And came, a youthful bride, to Lotus
	Farm."

So spake Jano Mario, Ramoun's wife,
The fond, proud mother who had given
	life
To our Mirèio. Unto her had hied,
The while were gathered the cocoons out-
	side,
Her neighbors. In the silk-worm-room
	they throng;
And, as they aid the picking, gossip long.

To these Mirèio tendered now and then
Oak-sprigs and sprays of rosemary; for
	when
The worms, lured by the mountain odor,
	come
In myriads, there to make their silken
	home,
The sprays and sprigs, adornèd in such
	wise,
Are like the golden palms of Paradise.

"On Mother Mary's altar yesterday,"
Jano Mario said, "I went to lay
My finer sprays, by way of tithe. And so
I do each year; for you, my women, know
That, when the holy Mother will, 'tis she
Who sendeth up the worms abundantly."

"Now, for my part," said Zèu of Host
	Farm,
"Great fears have I my worms will come
	to harm.
You mind that ugly day the east wind
	blew,—
I left my window open,—if you knew

Ever such folly!—and to my affright
Upon my floor are twenty, now turned
	white." [4]

To her replied Taven, the ancient crone,
Who from the heights of Baux had wan-
	dered down
To help at the cocooning: "Youth is bold,
The young think they know better than
	the old;
And age is torment, and we mourn the
	fate
Which bids us see and know,—but all too
	late,

"Ye are such giddy women, every one,
That, if the hatching promise well, ye run
Straightway about the streets the tale to
	tell.
'Come see my silk-worms! 'Tis incredible
How fine they are!' Envy can well dis-
	semble:
She hastens to your room, her heart
	a-tremble

"With wrath. And 'Well done, neighbor!'
	she says cheerly:
'This does one good! You've still your
	caul [5] on, clearly!'
But when your head is turned, she casts
	upon 'em—
The envious one—a look so full of
	venom,
It knots and burns 'em up. And then you
	say
It was the east wind plastered 'em that
	way!"

"I don't say that has naught to do with it,"
Quoth Zèu. "Still it had been quite as fit
For me to close the window."—"Doubt
	you, then,
The harm the eye can do," went on
	Taven,
"When in the head it glistens balefully?"
And herself scanned Zèu with piercing
	eye.

"Ye are such fools, ye seem to think,"
    she said,
"That scraping with a scalpel on the dead
Would win its honey-secret from the bee!
But may not a fierce look, now answer
    me,
The unborn babe for evermore deform,
And dry the cow's milk in her udders
    warm?

"An owl may fascinate a little bird;
A serpent, flying geese, as I have heard,
How high soe'er they mount. And if one
    keep
A fixed gaze upon silk-worms, will they
    sleep?
Moreover, is there, neighbors, in the land
So wise a virgin that she can withstand

"The fiery eyes of passionate youth?"
    Here stopped
The hag, and damsels four their cocoons
    dropped;
"In June as in October," murmuring,
"Her tongue hath evermore a barbèd
    sting,
The ancient viper! What! the lads, say
    you?
Let them come, then! We'll see what they
    can do!"

But other merry ones retorted, "No!
We want them not! Do we, Mirèio?"
"Not we! Nor is it always cocooning,
So I'll a bottle from the cellar bring
That you will find delicious." And she
    fled
Toward the house because her cheeks
    grew red.

"Now, friends," said haughty Lauro, with
    decision,
"This is my mind, though poor be my
    condition:
I'll smile on no one, even though my
    lover
As king of fairy-land his realm should
    offer.

A pleasure were it, could I see him lying,
And seven long years before my footstool
    sighing."

"Ah!" said Clemenço, "should a king me
    woo,
And say he loved me, without much ado
I'd grant the royal suit! And chiefly thus
Were he a young king and a glorious.
A king of men, in beauty, I'd let come
And freely lead me to his palace home!

"But see! If I were once enthronèd there,
A sovereign and an empress, in a fair
Mantle bedecked, of golden-flowered
    brocade,
With pearls and emeralds dazzling round
    my head,
Then would my heart for my poor coun-
    try yearn;
And I, the queen, would unto Baux re-
    turn.

"And I would make my capital at Baux,
And on the rock where lie its ruins low
I would rebuild our ancient castle, and
A white tower on the top thereof should
    stand
Whose head should touch the stars.
        Thither retiring,
It rest or solace were the queen desiring,

"We'd climb the turret-stair, my prince
    and I,
And gladly throw the crown and mantle
    by.
And would it not be blissful with my love,
Aloft, alone to sit, the world above?
Or, leaned upon the parapet by his side,
To search the lovely landscape far and
    wide,

"Our own glad kingdom of Provence
    descrying,
Like some great orange-grove beneath us
    lying
All fair? And, ever stretching dreamily

Beyond the hills and plains, the sapphire
    sea;
While noble ships, tricked out with
    streamers gay,
Just graze the Chateau d'If, and pass
    away?

"Or we would turn to lightning-scathed
    Ventour,[6]
Who, while the lesser heights before him
    cower,
His hoary head against the heaven raises,
As I have seen, in solitary places
Of beech and pine, with staff in agèd
    hand,
Some shepherd-chief, his flock o'erlook-
    ing, stand.

"Again, we'd follow the great Rhone
    awhile,
Adown whose banks the cities brave de-
    file,
And dip their lips and drink, with dance
    and song.
Stately is the Rhone's march, and very
    strong;
But even he must bend at Avignon
His haughty head to Notre Dame des
    Dom.[7]

"Or watch the ever-varying Durance,
Now like some fierce and ravenous goat
    advance
Devouring banks and bridges; now de-
    mure
As maid from rustic well who bears her
    ewer,
Spilling her scanty water as she dallies,
And every youth along her pathway
    rallies."

So spake her sweet Provençal majesty,
And rose with brimful apron, and put by
Her gathered treasure. Two more maids
    were there,
Twin sisters, the one dark, the other
    fair,—

Azalaïs, Viòulano. The stronghold
Of Estoublon sheltered their parents old.

And oft these two to Lotus Farmstead
    came;
While that mischievous lad, Cupid by
    name,
Who loves to sport with generous hearts
    and tender,
Had made the sisters both their love sur-
    render
To the same youth. So Azalaïs said,—
The dark one,—lifting up her raven head:

"Now, damsels, play awhile that I were
    queen.
The Marseilles ships, the Beaucaire mea-
    dows green,
Smiling La Ciotat, and fair Salon,
With all her almond-trees, to me belong.
Then the young maids I'd summon by
    decree,
From Arles, Baux, Barbentano, unto me.

" 'Come, fly like birds!' the order should
    be given;
And I, of these, would choose the fairest
    seven,
And royal charge upon the same would
    lay,
The false love and the true in scales to
    weigh.
And then would merry counsel holden be;
For sure it is a great calamity

"That half of those who love, with love
    most meet,
Can never marry, and their joy complete.
But when I, Azalaïs, hold the helm,
I proclamation make, that in my realm
When lovers true are tyrannously hurt
They shall find mercy at the maiden's
    court.

"And if one sell her robe of honor white,
Whether it be for gold or jewel bright,
And if one offer insult, or betray
A fond heart, unto such as these alway

The high court of the seven maids shall
    prove
The stern avenger of offended love.

"And if two lovers the same maid desire,
Or if two maids to the same lad aspire,
My council's duty it shall be to choose
Which loves the better, which the better
    sues,
And which is worthier of a happy fate.
Moreover, on my maidens there shall wait

"Seven sweet poets, who from time to
    time
Shall write the laws of love in lovely
    rhyme
Upon wild vine-leaves or the bark of
    trees;
And sometimes, in a stately chorus, these
Will sing the same, and then their couplets
    all
Like honey from the honey-comb will
    fall."

So, long ago, the whispering pines among,
Faneto de Gautèume[8] may have sung,
When she the glory of her star-crowned
    head
On Roumanin and on the Alpines shed;
Or Countess Dio,[9] of the passionate lays,
Who held her courts of love in the old
    days.

But now Mirèio, to the room returning,
With face as radiant as an Easter morn-
    ing,
A flagon bore; and, for their spirits' sake,
Besought them all her beverage to par-
    take:
"For this will make us work with heartier
    will;
So come, good women, and your goblets
    fill!"

Then, pouring from the wicker-covered
    flask
A generous drink for whosoe'er might
    ask,

(A string of gold the falling liquor made),
"I mixed this cordial mine own self," she
    said:
"One leaves it in a window forty days,
That it may mellow in the sun's hot rays.

"Herein are mountain herbs, in number
    three.
The liquor keeps their odor perfectly:
It strengthens one." Here brake in other
    voices:
"Listen, Mirèio! Tell us what your choice
    is;
For these have told what they would do,
    if they
Were queens, or came to great estate one
    day.

"In such a case, Mirèio, what would
    you?"
"Who, I? How can I tell what I would do?
I am so happy in our own La Crau
With my dear parents, wherefore should
    I go?"
"Ah, ha!" outspake another maiden bold:
"Little care you for silver or for gold.

"But on a certain morn, I mind it well,—
Forgive me, dear, that I the tale should
    tell!—
'Twas Tuesday: I had gathered sticks that
    day,
And, fagot on my hip, had won my way
Almost to La Crous-Blanco, when I 'spied
You in a tree, with some one by your side

"Who chatted gayly. A lithe form he
    had"—
"Whence did he come?" they cried. "Who
    was the lad?"
Said Noro, "To tell that were not so easy,
Because among the thick-leaved mulberry-
    trees he
Was hidden half; yet think I 'twas the
    clever
Vincen, the Valabregan basket-weaver!"

"Oh!" cried the damsels all, with peals of
laughter,
"See you not what the little cheat was
after?
A pretty basket she would fain receive,
And made this poor boy in her love believe!
The fairest maiden the whole country
over
Has chosen the barefoot Vincen for her
lover!"

So mocked they, till o'er each young
countenance
In turn there fell a dark and sidelong
glance,—
Taven's,—who cried, "A thousand curses
fall
Upon you, and the vampire[10] seize you
all!
If the good Lord from heaven this way
came,
You girls, I think, would giggle all the
same.

" 'Tis brave to laugh at this poor lad of
osiers;
But mark! the future may make strange
disclosures,
Poor though he be. Now hear the oracle!
God in his house once wrought a miracle;
And I can show the truth of what I say,
For, lasses, it all happened in my day.

"Once, in the wild woods of the
Luberon,[11]
A shepherd kept his flock. His days were
long;
But when at last the same were well-nigh
spent,
And toward the grave his iron frame was
bent,
He sought the hermit of Saint Ouquèri,
To make his last confession piously.

"Alone, in the Vaumasco[12] valley lost,
His foot had never sacred threshold crost,
Since he partook his first communion.

Even his prayers were from his memory
gone;
But now he rose and left his cottage lowly,
And came and bowed before the hermit
holy.

" 'With what sin chargest thou thyself,
my brother?'
The solitary said. Replied the other,
The aged man, 'Once, long ago, I slew
A little bird about my flock that flew,—
A cruel stone I flung its life to end:
It was a wag-tail, and the shepherds'
friend.'

" 'Is this a simple soul,' the hermit
thought,
'Or is it an impostor?' And he sought
Curiously to read the old man's face
Until, to solve the riddle, 'Go,' he says,
'And hang thy shepherd's cloak yon beam
upon,
And afterward I will absolve my son.'

"A single sunbeam through the chapel
strayed;
And there it was the priest the suppliant
bade
To hang his cloak! But the good soul
arose,
And drew it off with mien of all repose,
And threw it upward. And it hung in
sight
Suspended on the slender shaft of light!

"Then fell the hermit prostrate on the
floor,
'Oh, man of God!' he cried, and he wept
sore,
'Let but the blessed hand these tears
bedew,
Fulfill the sacred office for us two!
No sins of thine can I absolve, 'tis clear:
Thou art the saint, and I the sinner
here!' "

Her story ended, the crone said no more;
But all the laughter of the maids was o'er.

Only Laureto dared one little joke:
"This tells us ne'er to laugh at any cloak!
Good may the beast be, although rough
    the hide;
But, girls, methought young mistress I
    espied

"Grow crimson as an autumn grape, be-
    cause
Vincen's dear name so lightly uttered was.
There's mystery here! Mirèio, we are
    jealous!
Lasted the picking long that day? Pray,
    tell us!
When two friends meet, the hour is
    winged with pleasure;
And, for a lover, one has always leisure!"

"Oh, fie!" Mirèio said. "Enough of jok-
    ing!
Mind your work now, and be not so
    provoking!
You would make swear the very saints!
    But I
Promise you one and all, most faithfully,
I'll seek a convent while my years are
    tender,
Sooner than e'er my maiden heart sur-
    render!"

Then brake the damsels into merry
    chorus:
"Have we not pretty Magali before us?
Who love and lovers held in such disdain
That, to escape their torment, she was
    fain
To Saint Blasi's in Arles away to hie,
And bury her sweet self from every eye."

"Come, Noro, you, whose voice is ever
    thrilling,
Who charm us all, sing now, if you are
    willing,
The song of Magali, the cunning fairy,
Who love had shunned by all devices airy.
A bird, a vine, a sunbeam she became,
Yet fell herself, love's victim all the same!

"Queen of my soul!" sang Noro, and the
    rest
Fell straightway to their work with two-
    fold zest;
And as, when one cicala doth begin
Its high midsummer note, the rest fall in
And swell the chorus, so the damsels here
Sang the refrain with voices loud and
    clear:—

I.[13]

"Magali, queen of my soul,
    The dawn is near!
Hark to my tambourine,
Hide not thy bower within,
    Open and hear!

II.

"The sky is full of stars,
    And the wind soft;
But, when thine eyes they see,
The stars, O Magali,
    Will pale aloft!"

III.

"Idle as summer breeze
    The tune thou playest!
I'll vanish in the sea,
A silver eel will be,
    Ere thou me stayest."

IV.

"If thou become an eel,
    And so forsake me,
I will turn fisher too,
And fish the water blue
    Until I take thee!"

V.

"In vain with net or line
    Thou me implorest:
I'll be a bird that day,
And wing my trackless way
    Into the forest!"

VI.

"If thou become a bird,
    And so dost dare me,

I will a fowler be,
And follow cunningly
Until I snare thee!"

VII.
"When thou thy cruel snare
Settest full surely,
I will a flower become,
And in my prairie home
Hide me securely!"

VIII.
"If thou become a flower,
Before thou thinkest
I'll be a streamlet clear,
And all the water bear
That thou, love, drinkest!"

IX.
"When thou, a stream, dost feed
The flower yonder,
I will turn cloud straightway,
And to America
Away I'll wander."

X.
"Though thou to India
Fly from thy lover,
Still I will follow thee:
I the sea-breeze will be
To waft thee over!"

XI.
"I can outstrip the breeze
Fast as it flieth:
I'll be the swift sun-ray
That melts the ice away
And the grass drieth!"

XII.
"Sunlight if thou become,
Are my wiles ended?
I'll be a lizard green,
And quaff the golden sheen
To make me splendid!"

XIII.
"Be thou a Triton, hid
In the dark sedges!

I'm the moon by whose ray
Fairies and witches pay
Their mystic pledges!"

XIV.
"If thou the moon wilt be
Sailing in glory,
I'll be the halo white
Hovering every night
Around and o'er thee!"

XV.
"Yet shall thy shadowy arm
Embrace me never!
I will turn virgin rose,
And all my thorns oppose
To thee for ever!"

XVI.
"If thou become a rose,
Vain too shall this be!
Seest thou not that I,
As a bright butterfly,
Freely may kiss thee?"

XVII.
"Urge, then, thy mad pursuit:
Idly thou'lt follow!
I'll in the deep wood bide;
I'll in the old oak hide,
Gnarlèd and hollow."

XVIII.
"In the dim forest glade
Wilt thou be hidden?
I'll be the ivy-vine,
And my long arms entwine
Round thee unbidden!"

XIX.
"Fold thine arms tightly, then:
Clasp the oak only!
I'll a white sister be!
Far off in St. Blasi,
Secure and lonely!"

XX.
"Be thou a white-veiled nun
Come to confession,

I will be there as priest,
Thee freely to divest
Of all transgression!"

The startled women their cocoons let fall.
"Noro, make haste!" outspake they one
and all:
"What could our hunted Magali answer
then?
A nun, poor dear, who had already been
A cloud, a bird, a fish, an oak, a flower,
The sun, the moon, the stream, in one
short hour?"

"Ah, yes!" said Noro, "I the rest will sing:
She was, I think, the cloister entering;
And that mad fowler dared to promise
her
He would in the confessional appear,
And shrive her. Therefore hear what she
replies:
The maid hath yet another last device:"—

XXI.
"Enter the sacred house!
I shall be sleeping,
Robed in a winding-sheet,
Nuns at my head and feet,
Above me weeping."

XXII.
"If thou wert lifeless dust,
My toils were o'er:
I'd be the yawning grave,

Thee in my arms to have
For evermore!"

XXIII.
"Now know I thou art true,
Leave me not yet!
Come, singer fair, and take
And wear for my sake
This annulet!"

XXIV.
"Look up, my blessed one,
The heaven scan!
Since the stars came to see
Thee, O my Magali,
They are turned wan!"

A silence fell, the sweet song being ended:
Only with the last moving notes had
blended
The voices of the rest. Their heads were
drooping,
As they before the melody were stooping,
Like slender reeds that lean and sway for
ever
Before the flowing eddies of a river.

Till Noro said, "Now is the air serene;
And here the mowers come, their scythes
to clean
Beside the vivary brook. Mirèio, dear,
Bring us a few St. John's Day apples here.
And we will add a little new-made cheese,
And take our lunch beneath the lotus-
trees."

NOTES TO CANTO III.

[1] THE cocooning, or gathering of the cocoons, described in the seventh stanza of this
canto.

[2] The *Ferigoulet* is an excellent wine
grown on one of the hillsides of Graveson.
Ferigoulo is thyme, and the wine recalls the
perfume of that plant.

[3] "The Baume Muscat." Baume is a village in the department of Vaucluse. The
environs produce a Muscat that is much esteemed.

[4] "Turned white." The *canela*, or whitening, is the term used to describe the silk-
worms suffering from the terrible disease
called the *muscardine*, due to the development of a sort of mouldiness, and which
gives them a plaster-like appearance.

[5] "You've still your caul on,"—*as ta crespino. Crespino*, a cap, is also used for the
membrane some children have upon their

heads at birth, and which is supposed to be a sign of good luck.

⁶ "Ventour." A high mountain to the north-east of Avignon, abruptly rising 6,440 feet above the level of the sea, isolated, steep, visible forty leagues off, and for six months of the year capped with snow.

⁷ "Notre Dame des Dom." The cathedral church at Avignon, where the Popes formerly officiated.

⁸ "Faneto de Gautèume." Fanette, abridged from Estéfanette, of the noble family of Gautèume, or Gautelme, presided, about the year 1340, over the Court of Love at Roumanin. Courts of Love are known to have been poetical assizes, at which the noblest, most beautiful, and most learned ladies in Gay-saber decided on questions of gallantry and love, and awarded prizes for Provençal poetry. The celebrated and lovely Laura was niece to Fanette de Gautelme, and a member of her graceful areopagus. The ruins of the Castle of Roumanin may still be seen, not far from St. Rémy, at the foot of the northern slope of the Lower Alps.

⁹ "Countess Dio." A celebrated poetess of the middle of the twelfth century. Such of her poems as have come down to us contain strains more impassioned, and occasionally more voluptuous, than those of Sappho.

¹⁰ The vampire, or *roumeso,* is thus described in the "Castagnados" of the Marquis Lafare Alais:—

"On twenty spiders-legs its brown body, as on stilts, is mounted; its belly swelled with fever and rottenness; the horrid odor thereof exudes."

¹¹ The Luberon, or Luberoun, is a mountain-chain in the department of Vaucluse.

¹² The Vaumasco (from *Vau* and *Masco,* Valley of Sorcerers) is a valley of the Luberoun, formerly inhabited by the Vaudois.

¹³ The song of Magali belongs to the class of poems called *aubado,*—music performed under a window in early morning, as a serenade is in the evening.

CANTO IV.

THE SUITORS.

When violets are blue in the blue shadows
    Of the o'erhanging trees,
The youth who stray in pairs about the
      meadows
    Are glad to gather these.

When peace descends upon the troubled
      Ocean,
    And he his wrath forgets,
Flock from Martigue that boats with
      wing-like motion,
    The fishes fill their nets.

And when the girls of Crau bloom into
      beauty
    (And fairer earth knows not),
Aye are there suitors ready for their duty
    In castle and in cot.

Thus to Mirèio's home came seeking her
A trio notable,—a horse-tamer,

A herdsman, and a shepherd. It befell
The last was first who came his tale to tell.
Alari was his name, a wealthy man,—
He had a thousand sheep, the story ran.

The same were wont to feed the winter
      long
In rich salt-pastures by Lake Entressen.
And at wheat-bolling time, in burning
      May,
Himself would often lead his flock, they
      say,
Up through the hills to pastures green
      and high:
They say moreover, and full faith have I,

That ever as St. Mark's came round again
Nine noted shearers Alari would retain
Three days to shear his flock. Added to
      these
A man to bear away each heavy fleece,
And a sheep-boy who back and forward
      ran
And filled the shearer's quickly emptied
      can.

But when the days were shortening, and
    the snow
Whitened the mountain summits of
    Gavot,
A stately sight it was that flock to see
Wind from the upper vales of Dauphiny,
And o'er the Crau pursue their devious
    ways,
Upon the toothsome winter grass to graze.

Also to watch them there where they
    defile
Into the stony road were well worth
    while;
The early lambkins all the rest out-
    stripping
And merrily about the lamb-herd leaping,
The bell-decked asses with their foals
    beside,
Or following after them. These had for
    guide

A drover, who a patient mule bestrode.
Its wattled panniers bare a motley load:
Food for the shepherd-folk, and flasks of
    wine,
And the still bleeding hides of slaughtered
    kine;
And folded garments whereon oft there
    lay
Some weakly lamb, a-weary of the way.

Next came abreast—the captains of the
    host—
Five fiery bucks, their fearsome heads
    uptost:
With bells loud jingling and with sidelong
    glances,
And backward curving horns, each one
    advances.
The sober mothers follow close behind,
Striving their lawless little kids to mind.

A rude troop and a ravenous they are,
And these the goat-herd hath in anxious
    care.
And after them there follow presently

The great ram-chiefs, with muzzles lifted
    high:
You know them by the heavy horn that
    lies
Thrice curved about the ear in curious
    wise.

Their ribs and backs with tufts of wool
    are decked,
That they may have their meed of due
    respect
As the flock's grandsires. Plain to all be-
    holders,
With sheepskin cloak folded about his
    shoulders,
Strides the chief-shepherd next, with
    lordly swing;
The main corps of his army following.

Tumbling through clouds of dust, the
    great ewe-dams
Call with loud bleatings to their bleating
    lambs.
The little hornèd ones are gayly drest,
With tiny tufts of scarlet on the breast
And o'er the neck. While, filling the next
    place,
The woolly sheep advance at solemn
    pace.

Amid the tumult now and then the cries
Of shepherd-boy to shepherd-dog arise.
For now the pitch-marked herd innumer-
    able
Press forward: yearlings, two-year-olds as
    well,
Those who have lost their lambs, and
    those who carry
Twin lambs unborn with footsteps slow
    and weary.

A ragamuffin troop brings up the rear.
The barren and past-breeding ewes are
    here,
The lame, the toothless, and the remnant
    sorry

Of many a mighty ram, lean now and
    hoary,
Who from his earthly labors long hath
    rested,
Of honor and of horns alike divested.

All these who fill the road and mountain-
    passes—
Old, young, good, bad, and neither; sheep,
    goats, asses—
Are Alari's, every one. He stands the
    while
And watches them, a hundred in a file,
Pass on before him; and the man's eyes
    laugh.
His wand of office is a maple-staff.

And when to pasture with his dogs hies
    he,
And leathern gaiters buttoned to the knee,
His forehead to an ample wisdom grown
And air serene might be King David's
    own,
When in his youth he led, as the tale tells,
The flocks at eve beside his father's wells.

This was the chief toward Lotus Farm
    who drew,
And presently Mirèio's self who knew
Flitting about the doorway. His heart
    bounded.
"Good Heaven!" he cried, "her praises
    they have sounded
Nowise too loudly! Ne'er saw I such grace
Or high or low, in life or pictured face!"

Only that face to see, his flock forsaking,
Alari had come. Yet now his heart was
    quaking
When, standing in the presence of the
    maid,
"Would you so gracious be, fair one," he
    said,
"As to point out the way these hills to
    cross?
For else find I myself at utter loss."

"Oh, yes!" replied the girl, ingenuously,
"Thou takest the straight road, and com-
    est thereby
Into Pèiro-malo desert. Then
Follow the winding path till thou attain
A portico[1] with an old tomb anear:
Two statues of great generals it doth bear.

Antiquities they call them hereabout."
"Thanks, many!" said the youth. "I had
    come out
A thousand of my woolly tribe, or so,
To lead into the mountains from La Crau.
We leave to-morrow. I their way direct,
And sleeping-spots and feeding-ground
    select.

"They bear my mark, and are of fine
    breed, all;
And for my shepherdess, when one I call
My own, the nightingales will ever sing.
And dared I hope you'd take my offering,
Mirèio dear, no gems I'd tender you,
But a carved box-wood cup,—mine own
    work too!"

Therewith he brought to light a goblet
    fair,
Wrapped like some sacred relic with all
    care,
And carven of box-wood green. It was his
    pleasure
Such things to fashion in his hours of
    leisure;
And, sitting rapt upon some wayside
    stone,
He wrought divinely with a knife alone.

He carved him castanets with fingers
    light,
So that his flock would follow him at
    night
Through the dark fields, obedient to their
    tones.
And on the ringing collars, and the bones
That served for bell-tongues, he would cut
    with skill

Faces and figures, flowers and birds, at
    will.

As for the goblet he was tendering,
You would have said that no such fairy
    thing
Was ever wrought by shepherd's knife or
    wit:
A full-flowered poppy wreathed the rim
    of it;
And in among the languid flowers there
Two chamois browsed, and these the
    handles were.

A little lower down were maidens three,
And certes they were marvellous to see:
Near by, beneath a tree, a shepherd-lad
Slept, while on tiptoe stole the maidens
    glad,
And sought to seal his lips, ere he should
    waken,
With a grape-cluster from their basket
    taken.

Yet even now he smiles at their illusion,
So that the foremost maid is all confusion.
The odor of the goblet proved it new:
The giver had not drunk therefrom; and
    you
Had said, but for their woody coloring,
The carven shapes were each a living
    thing.

Mirèio scanned the fair cup curiously.
"A tempting offering thine, shepherd!"
    said she:
But suddenly, "A finer one than this
Hath my heart's lord! Shepherd, his love
    it is!
Mine eyes close, his impassioned glances
    feeling:
I falter with the rapture o'er me stealing!"

So saying, she vanished like a tricksy
    sprite;
And Alari turned, and in the gray twilight
Ruefully, carefully, he folded up

And bore away again his carven cup,
Deeming it sad and strange this winsome
    elf
Her love should yield to any but himself.

Soon to the farm came suitor number
    two,
A keeper of wild horses from Sambu,[2]—
Veran, by name. About his island home
In the great prairies, where the asters
    bloom,
He used to keep a hundred milk-white
    steeds,
Who nipped the heads of all the lofty
    reeds.

A hundred steeds! Their long manes flow-
    ing free
As the foam-crested billows of the sea!
Wavy and thick and all unshorn were
    they;
And when the horses on their headlong
    way
Plunged all together, their dishevelled
    hair
Seemed the white robes of creatures of
    the air.

I say it to the shame of human kind:
Camargan[3] steeds were never known to
    mind
The cruel spur more than the coaxing
    hand.
Only a few or so, I understand,
By treachery seduced, have halter worn,
And from their own salt prairies been
    borne;

Yet the day comes when, with a vicious
    start,
Their riders throwing, suddenly they part,
And twenty leagues of land unresting
    scour,
Snuffing the wind, till Vacarès[4] once more
They find, the salt air breathe, and joy to
    be
In freedom after ten years' slavery.

For these wild steeds are with the sea at
    home:
Have they not still the color of the foam?
Perchance they brake from old King
    Neptune's car;
For when the sea turns dark and moans
    afar,
And the ships part their cables in the bay,
The stallions of Camargue rejoicing
    neigh,

Their sweeping tails like whipcord snap-
    ping loudly;
Or pawing the earth, all, fiercely and
    proudly,
As though their flanks were stung as with
    a rod
By the sharp trident of the angry god,
Who makes the rain a deluge, and the
    ocean
Stirs to its depths in uttermost commo-
    tion.

And these were all Veran's. Therefore one
    day
The island-chieftain paused upon his way
Across La Crau beside Mirèio's door;
For she was famed, and shall be ever-
    more,
For beauty, all about the delta wide
Where the great Rhone meeteth the ocean
    tide.

Confident came Veran to tell his passion,
With paletot, in the Arlesian fashion,
Long, light, and backward from his shoul-
    ders flowing;
His gay-hued girdle like a lizard glowing,
The while his head an oil-skin cap pro-
    tected,
Wherefrom the dazzling sun-rays were
    reflected.

And first the youth to Master Ramoun
    drew.
"Good-morrow to you, and good fortune
    too!"

He said. "I come from the Camargan
    Rhone,
As keeper Pèire's grandson I am known.
Thou mindest him! For twenty years or
    more
My grandsire's horses trod thy threshing-
    floor.

"Three dozen had the old man venerable,
As thou, beyond a doubt, rememberest
    well.
But would I, Master Ramoun, it were
    given
To thee to see the increase of that leaven!
Let ply the sickles! We the rest will do,
For now have we an hundred lacking
    two!"

"And long, my son," the old man said,
    "pray I
That you may see them feed and multi-
    ply.
I knew your grandsire well for no brief
    time;
But now on him and me the hoary rime
Of age descends, and by the home lamp's
    ray
We sit content, and no more visits pay."

"But, Master Ramoun," cried the youth-
    ful lover,
"All that I want thou dost not yet dis-
    cover!
Far down at Sambu, in my island home,
When the Crau folk for loads of litter
    come,
And we help cord them down, it happens
    so
We talk sometimes about the girls of
    Crau.

"And thy Mirèio they have all portrayed
So charmingly, that, if thou wilt," he said,
"And if thou like me, I would gladly be
Thy son-in-law!" "God grant me this to
    see!"

Said Ramoun. "The brave scion of my
    friend
To me and mine can only honor lend."

Then did he fold his hands and them up-
    raise
In saint-like gratitude. "And yet," he says,
"The child must like you too, O Veranet! [5]
The only one will alway be a pet!
Meanwhile, in earnest of the dower I'll
    give her,
The blessing of the saints be yours for
    ever!"

Forthwith summoned Ramoun his little
    daughter,
And told her of the friend who thus had
    sought her.
Pale, trembling, and afraid, "O father
    dear!"
She said, "is not thy wisdom halting here?
For I am but a child: thou dost forget.
Surely thou wouldest not send me from
    thee yet!

"Slowly, so thou hast often said to me,
Folk learn to love and live in harmony.
For one must know, and also must be
    known;
And even then, my father, all's not done!"
Here the dark shadow on her brow was lit
By some bright thought that e'en trans-
    figured it.

So the drenched flowers, when morning
    rains are o'er,
Lift up their heavy heads, and smile once
    more.
Mirèio's mother held her daughter's view.
Then blandly rose the keeper, "Adieu,
Master," he said: "who in Camargue hath
    dwelt
Knows the mosquito-sting as soon as felt."

Also that summer came to Lotus Place
One from Petite Camargue,[6] called
    Ourrias.
Breaker and brander of wild cattle, he;

And black and furious all the cattle be
Over those briny pastures wild who run,
Maddened by flood and fog and scalding
    sun.

Alone this Ourrias had them all in charge
Summer and winter, where they roamed
    at large.
And so, among the cattle born and grown,
Their build, their cruel heart, became his
    own;
His the wild eye, dark color, dogged look.
How often, throwing off his coat, he took

His cudgel,—savage weaner!—never
    blenching,
And first the young calves from the
    udders wrenching,
Upon the wrathful mother fell so madly
That cudgel after cudgel brake he gladly,
Till she, by his brute fury masterèd,
Wild-eyed and lowing to the pine-copse
    fled!

Oft in the branding at Camargue had he
Oxen and heifers, two-year-olds and three,
Seized by the horns and stretched upon
    the ground.
His forehead bare the scar of an old
    wound
Fiery and forked like lightning. It was
    said
That once the green plain with his blood
    was red.

On a great branding-day befell this thing:
To aid the mighty herd in mustering,
Li Santo, Agui Morto,[7] Albaron,[8]
And Faraman[9] a hundred horsemen
    strong
Had sent into the desert. And the herd
Roused from its briny lairs, and, forward
    spurred

By tridents of the branders close behind,
Fell on the land like a destroying wind.
Heifers and bulls in headlong gallop
    borne

[157]

Plunged, crushing centaury[10] and sali-
　　corne;[11]
And at the branding-booth at last they
　　mustered,
Just where a crowd three hundred strong
　　had clustered.

A moment, as if scared, the beasts were
　　still.
Then, when the cruel spur once more they
　　feel,
They start afresh, into a run they break,
And thrice the circuit of the arena make;
As marterns fly a dog, or hawks afar
By eagles in the Luberon hunted are.

Then Ourrias—what ne'er was done be-
　　fore—
Leaped from his horse beside the circus-
　　door
Amid the crowd. The cattle start again,
All saving five young bulls, and scour the
　　plain;
But these, with flaming eyes and horns
　　defying
Heaven itself, are through the arena fly-
　　ing.

And he pursues them. As a mighty wind
Drives on the clouds, he goads them from
　　behind,
And presently outstrips them in the race;
Then thumps them with the cruel goad he
　　sways,
Dances before them as infuriate,
And lets them feel his own fists' heavy
　　weight.

The people clap and shout, while Ourrias
White with Olympic dust encountered has
One bull, and seized him by the horns at
　　length;
And now 'tis head to muzzle, strength for
　　strength.
The monster strains his prisoned horns to
　　free
Until he bleeds, and bellows horribly.

But vain his fury, useless all his trouble!
The neatherd had the art to turn and
　　double
And force the huge head with his shoulder
　　round,
And shove it roughly back, till on the
　　ground
Christian and beast together rolled, and
　　made
A formless heap like some huge barricade.

The tamarisks[12] are shaken by the cry
Of "Bravo Ourrias! That's done val-
　　iantly!"
While five stout youths the bull pin to the
　　sward;
And Ourrias, his triumph to record,
Seizes the red-hot iron with eager hand,
The vanquished monster on the hip to
　　brand.

Then come a troop of girls on milk-white
　　ponies,—
Arlesians,—flushed and panting every one
　　is,
As o'er the arena at full gallop borne
They offer him a noble drinking-horn
Brimful of wine; then turn and disappear,
Each followed by her faithful cavalier.

The hero heeds them not. His mind is set
On the four monsters to be branded yet:
The mower toils the harder for the grass
He sees unmown. And so this Ourrias
Fought the more savagely as his foes
　　warmed,
And conquered in the end,—but not un-
　　harmed.

White-spotted and with horns magnificent,
The fourth beast grazed the green in all
　　content.
"Now, man, enough!" in vain the
　　neatherds shouted;
Couched in the trident and the caution
　　flouted;
With perspiration streaming, bosom bare,

Ourrias the spotted bull charged then and
    there!

He meets his enemy, a blow delivers
Full in the face; but ah! the trident
    shivers.
The beast becomes a demon with the
    wound:
The brander grasps his horns, is whirled
    around,—
They start together, and are borne amain,
Crushing the salicornes along the plain.

The mounted herdsmen, on their long
    goads leaning,
Regard the mortal fray; for each is mean-
    ing
Dire vengeance now. The man the brute
    would crush.
The brute bears off the man with furious
    rush;
The while with heavy, frothy tongue he
    clears
The blood that to his hanging lip adheres.

The brute prevailed. The man fell dazed,
    and lay
Like a vile rakeful in the monster's way.
"Sham dead!" went up a cry of agony.
Vain words! The beast his victim lifted
    high
On cruel horns and savage head inclined,
And flung him six and forty feet behind!

Once more a deafening outcry filled the
    place
And shook the tamarisks. But Ourrias
Fell prone to earth, and ever after wore
    he
The ugly scar that marred his brow so
    sorely.
Now, mounted on his mare, he paces slow
With goad erect to seek Mirèio.

It chanced the little maid was all alone.
She had, that morning, to the fountain
    gone;

And here, with sleeves and petticoats up-
    rolled
And small feet dabbling in the water cold,
She was here cheese-forms cleaning with
    shave-grass;
And, lady saints! how beautiful she was!

"Good-morrow, pretty maid!" began the
    wooer,
"Thy forms will shine like mirrors, to be
    sure!
Will it offend thee, if I lead my mare
To drink out of thy limpid streamlet
    there?"
"Pray give her all thou wilt, at the dam
    head:
We've water here to spare!" the maiden
    said.

"Fair one!" spake the wild youth, "if e'er
    thou come
As pilgrim or as bride to make thy home
At Sylvaréal[13] by the noisy wave,
No life of toil like this down here thou'lt
    have!
Our fierce black cows are never milked,
    but these
Roam all at large, and women sit at ease."

"Young man, in cattle-land, I've heard
    them say,
Maids die of languor."—"Pretty maiden,
    nay:
There is no languor where two are to-
    gether!"
"But brows are blistered in that burning
    weather,
And bitter waters drunk."—"When the
    sun shines,
My lady, thou shalt sit beneath the pines!"

"Ah! but they say, young man, those pines
    are laden
With coils of emerald serpents."—"Fair-
    est maiden,
We've herons also, and flamingoes red
That chase them down the Rhone with
    wings outspread

Like rosy mantles."—"Then, be thou
  aware,
Thy pines are from my lotus-trees too
  far!"

"But priests and maidens, fair one, never
  know,
The proverb saith, the land where they
  may go
And eat their bread."—"Let mine but
  eaten be
With him I love: that were enough," said
  she,

"To lure me from the home-nest to remove."
"If that be so, sweet one, given me thy
  love!"

"Thy suit," Mirèio said, "mayhap I'll
  grant!
But first, young man, yon water-lily plant
Will bear a cluster of columbine[14] grapes.
Yon hills will melt from all their solid
  shapes,
That goad will flower, and all the world
  will go
In boats unto the citadel of Baux!"

NOTES TO CANTO IV.

[1] *A portico.* Within half an hour's walk from St. Rémy, at the foot of the Alpines, arise side by side two fine Roman monuments. One is a triumphal arch; the other, a magnificent mausoleum, of three stories, adorned with rich bas-reliefs and surmounted by a graceful cupola, supported by ten Corinthian pillars, through which are discerned two statues in a standing attitude. They are the last vestiges of Glanum, a Marseilles colony destroyed by the Barbarians.
[2] Sambu, a hamlet in the territory of Arles, in the isle of Camargue.
[3] Camargue is a vast delta, formed by the bifurcation of the Rhone. The island extends from Arles to the sea, and comprises 184,-482¼ acres. The immensity of its horizon, the awful silence of its level plain, its strange vegetation, meres, swarms of mosquitos, large herds of oxen and wild horses, amaze the traveller, and remind him of the *pampas* of South America.
[4] Vacarès, a large assemblage of salt-ponds, lagunes, and moors in the isle of Camargue. "Vacarès" is formed of the word

vaco and the Provençal desinence *arés* or *eirés*, indicating union, generality. It means a place where cows abound.
[5] *Veranet* is the diminutive of *Veran.*
[6] Petite Camargue, also called Sóuvage, is bounded on the east by the Petit Rhone, which separates it from Grande Camargue, on the south by the Mediterranean, and on the west and north by the Rhone Mort and the Aigui Morto canal. It is the principal resort of the wild black oxen.
[7][8][9] Faraman and Ambaroun are hamlets in Camargue. Aigui Morto is in the department of the Gard. It was at the port of this town that St. Louis twice embarked for the Holy Land. Here also Francis I. and Charles V. had an interview in 1579. (The French form is Aiguesmortes.—H.W.P.)
[10][11] *Centaury* and *Salicorne.* The *Centaurea solstitialis,* a species of star-thistle, abounds in the fields of Crau after harvest. *Salicornia fructicosa* is a species of samphire.
[12] *Tamarisk,* the *Tamarix gallica* of Linnæus.
[13] Sylvaréal, a forest of parasol-pines in Petite Camargue.
[14] "Columbine," the name of a large and superior sort of grape.

CANTO V.
THE BATTLE.

Cool with the coming eve the wind was
  blowing,
The shadows of the poplars longer growing;
Yet still the westering sun was two hours
  high,

As the tired ploughman noted wistfully,—
Two hours of toil ere the fresh twilight
  come,
And wifely greeting by the door at home.

But Ourrias the brander left the spring,
The insult he had suffered pondering.
So moved to wrath was he, so stung with
  shame,

The blood into his very forehead came;
And, muttering deadly spite beneath his
    teeth,
He drave at headlong gallop o'er the
    heath.

As damsons in a bush, the stones of Crau
Are plentiful; and Ourrias, fuming so,
Would gladly with the senseless flints
    have striven,
Or through the sun itself his lance have
    driven.
A wild boar from his lair forced to de-
    camp,
And scour the desert slopes of black
    Oulympe,[1]

Ere turning on the dogs upon his track,
Erects the rugged bristles of his back,
And whets his tusks upon the mountain
    oaks.
And now young Vincen with his comely
    looks
Must needs have chosen the herdsman's
    very path,
And meets him full face, boiling o'er with
    wrath.

Whereas the simple dreamer wandered
    smiling,
His memory with a sweet tale beguiling,
That he had heard a fond girl whispering
Beneath a mulberry-tree one morn in
    spring.
Straight is he as a cane from the Durance;
And love, peace, joy, beam from his
    countenance.

The soft air swells his loose, unbuttoned
    shirt:
His firm, bare feet are by the stones un-
    hurt,
And light as lizard slips he o'er the way.
Oh! many a time, when eve was cool and
    gray,
And all the land in shadow lay concealed,
He used to roam about the darkling field,

Where the chill airs had shut the tender
    clover;
Or, like a butterfly, descend and hover
About the homestead of Mirèio;
Or, hidden cleverly, his hiding show,
Like a gold-crested or an ivy wren,
By a soft chirrup uttered now and then.

And she would know who called her, and
    would fly
Swift, silent, to the mulberry-tree hard by,
With quickened pulses. Fair is the moon-
    light
Upon narcissus-buds in summer night,
And sweet the rustle of the zephyr borne
In summer eve over the ripening corn,

Until the whole, in infinite undulation,
Seems like a great heart palpitant with
    passion.
Also the chamois hath a joy most keen
When through the savage Queiras[2] ravine
All day before the huntsman he hath
    flown,
And stands at length upon a peak, alone

With larches and with ice fields, looking
    forth.
But all these joys and charms are little
    worth,
With the brief rapture of the hours com-
    pared—
Ah, brief!—that Vincen and Mirèio
    shared,
When, by the friendly shadows favorèd,
(Speak low, my lips, for trees can hear,
    'tis said,)

Their hands would seek each other and
    would meet,
And silence fall upon them, while their
    feet
Played idly with the pebbles in their way.
Until, not knowing better what to say,
The tyro-lover laughingly would tell
Of all the small mishaps that him befell;

Of nights he passed beneath the open
    heaven;
Of bites the farmers' dogs his legs had
    given,
And show his scars. And then the maid
    told o'er
Her tasks of that day and the day before;
And what her parents said; and how the
    goat
With trellis-flowers had filled his greedy
    throat.

Once only—Vincen knew not what he
    did;
But, stealthy as a wild-cat, he had slid
Along the grasses of the barren moor,
And prostrate lay his darling's feet before.
Then—soft, my lips, because the trees can
    hear—
He said, "Give me one kiss, Mirèio dear!

"I cannot eat nor drink," he made his
    moan,
"For the great love I bear you! Yea, mine
    own,
Your breath the life out of my blood has
    taken.
Go not, Mirèio! Leave me not forsaken!
From dawn to dawn, at least, let a true
    lover
Kneel, and your garment's hem with
    kisses cover!"

"Why, Vincen," said Mirèio, "that were
    sin!
Then would the black-cap and the pendu-
    line[3]
Tell everywhere the secret they had
    heard!"
"No fear of that! for every tell-tale bird
I'd banish from La Crau to Arles," said
    he;
"For you, Mirèio, are as heaven to me!

"Now list! There grows a plant in river
    Rhone,
Eel-grass[4] by name," said Master Am-
    broi's son:

"Two flowers it beareth, each on its own
    stem,
And a great space of water severs them,
For the plant groweth in the river's bed;
But when the time for wooing comes," he
    said,

"One flower comes to the surface of the
    flood,
And in the genial sunshine opes its bud.
Whereon the other, seeing this so fair,
Swims eagerly to seize and kiss her there;
But, for the tangled weeds, can she not
    gain
Her love, till her frail stem breaks with
    the strain.

"Now free at least, but dying, she doth
    raise
Her pale lips for her sister's last embrace.
So I! One kiss, and I will die to-night!
We are all alone!" Mirèio's cheek grew
    white.
Then sprang he, wild-eyed as a lissome
    beast,
And clasped her. Hurriedly the maid
    released

Herself from his too daring touch. Once
    more
He strove to seize,—but ah! my lips,
    speak lower,
For the trees hear,—"Give over!" cried
    the girl,
And all her slender frame did writhe and
    curl.
Yet would he frantic cling; but straight
    thereafter
She pinched him, bent, slipped, and, with
    ringing laughter,

The saucy little damsel sped away,
And lifted up her voice in mocking lay.
Thus sowed these two upon the twilight
    heath
Their pretty moon-wheat,[5] as the proverb
    saith.

Flowery the moments were, and fleet with
    pleasure:
Of such our Lord giveth abundant
    measure

To peasants and to kings alike. And so
I come to what befell that eve on Crau.
Ourrias and Vincen met. As lightning
    cleaves
The first tall tree, Ourrias his wrath re-
    lieves.
" 'Tis you, son of a hag, for aught I know,
Who have bewitched her,—this Mirèio;

"And, since your path would seem to lie
    her way,
Tell her, tatterdemalion, what I say!
No more for her nor for her weasel face
Care I than for the ancient clout," he says,
"That from your shoulders fluttering I see.
Go, pretty coxcomb, tell her this from
    me!"

Stopped Vincen thunderstruck. His wrath
    leaped high
As leaps a fiery rocket to the sky.
"Is it your pleasure that I strangle you,
Base churl," he said, "or double you in
    two?"
And faced him with a look he well might
    dread,
As when a starving leopard turns her
    head.

His face was purple, quivered all his
    frame.
"Oh, better try!" the mocking answer
    came.
"You'll roll headfirst upon the gravel,
    neighbor!
Bah, puny hands! meet for no better labor
Than to twist osiers when they're supple
    made;
Or to rob hen-roosts, lurking in the
    shade!"

Stung by the insult, "Yea, I can twist
    osier,

And I can twist your neck with all com-
    posure,"
Said Vincen. "Fly me, coward, while you
    may!
Or, by St. Jacques of Gallicia,
You'll never see your tamarisks any more!
This iron first shall bray your limbs be-
    fore!"

Wondering, and charmed to find by such
    quick chance
A man whereon to wreak his vengeance,
"Wait!" said the herdsman: "be not over-
    hot!
First let me have a pipe, young idiot!"
And brought to light a buckskin pouch,
    and set
Between his teeth a broken calumet.

Then scornfully, "While rocking you, my
    lamb,
Under the goose-foot,[6] did your gypsy-
    dam
Ne'er tell the tale of Jan de l'Ourse,[7]
    pray?—
Two men in one, who, having gone one
    day,
By orders, to plough stubble with two
    yoke,
Seized plough and teams, as shepherds do
    a crook,

"And hurled them o'er a poplar-tree hard
    by?
Well for you, urchin, there's no poplar
    nigh!
You couldn't lead a stray ass whence it
    came!"
But Vincen stood like pointer to the game.
"I say," he roared in tones stentorian,
"Will you come down, or must I fetch
    you, man

"Or hog? Come! Brag no more upon your
    beast:
You flinch now we are coming to the test.
Which sucked the better milk, or you or
    I?

Was it you, bearded scoundrel? We will
    try!
Why, I will tread you like a sheaf of
    wheat,
If you dare flout yon maiden true and
    sweet.

"No fairer flower in this land blossomed
    ever;
And I who am called Vincen, basket-
    weaver,
Yes, I—her suitor, be it understood—
Will wash your slanders out in your own
    blood,
If such you have!" Quoth Ourrias, "I am
    ready,
My gypsy-suitor to a cupboard! Steady!"

Therewith alights. They fling their coats
    away,
Fists fly, and pebbles roll before the fray.
They fall upon each other in the manner
Of two young bulls who, in the vast
    savannah,
Where the great sun glares in the tropic
    sky,
The sleek sides of a dark young heifer spy

In the tall grasses, lowing amorous.
The thunder bursts within them, chal-
    lenged thus.
Mad, blind with love, they paw, they
    stare, they spring;
And furious charge, their muzzles low-
    ering;
Retire, and charge again. The ominous
    sound
Of crashing horns fills all the spaces
    round.

And long, I ween, the battle is, and dire.
The combatants are maddened by desire.
Puissant Love urges and goads them on.
So here, with either doughty champion.
'Twas Ourrias who received the first hard
    touch;

And, being threatened with another such,

Lifts his huge fist and lays young Vincen
    flat
As with a club. "There, urchin, parry
    that!"
"See if I have a scratch, man!" cried the
    lad.
The other, "Bastard, count the knocks
    you've had!"
"Count you the ounces of hot blood," he
    shouted,
"Monster, that from your flattened nose
    have spouted!"

And then they grapple; bend and stretch
    their best,
With foot to foot, shoulder to shoulder,
    prest.
Their arms are wreathed and coiled like
    supple snakes,
The veins are swelled to bursting in their
    necks,
The muscles of their calves tense with the
    strain.
Long time they stiff and motionless re-
    main,

With pulsing flanks, like flap of bustard's
    wing.
And, one against the other steadying,
Bear up like the abutments huge and wide
Of that great bridge the Gardoun[8] doth
    bestride.
Anon they part: their doubled fists up-
    raise,
Once more the pestle in the mortar brays,

And in their fury ply they tooth or nail.
Good God! the blows of Vincen fall like
    hail.
Yet ah! what club-like hits the herdsman
    deals!
And, as their crushing weight the weaver
    feels,
He whirls as whirls a sling about his foe,
And backward bends to deal his fiercest
    blow.

"Look your last, villain!" Ere the word
    said he,
The mighty herdsman seized him bodily,
And flung him o'er his shoulder far away,
As a Provençal shovels wheat. He lay
A moment on his side, not sorely hurt.
"Pick up, O worm!" cried Ourrias,—"pick
    the dirt

"You have displaced, and eat it, if you
    will!"
"Enough of that! Brute who was broken
    ill,
We'll have three rounds before this game
    is over!"
With bitter hate retorts the poor boy-
    lover;
And, reddening to his very hair for shame,
Rears like a dragon to retrieve his fame.

And, daring death, he on the brute hath
    flown,
And dealt a blow marvellous in such an
    one
Straight from the shoulder to the other's
    breast,
Who reeled and groped for that whereon
    to rest,
With darkening eyes and brow cold-
    beaded, till
He crushed to earth, and all La Crau was
    still.

Its misty limit blent with the far sea;
The sea's with the blue ether, dreamily.
Still in mid-air there floated shining
    things,
Swans, and flamingoes on their rosy
    wings,
Come to salute the last of the sunset
Along the desert meres that glimmered
    yet.

The white mare of the herdsman lazily
Pulled at the dwarf-oak leaves that grew
    thereby:
The iron stirrups of the creature jangled,

As loose and heavy at her sides they
    dangled.
"Stir, and I crush you, ruffian!" Vincen
    said:
" 'Tis not by feet that men are measurèd!"

Then in the silent wold the victor pressed
His heel upon the brander's prostrate
    breast,
Who writhed beneath it vainly, while the
    blood
Sluggish and dark from lips and nostrils
    flowed.
Thrice did he strive the horny foot to
    move,
And thrice the basket-weaver from above

Dealt him a blow that levelled him once
    more,
Until he haggard lay, and gasping sore
Like some sea-monster. "So your mother,
    then,
Was not, it seems, the only mould of
    men,"
Said Vincen, jeeringly. "Go tell the tale
Of my fist's weight to bulls in Sylvaréal.

"Go to the waste of the Camargan isle,
And hide your bruises and your shame
    awhile
Among your beasts!" So saying, he loosed
    this one,
As shearer in the fold a ram full-grown
Pins with his knees till shorn; then, with
    a blow
Upon the crupper, bids him freely go.

Bursting with rage and all defiled with
    dust,
The herdsman went his ways. But where-
    fore must
He linger ferreting about the heath,
Amid the oaks and broom, under his
    breath
Muttering curses? until suddenly
He stoops, then swings his savage trident
    high,

And darts on Vincen. For him all is done.
Vain were the hope that murderous lance
    to shun,
And the boy paled as on the day he died;
Not fearing death, but that he could not
    bide
The treachery. A felon's prey to be!
That stung the manly soul to agony.

"Traitor, you dare not!" But the lad re-
    strains
The word, firm as a martyr in his pains;
For yon's the farmstead hidden by the
    trees.
Tenderly, wistfully, he turns to these.
"O my Mirèio!" said the eager eye,
"Look hither, darling,—'tis for you I
    die!"

Great heart, intent as ever on his love!
"Say your prayers!" thundered Ourrias
    from above
In a hoarse voice, and pitiless to hear,
And pierced the victim with his iron
    spear.
Then, with a heavy groan, the fated lover
Rolled upon the green-sward, and all was
    over.

The beaten grass is dark with human gore,
And the field-ants already coursing o'er
The prostrate limbs ere Ourrias mounts,
    and flies
Under the rising moon in frantic wise;
Muttering, as the flints beneath him fly,
"To-night the Crau wolves will feast mer-
    rily."

Deep stillness reigned in Crau. Its limit
    dim
Blent with the sea's on the horizon's rim,
The sea's with the blue ether. Gleaming
    things,
Swans, and flamingoes on their ruddy
    wings,
Came to salute the last declining light
Along the desert meres that glimmered
    white.

Away, Ourrias, away! Draw not the rein,
Urge thy unresting gallop o'er the plain,
While the green heron[9] shout their fear-
    some cries
In thy mare's ear, as the good creature
    flies,
Til her ear trembles, and her nostrils
    quiver,
And eyes dilate. That night the great
    Rhone River

Slept on his stony bed beneath the moon,
As pilgrim of Sainte Baume[10] may lay
    him down,
Fevered and weary, in a deep ravine.
"Ho!" cries the ruffian to three boatmen
    seen,
"Ho! Boat ahoy! We must cross, hark ye
    there!
On board or in the hold, I and my mare!"

"On board, my hearty, then, without
    delay!
There shines the night-lamp! And lured
    by its ray,"
Answered a cheery voice, "about our
    prow
And oars the fish frisk playfully enow.
It is good fishing, and the hour is fair.
On board at once! We have no time to
    spare."

Therewith upon the poop the villain
    clomb.
While, tethered to the stern, amid the
    foam
Swam the white mare. Now fishes huge
    and scaly
Forsook their grottoes, and leaped up-
    ward gayly,
And flashed on the smooth surface of the
    stream.
"Have a care, pilot! For this craft I deem

"Nowise too sound." And he who spake
    once more
Lay foot to stretcher, bent the supple oar.
"So I perceive. Ah!" was the pilot's word,

"I tell thee we've an evil freight on
  board."
No more. And all the while the vessel old
Staggered and pitched and like a drunkard
  rolled.

A crazy craft! Rotten its timbers all.
"Thunder of God!" Ourrias began to call,
Seizing the helm his tottering feet to stay.
Whereon the boat in some mysterious way
Seemed moved to writhing, as a wounded
  snake
Whose back a shepherd with a stone doth
  break.

"Doth all this tumult, comrades, bode
  disaster?"
Appealed the brander, growing pale as
  plaster.
"And will you drown me?" Brake the pilot
  out,
"I cannot hold the craft! She springs about
And wriggles like a carp. Villain, I know
You've murdered some one, and not long
  ago!"

"Who told you that? May Satan if I have
Thrust me with his pitch-fork beneath the
  wave."
"Ah!" said the livid pilot, "then I err!
I had forgot the cause of all this stir.
'Tis Saint Medard's to-night, when poor
  drowned men
Come from their dismal pits to land again,

"How deep and dark soe'er their watery
  prison.
Look! Even now hath from the wave
  arisen
The long procession of the weeping dead!
Barefoot, poor things! the shingly shore
  they tread,
The turbid water dripping, dripping, see,
From matted hair and stained clothes
  heavily.

"See them defile under the poplars tall,
Carrying lighted tapers, one and all.

While up the river's bank, now and anon,
Eagerly clambereth another one.
'Tis they who toss our wretched craft
  about
So like a raging storm, I make no doubt.

"Their cramped legs and their mottled
  arms—ah, see!—
And heavy heads they from the weeds
  would free.
Oh, how they watch the stars as on they
  go,
Quaff the fresh air and thrill at sight of
  Crau,
And scent the harvest odors the winds
  bring,
In their brief hour of motion revelling!

"And still the water from their garments
  raineth,
And still another and another gaineth
The river-bank. And there," the boatman
  moans,
"Are the old men, women, and little ones:
They spurn the clinging mud. Ah me!" he
  said,
"Yon ghastly things abhor the fisher's
  trade.

"The lamprey and the perch they made
  their game,
And now are they become food for the
  same.
But what is this? Another piteous band,
Travelling in a line along the sand?
Ah, yes! the poor deserted maids," quoth
  he,
"Who asked the Rhone for hospitality,

"And sought to hide their grief in the
  great river.
Alas! alas! They seem to moan for ever.
And, oh, how painfully, fond hearts, ill
  fated,
Labor the bosoms by the dank weeds
  weighted!
Is it the water dripping that one hears

From their long veils of hair, or is it
tears?"

He ceased. The wending souls bare each a
light,
Intently following in the silent night
The river-shore. And those two listening
Might even have heard the whirr of a
moth's wing.
"Are they not, pilot," asked the awe-
struck brander,
"Seeking somewhat in the gloom where
they wander?"

"Ah, yes, poor things!" the master-
boatman said.
"See how from side to side is turned each
head.
'Tis their good works they seek,—their
acts of faith
Sown upon earth ere their untimely death.
And when they spy the same, 'tis said
moreover,
They haste thereto, as haste the sheep to
clover,

"The good work or the act of faith to cull.
And when of such as these their hands are
full,
Lo, they all turn to flowers! And they who
gather
Go tender them with joy to God the
Father,
Being by the flowers to Peter's gate con-
veyed.
Thus those who find a watery grave," he
said,

"The gracious God granteth a respite to,
That they may save themselves. But some
anew
Ere the day dawn will bury their good
deeds
Deep underneath the surging river-weeds.
And some," the pilot whispered,—"some
are worse,
Devourers of the needy, *murderers*,

"Atheists, traitors, that worm-eaten kind.
These hunt the river-shore, but only find
Their sins and crimes like great stones in
the gravel
Whereon their bare feet stumble as they
travel.
The mule when dead is beaten never
more;
But these God's mercy shall in vain im-
plore

"Under the roaring wave." Here, sore
afraid,
Ourrias a hand upon the pilot laid,
Like robber at a turning. "Look!" he cries,
"There's water in the hold!" Whereon
replies
The pilot, coolly, "And the bucket's
there!"
The herdsman bales for life in his despair.

Ay, bale, brave Ourrias! But there danced
that night,
On Trincataio[11] bridge, the water-sprite.[12]
Madly the white mare strove to break her
halter.
"What ails you, Blanco?" Ourrias 'gan
falter.
"Fear you the dead yonder upon the
verge?"
Over the gunnel plashed the rising surge.

"Captain, the craft sinks, and I cannot
swim!"
"I know no help," the pilot answered him.
"We must go down. But, presently," he
said,
"A cable will be heaved us by the dead,—
The dead you fear so,—on the river-
bank."
And even as he spake the vessel sank.

The tapers gleaming far and fitfully
In the poor ghostly hands flared forth so
high,
They sent a shaft of vivid brilliance
Across the murky river's broad expanse;
Then, as a spider in the morn you see

[168]

Glide o'er his late-spun thread, the boatmen three,

Being all spirits, leaped out of the stream,
And caught and swooped along the
dazzling beam.

¹ OULYMPE, or Oulimpe, is a lofty mountain on the boundary-line of the Var and
Bouches-du-Rhone.

² Queiras, a valley of the Upper Alps.

³ Penduline, *Motacilla pendulina.*

⁴ Eel-grass, *Valisneria spiralis* of Linnæus.

⁵ "Pretty moon-wheat," *poulit blad de
luno. Faire de blad de luno* signifies, literally,
to rob parents of their wheat by moonlight.
Figuratively, it is used for love-making on
the sly.

⁶ Goose-foot, *Chenopadium fructicum* of
Linnæus.

⁷ Jan de l'Ourse is a story-book hero, a
kind of Provençal Hercules, to whom many

exploits are attributed. He was the son of a
shepherdess and a bear, and had for companions in his exploits two adventurers of
marvellous strength. The name of the one
was Arrache Montagne; that of the other,
Pierre de Moulin.

⁸ This bridge is the Roman antiquity
known as the "Pont du Gard."

⁹ Green heron, *Ardea virides.*

¹⁰ Sainte Baume, a grotto in the midst of
a virgin forest near St. Maximin, to which
Ste. Magdalene used to repair, to do penance.

¹¹ ¹² Trincataio is a suburb of Arles, in
Camargue, united to the town by a bridge
of boats. The water-sprites, or *trevi,* were
said to dance on the tips of the waves by the
light of the sun or moon.

CANTO VI.

THE WITCH.

The merry birds, until the white dawn
showeth
Clear in the east, are silent every one.
Silent the odorous Earth until she
knoweth
In her warm heart the coming of the Sun,
As maiden in her fairest robes bedight
Breathless awaits her lover and her flight.

Across La Crau three swineherds held
their way
From St. Chamas the wealthy, whither
they
Had to the market gone. Their herds were
sold,
And o'er their shoulders pouches full of
gold
Were hung, and by their hanging cloaks
concealed:
So, chatting idly, they attained the field

Of the late strife. Suddenly one cried,
"Hush!

And Ourrias, too, the cable sought to
seize
Amid the gurgling waters, even as these;
But sought it vainly. And the water-
sprite
Danced upon Trincataio bridge that night.

Comrades, I hear a moaning in the bush."
" 'Tis but a tolling bell," the rest averred,
"From Saint Martin's or from Maussano¹
heard,
Or the north wind the dwarf-oak limbs
a-swaying."
But, ere they spake, all were their steps
delaying,

Arrested by so piteous a moan
It rent the very heart. And every one
Cried, "Holy Jesus! Here has been foul
play!"
Then crossed themselves, and gently took
their way
Toward the sound. Ah, what a sight there
was!
Vincen, supine upon the stony grass,—

The grass blood-stained, the trampled
earth besprent
With willow rods. His shirt to ribbons
rent,
Stabbed in the breast, left on the moor
alone,

Had lain the poor lad through the night
    now gone,
With but the stars to watch. But the dim
    ray
Of early dawn as ebbed his life away,

Falling upon his lids had oped them wide.
Straightway the good Samaritans turned
    aside
From their home-path, stooped, and a
    hammock made
Of their three cloaks, thereon the victim
    laid,
Then bare him tenderly upon their arms
Unto the nearest door,—the Lotus-
    Farm's. . . .

O friends,—Provençal poets brave and
    dear,
Who love my songs of other days to hear!
You, Roumanille, who blend with songs
    you sing
Tears, girlish laughter, and the breath of
    spring;
And you, proud Aubanel, who stray
    where quiver
The changing lights and shades of wood
    and river,

To soothe a heart oppressed by love's
    fond dream;
You, Crousillat, who your belovèd stream,
The bright Touloubro, make more truly
    famous
Than did the grim star-gazer Nostrada-
    mus;[2]
And you, Anselme, who see, half-sad,
    half-smiling,
Fair girls under the trellised arbors
    whiling

Their hours away; and you, my Paul, the
    witty,
And peasant Tavan, who attune your ditty
Unto the crickets' chirrup, while you peer
Wistful at your poor pickaxe; and most
    dear,

Adolphe Dumas, who, when Durance is
    deep
With his spring flood, come back your
    thoughts to steep,

And warm the Frenchman at Provençal
    suns,
'Twas you who met my own Mirèio once
At your great Paris,—met her tenderly,
Where she had flown, impetuous, daring,
    shy;
And last Garcin, brave son of a brave sire,
Whose soul mounts upward on a wind of
    fire;—

Upbear me with your holy breath as now
I climb for the fair fruit on that high
    bough! . . .
The swineherds paused at Master
    Ramoun's door,
Crying, "Good-morrow! Yonder, on the
    moor,
We found this poor lad wounded in the
    breast.
'Twere well that his sore hurt were
    quickly drest."

So laid their burden on the broad, flat
    stone.
They tell Mirèio, to the garden gone
To gather fruit, who, basket on her side,
Fled wildly to the spot. Thither, too, hied
The laborers all; but she, her basket fall-
    ing,
Stretched forth her hands on Mother
    Mary calling.

"Vincen is bleeding! Ah, what have they
    done?"
Then, lovingly, the head of the dear one
She lifted, turned, and long and mutely
    gazed
As though with horror and with grief
    amazed,
Her large tears dropping fast. And well he
    knows
That tender touch to be Mirèio's,

And faintly breathes, "Pity, and pray for
    me,
Because I need the good God's company!"
"Your parched throat moisten with this
    cordial.³ Strive
To drink," old Ramoun said: "you will
    revive."
The maiden seized the cup, and drop by
    drop
She made him drink, and spake to him of
    hope

Till his pain lulled. "May God keep you
    alway
From such distress, and your sweet care
    repay!"
Said Vincen; and the brave boy would not
    tell
It was for her sake that he fought and fell;
But "Splitting osier on my breast," he
    said,
"The sharp knife slipped, and pierced
    me." Therewith strayed

His thought back to his love as bee to
    flower.
"The anguish on thy face, dear, in this
    hour
Is far more bitter than my wound to me.
The pretty basket that in company
We once began will be unfinished now.
Would I had seen it full to overflow,

"Dear, with thy love! Oh, stay! Life's in
    thine eyes.
Ah, if thou couldst do something," the lad
    cries,
"For him,—the poor old basket-weaver
    there,—
My father, worn with toil!" In her despair,
Mirèio bathes the wound, while some
    bring lint,
And some run to the hills for healing
    mint.

Then the maid's mother spake: "Let four
    men rally,
And to the Fairies' Cavern,⁴ in the valley

They call Enfer, bear up this wounded
    man.
The deadlier the hurt, the sooner can
The old witch heal. Scale first the cliffs of
    Baux,
And circling vultures the cave's mouth
    will show."

A hole flush with the rocks, by lizards
    haunted,
And veiled by tufts of rosemary thereby
    planted.
For ever, since the holy Angelus swells
In Mary's honor from the minster-bells,
The antique fairies have been forced to
    hide
From sunlight, and in this deep cavern
    bide.

Strange, airy things, they used to flit about
Dimly, 'twixt form and substance, in and
    out:
Half-earthly made, to be the visible
Spirit of Nature; female made as well,
To tame the savagery of primal men.
But these were fair in fairies' eyes, and
    then

They loved: and so, infatuate, lifted not
Mortals unto their own celestial lot;
But, lusting, fell into our low estate,
As birds fall, whom a snake doth fasci-
    nate,
From their high places. But, while thus
    I write,
The bearers have borne Vincen up the
    height.

A dim, straight passage led the cavern
    toward,
A rocky funnel where they gently low-
    ered
The sufferer; and he did not go alone,—
Yet was Mirèio's self the only one
Who dared to follow down that awesome
    road,
Commending, as she went, his soul to
    God.

The bottom gained, they found a grotto cold
And vast; midway whereof a beldam old,
The witch Taven, sat silent, crouching lowly
As lost in thought and utter melancholy,
Holding a sprig of brome, and muttering,
"Some call thee devil's wheat, poor little thing,

"Yet art thou one of God's own signs for good!"
Therewith Mirèio, trembling where she stood,
Was fain to tell why they had sought her thus.
"I knew it!" cried the witch, impervious,
The brome addressing still, with bended head.
"Thou poor field-flower! The trampling flock," she said,

"Browse on thy leaves and stems the whole year long;
But all the more thou spreadest and art strong,
And north and south with verdure deckest yet."
She ceased. A dim light, in a snail-shell set,
Danced o'er the dank rock-wall in lurid search:
Here hung a sieve; there, on a forkèd perch,

Roosted a raven, a white hen beside.
Suddenly, as if drunken, rose and cried
The witch, "And what care I whoe'er you be?
Faith walketh blindfold, so doth Charity,
Nor from her even tenor wandereth.
Say, Valabregan weaver, have you faith?"

"I have." Then wildly, their pursuit inviting,
Like a she-wolf her flanks with her tail smiting,
Darted the hag into a deeper shaft,

While the fowl cackled and the raven laughed
Before her footsteps; and the boy and maid
Followed her through the darkness, sore afraid.

"Stay not!" she cried. "The time is now to gather
The mandrake!" And, fast holding one another,
Obedient to the voice the two crept on,
Through the infernal passage, till they won
A grotto larger than the rest. "Lo! now,
Lord Nostradamus' plant, the golden bough,

"The staff of Joseph and the rod of Moses!"
Thus crying, Taven a slender shrub discloses,
And, kneeling, with her chaplet crowns. Then said,
Arising, "We too must be garlanded
With mandrake"; and the plant in the rock's cleft
Of three fair sprays mysteriously bereft,

Herself crowned first, and next the wounded man,
And last the maid. Then, crying, "Forward!" ran
Down the weird way, before her footsteps lit
By shining beetles trooping over it.
Yet turned with a sage word,—"All paths of glory,
My children, have their space of purgatory!

"Therefore have courage! for we must, alas!
The terrors of the Sabatori[5] pass."
And, while she spake, their faces cut they find,
And breathing stopped, by rush of keenest wind.

"Lie down!" she whispered hurriedly,—
    "lie low!
The triumph of the Whirlwind Sprites is
    now!"

Then fell upon them, like a sudden gale
Or white squall on the water fraught with
    hail,
A swarm of whirling, yelping, vicious
    things,
Under the fanning of whose icy wings
The mortals, drenched with sweat and
    struck with cold,
Stood shivering. "Away, ye over-bold,

"Ye spoilers of the harvest, unlicked
    whelps!"
Taven exclaimed. "Must we then use such
    helps
To the fair deeds we do? Yet, as by skill
The sage physician bringeth good from ill,
We witches, by our hidden arts, compel
Evil to yield its fruit of good as well.

"Naught's hid from us. For where the
    vulgar see
A stone, a whip, a stag, a malady,
We witches can the inner force divine
Like that which works under the scum
    of wine
In fermentation. Pierce the vat, you know,
A seething, boiling scum will outward
    flow.

"Find, if you can, the key of Solomon!
Or speak unto the mountain in its own
Dread language! It shall move at your
    behest,
And roll into the valley ere it rest."
Meanwhile they wended lower, and were
    'ware
Of a small, roguish voice a-piping there,

Most like a goldfinch: "Our good granny
    spins,
And winds and spins, and then anew
    begins,

And thinks that she spins worsted night
    and day,
And ha! ha! gossip, she spins only hay!
Te! he! spin, Aunty, spin!" And long-
    drawn laughter,
Like whinnying of young colts, followed
    thereafter.

"Why, what can that be?" asked
    Mirèio,—
"The little voice that laughs and jeers us
    so?"
Again the childish treble came, "Te! he!
Who is this pretty mortal? Let us see!
We'll raise the neckerchief a little bit:
Are nuts and pomegranates under it?"

Then the poor maid had nearly cried out-
    right;
But the hag stayed her, "Here's no cause
    for fright.
The singing, jeering thing is but a Glari:
Fantasti is his name, a sprightly fairy.
In his good mood he will your kitchen
    sweep,
Mind fire, turn roast, and a full hen's-
    nest keep.

"But what a marplot when he takes the
    whim!
He'll salt your broth just as it pleaseth
    him,
Or blow your light out ere you're half in
    bed!
Or, if to vespers you would go," she said,
"At great Saint Trophimus',[6] gayly
    bedight,
He'll hide your Sunday suit, or spoil it
    quite!"

"Hear!" shrieked the imp: "now hear the
    old hag talk!
'Tis like the creak of an ill-greasèd block!
No doubt, my withered olive," the thing
    said,
"I twitch the bedclothes off a sleeping
    maid

Sometimes at midnight, and she starts
     with fear
And trembles, and her breast heaves. Oh,
     I see her!"

And with its whinnying laugh the sprite
     was gone;
Then, for a brief space, as they journeyed
     on
Under the grots, the witcheries were
     stayed;
And in the gloomy silence, long delayed,
They heard the water drop from vaulted
     roof
To crystal ground. Now there had sat
     aloof,

Upon a ledge of rock, a tall, white thing,
Which rose in the half-light as menacing
With one long arm. Then stiff as a quartz
     rock
Stood Vincen; while, transported by the
     shock,
Mirèio would have leaped a precipice,
Had such been there. "Old scare-crow,
     what is this?

"What mean you," cried Taven, "by
     swaying so
Your limp head like a poplar to and fro?"
Then turning to the stricken twain, "My
     dears,
You know the Laundress? Oft-times she
     appears
On Mount Ventour, and then the common
     crowd
Are wont to take her for a long, white
     cloud.

"But shepherds, when they see her, pen
     their sheep.
The Laundress of destruction, who doth
     keep
The errant clouds in hand, is known too
     well.
She scrubs them with a strength right
     terrible;

Wringing out buckets full of rain, and
     flame.
And neatherds house their cattle at her
     name;

"And seamen, on the angry, tossing wave,
Upon our Lady call, their craft to save."
Here drowned her speech a discord most
     appalling,
Rattling of latches, whimpering, cater-
     wauling,
With uncouth words half-uttered inter-
     vening,
Whereof the devil only knows the mean-
     ing;

And brazen din through all the cave
     resounding,
As one were on a witch-caldron pounding.
Then whence those shrieks of laughter,
     and those wails
As of a woman in her pains? Prevails
Hardly amid the howl the beldam's
     speech,
"Give me a hand that I may hold you
     each,

"And let your magic garlands not be lost!"
Here were they jostled from their feet
     almost
By rush of something puffing, grunting,
     snorting,
Most like a herd of ghostly swine com-
     porting.
On starlit winter-nights, when Nature
     slumbers
Under her snowy sheets, come forth in
     numbers

The fowlers, torch in hand, who bush and
     tree
By river-side will beat right vigorously,
Till all the birds at roost arise in haste,
And, as by breath of smithy-bellows
     chased,
Affrighted, rush until the net receive:
So drave Taven the foul herd with her
     sieve

[174]

Into the outer darkness. With the same
She circles traced, luminous, red as flame,
And divers other figures. All the while,
"Avaunt!" she cried, "ye locusts, ye who
        spoil
The harvest! Quit my sight, or woe betide
        you!
Workers of evil, in your burrows hide
        you!

"Since, by the pricking of your flesh, ye
        know
The hills are still with sunshine all aglow,
Go hang yourselves again on the rock-
        angles,
Ye bats!" They flit. The clamour disen-
        tangles,
And dies away. Then to the children
        spake
The witch: "All birds of night themselves
        betake

"To this retreat what time shines the day-
        light
On the ploughed land and fallow; but at
        night,—
At night the lamps are lighted without
        hand
In churches void and triply fastened, and
The bells toll of themselves, and pave-
        ment stones
Upstart, and tremble all the buried bones,

"And the poor dead arise and kneel to
        pray,
And mass is said by priests as pale as
        they.
Ask the owls else, who clamber down the
        steeple
To drain the lamps of oil; and if the
        people
Who thus partake of the communion
Be not all dead except the priests alone!

"What time the beldam jeers at Febru-
        ary,[7]
Let women everywhere be wondrous
        wary,

Nor fall asleep on chairs for awful reason!
Shepherds as well, at yon uncanny season
Early your charges fold, it mislike you
A spell should motionless and rigid strike
        you

"For seven years' time. The Fairies'
        Cavern, too,
Looses about these days its eerie crew.
Winged or four-footed, they o'er Crau
        disperse;
While, from their lairs aroused, the
        sorcerers
Gather, the *farandoulo*[8] dance, and sup
An evil potion from a golden cup.

"The dwarf-oaks dance as well. Lord, how
        they trip it!
Meanwhile there's Garamaude[9] in wait
        for Gripet.[10]
Fie, cruel flirt! Ay, seize the carrion,
And claw her bowels out! Now they are
        gone,—
Nay, but they come again! And, oh,
        despair!
The monster stealing through the sea-kale
        there,

"The one who like a burglar crouched
        and ran,
Is Bambarouche, babe-stealing harridan.
Her wailing prey in her long claw she
        takes,
Lifts on her horny head, and off she
        makes.
And yon's another! She's the Nightmare-
        sprite
Comes down the chimney-flue at dead of
        night,

"And stealthy climbs upon the sleeper's
        breast,
Who, as with weight of a tall tower
        opprest,
Hath horrid dreams. Hi! What a hideous
        racket!
My dears, 'tis the foul-weather fiends who
        make it!

That sound of rusty hinges, groaning
    doors,
Is they who beat up fog upon the moors,

"And ride the winds that homestead-roofs
    uptear
And bear afar. Ha, Moon! What ails you
    there?
What dire indignity hath made you scowl
So red and large o'er Baux? 'Ware the
    dog's howl!
Yon dog can snap you like a cake, be
    sure!
He minds the filthy Demon of the Sewer!

"Now see the holm-oaks bend their heads
    like ferns,
And see that flame that leaps and writhes
    and burns.
It is St. Elmo's. And that ringing sound
Of rapid hoofs upon the stony ground
Is the wild huntsman riding over Crau."
Here hoarse and breathless paused the
    witch of Baux.

But straight thereafter, "Cover ears and
    eyes,
For the black lamb is bleating!" wildly
    cries.
"That baaing lambkin!" Vincen dared to
    say;
But she, "Hide eyes and ears without
    delay!
Woe to the stumbler here! Sambuco's[11]
    Path
Less peril than the black horn's passage
    hath.

"Tender his bleating, as you hear, and
    soft:
Thereby he lures to their destruction oft
The heedless Christians who attend his
    moan.
To them he shows the sheen of Herod's
    throne,
The gold of Judas, and the fatal spot
Where Saracens made fast the golden
    goat.

"Her they may milk till death, to hearts'
    content.
But, when they call for holy sacrament,
The black lamb only butts them savagely.
And yet, so evil is the time," quoth she,
"Unnumbered greedy souls that bait will
    seize,
Burn incense unto gold, then die as
    these!"

Now, while the white hen gave three
    piercing crows,
The eerie guide did to her guests disclose
The thirteenth grotto, and the last; and lo!
A huge, wide chimney and a hearth
    aglow,
And seven black tom-cats warming round
    the flame.
And, hanging from a hook above the
    same,

An iron caldron of gigantic size,
And underneath two fire-brands, dragon-
    wise
Belching blue flame. "Is it with these you
    brew,
Grandmother," asked the lad, "your
    magic stew?"
"With these, my son. They're branches of
    wild vine:
No better logs for burning be than mine."

"Well, call them branches if it be your
    taste;
But—but I may not jest. Haste, mother,
    haste!"
Now, midway of the grotto, they descry
A large, round table of red porphyry;
And, radiating from this wondrous place,
Lower than root of oak or mountain base,

Infinite aisles whose gleaming columns
    cluster
Like pendant icicles in shape and lustre.
These are the far-famed galleries of the
    fays,
Here evermore a hazy brightness plays,

Temples and shining palaces are here,
Majestic porticoes their fronts uprear,

And many a labyrinth and peristyle
The like whereof was never seen erewhile,
Even in Corinth or in Babylon.
Yet let a fairy breathe, and these are
    gone!
And here, like flickering rays of light,
    disperse
Through the dim walks of this serene
    Chartreuse,

The fairies with their knights long since
    enchanted.
Peace to the aisles by their fair presence
    haunted!
And now the witch was ready. First of all,
She lifted high her hands, then let them
    fall,
While Vincen had like holy Lawrence
    lain
Upon the porphyry table, mute with pain.

And mightily the spirit of the crone
Appeared to work within her; and as
    grown
She seemed, when, rising to her height
    anew,
She plunged her ladle in the boiling stew
That overflowed the caldron in the heat,
While all the cats arose and ringed her
    feet,

And, with her left hand, unto Vincen's
    breast
Applied the scalding drops with solemn
    zest,
Gazing intently on him where he lay,
Until the cruel hurt was charmed away;
And all the while, "The Lord is born, is
    dead,
Is risen, shall rise again," she murmurèd.

Last on the quivering flesh the cross she
    made
Thrice with her toe-nail; as in forest glade

A tigress fiercely claws her fallen prey.
And now her speech maketh tumultuous
    way
To where the dim gates of the future are.
"Yea, he shall rise! I see him now afar

"Amid the stones and thistles of the hill,
His forehead bleeding heavily. And still
Over the stones and briers he makes his
    way,
Bowed by his cross. Where is Veronica
To wipe the blood? And him of Cyrene
To stay him when he fainteth,—where is
    he?

"And where the weeping Maries, hair
    dishevelled?
All gone! And rich and poor, before him
    levelled,
Gaze while he mounts; and 'Who is this,'
    one saith,
'Who climbs with shouldered beam, and
    and never stayeth?'
O carnal sons of men! The Cross-bearer
Is unto you but as a beaten cur.

"O cruel Jews! Wherefore so fiercely bite
    you
The hands that feed, and lick the hands
    that smite you?
Receive the fruit of your foul deeds you
    must.
Your precious gems shall crumble into
    dust,
And that you deemed fair pulse or whole-
    some wheat
Shall turn to ashes even while you eat,

"And scare your very hunger. Woe is me!
Rivers that foam o'er carrion-heaps I see,
And swords and lances in tumultuous
    motion.
Peace to thy stormy waves, thou vexèd
    Ocean!
Shall Peter's ancient bark withstand the
    shock?
Alas, it strikes upon the senseless rock!

"Nay, but there cometh One with power
　　to save!
Fisher of men, he quells the rebel wave.
A fair new bark the Rhone is entering
　　now:
She hath God's cross uplifted on her
　　prow,
Rainbow divine! Eternal clemency!
Another land, another sun, I see!

"Dance olive-pickers, where the fruit is
　　shining;
Drink reapers, on the barley-sheaves
　　reclining!
Revealed by signs so many, God," she
　　said,

"Is in his holy temple worshippèd."
And, stretching forth her hand, the witch
　　of Baux
Pointed the way and bade the children go.

Light gleamed afar. They haste the ray to
　　follow;
They thread their way to the Cordovan
　　Hollow,[12]
Where sun and air await them, and they
　　seem
To see Mont Majour's wrecks, as in a
　　dream,
Strewn o'er the hill; yet on the sunlit
　　verge
Pause for one kiss or ever they emerge.

NOTES TO CANTO VI.

[1] MAUSSANO and Saint Martin are villages
in Crau.

[2] Nostradamus. Michel de Nostradame, or
Nostradamus, was born at Saint Rémy, in
1503, and died at Salon, in 1565. He prac-
tised medicine very successfully under the
latter Valois, applied himself to mathematics
and astrology, and published in 1557, under
the title of "The Centuries," the prophesies
which have rendered his name popular.
Charles IX. appointed him physician in ordinary, and loaded him with honor.

[3] "This cordial," Agrioutas, a liquor, composed of brandy and sugar, with which is
mixed a certain quantity of short-stalked
cherry, well bruised.

[4] "The Fairies' Cavern." The following is
Jules Canonge's description of this locality:—
"From the bottom of the gorge, aptly
named Enfer, I descended into the Fairies'
Grotto. But, instead of the graceful phan-
toms with which my imagination had peopled it, I saw nothing but low vaults under
which I was forced to crawl, blocks of stone
heaped up, and gloomy depths. I have just
observed that this gorge is aptly called
Enfer. Nowhere else have I ever seen rocks
so tormented. They stand erect, with cavities
in their side; and their gigantic entablements,
covered with aerial gardens, in which a dishevelled sort of vegetation obtains, defile out
like the Pyrenean rock cleft by the sword of
Roland."
On comparing the description of Dante's
"Inferno" with this tortured Cyclopean, fantastic vista, one is persuaded that the great

Florentine poet, who travelled in our parts
and even sojourned in Arles, must have
visited the town of Baux, sat on the escarpments of the Valoun d'Infer, and, being
struck with the grandeur of its desolation,
conceived in its midst the outline of his "Inferno." Every thing leads to this idea, even
the name of the gorge itself, its amphitheatri-
cal form, the same given by Dante to Hell,
and the large detached rocks forming its
escarpments.

"In su l'estremita d'un alta ripa
　Che facevan gran pietre rotte in
　　cerchio."

And the Provençal name of these same baus,
Italianized by the poet into balzo, was given
by him to the escarpments of his own lugu-
brious funnel.

[5] "Sabatori." Beside its etymological meaning, this word is used to designate a meeting
held by sorcerers at night to worship the
devil. (The Witches' Sabbath of our own
witchcraft delusion.—AM. TR.)

[6] "Saint Trophimus'," the cathedral of
Arles, built in the seventh century, by Arch-
bishop St. Virgile, in which Frederic Barba-
rossa was consecrated emperor in 1178.

[7] Peasants in Southern France have remarked that the last three days of February
and the first three of March are almost always visited by a renewal of cold; and this
is how their poetic imagination accounts for
the fact:—
An old woman was once tending her
sheep. It was toward the end of February,
which that year had not been severe. The
old woman, believing herself clear of winter,
began jeering February as follows:—

"Adieu, Febriè. Mè ta feberado
M'as fa ni peu ni pelado."

("Farewell, February. With your
frost
Harmed me you have not, and nothing cost.")

This jeer enraged February, who went in
search of March, and said, "March, do me
a favor!"—"Two, if you like," answered
March."—"Lend me three days; and, with
the three I have left, I will both harm her
and cost her plenty." The weather immediately afterward became intolerably bad, all
the sheep of the old woman were killed by
the frost, and she, the peasants say, kicked
against it. This inclement period has ever
since been known as the *reguignado de la
Vièio,* or kicking of the old woman.

8 The *farandoulo* is a Provençal dance.
9 10 Garamaude is the imp of flirtation;
Gripet, the demon of influenza, from *gripa,*
to grip.

11 Sambuco's Path, in the mountains of
Sambuco, to the east of Aix, is much
dreaded by travellers.

12 The Cordovan Hollow, or *Trau de
Cordo.* To the east of Arles arise two hills,
which must originally have formed but one,
but are now separated by a morass. Upon
the flat, rocky summit of the lower, the Celts
had once made an excavation. It is believed
that the Saracens once encamped upon this
hill, and gave it its name of "Cordo," in
memory of Cordova. Wonderful traditions
cluster around this spot. It is the haunt of
the Fairy Serpent, or *Melusine Provençale;*
of the golden goat, that enables people to
discover hidden treasure. The larger hill
bears the almost Roman name of Mont
Majour. Upon this hill are the gigantic ruins
of the Abbey of Mont Majour. Both the
Grotte de Corde and the Grotte des Baus
bear the name of "Trau di Fado," or
"Fairies' Cave," and the popular belief is
that the excavations communicate.

CANTO VII.

THE OLD MEN.

Fixing a troubled eye on the old man,
Vincen to Master Ambroi thus began,
The while a mighty wind,¹ the poplars
bending,
Its howl unto the poor lad's voice was
lending:
"I am mad, father, as I oft of late
Have said. Thinkest thou I'm jesting
when I say't?"

Before his nut-shell cot the Rhone beside
Sat Ambroi on a fallen trunk, and plied
His trade. And, as he peeled the osier
withe,
Vincen received it, and, with fingers lithe
And strong, bent the white rods to basket
form,
Sitting upon the door-stone. With the
storm

Of wind was the Rhone's bosom agitated,
The waves drove seaward like a herd
belated;
But round about the hut an azure mere

Spread tranquilly. The billows brake not
here:
A pleasant shelter gave the willow-trees,
And beavers gnawed their bitter bark in
peace.

While yonder, through the deep of limpid
water,
Darted at intervals the dark brown otter,
Following the silver-flashing fish. Among
The reeds and willows, pendulines had
hung
Their tiny nests, white woven with the
wool
Plucked from the poplar when its flowers
are full.

And here the small things fluttered full of
glee,
Or swang on wind-rocked stems right
lazily.
Here, too, a sprightly lassie, golden-
haired,—
Head like a crown-cake! ²—back and
forward fared,
And spread on a fig-tree a fishing-net
Unwieldy and with water dripping yet.

Birds, beavers, otters, feared the maid no
    more
Than whispering reeds or willows of the
    shore.
This was the daughter of the basket-
    weaver,
The little Vinceneto. No one ever
Had even bored her ears, poor child! yet
    so
Her eyes were damson-blue, her bosom
    low,—

A caper-blossom by the river-side,
Wooed by the splashing of the amorous
    tide.
But now old Ambroi, with his long white
    beard
Flowing o'er all his breast, his head up-
    reared,
And answered Vincen's outcry: "What
    is't? Mad?
You are a blockhead! that is all, my lad!"

"Ah!" said the other, "for the ass to stray,
Sweet must the mead be. But what do I
    say?
Thou knowest her! If she to Arles should
    fare,
All other maids would hide them in des-
    pair;
For, after her, I think the mould was
    broken.
And what say to the words herself hath
    spoken,

" 'You I will have!' "—"Why, naught,
    poor fool! say I:
Let poverty and riches make reply!"
"O father!" Vincen cried, "go, I implore
    thee,
To Lotus Farm, and tell them all the
    story!
Tell them to look for virtue, not for gain!
Tell them that I can plough a stony plain,

"Or harrow, or prune vines with any
    man!

Tell them their six yoke, with my guiding,
    can
Plough double! Tell them I revere the old;
And, if they part us for the sake of gold,
We shall both die, and they may bury us!"
"Oh, fie! But you are young who maunder
    thus,"

Quoth Master Ambroi. "All this talk I
    know.
The white hen's egg,[3] the chaffinch on the
    bough,
You'll have the pretty bird this very
    minute!
Whistle, bring sugared cake, or die to win
    it;
Yet will the chaffinch never come, be
    sure,
And perch upon your finger! You are
    poor!"

"Plague on my poverty!" poor Vincen
    cried,
Tearing his hair. "Is God who hath denied
All that could make life worthy,—is He
    just?
And wherefore are we poor? And where-
    fore must
We still the refuse of the vineyard gather,
While others pluck the purple clusters
    rather?"

Lifting his hands, the old man sternly
    said,
"Weave on, and drive this folly from your
    head!
Shall the corn-ears rebuke the reaper,
    pray?
Or silly worm to God the Father say,
'Why am I not a star in heaven to shine?'
Or shall the ox to be a drover pine,

"So to eat corn instead of straw? Nay,
    nay!
Through good and ill we all must hold
    our way.
The hand's five fingers were unequal
    made.

Be you a lizard, as your Master bade,
And dwell content upon your wall apart,
And drink your sunbeam with a thankful
      heart!"

"I tell thee, father, I this maid adore
More than my sister, than my Maker
      more;
And if I have her not, 'tis death, I say!"
Then to the rough stream Vincen fled
      away;
While little Vinceneto burst out weeping,
Let fall her net, and near the weaver
      creeping,—

"O father! ere thou drive my brother wild,
Listen to me!" began the eager child:
"For where I served the master had a
      daughter;
And had a laborer, too, who loved and
      sought her,
Just as our Vincen loves Mirèio.
She was named Alis; he, Sivèstre: and so

"He labored like a wolf because he loved.
Skilful and prompt, quiet and saving
      proved,
And took such care, master slept tran-
      quilly;
But once—mark, father, how perverse
      men be!—
One morning master's wife, as it befell,
O'erheard Sivèstre his love to Alis tell.

"So when at dinner all the men were
      sitting,
The master gave Sivèstre a wrathful
      greeting.
'Traitor!' he cried, with his eyes all aglow,
'You are discovered! Take your wage,
      and go!'
We looked at one another in dismay,
As the good servant rose, and went his
      way.

"Thereafter, for three weeks, when we
      were working,

We used to see him round the farmstead
      lurking,—
A sorry sight; for all his clothes were torn,
And his face very pale and wild and
      worn.
And oft at eve he to the trellis came,
And called the little mistress by her name.

"Erelong the hay-rick at its corners four
Burnt all a-flame. And, father, something
      more!
They drew a drownèd man out of the
      well."
Then Ambroi, in gruff tones half-audible,
"A little child a little trouble gives,
And more and more for every year he
      lives."

Therewith put his long spatterdashes on
Which he himself had made in days
      bygone,
His hobnailed shoes, and long red cap,
      and so
Straightway set forth upon the road to
      Crau.
'Twas harvest-time, the eve of St. John's
      day,
The hedgerow paths were crowded all the
      way

With troops of dusty, sunburnt moun-
      taineers
Come down to work awhile as harvesters.
In fig-wood quivers were their sickles
      borne,
Slung to a belt across the shoulder worn.
By twos and twos they came, and every
      pair
Had its own sheaf-binder. And carts were
      there,

Bearing the weary elders, and beside
The pipes and tambourines with ribbons
      tied.
Anon by fields of beardless wheat they
      passed,
Lashed into billows by the noisy blast;
And "Mon Dieu, but that is noble grain!"

They cried. "What tufts of ears! There
    shall we gain

"Right pleasant reaping! The wind bows
    them over;
But see you not how quickly they re-
    cover?
Does all your Provence wheat-crop look
    as cheering,
Grandfather?" asked a youth, old Ambroi
    nearing.
"The red is backward still," he made
    reply;
"But, if this windy weather last, deem I

"Sickles will fail us ere the work be done.
How like three stars the Christmas
    candles shone!
That was a blessed sign of a good year!"
"Now, grandfather, may the good God
    thee hear,
And in thy granary the same fulfil!"
So Ambroi and the reapers chatted still

In friendly wise, under the willows wend-
    ing;
For these as well to Lotus Farm were
    tending.
It also chanced that Master Ramoun
    went
That eve to hearken for the wheat's
    complaint
Against the wind, wild waster of the
    grain;
And, as he strode over the yellow plain

From north to south, he heard the golden
    corn
Murmuring, "See the ills that we have
    borne,
Master, from this great gale. It spills our
    seed
And blurs our bloom!"—"Put on your
    gloves of reed,"
Sang others, "else the ants will be more
    fleet,
And rob us of our all but hardened wheat.

"When will the sickles come?" And
    Ramoun turned
Toward the trees, and even then discerned
The reapers rising in the distance dim;
Who, as they nearer drew, saluted him
With waving sickles flashing in the sun.
Then roared the master, "Welcome, every
    one!

"A very God-send!" cried he, loud and
    long;
And soon the sheaf-binders about him
    throng,
Saying, "Shake hands! Why, Holy Cross,
    look here!
What heaps of sheaves, good master, will
    this year
Cumber your treading-floor!"—"May-
    hap," said he:
"We cannot alway judge by what we see.

"Till all is trod, the truth will not be
    known.
I have known years that promised," he
    went on,
"Eighty full bushels to the acre fairly,
And yielded in their stead a dozen barely.
Yet let us be content!" And, with a smile,
He shook their hands all round in friendly
    style,

And gossiped with old Ambroi affably.
So entered all the homestead path, and he
Called out once more, "Come forth,
    Mirèio mine,
Prepare the chiccory and draw the wine!"
And she right lavishly the table spread;
While Ramoun first him seated at its
    head,

And the rest in their order, for the lunch.
Forthwith the laborers began to crunch
Hard-crusted bread their sturdy teeth
    between,
And hail the salad made of goats-beard
    green;
While fair as an oat-leaf the table shone,
And in superb profusion heaped thereon

Were odorous cheese, onions and garlic
hot,
Grilled egg-plant, fiery peppers, and what
not,
To sting the palate. Master Ramoun
poured
The wine, king in the field and at the
board;
Raising his mighty flagon now and then,
And calling for a bumper on the men.

"To keep the sickles keen on stony
ground,
They must be often whetted, I have
found."
The reapers held their goblets, bidden so,
And red and clear the wine began to flow.
"Ay, whet the blades!" the cheery master
cries;
And furthermore gives order in this wise:

"Now eat your fill, and all your strength
restore.
But go thereafter, as you used of yore,
And branches in the copse-wood cut, and
bring
In fagots; thus a great heap gathering.
And when 'tis night, my lads, we'll do the
rest!
For this the fête is of Saint John the
blest,—

"Saint John the reaper, and the friend
of God."
So spake the lord of all these acres broad.
The high and noble art of husbandry,
The rule of men, none better knew than
he,
Or how to make a golden harvest grow
From dark sods moistened by the toiler's
brow.

A grave and simple master of the soil,
Whose frame was bending now with years
and toil;
Yet oft, of old, when floors were full of
wheat,

Glowing with pride he had performed the
feat,
Before his youthful corps, upright to
stand
Bearing two pecks upon each horny hand.

He could the influence of the moon re-
hearse;
Tell when her look is friendly, when
adverse;
When she will raise the sap, and when
depress;
The coming weather from her halo guess,
And from her silver-pale or fiery face.
Clear signs to him were birds and keen
March days,

And mouldy bread and noisome August
fogs,
St. Clara's dawn, the rainbow-hued sun-
dogs,
Wet seasons, times of drought and frost
and plenty.
Full oft, in pleasant years, a-ploughing
went he,
With six fair, handsome beasts. And,
verily,
Myself have seen, and it was good to see,

The soil part silently before the share,
And its dark bosom to the sun lay bare:
The comely mules, ne'er from the furrow
breaking,
Toiled on as though they care and thought
were taking
For what they did. With muzzles low
they went,
And arching necks like bows when these
are bent,

And hasted not, nor lagged. Followed
along—
Eye on the mules, and on his lips a
song—
The ploughman, with one handle only
guiding.
So, in the realm where we have seen
presiding

Our old friend Ramoun, flourished every
    thing,
And he bare sceptre like a very king.

Now says he grace, and lifts his eyes
    above,
And signs the holy cross. The laborers
    move
Away to make the bonfire ready. These
Bring kindling; those, the boughs of dark
    pine-trees;
And the old men alone at table staying,
A silence fell. But Ambroi brake it, say-
    ing,—

"For counsel, Ramoun, am I come to
    thee;
For I am in a great perplexity
Thou only canst resolve. Cure see I none.
Thou knowest, Master, that I have a son
Who has been passing good until this
    day,—
It were ingratitude aught else to say;

"But there are flaws even in precious
    stones,
And tender lambs will have convulsions,
And the still waters are perfidious ever:
So my mad boy,—thou wilt believe it
    never,—
He loves the daughter of a rich free-
    holder,
And swears he will in his embrace enfold
    her!

"Ay, swears he will, the maniac! And his
    love
And his despair my soul to terror move.
I showed him all his folly, be thou sure,
And how wealth gains, and poverty grows
    poor
In this hard world. In vain! He would
    but call,
'Cost what it may, tell thou her parents
    all,—

" 'Tell them to look for virtue, not for
    gain!

Tell them that I can plough a stony plain,
Or harrow, or prune vines with any man!
Tell them their six yoke, with my guiding,
    can
Plough double! Tell them I revere the old;
And, if they part us for the sake of gold,

" 'We shall both die, and need but burial.'
Now, Master Ramoun, I have told thee
    all.
Shall I, clad in my rags, for this maid sue,
Or leave my son to die of sorrow?"—
    "Whew!"
The other. "To such wind spread thou no
    sail!
Nor he, nor she, will perish of this ail.

"So much, good friend, I say in utmost
    faith.
Nor would I, Ambroi, fret myself to death
If I were thou; but, seeing him so mad,
I would say plainly, 'Calm your mind, my
    lad!
For if you raise a tempest by your
    passions,
I'll teach you with a cudgel better
    fashions!'

"If an ass, Ambroi, for more fodder bray,
Throw him none down, but let thy
    bludgeon play.
Provençal families in days bygone
Were healthy, brave, and evermore at
    one,
And strong as plane-trees when a storm
    befell.
They had their strifes, indeed,—we know
    it well;

"But, when returned the holy Christmas
    eve,
The grandsire all his children would
    receive
At his own board, under a star-sown tent;
And ceased the voice of strife and all
    dissent,
When, lifting hands that wrinkled were
    and trembled,

He blessed the generations there as-
    sembled.

"Moreover, he who is a father truly
Will have his child yield him obedience
    duly:
The flock that drives the shepherd, soon
    or late,
Will meet a wolf and a disastrous fate.
When we were young, had any son with-
    stood
His father, he, belike, had shed his
    blood!"

"Thou wilt kill me then, father! It is I
Whom Vincen worships thus despair-
    ingly;
And before God and our most holy
    Mother,
I give my soul to him, and to no other!"
A deathlike hush followed Mirèio's word.
The wife of Ramoun was the first who
    stirred.

Upspringing with clasped hands and
    utterance wild,
"Your speech is an atrocious insult, child!
Your love's a thorn that long hath stung
    us deep.
Alari, the owner of a thousand sheep,
You sent away; and keeper Veran too,
Disgusted with your scorn, his suit with-
    drew;

"Also the wealthy herdsman, Ourrias,
You treated as a dog and a scapegrace!
Tramp through the country with your
    beggar, then!
Herd with strange women and with out-
    cast men!
And cook your pot with fortune-telling
    crones
Under a bridge mayhap, upon three
    stones.

"Go, gypsy, you are free!" the mother
    said;

Nor stayed Ramoun her pitiless tirade,
Though his eye like a taper burned. But
    now
The lightning flashed under his shaggy
    brow,
And his wrath brake, all barriers over-
    bearing,
Like swollen torrent down a mountain
    tearing.

"Your mother's right!" he said. "Go!
    travel yonder,
And take the tempest with you where you
    wander!
Nay, but you shall not! Here you shall
    remain,
Though I should bind you with an iron
    chain,
Or hold like a rebellious jumart, look!
Dragged by the nostrils with an iron
    hook!

"Yea, though you pine with sickly
    melancholy,
Till from your cheeks the roses perish
    wholly,
Or fade as snow fades when the sun is
    hot
On the hill-sides in spring, go shall you
    not!
And mark, Mirèio! Sure as the hearth's
    ashes
Rest on that brick, and sure as the Rhone
    dashes

"Above its banks when it is overfull,
And sure as that's a lamp, and here I
    rule,
You'll see him never more!" The table
    leapt
Beneath his fist. Mirèio only wept.
Her heavy tears like dew on smallage
    rain,
Or grapes o'er ripe before a hurricane.

"And who," resumed the old man, blind
    with rage,—

"Curse it!—I say, who, Ambroi, will en-
    gage
Thou didst not with the younger ruffian
    plot
This vile abduction, yonder in thy cot?"
Then Ambroi also sprang infuriate,—
"Good God!" he cried, "we are of low
    estate;

"But let me tell you that our hearts are
    high!
No shame, no stain, is honest poverty!
I've served my country forty years or
    more
On shipboard, and I know the cannon's
    roar,
So young that I could scarce a boat-hook
    swing
When on my first cruise I went wandering.

"I've seen Melinda's empire far away,
And with Suffren have haunted India,
And done my duty over all the world
In the great wars, where'er our flag un-
    furled
That southern chief who passed his
    conquering hand
With one red sweep from Spain to Rus-
    sian land,

"And at whose drum-beat every clime
    was quaking
Like aspen-tree before the tempest shak-
    ing;
Horrors of boarding, shipwreck's
    agonies,—
These have I known, and darker things
    than these,
Days than the sea more bitter. Being
    poor,
No bit of motherland might I secure.

"Scorned of the rich, I might not dress
    the sward,
But suffer forty years without reward.
We ate dog's food, on the hoar-frost we
    lay:
Weary of life, we rushed into the fray,

And so upbore the glorious name of
    France.
But no one holds it in remembrance!"

His caddis-cloak upon the ground he
    threw,
And spake no more. "What great thing
    wilt thou do?"
Asked Ramoun, and his tone was full of
    scorn.
"I, too, have heard the cannon-thunder
    borne
Along the valley of Toulon, have seen
The bridge of Arcole stormed, and I have
    been

"In Egypt when her sands were red with
    gore;
But we, like men, when those great wars
    were o'er,
Returning, fiercely fell upon the soil,
And dried our very marrow up with toil.
The day began long ere the eastern glow,
The rising moon surprised us at the hoe.

"They say the Earth is generous. It is
    true!
But, like a nut-tree, naught she gives to
    you
Unless well-beaten. And if all were
    known,
Each clod of landed ease thus hardly won,
He who should number them would also
    know
The sweat-drops that have fallen from
    my brow.

"And must I, by Ste. Ann of Apt, be still?
Like satyr toil, of siftings eat my fill,
That all the homestead may grow wealthy,
    and
Myself before the world with honor stand,
Yet go and give my daughter to a tramp,
A vagabond, a straw-loft-sleeping scamp?

"God's thunder strike you and your dog!
    Begone!

But I," the master said, "will keep my
    swan."
These were his last rough words; and
    steadily
Ambroi arose, and his cloak lifted he,
And only rested on his staff to say,
"Adieu! Mayst thou not regret this day!"

"And may the good God and his angels
    guide
The orange-laden bark across the tide!"
Then, as he passed into the falling night,
From the branch-heap arose a ruddy light,
And one long tongue of flame the wan-
    derer sees,
Curled like a horn by the careering
    breeze;

And round it reapers dancing blithe-
    somely,
With pulsing feet, and haughty heads and
    free
Thrown back, and faces by the bonfire lit,
Loud crackling as the night-wind fanneth
    it.
The sound of coals that to the brazier fall
Blends with the fife-notes fine but musical,

And merry as the song of the hedge-
    sparrow.

Ah, but it thrills the old Earth to her
    marrow
When thou dost visit her, beloved St.
    John!
The sparks went whirling upward, and
    hummed on
The tabor gravely and incessantly,
Like the low surging of a tranquil sea.

Then did the dusky troop their sickles
    wave,
And three great leaps athwart the flame
    they gave,
And cloves of odorous garlic from a
    string
Upon the glowing embers they did fling,
And holy herb and John's-wort bare
    anigh;
And these were purified and blessed
    thereby.

Then "Hail, St. John!" thrice rose a
    deafening shout;
And hills and plain, illumined round
    about,
Sparkled as though the dark were shower-
    ing stars.
And sure the Saint, above the heaven's
    blue bars,
The breath of all this incense doth inhale,
Wafted aloft by the unconscious gale.

NOTES TO CANTO VII.

[1] THE *mistral,* or north-west wind, which
blows down the valley with great violence.
[2] *Tourtihado,* a cake baked in the form of
a crown and made of fine paste, sugar, eggs,
and anise-seed.
[3] "The white hen's egg," a proverbial expression for something rare and precious.

CANTO VIII.

LA CRAU.

The rage of the mighty lioness
    Who shall restrain?
She came to her den, and she found it bare:
A Moorish huntsman had entered there.
The huntsman came, and the whelp is
    gone.
Away through the canebrake they have
    flown,

Galloping far at a headlong pace.
    To follow—vain!
She roars awhile in her deep despite,
Then rises and courses, lank and
    light,
Over the hills of Barbary.
As a maid bereft of her love is she.

Mirèio lay upon her little bed,
Clasping in both her hands her burning
    head.

Dim was the chamber; for the stars alone
Saw the maid weep, and heard her piteous
    moan,—
"Help, Mother Mary, in my sore distress!
Oh, cruel fate! Oh, father pitiless,

"Who tread me underfoot! Could you but
    see
My heart's mad tumult, you would pity
    me!
You used to call me darling long ago,
And now you bend me to the yoke as
    though
I were a vicious colt that you were fain
To break. Why does the sea not flood this
    plain?

"I would the wealthy lands that make me
    weep
Were hid for evermore in the great deep!
Ah, had I in a serpent's hole been born,
Of some poor vagrant, I were less forlorn!
For then if any lad, my Vincen even,
Had asked my hand, mayhap it had been
    given.

"O Vincen, who so handsome are and
    true!
If only they would let me go to you,
I'd cling as clings the tender ivy-vine
Unto the oak: I would not ever pine
For food, but life in your caresses find,
And drink at wayside pools with happy
    mind."

So on her pallet the sweet maid lay
    sobbing,
Fire in her heart and every vein
    a-throbbing,
And all the happy time remembering—
Oh, calm and happy!—of her love's fair
    spring,
Until a word in Vincen's very tone
Comes to her memory. " 'Twas you, my
    own,—

" 'Twas you," she cried, "came one day to
    the farm,

And said, 'If ever thou dost come to
    harm,—
If any lizard, wolf, or poisonous snake
Ever should wound thee with its fang,—
    betake
Thyself forthwith to the most holy Saints,
Who cure all ills and hearken all com-
    plaints.'

"And sure I am in trouble now," she said:
"Therefore we'll go, and come back
    comforted."
Then lightly from her white cot glided
    she,
And straightway opened, with a shining
    key,
The wardrobe where her own possessions
    lay:
It was of walnut wood, and carven gay.

Here were her childhood's little treasures
    all:
Here sacredly she kept the coronal
Worn at her first communion; and anear
There lay a withered sprig of lavender;
And a wax taper almost burned, as well,
Once blessed, the distant thunder to
    dispel.

A smart red petticoat she first prepares,
Which she herself had quilted into
    squares,—
Of needlework a very masterpiece;
And round her slender waist she fastens
    this;
And over it another, finer one
She draws; and next doth a black bodice
    don,

And fasten firmly with a pin of gold.
On her white shoulders, her long hair
    unrolled,
Curling, and loose like a dark garment,
    lay,
Which, gathering up, she swiftly coils
    away
Under a cap of fine, transparent lace;

Then decks the veilèd tresses with all
    grace,

Thrice with a ribbon blue encircling
    them,—
The fair young brow's Arlesian diadem.
Lastly, she adds an apron to the rest,
And folds a muslin kerchief o'er her
    breast.
In her dire haste, alone, the child forgat
The shallow-crowned, broad-brimmed
    Provençal hat,

That might have screened her from the
    mortal heat.
But, so arrayed, crept forth on soundless
    feet
Adown the wooden staircase, in her hand
Her shoes, undid the heavy door-bar, and
Her soul unto the watchful saints com-
    mended,
As away like a wind of night she wended.

It was the hour when constellations keep
Their friendly watch o'er followers of the
    deep.
The eye of St. John's eagle flashed afar,
As it alighted on a burning star,
One of the three where the evangelist
Hath his alternate dwelling. Cloud nor
    mist

Defaced the dark serene of star-lit sky;
But the great chariot of souls went by
On wingèd wheels along the heavenly
    road,
Bearing away from earth its blessed load.
Far up the shining steeps of Paradise,
The circling hills behold it as it flies.

Mirèio hasted no less anxiously
Than Magalouno[1] in the days gone by,
Who searched the wood with sad, inquir-
    ing glance
For her lost lover, Pèire of Provence,
When cruel waves divorced him from
    her side,

And left her lone and wretched. Soon
    espied

The maid, upon the boundary of the lea,
Folds where her sire's own shepherds
    could she see
Already milking. Some the sheep com-
    pelled,
Against the pen-side by the muzzle held,
To suckle quietly their tawny lambs.
Always arose the bleat of certain dams;

While other childless ones the shepherds
    guide
Toward the milker. On a stone astride,
Mute as the very night, sits he, and dim;
While, pressed from swollen udders, a
    long stream
Of warm fine milk into the pail goes
    leaping,
The white froth high about its border
    creeping.

The sheep-dogs all in tranquil slumber
    lay.
The fine, large dogs—as white as lilies
    they—
Stretched round the enclosure, muzzles
    deep in thyme.
And peace was everywhere, and summer
    clime;
And o'er the balmy country, far and near,
Brooded a heaven full of stars, and clear.

So in the stillness doth Mirèio dash
Along the hurdles, like a lightning flash,
Lifting a wailing cry that never varies,—
"Will none go with me to the holy Maries,
Of all the shepherds?" They and the sheep
    hear it,
And see the maiden flitting like a spirit,

And huddle up, and bow their heads, as
    though
Smit by a sudden gale. The farm-dogs
    know
Her voice, but never stir her flight to stay.
And now is she already far away,

Threads the dwarf-oaks, and like a par-
    tridge rushes
Over the holly and the camphyre bushes,

Her feet scarce touching earth. And now
    she passes
Curlews in flocks asleep amid the grasses
Under the oaks, who, roused from
    slumber soft,
Arise in haste, and wing their flight aloft
Over the sad and barren plain; and all
Together "Cour'li! cour'li! cour'li!" call,

Until the Dawn, with her dew-glittering
    tresses,
From mountain-top to level slow progres-
    ses,
Sweetly saluted by the tufted lark,
Soaring and singing o'er the caverns dark
In the great hills, whose pinnacles each
    one
Appear to sway before the rising sun.

Then was revealed La Crau, the bare, the
    waste,
The rough with stones, the ancient, and
    the vast,
Whose proud old giants, if the tale be
    true,
Once dreamed, poor fools, the Almighty
    to subdue
With but a ladder and their shoulders
    brave;
But He them 'whelmed in a destroying
    wave.

Already had the rebels dispossest
The Mount of Victory[2] of his tall crest,
Lifted with lever from its place; and sure
They would have heaped it high upon
    Ventour,
As they had piled the rugged escarpment
They from the Alpine range had earlier
    rent.

But God his hand extended o'er the plain:
The north-west wind, thunder, and hurri-
    cane

He loosed; and these arose like eagles
    three
From mountain clefts and caverns and the
    sea,
Wrapped in thick fog, with fury terrible,
And on the marble pile together fell.

Then were the rude Colossi overthrown;
And a dense covering of pudding-stone
Spread o'er La Crau, the desolate, the
    vast,
The mute, the bare to every stormy blast;
Who wears the hideous garment to this
    day.
Meanwhile Mirèio farther speeds away

From the home-lands, while the sun's
    ardent glare
Makes visible all round the shimmering
    air;
And shrill cicalas, grilling in the grass,
Beat madly evermore their tiny brass.
Nor tree for shade was there, nor any
    beast:
The many flocks, that in the winter feast

On the short, savory grasses of the moor,
Had climbed the Alps, where airs are cool
    and pure,
And pastures fadeless. Yet the maid doth
    fly
Under the pouring fire of a June sky,—
Fly, fly, like lightning. Lizards large and
    gray
Peep from their holes, and to each other
    say,

"She must be mad who thus the shingle
    clears,
Under a heat that sets the junipers[3]
A-dancing on the hills; on Crau, the
    sands."
The praying mantes[4] lift beseeching
    hands,
"Return, return, O pilgrim!" murmuring,
"For God hath opened many a crystal
    spring;

"And shady trees hath planted, so the rose
To save upon your cheeks. Why, then,
        expose
Your brow to the unpitying summer
        heat?"
Vainly as well the butterflies entreat.
For her the wings of love, the wind of
        faith,
Bear on together, as the tempest's breath

White gulls astray over the briny plains
Of Agui-Morto. Utter sadness reigns
In scattered sheep-cots of their tenants
        left,
And overrun with salicorne. Bereft
In the hot desert, seemed the maid to
        wake,
And see nor spring nor pool her thirst to
        slake,

And slightly shuddered. "Great St.
        Gent!" [5] she cried,
"O hermit of the Bausset mountain-side!
O fair young laborer, who to thy plough
Didst harness the fierce mountain-wolf
        ere now,
And in the flinty rock, recluse divine,
Didst open springs of water and of wine,

"And so revive thy mother, perishing
Of heat! like me, when they were slum-
        bering,
Thou didst forsake thy household, and
        didst fare
Alone with God through mountain-passes,
        where
Thy mother found thee! For me, too, dear
        Saint,
Open a spring; for I am very faint,

"And my feet by the hot stones blisterèd!"
Then, in high heaven, heard what Mirèio
        said
The good St. Gent: and soon she doth
        discover
A well far off, with a bright stone laid
        over;

And, like a marten through a shower of
        rain,
Speeds through the flaming sun-rays, this
        to gain.

The well was old, with ivy overrun,—
A watering-place for flocks; and from the
        sun
Scarce by it sheltered sat a little boy,
With basket-full of small white snails for
        toy.
With his brown hands, he one by one
        withdrew them,
The tiny harvest-snails; and than sang to
        them,—

        "Snaily, snaily, little nun,
    Come out of the cell, come into the
        sun!
    Show me your horns without delay,
    Or I'll tear your convent-walls
        away."

Then the fair maid of Crau, when she had
        dipped
Her burning lips into the pail, and sipped,
Quickly upraised a lovely, rosy face,
And, "Little one! what dost thou here?"
        she says.
A pause. "Pick snailies from the stones
        and grass?"
"Thou hast guessed right!" the urchin's
        answer was.

"Here in my basket have I— see, how
        many!
Nuns,[6] harvest-snails,[7] and these,[8] as
        good as any!"
"Well, and you eat them?"—"Nay, not I,"
        replied he;
"But mother carries them to Arles on
        Friday,
And sells them; and brings back nice,
        tender bread.
Thou wilt have been to Arles?"—
        "Never!" she said.

"What, never been to Arles! But I've
    been there!
Ah, poor young lady! Couldst thou see
    how fair
And large a city that same Arles is grown!
She covers all the seven mouths of the
    Rhone.
Sea-cattle has she on the isles, who graze
Of the salt-meres. Wild horses, too, she
    has;

"And, in one summer, corn enough she
    raises
To feed her seven full years, if so she
    pleases.
She's fishermen who fish on every sea,—
Seamen who front the storms right val-
    iantly
Of distant waters." Thus with pretty pride
The boy his sunny country glorified,

In golden speech;—her blue and heaving
    ocean;
Her Mont Majour, that keeps the mills in
    motion,—
These with soft olives ever feeding fully;
Her bitterns in the marshes booming
    dully.
One thing alone, thou lovely, dusky town,
The child forgat,—of all thy charms the
    crown:

He said not, fruitful Arles, that thy fine
    air
Gives to thy daughters beauty rich and
    rare,
As grapes to autumn, or as wings to bird,
Or fragrance to the hill-sides. Him had
    heard
The country maiden, sadly, absently.
But now, "Bright boy, wilt thou not go
    with me?"

She said; "for, ere the frogs croak in the
    willow,
My foot must planted be beyond the
    billow.

Come with me! I must o'er the Rhone be
    rowed,
And left there in the keeping of my God!"
"Now, then," the urchin cried, "thou
    poor, dear lady,
Thou art in luck! for we are fishers," said
    he;

"And thou shalt sleep under our tent this
    night,
Pitched in the shadow of the poplars
    white,
So keeping all thy pretty clothing on;
And father, with the earliest ray of dawn,
In our own little boat will put thee o'er!"
But she, "Do not detain me, I implore:

"I am yet strong enough this night to
    wander."
"Now God forbid!" was the lad's prompt
    rejoinder:
"Wouldst thou see, then, the crowd of
    sorry shapes
From the Trau-de-la-Capo that escapes?
For if they meet thee, be thou sure of
    this,—
They'll drag thee with them into the
    abyss!"

"Trau-de-la-Capo! What may that be,
    pray?"
"I'll tell thee, lady, as we pick our way
Over the stones." And forthwith he
    began:
"Once was a treading-floor that overran
With wealth of sheaves. To-morrow, on
    thy ways,
Thou 'lt pass, upon the riverside, the
    place.

"Trod by a circle of Camargan steeds,
The tall sheaves had been yielding up
    their seeds
To the incessant hoofs, a month or more.
No pause, no rest; and, on the treading-
    floor,

Dusty and winding, there was yet be-
     stowed
Of sheaves a very mountain to be trod.

"Also, the weather was so fiercely hot,
The floor would burn like fire; and rested
     not
The wooden forks that more sheaves yet
     supplied;
While at the horses' muzzles there were
     shied
Clusters of bearded ears unceasingly,—
They flew as arrows from the cross-bow
     fly.

"And on St. Peter's day and on St.
     Charles'
Rang, and rang vainly, all the bells of
     Arles:
There was no Sunday and no holiday
For the unhappy horses; but alway
The heavy tramp around the weary road,
Alway the pricking of the keeper's goad,

"Alway the orders issued huskily,
As in the fiery whirlwind still stood he.
The greedy master of the treaders white
Had even muzzled them, in his despite.
And, when Our Lady's⁹ day in August
     came,
The coupled beasts were treading, all the
     same,

"The pilèd sheaves, foam-drenched. Their
     livers clung
Fast to their ribs, and their jaws drivelling
     hung,
When suddenly an icy, northern gale
Smit, swept the floor,—and God's blas-
     phemers feel
It quake and part! On a black caldron's
     brink
They stand now, and their eyes with
     horror sink.

"Then the sheaves whirl with fury
     terrible.

Pitch-forkers, keepers, keepers-aids as
     well,
Struggle to save them; but they naught
     can do:
The van, the van-goats, and the mill-
     stones too,
Horses and drivers, treading-floor, and
     master
Are swallowed up in one immense
     disaster!"

"You make me shudder!" poor Mirèio
     said.
"Ah, but that is not all, my pretty maid!
Thou thinkest me a little mad, may be:
But on the morrow thou the spot wilt see;
And carp and tench in the blue water
     playing,
And, in the reeds, marsh-blackbirds
     roundelaying.

"But on Our Lady's day, when mounts
     again
The fire-crowned sun to the meridian,
Lay thee down softly, ear to earth," said
     he,
"And eye a-watch, and presently thou 'lt
     see
The gulf, at first so limpid, will begin
To darken with the shadow of the sin;

"And slowly up from the unquiet deep
A murmuring sound, like buzzing flies,
     will creep;
And then a tinkling, as of tiny bells,
That soon into an awful uproar swells
Among the water-weeds! Like human
     voices
Inside an amphora the fearsome noise is!

"And then it is the trot of wasted horses
Painfully tramping round their weary
     courses
Upon a hard, dry surface, evermore
Echoing like a summer threshing-floor,
Whom drives a brutal keeper, nothing
     loth,

And hurries them with insult and with
    oath.

"But, when the holy sun is sinking low,
The blasphemies turn hoarse and fainter
    grow,
The tinkling dies among the weeds. Far
    off,
The limping, sorry steed is heard to
    cough;
And, on the top of the tall reeds
    a-swinging,
Once more the blackbirds begin sweetly
    singing."

So, full of chat, and with his basket laden,
Travelled the little man before the
    maiden;
While the descending sun with rose
    invests
The great blue ramparts and the golden
    crests
Of the hill-range, peaceful and pure and
    high,
Blending its outline with the evening sky.

Seemed the great orb, as he withdrew in
    splendor,
God's peace unto the marshes to sur-
    render,
And to the great lake, and the olives
    gray
Of the Vaulungo, and the Rhone away

There in the distance, and the reapers
    weary,
Who now unbend, and quaff the sea-air,
    cheery.

Till the boy cries that far away he sees
The home-tent's canvas fluttering in the
    breeze.
"And the white poplar, dear maid, seest
    thou?
And brother Not, who climbs it even
    now?
He's there after cicalas, be thou sure;
Or to spy me returning o'er the moor.
"Ah, now he sees us! And my sister Zeto,
Who helped him with her shoulder, turns
    this way too;
And seems to tell my mother that she
    may
Put the fish-broth[10] to boil without delay.
And mother also, I can see her leaning
Over the boat, and the fresh fish
    a-gleaning."

Then, as the two made haste with one
    accord
To mount the dike, the lusty fisher roared,
"Now this is charming! Look this way,
    my wife!
Our little Andreloun, upon my life,
Will be the prince of fishers one day," said
    he;
"For he has caught the queen of eels
    already!"

NOTES TO CANTO VIII.

1 "MAGALOUNO." According to the old
chivalrous romance, Count Pierre of Provence, having eloped with Magalouno, daughter of the King of Naples, fled with her over
hill and vale. One day, as Magalouno was
sleeping by the seaside, a bird of prey carried
off a jewel that was glittering on her neck.
Her lover followed the bird in a boat out to
sea; but a storm arose, whereby he was
driven to Egypt, where he was received and
loaded with honors by the Soldan. After
many romantic adventures, they met again
in Provence, where Magalouno, having become an abbess, had founded a hospital,
around which the town of Magalouno was
afterwards built.

2 Santo Vitori, a lofty peak east of Aix.
It derives its name from the victory gained
by Marius over the Teutons, close by.

3 Juniper, *Juniparus phœnicea.*

4 Praying mantes, *Orthoptera raptoria.*

5 St. Gent. A young laborer of Monteux,
who, at the beginning of the eleventh century, retired to the gorge of Bausset, near
Vaucluse, to live as a hermit. His hermitage,
and the miraculous fountain he caused to
spring, tradition says, by touching the rock
with his finger, are objects of many pil-
grimages.

6 7 8 *Helix hermiculata, Helix exepitum,* and *Helix algira.*

9 August 15, the fête of Napoleon III.

10 "The fish-broth," *bouibaisso,* a favorite Provençal stew, made of all sorts of fish, and poured, boiling hot, upon pieces of bread.

CANTO IX.

THE MUSTER.

All sorrowfully droop the lotus-trees;
And heart-sick to their hives withdraw
    the bees,
Forgetful of the heath with savory sweet,
And with milk-thistle. Water-lilies greet
King-fishers blue that to the vivary hie,
And "Have you seen Mirèio?" is their
    cry.

While Ramoun and his wife by the fire-
    side
Are sitting, lost in grief, and swollen-
    eyed,
And at their hearts the bitterness of death.
"Doubtless," they said, "her reason wan-
    dereth.
Oh, what a mad and wretched maid it is!
Oh, what a heavy, cruel downfall this!

"Oh, dire disgrace! Our beauty and our
    hope
So with the last of trampers to elope!
Fled with a gypsy! And who shall dis-
    cover
The secret hole of this kidnapping lover,
Where he the shameless one concealèd
    hath?"
And, as they spake, they knit their brows
    in wrath.

Now came the cup-bearer with ass and
    pannier,
And on the threshold, in his wonted
    manner,
Pausing, "Good-morrow, master fair!" he
    cried.
"I'm come to fetch the lunch." [1]—"Curse
    it!" replied
The poor old man. "Begone! Without my
    child,

I'm like a cork-tree of its bark despoiled.

"Yet hark ye, cup-bearer, upon your
    track
Across the fields like lightning go you
    back,
And bid the ploughmen and the mowers
    all
Quit ploughs and scythes, the harvesters
    let fall
Their sickles, and the shepherds too,"
    said he,
"Forsake their flocks, and instant come to
    me!"

Then, fleeter than a goat, the faithful man
O'er stony fallow and red clover ran,
Threaded holm-oaks[2] on long declivities,
Leaped o'er the roads along the base of
    these,
And now already scents the sweet per-
    fume
Of new-mown hay, and the blue-tufted
    bloom

Of tall lucerne descries; and presently
The measured sweep of the long scythes
    hears he,
And lusty mowers bending in a row
Beholds, and grass by the keen steel laid
    low
In verdant swaths,—ever a pleasant
    sight,—
And children, and young maidens, with
    delight

Raking the hay and in cocks piling it;
While crickets, that before the mowers
    flit,
Hark to their singing. Also, farther on,
An ash-wood cart, by two white oxen
    drawn,

Heaped with cured grass, where a skilled
    waggoner
Doth, by huge armfuls, high and higher
    rear

The forage round his waist, till it conceals
The rails, the cart-beam, and the very
    wheels;
And, when the cart moves on, with the
    hay trailing,
It seems like some unwieldy vessel
    sailing.
But now the loader rises, and descries
The runner, and "Hold, men! there's
    trouble!" cries;

And cartman's aids, who in great forkfuls
    carry
To him the hay, now for a moment tarry,
And wipe their streaming brows; and
    mowers rest
The scythe-back carefully upon the
    breast,
And whet the edge, as they the plain
    explore
That Phœbus wings his burning arrows
    o'er.

Began the rustic messenger straightway,
"Hear, men, what our good master bade
    me say:
" 'Cup-bearer,' was his word, 'upon your
    track
Across the fields like lightning go you
    back,
And bid the ploughmen and the mowers
    all
Quit ploughs and scythes, the harvesters
    let fall

" 'Their sickles, and the shepherds hastily
Forsake their flocks, and hither come to
    me!' "
Then, fleeter than a goat, the faithful man
O'er the rich, madder-growing³ hillocks
    ran,—
Althen's bequest,—and saw on every
    hand

The gold of perfect ripeness tinge the
    land,

And centaury-starred fields, and plough-
    men bent
Above their ploughs and on their mules
    intent,
And earth, awakened from her winter-
    sleep,
And shapeless clods upturned from fur-
    rows deep,
And wagtails frisking o'er; and yet again,
"Hearken to what our master saith, good
    men!

" 'Cup-bearer,' was his word, 'upon your
    track
Across the fields like lightning go you
    back,
And bid the ploughmen and the mowers
    all
Quit ploughs and scythes, the harvesters
    let fall
Their sickles, and the shepherds hastily
Forsake their flocks, and hither come to
    me!' "

Then the stout runner, fleeter than the
    goats,
Dashed through the pieces waving with
    wild-oats,
Fosses o'erleaped with meadow-flowers
    bright,
And in great yellow wheat-fields passed
    from sight,
Where reapers forty, sickle each in hand,
Like a devouring fire fall on the land,

And strip her mantle rich and odorous
From off her breast, and, ever gaining
    thus
As wolves gain on their prey, rob, hour
    by hour,
Earth of her gold, and summer of her
    flower;
While in the wake of each, in ordered
    line,

Falls the loose grain, like tendrils of the
vine.

And the sheaf-binders, ever on the watch,
The dropping wheat in handfuls deftly
catch,
And underneath the arm the same bestow
Until, so gathering, they have enow;
When, pressing with the knee, they tightly
bind,
And lastly fling the perfect sheaf behind.

Twinkle the sickles keen like swarming
bees,
Or laughing ripple upon sunny seas
Where flounders are at play. Erect and
tall,
With rough beards blent, in heaps
pyramidal,
The sheaves by hundreds rise. The plain
afar
Shows like a tented camp in days of war;

Even like that which once arose upon
Our own Beaucaire, in days how long
withdrawn!
When came a host of terrible invaders,
The great Simon and all the French
crusaders,
Led by a legate, and in fierce advance
Count Raymond slaughtered and laid
waste Provence.

And here, with gleanings falling from her
fingers,
Full many a merry gleaner strays and
lingers;
Or in the warm lea of the stacks of corn,
Or 'mid the canes,[4] drops languidly,
o'erborne
By some long look, that e'en bewilders
her,
Because Love also is a harvester.

And yet again the master's word,—"Go
back
Like lightning, cup-bearer, upon your
track,

And bid the ploughmen and the mowers
all
Quit ploughs and scythes, the harvesters
let fall
Their sickles, and the shepherds instantly
Forsake their flocks, and hither come to
me!"

Then fleeter than a goat sped on his way
The faithful soul, straight through the
olives gray,
On, on, like a north-eastern gale descending
Upon the vineyards, and the branches
rending,
Until, away in Crau, the waste, the
lonely,
Behold him, where the partridge whirreth
only;

And, still remote, discovers he the flocks
Tranquilly lying under the dwarf-oaks,
And the chief-shepherd, with his helpers
young,
For noon-tide rest about the heather
flung,
And little wag-tails hopping at their ease
O'er sheep that ruminate unmoved by
these.

And slowly, slowly sailing o'er the sea
Diaphanous vapors, light and white, sees
he,
And deems that up in heaven some fair
saint,
Gliding too near the sun, is stricken faint
On the aerial heights, and hath let fall
Her convent-veil. And still the herald's
call:—

"Hark, shepherds, to the master's word,—
'Go back
Like lightning, cup-bearer, upon your
track,
And bid the ploughmen and the mowers
all
Quit ploughs and scythes, the reapers too
let fall

Their sickles, and the shepherds instantly
Forsake their flocks, and hither come to
me!' ''

Then the scythes rested and the ploughs
were stayed,
The forty highland reapers each his blade
Let fall, and rushed as bees on new-found
wings
Forsake the hive, begin their wanderings,
And, by the din of clanging cymbals led,
Gather them to a pine. So also fled

The laborers one and all; the waggoners,
And they who tended them; the rick-
builders,
Gleaners, and shepherds, and of sheaves
the heapers,
Binders of sheaves, rakers, mowers, and
reapers,
Mustered them at the homestead. There,
heart-sore
And silent, on the grass-grown treading-
floor,

The master and his wife sat down to bide
The coming of the hands; who, as they
hied
Thither, much marvelled at the strange
behest
So calling them from toil, and who
addrest
These words unto old Ramoun, drawing
near:
"Thou sentest for us, master. We are
here."

Then Ramoun raised his head, and thus
replied:
"The great storm alway comes at harvest-
tide.
However well-advised, as we advance
We must, poor souls, all stumble on
mischance:
I cannot say it plainer. Friends, I pray,
Let each tell what he knows, without
delay!"

Lauren de Gout came forward first. Now
he
Had failed no single year since infancy
His quivered sickle from the hills to bring
Down into Arles when ears were yellow-
ing.
Brown as a church-stone, he, with
weather-stain,
Or ancient rock the sea-waves charge in
vain.

The sun might scorch, the north-west
wind might roar,
But this old king of reapers evermore
Was first at work. And now with him
there came
Seven rough and stalwart boys who bore
his name.
Him with one voice the harvesters did
make
Their chief, and justly: therefore thus he
spake:

"If it be true that, when the dawning sky
Is ruddy, there is rain or snow close by,
Then what I saw this very morn, my
master,
Presageth surely sorrow and disaster.
So may God stay the earthquake! But as
night
Fled westward, followed by the early
light,

"And wet with dew as ever, I the men
First summoned briskly to their toil again,
And then myself, my sleeves uprolling
gayly,
Bent me to mine own task, as I do daily;
But at the first stroke wounded thus my
hand,—
A thing which hath not happened, under-
stand,

"For thirty years." His fingers then he
showed,
And the deep gash, wherefrom the blood
yet flowed.

Then groaned, more piteously than be-
fore,
Mirèio's parents; while a lusty mower,
One Jan Bouquet, a knight of La
Tarasque[5]
From Tarascon, a hearing rose to ask.

A rough lad he, yet kind and comely too.
None with such grace in Condamino
threw
The pike and flag,[6] and never merrier
fellow
Sang Lagadigadèu's ritournello[7]
About the gloomy streets of Tarascon,
When, once a year, they ring with shout
and song,

And brighten up with dances and are
blithe.
He might have been a master of the
scythe,
Could he have held the straight, laborious
path;
But, when the fête-days came, farewell
the swath,
And welcome revels underneath the trees,
And orgies in the vaulted hostelries,

And bull-baitings, and never-ending
dances!
A very roisterer he who now advances,
With, "As we, master, in long sweeps
were mowing,
I hailed a nest of francolines, just show-
ing
Under a tuft of tares; and, as I bent
Over the pendent grass, with the intent

"To count the fluttering things, what do I
see
But horrible red ants—oh, misery!—
In full possession of the nest and young!
Three were then dead. The rest, with
vermin stung,
Their little heads out of the nest ex-
tended,
As though, poor things, they cried to be
defended;

"But a great cloud of ants, more
venomous
Than nettles, greedy, eager, furious,
Them were o'erwhelming even then; and
I,
Leaning upon my scythe right pensively,
Could hear, far off, the mother agonize
Over their cruel fate, with piteous cries."

This tale of woe, following upon the
other,
Is a lance-thrust to father and to mother:
Their worst foreboding it hath justified.
Then, as a tempest in the hot June-tide,
Gathering silently, ascends the air,
The weather darkening ever, till the glare

Of lightning shows in the north-east, and
loud
Peal follows peal, another left the crowd,
One Lou Marran. It was a name renowned
In all the farms when winter-eves came
round,
And laborers, chatting while the mules
were stalled
And pulling lucerne from the rack,
recalled

What things befell when first this man was
hired,
Until the lights for lack of oil expired.
Seed-time it was, and every other man
Was opening up his furrow save Marran;
Who, hanging back, eyed coulter, tackle,
share,
As he the like had seen not anywhere.

Till the chief-ploughman spake: "Here is
a lout
To plough for hire! Why, a hog with his
snout
I wager would work better!"—"I will take
Thy bet," said Lou Marran; "and be the
stake
Three golden louis! Either thou or I,
Master, that sum will forfeit presently."

"Let blow the trumpet!" Then the plough-
  men twain
In two unswerving lines upturn the plain,
Making for the chosen goal,—two poplars
  high.
The sun-rays gild the ridges equally,
And all the laborers call out, "Well done!
Thy furrow, chieftain, is a noble one;

"Yet, sooth to say, so straight the other is,
One might an arrow shoot the length of
  this."
And Lou Marran was winner,—he who
  here
Before the baffled council doth appear,
All pale, to bear his bitter evidence:
"Comrades, as I was whistling, not long
  since,

"Over my share, methought the land was
  rough,
And we would stretch, the day to finish
  off;
When, lo! my beasts with fear began to
  quake,
Bristled their hairy sides, their ears lay
  back.
They stopped; and, with dazed eyes, I saw
  all round
The field-herbs fade, and wither to the
  ground.

"I touch my pair. Baiardo sadly eyes
His master, but stirs not. Falet applies
His nostril to the furrow. Then I lash
Their shin; and, all in terror, off they dash,
So that the ash-wood beam—the beam, I
  say—
Is rent, and yoke and tackle borne away.

"Then I grew pale, and all my breath was
  gone;
And, seized as with a strong convulsion,
I ground my jaws. A dreadful shudder
  grew
Upon me,—and my hair upraised, I
  knew,

As thistle-down is raised by the wind's
  breath;
But the wind sweeping over me was
  Death."

"Mother of God!" Mirèio's mother cried
In anguish, "do thou in thy mantle hide
Mine own sweet child!" and on her knees
  she dropped,
With lifted eyes and parted lips; yet
  stopped
Ere any word was spoken, for she saw
Antéume, shepherd-chief and milker,
  draw

Hurriedly toward them. "And why," he
  was panting,
"Was she the junipers untimely haunt-
  ing?"
Then, the ring entering, his tale he told.
"This morn, as we were milking in the
  fold,—
So early that above the bare plain showed
The sky yet hob-nailed with the stars of
  God,—

"A soul, a shadow, or a spectre swept
Across the way. The dogs all silence kept,
As if afraid, and the sheep huddled close.
Thought I,—who scarce have time, as
  master knows,
Ever an *Ave* in the church to offer,—
'Speak, soul, if thou art blest. If not, go
  suffer!'

"Then came a voice I knew,—it never
  varies,—
'Will none go with me to the holy Maries,
Of all the shepherds?' Ere the word was
  said,
Afar over the plain the voice had fled.
Wilt thou believe it, master?—it was she,
Mirèio!" Cried the people, "Can it be?"

"It was herself!" the shepherd-chief re-
  plied:
"I saw her in the star-light past me glide,
Not, surely, as she was in other days,

But lifting up a wan, affrighted face;
Whereby she was a living soul, I knew,
And stung by some exquisite anguish
    too."

At this dread word, the laborers groan,
    and wring
Each other's horny palms. "But who will
    bring,"
The stricken mother began wildly shriek-
    ing,
"Me to the saints? My bird I must be
    seeking!
My partridge of the stony field," she said,
"I must o'ertake, wherever she has fled.

"And if the ants attack her, then these
    teeth
Shall grind them and their hill! If greedy
    Death
Dare touch my darling rudely, then will I
Break his old, rusty scythe, and she shall
    fly
Away across the jungle!" Crying thus,
Jano Mario fled delirious

Back to the home; while Ramoun order
    gave,
"Cartman, set up the cart-tilt, wet the
    nave,
And oil the axle, and without delay
Harness Moureto.[8] We go far to-day,

And it is late." The mother, in despair,
Mounted the cart; and more and more
    the air

Resounded with the transports of her
    woe:
"O pretty dear! O wilderness of Crau!
O endless, briny plains! O dreadful sun,
Be kind, I pray you, to the fainting one!
But for her,—the accursèd witch
    Taven,—
Who lured my darling into her foul den,

And poured before her, as I know right
    well,
Her philters and her potions horrible,
And made her drink,—now may the
    demons all
Who bind St. Anthony upon her fall,
And drag her body o'er the rocks of
    Baux!"
As the unhappy soul lamented so,

Her tones were smothered by the cart's
    rude shaking;
And the farm-laborers, a last look taking
To see if none were coming o'er the plain,
Turned slowly, sadly, to their toil again;
While swarms of gnats, the idle, happy
    things,
Filled the green walks with sound of
    humming wings.

NOTES TO CANTO IX.

[1] LUNCH, a light meal taken by the reapers about ten in the morning.

[2] *Quercus ilex.*

[3] Jean Althen, an Arminian adventurer, introduced in 1774 the cultivation of madder into the Comtat Venaissen (department of Vaucluse). In 1850, a statue was erected to him on the rock of Avignon.

[4] The Provence cane, *Arundo vulgaris,* is very common in this region. Cattle-pens and angling-rods are made of it.

[5][6][7] All the world has heard of La Tarasque, a monster who, according to tradition, ravaged the banks of the Rhone, and was destroyed by Ste. Martha. Every year the people of Tarascon celebrate this deliverance by burning the monster in effigy; and, at intervals of time more or less long, the fête is enhanced by various games,—such as that of the pike and flag here mentioned, which consists in gracefully waving, throwing to a great height, and then catching with address, a standard with large folds, or a javelin. Lagadigadèu is the *ritournello* of a popular song ascribed to King René, and sung at Tarascon at this fête.

Condamino (Campus Domini) is the name of a certain quarter in Tarascon.

[8] *Moureto* is the name of the female, *Mouret* that of the male animal. In this country, beasts of burthen are usually named for their color,—*Mouret,* black; *Blanquet,* white; *Brunen,* brown; *Falet,* gray; *Baiard,* bay; *Roubin,* light bay.

CANTO X.
CAMARGUE.

Listen to me, good people of Provence,
Countrymen one and all, from Arles to
    Vence,
From Valensolo even to Marseilles,
And, if the heat oppress you, come, I
    pray,
To Durancolo[1] banks, and lying low,
Hear the maid's tale, and weep the lover's
    woe!

The little boat, in Andreloun's control,
Parted the water silent as a sole,
The while the enamoured maiden whom
    I sing,
Herself on the great Rhone adventuring,
Beside the urchin sat, and scanned the
    wave
Intently, with a dreamy eye and grave,

Till the boy-boatman spake: "Now
    knewest thou ever,
Young lady, how immense is the Rhone
    river?
Betwixt Camargue and Crau might
    holden be
Right noble jousts! That is Camargue!"
    said he;
"That isle so vast it can discern, I deem,
All the seven mouths of the Arlesian
    stream."

The rose-lights of the morn were beau-
    teous
Upon the river, as he chatted thus.
And the tartanes,[2] with snowy sails out-
    swelled,
Tranquilly glided up the stream,
    impelled

By the light breeze that blew from off the
    deep,
As by a shepherdess her milk-white sheep.

And all along the shore was noble shade
By feathery ash and silver poplar made,
Whose hoary trunks the river did reflect,
And giant limbs with wild vines all be-
    deckt
With ancient vines and tortuous, that
    upbore
Their knotty, clustered fruit the waters
    o'er.

Majestically calm, but wearily
And as he fain would sleep, the Rhone
    passed by
Like some great veteran dying. He recalls
Music and feasting in Avignon's halls
And castles, and profoundly sad is he
To lose his name and waters in the sea.

Meanwhile the enamoured maiden whom
    I sing
Had leaped ashore; and the boy, tarrying
Only to say, "The road that lies before
Is thine! The Saints will guide thee to the
    door
Of their great chapel," took his oars in
    hand,
And swiftly turned his shallop from the
    land.

Under the pouring fire of the June sky,
Like lightning doth Mirèio fly and fly.
East, west, north, south, she seems to see
    extend
One weary plain, savannas without end,
With glimpses of the sea, and here and
    there
Tamarisks lifting their light heads in air.

Golden-herb, samphire, shave-grass,
    soda,—these
Alone grow on the bitter prairies,
Where the black bulls in savage liberty
Rejoice, where the white horses all are
    free
To roam abroad and breast the briny gale,
Or air surcharged with sea-fog to inhale.

But now o'er all the marsh, dazzling to
    view,
Soars an immeasurable vault of blue,
Intense, profound. The only living thing
A solitary gull upon the wing
Or a gaunt hermit,[3] whose dark shadow
    falls
Over the desert meres at intervals,

Or red-legged chevalier,[4] or hern,[5] wild-
    eyed
With crest of three white plumes upraised
    in pride.
But soon the sun so beats upon the plain
That the poor, weary wanderer is fain
To loose and lift her folded neckerchief,
So from the burning heat to find relief.

Yet grows the torment ever more and
    more;
The sun ascending higher than before,
Until it rides in the unshaded zenith,
And thence a very flood of fire raineth,—
As a starved lion with his eye devours
The Abyssinian desert in his course.

Now were it sweet beneath a beech to
    slumber!
Now, like a swarm of hornets without
    number,—
An angry swarm, fierce darting high and
    low,—
Or like the hot sparks from a grindstone,
    grow
The pitiless rays; and Love's poor pilgrim,
    worn
And gasping, and by weariness o'erborne,

Forth from her bodice draws its golden
    pin,
So that her panting bosom shows within.
All dazzling white, like the campanulas[6]
That bloom beside the summer sea, it was,
And, like twin-billows in a brooklet, full.
Anon, the solitary scene and dull

Loses a little of its sadness, and
A lake shows on the limit of the land,—
A spacious lake, whose wavelets dance
    and shine,—
While shrubs of golden-herb[7] and jes-
    samine[8]
On the dark shore appear to soar aloft
Until they cast a shadow cool and soft.

It seems to the poor maid a heavenly
    vision,
A heartening glimpse into the land
    elysian.
And soon, afar, by that blue wave she sees
A town with circling walls and palaces,
And fountains gay, and churches without
    end,
And slender spires that to the sun ascend,

And ships and lesser sailing-craft, sun-
    bright,
Entering the port; and the wind seemeth
    light.
So that the oriflambs and streamers all
Languidly round the masts arise and fall.
"A miracle!" the maiden thought, and
    now
Wipes the abundant moisture from her
    brow,

And, with new hope, toward the town
    doth fare,
Deeming the Maries' tomb is surely there.
Alas! alas! be her flight ne'er so speedy,
A change will pass upon the scene.
    Already
The sweet illusion seems to fade and flit;
Recedes the vision as she follows it.

An airy show, the substance of a dream,
By spirit woven out of a sunbeam,
And all its fair hues borrowed from the
    sky,—
The filmy fabric wavers presently,
And melts away, and like a mist is gone.
Bewildered by the heat, and quite alone,

Is left Mirèio: yet her course she keeps,
Toiling over the burning, moving heaps
Of sand; over the salt-encrusted waste—
Seamed, swollen, dazzling to the eye—
    doth haste.
On through the tall marsh-grasses and the
    reeds
And rushes, haunted by the gnat, she
    speeds,

With Vincen ever in her thought. And
    soon,
Skirting the lonesome Vacarès lagune,
She sees it loom at last in distance dim,—
She sees it grow on the horizon's rim,—
The Saints' white tower, across the
    billowy plain,
Like vessel homeward bound upon the
    main.

And, even at that blessed moment, one
Of the hot shafts of the unpitying sun
The ill-starred maiden's forehead pierced,
    and she
Staggered, death-smitten, by the glassy
    sea,
And dropped upon the sand. Weep, sons
    of Crau,
The sweetest flower in all the land lies
    low.

When, in a valley by the river-side,
Young turtle-doves a huntsman hath
    espied,
Some innocently drinking, others cooing,
He, through the copse-wood with his gun
    pursuing,
At the most fair takes alway his first
    aim,—
The cruel sun had only done the same.

Now, as she lay in swoon upon the shore,
A swarm of busy gnats came hovering
    o'er,
Who seeing the white breast and fluttering
    breath,
And the poor maiden fainting to her
    death,
With ne'er a friendly spray of juniper
From all the pulsing fire to shelter her,

Each one the viol of his tiny wings
Imploring played with plaintive mur-
    murings,—
"Get thee up quickly, quickly, damsel
    fair!
For aye malignant is this burning air,"
And stung the drooping head; and sea-
    spray flew,
Sprinkling the fevered face with bitter
    dew:

Until at last Mirèio rose again,
And, with a feeble moan of mortal pain,
"My head! my head!" she dragged her
    way forlorn
And slow from salicorne to salicorne,—
Poor little one!—until her heavy feet
Arrived before the seaside Saints' retreat.

There, her sad eyes with tears all brim-
    ming o'er,
Upon the cold flags of the chapel-floor,
Wet with the infiltration of the sea,
She sank, and clasped her brow in agony;
And on the pinions of the waiting air
Was borne aloft Mirèio's faltering
    prayer:—

"O holy Maries, who can cheer
    The sorrow-laden,
Lend, I beseech, a pitying ear
    To one poor maiden!

"And when you see my cruel care
    And misery,
Then look in mercy down the air,
    And side with me!

"I am so young, dear Saints above,
     And there's a youth—
My handsome Vincen—whom I love
     With utter truth!

"I love him as the wayward stream
     Its wanderings;
As loves the new-fledged bird, I deem,
     To try its wings.

"And now they tell me I must quench
     This fire eternal;
Must from the blossoming almond wrench
     Its flowers vernal.

"O holy Maries, who can cheer
     The sorrow-laden,
Lend, I beseech, a pitying ear
     To one poor maiden!

"Now am I come, dear Saints, from far,
     To sue for peace:
Nor mother-prayer my way could bar,
     Nor wilderness;

"The sun, that cruel archer, shot
     Into my brain,—
Thorns, as it were, and nails red-hot,—
     Sharp is the pain;

"Yet give me but my Vincen dear:
     Then will we duly,
We two, with glad hearts worship here,—
     Oh, I say truly!

"Then the dire pain will rend no more
     These brows of mine,
And the face bathed in tears before
     Will smile and shine.

"My sire mislikes our love; is cold
     And cruel often:
'Twere naught to you, fair Saints of gold,
     His heart to soften.

"Howe'er so hard the olive grow,
     'Tis mollified

By all the winds that alway blow
     At Advent-tide.

"The medlar and the service-plum,
     So sharp to taste
When gathered, strewn on straw become
     A pleasant feast.

"O holy Maries, who can cheer
     The sorrow-laden,
Lend, I beseech, a pitying ear
     To one poor maiden!

.   .   .   .   .

"Oh, what can mean this dazzling light?
     The church is riven
O'erhead; the vault with stars is bright
     Can this be heaven?

"Oh, who so happy now as I?
     The Saints, my God,—
The shining Saints,—toward me fly,
     Down yon bright road!

"O blessed patrons, are you there
     To help, to stay me?
Yet hide the dazzling crowns you wear,
     Or these will slay me.

"Veil in a cloud the light appalling!
     My eyes are heavy.
Where is the chapel? Are you calling?
     O Saints, receive me!"

So, in a trance and past all earthly feeling,
The stricken girl upon the pavement
          kneeling,
With pleading hands, and head thrown
          backward, cried.
Her large and lovely eyes were opened
          wide,
As she beyond the veil of flesh discerned
St. Peter's gates, and for the glory
          yearned.

Mute were her lips now; but her face yet
          shone,

And wrapped in glorious contemplation
She seemed. So, when the gold-red rays of
    dawn
Early alight the poplar-tips upon,
The flickering night-lamp turneth pale
    and wan
In the dim chamber of a dying man.

And, as at daybreak, also, flocks arouse
From slumber and disperse, the sacred
    house
Appeared to open, all its vaulted roof
To part, and pillars tall to stand aloof,
Before the three fair women,—heavenly
    fair,—
Who on a starry path came down the air.

White in the ether pure, and luminous,
Came the three Maries out of heaven
    thus.
One of them clasped an alabaster vase
Close to her breast, and her celestial face
In splendor had that star alone for peer
That beams on shepherds when the nights
    are clear.

The next came with a palm in her hand
    holden,
And the wind lifting her long hair and
    golden.
The third was young, and wound a mantle
    white
About her sweet brown visage; and the
    light
Of her dark eyes, under their falling
    lashes,
Was greater than a diamond's when it
    flashes.

So, nearer to the mourner drew these
    three,
And leaned above, and spake consolingly.
And bright and tender were the smiles
    that wreathed
Their lips, and soft the message that they
    breathed.

They made the thorns of cruel martyr-
    dom,
That pierced Mirèio, into flowers bloom.

"Be of good cheer, thou poor Mirèio;
For we are they men call the Saints of
    Baux,—
The Maries of Judæa: and we three—
Be of good cheer!—we watch the stormy
    sea,
That we may succor vessels in distress.
Beholding us, the vexèd waves have
    peace.

"Now lift thine eyes, and see St. James's
    road!
A moment since, and we together stood
On high at its extremity remote;
And, gazing through the clustered stars,
    took note
How faithful souls to Campoustello[9] fare,
To seek the dear Saint's tomb, and wor-
    ship there.

"And, with the tune of falling fountains
    blending,
We heard the solemn litanies ascending
From pilgrims gathered in the fields at
    even,
And pealing of church-bells, and glory
    given
Unto our son and nephew, by his names
Of Spain's apostle and the greater James.

"Then were we glad of all the pious vows
Paid to his memory; and, on the brows
Of those poor pilgrims, dews of peace
    shed we,
And their souls flooded with serenity;
When, suddenly, thy warm petition came,
And seemed to smite us like a jet of flame.

"Dear child, thy faith is great; yet thy
    request
Our pitying hearts right sorely hath
    opprest.
For thou wouldst drink the waters of
    pure love,

Or ever to its source thee Death remove,
The bliss we have in God himself to share.
Hast thou, then, seen contentment any-
    where

"On earth? Is the rich blest, who softly
    lies,
And in his haughty heart his God denies,
And cares not for his fellow-man at all?
Thou knowest the leech when it is gorged
    will fall,
And he before the judgment-seat must
    pass
Of One who meekly rode upon an ass.

"Is the young mother happy to impart
Unto her baby, with a swelling heart,
The first warm jet of milk? One bitter
    drop,
Mingled therewith, may poison all her
    hope.
Now see her lean, distraught, the cradle
    over,
And a fair little corse with kisses cover.

"And hath she happiness, the promised
    bride,
Wandering churchward by her lover's
    side?
Ah, no! The path under those lingering
    feet
Thornier shall prove, to those who travel
    it,
Than sloe-bush of the moorland. Here
    below
Are only trial sharp and weary woe.

"And here below the purest waters ever
Are bitter on the lips of the receiver;
The worm is born within the fruit alway;
And all things haste to ruin and decay.
The orange thou hast chosen, out of all
The basket's wealth, shall one day taste
    as gall.

"And in thy world, Mirèio, they who
    seem

To breathe sigh only. And should any
    dream
Of drinking at the founts that run not dry,
Anguish alone such bitter draught will
    buy.
So must the stone be broken evermore,
Ere thou extract the shining silver ore.

"Happy is he who cares for others' woe,
And toils for men, and wearies only so;
From his own shoulders tears their mantle
    warm,
Therein to fold some pale and shivering
    form;
Is lowly with the lowly, and can waken
Fire-light on cold hearths of the world-
    forsaken.

"The sovereign word, that man remem-
    bereth not,
Is, 'Death is Life'; and happy is the lot
Of the meek soul and simple,—he who
    fares
Quietly heavenward, wafted by soft airs;
And lily-white forsakes this low abode,
Where men have stoned the very saints
    of God.

"And if, Mirèio, thou couldst see before
    thee,
As we from empyrean heights of glory,
This world; and what a sad and foolish
    thing
Is all its passion for the perishing,
Its churchyard terrors,—then, O lambkin
    sweet,
Mayhap thou wouldst for death and
    pardon bleat!

"But, ere the wheat-ear hath its feathery
    birth,
Ferments the grain within the darksome
    earth,—
Such ever is the law; and even we,
Before we wore our crowns of majesty,
Drank bitter draughts. Therefore, thy soul
    to stay,
We'll tell the pains and perils of our way."

Paused for a moment, then, the holy
three.
The waves, being fain to listen, coaxingly
Had flocked along the ocean sand; the
pines
Unto the rustling water-weeds made signs;
And teal and gull beheld, with deep
amaze,
Peace on the restless heart of Vacarès;

The sun and moon, afar the desert o'er,
Bow their great crimson foreheads, and
adore;
And all Camargue—salt-sown, forsaken
isle—
Seems thrilled with sacred expectation;
while
The saints, to hearten for her mortal strife
Love's martyr, tell the story of their life.

NOTES TO CANTO X.

1 *Durancolo:* this name is given to the canals derived from the Duranse.
2 *Tartanes,* the name of a small trading-craft common in the Mediterranean.
3 4 5 Birds common in Camargue. The Provençal name *Cambet* designates several birds of the order of the *échassiers,* chiefly the large red-legged chevalier, *Scolopax celidrix,* and the small red-legged chevalier.

6 The *Pancratian maritimus.*
7 8 *Atriplex portulacoides* and *Phylleria latifolia,* a large shrub of the jessamine family.
9 Campoustello, in the Middle Ages Campus Stellæ, once the capital of Gallicia, in Spain, now a town of thirty thousand inhabitants, with a fine old cathedral, containing the tomb of St. James the Major, patron saint of Spain.

CANTO XI.

THE SAINTS.

"The cross was looming yet, Mirèio,
Aloft on the Judæan mount of woe,
Wet with the blood of God; and all the
time
Seemed crying to the city of the crime,
'What hast thou done, thou lost and
slumbering,—
What hast thou done, I say, with Beth-
lehem's King?'

"The angry clamors of the streets were
stayed:
Cedron alone a low lamenting made
Afar; and Jordan rolled a gloomy tide,
Hasting into the desert, there to hide
The overflowings of his grief and rage
'Mid terebinth and lentisk foliage.

"And all the poorer folk were heavy-
hearted,
Knowing it was the Christ who had departed,
First having opened his own prison-door,

On friends and followers to look once
more,
The sacred keys unto St. Peter given,
And, like an eagle, soared away to
heaven.

"Oh! then in Jewry woe and weeping were
For the fair Galilean carpenter,—
Him who his honeyed parables distilled
Over their hearts, and fainting thousands
filled
Upon the hillsides with unleavened bread,
And healed the leper and revived the
dead.

"But scribes and kings and priests, and
all the horde
Of sacrilegious vendors whom the Lord
Had driven from his house, their hatred
uttered,
'And who the people will restrain,' they
muttered,
'Unless in all the region round about
The glory of this cross be soon put out?'

"So raged they, and the martyrs testified:
Stephen the first was stoned until he died,

MIRÈIO

James with the sword was slain, and many
a one
Cruelly crushed beneath a weight of
stone.
Yet, dying, all bear record undismayed:
'Christ Jesus is the Son of God!' they said.

"Then us, brothers and sisters of the slain,
Who him had followed in a loving train,
They thrust into a crazy bark; and we,
Oarless and sailless, drifted out to sea.
We women sorely wept, the men their
eyes
Anxiously lifted to the lowering skies.

"Palaces, temples, olive-trees, we saw—
Swiftly, oh swiftly!—from our gaze with-
draw,
All saving Carmel's rugged crests, and
those
But as a wave on the horizon rose.
When suddenly a sharp cry toward us
drifted.
We turned, and saw a maid with arms
uplifted.

" 'Oh, take me with you!' cried she in
distress;
'Oh, take me in the bark, my mistresses,
With you! I, too, must die for Jesus' sake!'
It was our handmaid Sarah thus who
spake.
Up there in heaven, whither she is gone,
She shineth sweetly as an April dawn!

"Seaward before the wind our vessel
drave.
Then God a thought unto Salome gave:
Her veil upon the foamy deep she
threw,—
Oh, wondrous faith!—and on the water,
blue
And white commingling wildly, it sustained
The maid until our fragile craft she
gained,

"To her as well the strong breeze lending
aid.
Now saw we in the hazy distance fade,
Hilltop by hilltop, our dear native land;
The sea encompassed us on every hand;
And a sharp home-sickness upon us fell,
The pangs whereof he who hath felt may
tell.

"So must we say farewell, O sacred shore!
O doomed Judæa, farewell evermore!
Thy just are banished, thy God crucified!
Henceforth let serpents in thy halls abide;
And wandering lions, tawny, terrible,
Feed on thy vines and dates. Farewell!
farewell!

"The gale had grown into a tempest now:
The vessel fled before it. On the prow
Martial was kneeling, and Saturnius:
While, in his mantle folded, Trophimus
The aged saint silently meditated;
And Maximin the bishop near him waited.

"High on the main-deck Lazarus held his
place.
There was an awful pallor on his face,—
Hues of the winding-sheet and of the
grave.
He seemed to face the anger of the wave.
Martha his sister to his side had crept,
And Magdalene behind them cowered
and wept.

"The slender bark, pursued of demons
thus,
Contained, beside, Cléon, Eutropius,
Marcellus, Joseph of Arimathea,
Sidonius. And sweet it was to hear
The psalms they sang on the blue waste
of sea,
Leaned o'er the tholes. Te Deum, too,
said we.

"How rushed the boat the sparkling billows by!
E'en yet that sea seems present to the
eye.

[209]

The breeze, careering, on the waters
    hurled,
Whereby the snowy spray was tossed and
    whirled,
And lifted in light wreaths into the air,
That soared like souls aloft, and vanished
    there.

"Out of the waves at morning rose the
    Sun,
And set therein when his day's course was
    run.
Mere waifs were we upon the briny plain,
The sport of all the winds that scour the
    main;
Yet of our God withheld from all mis-
    chance,
That we might bear His gospel to
    Provence.

"At last there came a morning still and
    bright.
We noted how, with lamp in hand, the
    night
Most like an anxious widow from us fled,
Risen betimes to turn her household
    bread
Within the oven. Ocean seemed as nap-
    ping.
The languid waves the boatside barely
    tapping.

"Till a dull, bellowing noise assailed the
    ear.
Unknown before, it chilled our blood to
    hear.
And next we marked a strange, upheav-
    ing motion
Upon the utmost limit of the ocean,
And, stricken speechless by the gathering
    roar,
Helplessly gazed the troubled waters o'er.

"Then saw we all the deep with horror
    lower,
As the swift squall descended in its power;
The waves drop dead still,—'twas a por-
    tent fell;

The bark hang motionless, as by a spell
Entranced; and far away, against the
    skies,
A mountain of black water seemed to
    rise.

"And all the heaped-up sea, with vapor
    crested,
To burst upon our vessel, thus arrested.
God, 'twas an awful hour! One monster
    wave
Seemed thrusting us into a watery grave,
Fainting to death. Or ever it closed o'er
    us,
The next upon a dizzy height upbore us.

"The lightning cleft the gloom with blades
    of fire;
Peal followed peal of thunder, deafening,
    dire.
It was as if all hell had been unchained
Upon our tiny craft, which groaned and
    strained
So hunted, and seemed rushing on her
    wreck,
And smote our foreheads with her heav-
    ing deck.

"Now rode we on the shoulders of the
    main;
Now sank into its inky gulfs again,
Where the seal dwelleth and the mighty
    shark,
And the sea-peacock; and we seemed to
    hark
To the sad cry, lifted unceasingly,
By the unresting victims of the sea.

"A great wave brake above us, and hope
    died.
Then Lazarus prayed: 'O Lord, be thou
    our guide,
Who me ere now out of the tomb didst
    bring!
Succor the bark, for she is foundering!'
Like a wood-pigeon's wing, this outcry
    clove

The tempest, and went up to realms
above.

"And Jesus, looking from the palace fair
Where he sat throned, beheld his friend's
despair,
And the fierce deep yawning to swallow
him.
Straightway the Master's gentle eyes grew
dim,
His heart yearned over us with pity warm,
And one long sun-ray leaped athwart the
storm.

"Now God be praised! For, though we
yet were tost
Right roughly up and down, and sank
almost
With bitter sea-sickness, our fears were
stayed:
The haughty waves began to be allayed;
Clouds brake afar, then vanished altogether,
And a green shore gleamed through the
bright'ning weather.

"Long was it yet ere the shocks quite
subsided
Of the tempestuous waves; and our boat
glided,
Our crazy boat, nearer that welcome
shore
All tranquilly, a dying breeze before.
Smooth as a grebe our keel the breakers
clomb,
Furrowing into great flakes the snowy
foam.

"Until—once more all glory be to God!—
Upon a rockless beach we safely trod,
And knelt on the wet sand, crying, 'O
Thou
Who saved from sword and tempest, hear
our vow!
Each one of us is an evangelist
Thy law to preach. We swear it, O Lord
Christ!'

"At that great name, that cry till then
unheard,
Noble Provence, wert thou not deeply
stirred?
Thy woods and fields, in all their fair
extent,
Thrilled with the rapture of a sweet content;
As a dog scents his master's coming feet,
And flies with bounding welcome him to
meet.

"Thou, Heavenly Father, also didst pro-
vide
A feast of shell-fish, stranded by the tide,
To stay our hunger; and, to quench our
thirst,
Madest among the salicornes outburst
The same clear, healing spring, which
flows alway
Inside the church where our dust sleeps
to-day.

"Glowing with zeal, we track the shingly
Rhone
From moor to moor. In faith we travel on
Until right gladly we discern the traces
Of human husbandry in those wild places,
And soon, afar, the tall Arlesian towers,
Crowned by the standard of the emperors.

"To-day, fair Arles, a harvester thou
seemest,
Who sleepest on thy threshing-floor, and
dreamest
Of glories past; but a queen wert thou
then,
And mother of so brave sea-faring men,
The noisy winds themselves aye lost their
way
In the great harbor where thy shipping
lay.

"Rome had arrayed thee in white marble
newly,
As an imperial princess decked thee duly.
Thy brow a crown of stately columns
wore;

The gates of thy arenas were sixscore;
Thou hadst thy theatre and hippodrome,
So to make mirth in thy resplendent
    home!

"We pass within the gates. A crowd ad-
    vances
Toward the theatre, with songs and
    dances.
We join them; and the eager thousands
    press
Through the cool colonnades of palaces;
As thou, mayhap, a mighty flood hast
    seen
Rush through a maple-shaded, deep
    ravine.

"Arrived,—oh, shame and sorrow!—we
    saw there
On the proscenium, with bosoms bare,
Young maidens waltzing to a languid
    lyre,
And high refrain sung by a shrill-voiced
    choir.
They in the mazes of their dance sur-
    rounded
A marble shape, whose name like 'Venus'
    sounded.

"The frenzied populace its clamor adds
Unto the cries of lasses and of lads,
Who shout their idol's praises o'er and
    o'er,—
'Hail to the Venus, of joy the bestower!
Hail to thee, Venus, goddess of all grace!
Mother of earth and of the Arlesian race!'

"The statue, myrtle-crowned, with nostrils
    wide
And head high-borne, appears to swell
    with pride
Amid the incense-clouds; when suddenly,
In horror of so great audacity,
Leaps Trophimus amid the maddened
    wretches,
And o'er the bewildered throng his arms
    outstretches.

" 'People of Arles!' in mighty tones he
    cried,
'Hear me, even for the sake of Christ who
    died!'
No more. But, smitten by his shaggy
    frown,
The idol groaned and staggered, and fell
    down,
Headlong, from off its marble pedestal.
Fell, too, the awe-struck dancers, one and
    all.

"Therewith went up, as 'twere, a single
    howl;
Choked were the gateways with a rabble
    foul,
Who through all Arles spread terror and
    dismay,
So that patricians tore their crowns away;
And all the enragèd youth closed round
    us there,
While flashed a thousand poniards in the
    air.

"Yet they recoiled;—whether it were the
    sight
Of us, in our salt-crusted robes bedight;
Or Trophimus' calm brow which beamed
    on them,
As wreathed with a celestial diadem;
Or tear-veiled Magdalene, who stood be-
    tween us,—
How tenfold fairer than their sculptured
    Venus!

"And the old saint resumed: 'Arlesian
    men,
Hear ye my message first; and slay me
    then,
If need be. Ye have seen your goddess
    famed
Shiver like glass when my God was but
    named:
Deem not, Arlesians, that the thing was
    wrought
By my poor, feeble voice; for we are
    naught.

" 'The God who laid, erewhile, your idol
        low
No lofty temple hath on the hill's brow;
But Day and Night see him alone up
        there!
And stern to sin, but generous to prayer,
Is he; and he hath made, with his own
        hand,
The sky, the sea, the mountains, and the
        land.

" 'One day he saw, from his high dwel-
        ling-place,
All his good things devoured by vermin
        base;
Slaves who drank hatred with their tears,
        and had
No comforter; and Evil, priestly clad,
At altars keeping school; and, in the
        street,
Maids who ran out the libertines to meet.

" 'Wherefore, to purge this vileness, and
        to end
Man's torment and our pilloried race be-
        friend,
He sent his own Son out of heaven down.
Naked and poor, wearing no golden
        crown,
He came, was of a virgin born, and saw
The daylight first pillowed on stable-
        straw.

" 'People of Arles, turn to this lowly One.
Ourselves can show the wonders he hath
        done,
Who were his comrades; and, in that far
        land
Where rolls the yellow Jordan, saw him
        stand,
In his white linen robe, amid the crowd,
Who him assailed with maledictions loud.

" 'Full gentle was his message: for he
        showed
That men should love each other, and that
        God
Is both almighty and all merciful;

And that the kingdom where he beareth
        rule
Descendeth not to tyrants, cheats, and
        scorners,
But to the poor, the lowly, and the
        mourners.

" 'These were his teachings: and he them
        attested
By walking on the waters; and arrested
Sickness most bitter by a glance, a word.
The dead, by the grim rampart un-
        deterred,
Came back to earth. This Lazarus whom
        you see
Once rotted in the grave. But jealousy

" 'Inflamed the bad hearts of the Jewish
        kings.
They led him to a mountain for these
        things,
And cruelly unto a tree-trunk nailed,
Spat on the sacred face, and coarsely
        railed
And lifted him on high.' Here all the
        throng
Brake into loud lament and sobbing
        strong.

" 'Mercy,' they cried, 'for our iniquities!
What shall we do the Father to appease?
Answer us, man of God! If blood must
        flow,
He shall have hecatombs.'—'Ah, no! ah,
        no!'
Replied the saint; 'but slay before the
        Father
Your vices and your evil passions rather!'

"So knelt, and prayed: 'Lord, thou dost
        not desire
Odor of slaying, sacrificial fire,
Or stately temples! Dearer far to thee
Is the bread given to those who fainting
        be;
Or sweet girl's timid coming, who doth
        bring

[213]

Her pure heart, like a May-flower, to her
    king.'

"As o'er the Apostle's lips, like sacred oil,
The word of God was flowing, 'gan recoil
The idols everywhere, and plunged at last
Adown the temple stairs; while tears
    dropped fast,
And rich and poor and working-men all
    ran
To kiss the garment of the holy man.

"Then bare Sidonius witness. In his
    night—
He was born blind—he led to the true
    light
The men of Arles. And Maximin, beside,
The resurrection of the Crucified
Set forth, and bade them turn from sin
    away.
Arles was baptized upon that very day.

"The Spirit of the Lord hurried us on,
Like wind upon a fire of shavings blown.
Then, as we turned of these to take fare-
    well,
Came messengers, before our feet who
    fell,
And passionately cried, 'O god-sent
    strangers!
Hear yet the story of our cruel dangers.

" 'To our unhappy city came the sound
Of marvels wrought and oracles new
    found.
She sends us hither. We are dead who
    stand
Before you! Such a monster wastes our
    land!
A scourge of God, greedy of human gore,
It haunts our woods and gorges. We im-
    plore

" 'Your pity. The beast hath a dragon's
    tail;
Bristles its back with many a horrid scale.
It hath six human feet, and fleet they are;
A lion's jaw; eyes red like cinnabar.

Its prey it hideth in a cavern lone,
Under a rock that beetles o'er the Rhone.

" 'Now day by day our fishermen grow
    few
And fewer.' Saying this, they wept anew
And bitterly,—the men of Tarascon.
Then maiden Martha said, serene and
    strong,
'Ready am I, and my heart yearns with
    pity.
Marcellus, haste: we two will save the
    city!'

"For the last time on earth we did em-
    brace,
With hope of meeting in a happy place,
And parted. Martial did Limoges choose;
Saturnius was wedded to Toulouse;
Eutropius was first this cause to plead,
And sow in stately Orange the good seed.

"And thou, sweet virgin, whither goest
    thou?
With step unfaltering and untroubled
    brow,
Martha her cross and holy-water carried
Against the dragon dire, and never
    tarried.
The wild men clomb the pine-trees round
    about,
The fray to witness and the maiden's rout.

"Startled from slumber in his darksome
    cave,
Thou shouldst have seen the leap the
    monster gave!
Yet vainly writhed he 'neath the holy
    dew,
And growled and hissed as Martha near
    him drew,
Bound with a frail moss-halter, and forth
    led
Snorting. Then all the people worshippèd.

" 'Huntress Diana art thou?' prostrate
    falling

Before the Christian maid, began they
    calling;
'Or yet Minerva, the all-wise and chaste?'
'Nay, nay!' the damsel answered in all
    haste:
'I am God's handmaid only.' And the
    crowd
She taught until with her to Him they
    bowed.

"Then by the power of her young voice
    alone,
She smote Avignon's rock; and from the
    stone
Welled faith in so pellucid stream, that,
    later,
Clements and Gregories in that fair water
Dipped holy chalices their thirst to slake,
And Rome long years did for her glory
    quake.

"And all Provence, regenerate, sang so
    clear
A hymn of praise, that God was glad to
    hear.
Hast thou not marked, when rain begins
    to fall,
How spring the drooping trees and grasses
    all,
How soon the foliage with joy will quiver?
So fevered souls drank of this cooling
    river!

"Thou fair Marseilles, who openest on the
    sea
Thy haughty eyes and gazest languidly,
As though naught else were worthy to
    behold,
And, though the winds rage, dreamest but
    of gold,
When Lazarus preached to thee, thou
    didst begin
Those eyes to close, and see the night
    within,

"And to the fountain of l'Huveaune[1]
    speeding,

The source whereof Magdalene's tears
    were feeding,
Didst wash thy sins away: and in this
    hour
Art proud once more; but other storms
    may lower.
Forget not, then, amid thy revelries,
Whose tears they are that bathe thine
    olive-trees!

"Dark cedars that on Mount Sambuco[2]
    grew,
Sheer ledges of the hills of Aix, and you,
Tall pines, clothing the flanks of Estérel,[3]
And junipers of Trevaresso,[4] tell
How thrilled your vales with joy, when,
    his cross bearing,
The bishop Maximin was through them
    faring.

"Seest thou one with white arms on her
    breast,
Who kneels and prays in yonder grotto,
    dressed
In the bright garment of her floating hair?
Poor sufferer! Her tender knees are bare,
And cruelly by the sharp flints are torn.
The moon, with pale torch, watches the
    forlorn

"And sad recluse. The woods in silence
    bow.
The angels hush their very heart-throbs
    now,
As, gazing through a crevice, they espy
A pearly tear fall from the lifted eye,
And haste the precious gem to gather up,
And keep for ever in a golden cup.

"Enough, O Magdalene! Thirty years ago,
The wind that in the forest whispers low
Bare thee the pardon of the Man divine!
The tears that the rock weeps are tears of
    thine.
These, like a snowfall softly sprinkled
    o'er,
Shall whiten woman's love for ever more!

"But naught can stay the mourner's gnaw-
ing grief.
Even the little birds bring not relief,
That flock around her, building many a
nest
On Saint Pilon; nor spirits of the blest,
Who lift and rock her in their arms of
love,
And soar, seven times a day, the vales
above.

"O Lord, be thine the glory! And may we
In thy full brightness and reality
Behold thee ever! Poor and fugitive,
We women did of thy great grace receive.
We, even we, touched by thy love
supernal,
Shed some faint reflex of the light eternal.

"Ye, Alpine peaks and all blue hills of
Baux,
Unto the latest hour of time will show
The traces of our teaching carved in
stone! 5
And so Death found us on the marshes
lone,
Deep in Camargue, encircled by the sea,
And from our day's long labor set us free.

"And as, on earth, haste all things to
decay,
Faded the memory of our tombs away.
While sang Provence her songs, and time
rolled on,
Till, as Durance is blended with the
Rhone,
Ended the merry kingdom of Provence,
And fell asleep upon the breast of France.

" 'France, take thy sister by the hand!' So
saith
Our land's last king, he drawing near to
death.
'On the great work the future has in store,
Together counsel take! Thou art the more
Strong; she, the more fair: and rebel night
Before your wedded glory shall take flight.'

"This did René. Therefore we sought the
king,
As on his feathers he lay slumbering,
And showed the spot where long our
bones had lain;
And he, with bishops twelve and courtly
train,
Came down into this waste of sand and
waves,
And found, among the salicornes, our
graves.

"Adieu, dear Mirèio! The hour flies;
And, like a taper's flame before it dies,
We see life's light within thy body flicker.
Yet, ere the soul is loosed,—come quick,
oh quicker,
My sisters!—we the hills of heaven must
scale
Or ever she arrive within the veil.

"Roses and a white robe we must prepare!
She is love's martyr and a virgin fair
Who dies to-day! With sweetest flowers
blow,
Celestial paths! and on Mirèio
Shine saintly splendors of the heavenly
host!
Glory to Father, Son, and Holy Ghost!"

NOTES TO CANTO XI.

1 L'HUVEAUNE, a small river that rises in
the Sainte Baume mountain (Var), flows
past Aubagne, and reaches the sea at Marseilles, near the Prado. A legend ascribes its
origin to the tears of St. Magdalene.
2 Sambuco, a mountain to the east of Aix.
3 Estérel, a mountain and forest in the Var.

4 Trevaresso, a mountain-chain between
the Touloulero and the Durance.
5 It has been seen, in the relation of the
holy Maries, that the bark of the proscribed
saints was cast upon the extremity of the isle
of Camargue. These first apostles to the
Gauls ascended the Rhone to Arles, and then
dispersed over the South. It is even held that

Joseph of Arimathea proceeded as far as England. Such is the Arlesian tradition. That of Baux continues the Odyssey of the holy women. It states that they went and preached the faith in the Alpines; and, to eternalize the memory of their doctrine, they miraculously carved their effigies on a rock. On the eastern side of Baux this mysterious and antique monument may still be seen. It is an enormous upright block, detached, and standing over the brink of a precipice. Upon its eastern side are sculptured three colossal faces, which are objects of veneration to all the people of the region.

CANTO XII.

DEATH.

As, when in orange-lands God's day is
    ending,
The maids let fly the leafy boughs, and,
    lending
A helpful hand, the laden baskets lift
On head or hip, and fishing-boats adrift
Are drawn ashore, and, following the sun,
The golden clouds evanish, one by one;

As the full harmonies of eventide,
Swelling from hill and plain and river-side
Along the sinuous Argens,—airy notes
Of pastoral pipe, love-songs, and bleat of
    goats,—
Grow fainter, and then wholly fade away,
And sombre night falls on the mountains
    gray;

Or as the last sigh of an anthem soft,
Or dying organ-peal, is borne aloft
O'er some old church, and on the wan-
    dering wind
Passes afar,—so passed the music twined
Of the three Maries' voices, heavenward
    carried.
For her, she seemed asleep; for yet she
    tarried

Kneeling: and was more fair than ever
    now,
So strange a freak of sunlight crowned
    her brow.
And here they who had sought her
    through the wild,
The aged parents, came, and found their
    child;
Yet stayed their faltering steps the portal
    under,

To gaze on her entranced with awe and
    wonder;

Then crossed their foreheads with the
    holy water,
And, hasting o'er the sounding flags,
    besought her
To wake. But, as a frighted vireo
Who spies the huntsman, shrieked
    Mirèio,
"O God, what is it? Father, mother, tell!
Where will you go?" And therewith
    swooned and fell.

The weeping mother lifts her head, and
    yearns
Over her. "My sweet, your forehead
    burns!
What means it?" And again, "No dream
    is this.
My own sweet child,—my very own it
    is,—
Low lying at my feet!" And then she wept
And laughed together; and old Ramoun
    crept

Beside them. "Little darling, it is I,
Your father, has your hand!" Then sud-
    denly
His anguish choked him, and he could
    but hold
And chafe and strive to warm those
    fingers cold.
Meanwhile the wind the mournful tidings
    bore
Abroad, and all Li Santo thronged the
    door,

And anxiously. "Bear the sick child," they
    say,

"Into the upper chapel, nor delay;
And let her touch the dear Saints' relics
    thus
Within their reliquaries marvellous;
Or kiss, at least, with dying lips!" And
    there
Two women raised, and bore her up the
    stair.

In this fair church, altars and chapels
    three,
Built one upon the other, you may see,
Of solid stone. In that beneath the ground
The dusky gypsies kneel, with awe pro-
    found,
Before Saint Sarah. One is over it
That hath God's altar. And one higher
    yet,

On pillars borne,—last of the sanc-
    tuaries,—
The small, funereal chapel of the Maries,
With heavenward vault. And here long
    years have lain
Rich legacy,—whence falleth grace like
    rain!—
The ever-blessed relics. Four great keys
Enlock the cypress chests that shelter
    these.

Once are they opened in each hundred
    years;
And happy, happy shall he be who nears
And sees and touches them! Upon the
    wave
Bright star and weather fair his bark shall
    have,
His trees be with abundant fruitage
    graced,
His faithful soul eternal blessing taste!

An oaken door, with carvings rich and
    rare,
Gift of the pious people of Beaucaire,
Closes the holy precinct. And yet surely
That which defends is not the portal
    purely,—
Is not the circling rampart; but the grace

Descending from the azure depths of
    space.

So to the chapel bare they the sick child,
While up the winding stair the folk de-
    filed;
And, as a white-robed priest threw wide
    the door,
They, entering, fell on the dusty floor,
As falls full-bearded barley when a squall
Hath smitten it, and worshipped one and
    all.

"O lovely Saints! O friendly Saints!" they
    said,
"O Saints of God, pity this poor young
    maid!"
"Pity her!" sobbed the mother. "I will
    bring,
When she is well, so fair an offering!
My flower-carved cross, my golden ring!"
    she cried,
"And tell the tale through town and
    country-side!"

"O Saints," groaned Ramoun, stumbling
    in the gloom,
While shook his aged head, "be kind, and
    come!
Look on this little one! She is my treas-
    ure!
She is my plover! Pretty beyond measure,
And good and meet for life! Send my old
    bones
To dung the mallows, but save her!" he
    moans.

And all the while Mirèio lay in swoon,
Till a breeze, with declining afternoon,
Blew from the tamarisks. Then, in the
    hope
To call her back to life, they lifted up
The flower of Lotus Farm, and tenderly
Laid on the tiles that overlook the sea.

There, from the doorway leading on the
    roof,—

[218]

The chapel's eye,—one may look far, far
    off,
Even to the pallid limit of the brine,
The blending and the separating line
'Twixt vaulted sky and weary sea explore,
And the great waves that roll for ever-
    more.

Insensate and unceasing and untiring,
They follow one another on; expiring,
With sullen roar, amid the drifted sand:
While vast savannas, on the other hand,
Stretch till they meet a heaven without a
    stain,
Unfathomed blue over unmeasured plain.

Only a light-green tamarisk, here and
    there,
Quivering in the faintest breath of air,
Or a long belt of salicornes, appears,
With swans that dip them in the desert
    meres,
With oxen roaming the waste moor at
    large,
Or swimming Vacarès from marge to
    marge.

At last the maiden murmured, but how
    weak
The voice! how vague the words! "On
    either cheek
I seem to feel a breeze,—one from the
    sea,
One from the land: and this refreshes me
Like morning airs; but that doth sore
    oppress
And burn me, and is full of bitterness."

So ceased. The people of Li Santo turn
Blankly from plain to ocean: then discern
A lad who nears them, at so fleet a pace
The dust in clouds is raised; and, in the
    race
Outstripped, the tamarisks are growing
    small,
And far behind the runner seem to fall.

Vincen it was. Ah, poor unhappy youth!

When Master Ambroi spake that sorry
    truth,
"My son, the pretty little lotus-spray
Is not for you!" he turned, and fled away;
From Valabrègo like a bandit fled,
To see her once again. And when they
    said

In Crau, "She in Li Santo must be
    sought,"
Rhone, marshes, weary Crau, withheld
    him not;
Nor stayed he ever in his frantic search
Till, seeing that great throng inside the
    church,
He rose on tiptoe deadly pale, and crying,
"Where is she?" And they answered, "She
    is dying

"Above there in the chapel." In despair
And all distraught, he hurried up the
    stair;
But, when his eye fell on the prostrate
    one,
Threw his hands wildly up. "What have
    I done,—
What have I done against my God and
    hers
To call down on me such a heavy curse

"From Heaven? Have I cut the throat of
    her
Who gave me birth? or at a church taper
Lighted my pipe? or dared I, like the
    Jews,
The holy crucifix 'mong thistles bruise?
What is it, thou accursèd year of God,—
Why must I bear so terrible a load?

" 'Twas not enough my darling they
    denied
To me! They've hunted her to death!" he
    cried;
And then he knelt, and kissed her
    passionately;
And all the people, when they saw how
    greatly

His heart was wrung, felt theirs too swell
    with pain,
And wept aloud above the stricken twain.

Then, as the sound of many waters,
    falling
Far down a rocky valley, rises calling
Unto the shepherd high the hills among,
Rose from the church a sound of full-
    choired song,
And all the temple trembled with the
    swell
Of that sweet psalm the Santen sing so
    well:—

  "Saints of God, ere now sea-faring
    On these briny plains of ours,
  Who have set a temple bearing
    Massy walls and snowy towers,

  "Watch the wave-tossed seaman
    kindly;
    Lend him aid the bark to guide;
  Send him fair winds, lest he blindly
    Perish on the pathless tide!

  "See the woman poor and sightless:
    Ne'er a word she uttereth;
  Dark her days are and delightless,—
    Darkness aye is worse than death.

  "Vain the spells they have told o'er
    her,
    Blank is all her memory.
  Queens of Paradise, restore her!
    Touch those eyes that they may
    see!

  "We who are but fishers lowly,
    Lift our hearts ere forth we go;
  Ye, the helpful saints and holy,
    Fill our nets to overflow.

  "So, when penitents heart-broken
    Sue for pardon at your door,
  Flood their souls with peace un-
    spoken,
    White flowers of our briny moor!"

So prayed the Santen, with tears and
    strong crying.
Then came the patrons to the maid low-
    lying,
And breathed a little life into her frame;
So that her wan eyes brightened, and
    there came
A tender flush of joy her visage over,
At the sweet sight of Vincen bent above
    her.

"Why love, whence came you? Do you
    mind, I pray,
A word you said down at the Farm one
    day,
Walking under the trellis, by my side?
You said, 'If ever any harm betide,
Hie thee right quickly to the holy Saints,
Who cure all ills and hearken all com-
    plaints.'

"Dearest, I would you saw my heart this
    minute,
As in a glass, and all the comfort in it!
Comfort and peace like a full fountain
    welling
Through all my happy spirit! There's no
    telling—
A grace beyond my uttermost desires!
Look, Vincen: see you not God's angel-
    choirs?"

Pausing, she gazed into the deep blue air.
It was as if she could discern up there
Wonderful things hidden from mortal
    men.
But soon her dreamy speech began again:
"Ah, they are happy, happy souls that
    soar
Aloft, tethered by flesh to earth no more!

"Did you mark, Vincen dear, the flakes
    of light
That fell when they began their heaven-
    ward flight?
If all their words to me had written been,
They would have made a precious book,
    I ween."

Here Vincen, who had striven his tears to
    stay,
Brake forth in sobs, and gave his anguish
    way.

"Would to God I *had* seen them ere they
    went!
Ah, would to God! Then to their white
    raiment,
Like a tick fastening, I would have cried,
'O queens of heaven! Sole ark where we
    may bide,
In this late hour, do what you will with
    me!
Maimed, sightless, toothless, I would
    gladly be;

" 'But leave my pretty little fairy sane
And sound!' " Here brake Mirèio in
    again:
"There are they, in their linen robes of
    grace!
They come!" and from her mother's fond
    embrace
Began to struggle wildly to be free,
And waved her hand afar toward the sea.

Then all the folk turned also to the main,
And under shading hands their eyes 'gan
    strain;
Yet, save the pallid limit of the brine,
The blending and the separating line
'Twixt sea and heaven, nought might
    they descry.
"Naught cometh," said they. But the
    child, "Oh, ay!

"Look closer! There's a bark, without a
    sail,
Wafted toward us by a gentle gale,
And they are on it! And the swell sub-
    sides
Before them, and the bark so softly
    glides!
Clear is the air and all the sea like glass,
And the sea-birds do homage as they
    pass!"

"Poor child! she wanders," murmured
    they; "for we
See only the red sunset on the sea!"
"Yet it is they! Mine eyes deceive me
    not,"
The sick one answered eagerly. "The
    boat—
Now low, now lifted—I see drawing near.
Oh, miracle of God!—the boat is here!"

Now was she paling, as a marguerite
Half-blown and smitten by a tropic heat,
While crouching Vincen, horror in his
    heart,
Or ere his well-belovèd quite depart
Hath her in charge unto our Lady given,
To the Saints of the chapel and of heaven.

Lit are the tapers, and, in violet stole
Begirt, the priest, to stay the passing soul,
Lays angel's bread to those dry lips of
    hers,
And the last unction so administers;
Then of her body the seven parts anoints
With holy oil, as holy church appoints.

The hour was calm. Upon the tiles no
    word
Save the *oremus* of the priest was heard.
The last red shaft of the declining day
Struck on the wall and passed, and
    heaven turned gray.
The sea's long waves came slowly up the
    shore,
Brake with a murmur soft, and were no
    more.

Beside the maid knelt father, mother,
    lover,
And hoarsely sobbed at intervals above
    her;
Till once again her lips moved, and she
    spake:
"Now is the parting close at hand! So
    take
My hand, and press it quickly, dears. Lo,
    now
The glory grows on either Mary's brow!

"The pink flamingoes flock from the
Rhone shore,
The tamarisks in blossom all adore.
The dear Saints beckon me to them," she
said.
"They tell me I need never be afraid:
They know the constellations of the skies;
Their bark will take us quick to Para-
dise!"

"My little pet," said Ramoun, quite undone,
"You will not go, and leave the home so
lone!
Why have I felled my oaks with such
ado?
The zeal that nerved me only came of
you.
If the hot sun on sultry glebe o'ertook
me,
I thought of you, and heat and thirst
forsook me."

"Dear father, if a moth shall sometime fly
About your lamp at night, that will be I.
But see! the Saints are standing on the
prow!
They wait. I'm coming in a moment now!
Slowly I move, good Saints, for I am
ailing."
"It is too much!" the mother brake out,
wailing.

"Oh, stay with me! I cannot let you die.
And, when you're well, Mirèio, by and by
We'll go some day to Aunt Aurano's,
dear,
And carry pomegranates. Do you hear?
Maiano is not distant from our home;
And, in one day, one may both go and
come."

"Not very distant, mother,—that I know;
But all alone thou wilt the journey go!
Now give me my white raiment, mother
mine.
Oh, how the mantles of the Maries
shine!

Sawest thou ever such a dazzling sight?
The snow upon the hillsides is less white!"

"O thou," cried the dark weaver, "who
didst ope
The palace of thy love to me, my hope,
My queen, my all! A blossoming alms
thou gavest;
The mire of my low life in thine thou
lavest,
Till it shines like a mirror, and dost place
Me in eternal honor by thy grace.

"Pearl of Provence! of my young days the
sun!
Shall it be ever said of such an one,
I saw upon her forehead the death-dew?
Shall it be said, puissant Saints, of you,
You looked unmoved upon her mortal
pain,
Letting her clasp your sacred sill in
vain?"

Slowly the maiden answered, "My poor
friend,
What is it doth affright you, and offend?
Believe me, dear, the thing that we call
death
Is a delusion. Lo! it vanisheth,
As a fog when the bells begin their
pealing;
As dreams with daylight through the
window stealing.

"I am not dying! See, I mount the boat
With a light foot! And now we are afloat!
Good-by! good-by! We are drifting out to
sea.
The waves encompass us, and needs must
be
The very avenue to Paradise,
For all round they touch the azure skies!

"Gently they rock us now. And overhead
So many stars are shining! Ah," she said,
"Among those worlds one surely may be
found

Where two may love in peace! Hark,
    Saints, that sound!
Is it an organ played across the deep?"
Then sighed, and fell, as it had been,
    asleep.

And, by her smiling lips, you might have
    guessed
That yet she spake. Only the Santen
    pressed
About the sleeper in a mournful band,
And, with a taper passed from hand to
    hand,
Signed the cross o'er her. While, as turned
    to stone,
The parents gazed on what themselves
    had done.

To them her form is all enrayed with
    light.
Vainly they feel her cold, they see her
    white:
The awful stroke they comprehend not
    now.
But, soon as Vincen marked the level
    brow,
The rigid arms, the sweet eyes wholly
    veiled,
"See you not she is dead?" he loudly
    wailed.

"Quite dead?" And therewith fiercely
    wrung his hands,
As he of old had wrung the osier-strands,
And threw his naked arms abroad. "My
    own!"
He cried, "they will not weep for you
    alone:
With yours, the trunk of my life too they
    fell.
'Dead' was I saying? 'Tis impossible:

"A demon whispered me the word, no
    doubt!
Tell me, in God's name, ye who stand
    about,—
Ye who have seen dead women ere to-
    day,—

If, passing through the gates, they smile
    that way.
Her look is well-nigh merry, do you see?
Why do they turn their heads away from
    me,

"And weep? This means, I think, that all
    is o'er.
Her pretty prattle I shall hear no more:
Still is the voice I loved!" All hearts were
    thrilled;
Tears rushed like rain, and sobs would
    not be stilled.
One sound went up of weeping and
    lament,
Till the waves on the beach returned the
    plaint.

So when in some great herd a heifer dies,
About the carcass where it starkly lies
Nine following eves the beasts take up
    their station,
And seem to mourn after their speechless
    fashion;
The sea, the plain, the winds, thereover
    blowing,
Echo nine days with melancholy low-
    ing,—

"Poor Master Ambroi!" Vincen wandered
    on,
"Thou wilt weep heavy tears over thy son!
And now, good Santen, one last wish is
    mine,—
Bury me with my love, below the brine;
Scoop in the oozy sand a crib for two:
Tears for so great a mourning will not do.

"And a stone wall about the basin set,
So the sea flow not in, and part us yet!
Santen, I trust you! Then, while they are
    beating
Their brows, and with remorse her name
    repeating,
There at the farm where her home used
    to be,
Far from the unrest of the upper sea,

"Down in the peaceful blue we will abide,
My oh so pretty, alway side by side;
And you shall tell me of your Maries
over,
Over, until with shells the great storms
cover."
Here the crazed weaver on the corse him
threw,

And from the church arose the psalm
anew.

.   .   .   .   .

"So, when penitents heart-broken
Sue for pardon at your door,
Flood their souls with peace un-
spoken,
White flowers of our briny moor!"

THE LIFE AND WORKS OF
FRÉDÉRIC MISTRAL

By ANDRÉ CHAMSON

I WAS SIXTEEN when I first met *Mirèio*. To celebrate my birthday, I had set out on a journey. It was my first one—a long journey, from Alès to Arles, from the Cévennes to Provence. I had discovered the avenue of tombs, the amphitheater, and the St. Trophime cloister. A whole procession of Venuses and marble dancers had guided my steps to the Arlaten Museum, which Mistral dedicated to Provence after receiving the Nobel Prize.

I had bought *Mirèio* in this sanctuary of poetry and folk tradition and, as I sat in the train on my way home, I had immersed myself in the poem. Wonder of wonders! I understood it in the original and seemed to hear the voice of the fifteen-year-old girl with eyes like the dew. There she stood before me, a living being. For *Mirèio* is not a book, but a real person who takes you by the hand and leads you to Mistral, just as a young girl you meet in the heart of the countryside may take you to her father's house and introduce you to him. There was a time when *Mirèio* actually drew her new friends to the poet's home, in the gardens of Maillane, in front of the grey wall of the Alpilles and the black line of cypress trees. For many men, whether young or old, meeting *Mirèio* is like a thunderbolt.

One such man was Bonaparte Wyse (an Irish gentleman, the son of Sir Thomas

Wyse and Laetitia, daughter of Prince Lucien). When passing through Avignon on his way to Italy, he bought the twelve-canto poem, which had only just been published, at the Roumanille bookshop and devoured it from cover to cover that night. Just as I did later on my Arles journey, he saw the girl of fifteen coming toward him and the next morning, in the snow and icy wind of Christmas, he set out on foot and followed her to the poet's house, where he formed a friendship that was to be lifelong. I was not so fortunate. Mistral had been dead for two years when I met the girl who would have led me to his home—but she led me to his works, where I found him still alive.

On that day the sixteen-year-old boy, as I was then, fell in love with the girl of fifteen. I am now nearly sixty; she is still fifteen and the centuries are powerless in the face of this immortal youth which makes us realize more fully the value of our own and takes us back to ourselves beyond the bounds of time.

Since then I have not ceased to be under the spell of Provençal poetry and for more than forty years I have lived on intimate terms with the master of Maillane. Without every trying to learn them, I know thousands of lines of *Mirèio*, *Calendau*, *Islands of Gold*, and *The Song of the Rhône*. They have their place in my memory side by side with the poetry of Hugo, Nerval, Vigny, Baudelaire, and Valéry. They bring to my mind echoes of the songs of Peire Vidal, Marcabrun, and the Countess of Die, and some tercets by Dante. All these songs make up an invisible universe for me which is rooted in permanence and gives the one I live in its depth.

Almost thirty years ago, when I was still very young, I received an invitation from some learned Romance language scholars at the University of Berlin. Before the great madness overtook her, Germany had kept touch with all the traditions of our Western culture. My hosts upheld them with an enthusiasm not untinged with charming naiveness and, in the evening, when we were gathered round a blazing fire, they asked me to read aloud some passages from Mistral. We know Provençal, they told me, but we have difficulty in hearing its music—perhaps this music is the only secret that learning does not teach.

Edward Wechssler, who interpreted the poets, from Heraclitus to Paul Valéry, in the same way that people consult the stars, smiled as he handed me an old, well-thumbed copy of *Mirèio*. I took the book; it was open at the beginning of the first canto. I closed it and gently laid it on the edge of the fireplace.

"Why refuse us this pleasure?" asked my hosts.

"In Provence," I replied, half-jokingly, half in earnest, "we all know the beginning of the first canto of *Mirèio* by heart" —and I started to recite it.

In thirty years I have not forgotten a single line.

I have not told this story to marvel at my memory; what seems miraculous to me is the power of poems that we cannot forget. The only songs that remain alive in us are those that possess a special virtue and it is this virtue that imprints them on our mind. Mistral's poetry has

this power. Once you have met *Mirèio*, you will hear her whispering to you all your life.

I do not want to confine myself to expressing my admiration for Mistral's works. As a French writer, I must also attempt to explain what Provençal poetry meant to many of the writers of France. Although *Mirèio* was created in solitude by an unknown young poet working for seven years in the heart of his province, far from the tumult of Paris, it was in Paris that she set her foot on the road to fame when a great French writer, Lamartine, took her by the hand. This great poet was in exile right in the heart of his homeland—the exile of destitution and old age —and he was the first to discover the girl from Provence. His name was famous enough for a young boy fresh from his provincial solitude to think that his whole future was at stake when he brought his poem to the great man.

It was in this spirit of veneration that Mistral took his *Mirèio* to Lamartine. The house where the poet was living at the time in the rue de la Ville-l'Evêque has now disappeared, but we still have some engravings from which we can imagine what it was like, with its low wall crowned by railing, its small garden, and its front steps sheltered by a porch. This is where Lamartine received the young poet, who came to see him several times in the company of Adolphe Dumas, a Provençal turned Parisian who had nevertheless remained faithful to Provence and had visited Mistral while he was writing his poem.

In his fortieth "Entretien," Lamartine tells of his meeting with *Mirèio*. "The young man recited a few lines to us," he says, "in the soft but virile Provençal idiom, reminiscent at times of Latin, at times of Attic grace or again of Tuscan roughness. My familiarity with Latin provincial dialects—for up to the age of twelve I spoke nothing else in the mountains where I grew up—helped me to understand this beautiful idiom."

We need only reread the beginning of *Mirèio*, as Mistral must have done, first in French, then in Provençal, and finally in English to understand the great effect it had on Lamartine:

> Toi, Seigneur Dieu de ma patrie,/qui naquis parmi les pâtres,/enflamme mes paroles et donne-moi du souffle!/Tu le sais: parmi la verdure,/au soleil et aux rosées,/quand les figues mûrissent,/ vient l'homme, avide comme un loup, dépouiller entièrement l'arbre de ses fruits.

> Tu, Segnour Diéu de ma patrio,
> Que nasquères dins la pastriho,
> Enfioco mi paraulo e douno-me d'alen!
> Lou sabes: entre la verduro,
> Au soulèu em'i bagnaduro,
> Quand li figo so fan maduro,
> Vèn l'ome aloubati desfrucha l'aubre en plen.

> God of my country, who didst have
> Thy birth
> Among poor shepherds when Thou
> wast on earth,
> Breathe fire into my song! Thou know-
> est, my God,
> How, when the lusty summer is abroad,
> And figs turn ripe in sun and dew,
> comes he—
> Brute, greedy man—and quite despoils
> the tree.

> Mais sur l'arbre dont il brise les ra-meaux,/toi, toujours tu élèves quelque branche/où l'homme insatiable ne puisse porter la main,/belle pousse hâtive/ et odorante et virginale,/beau fruit mûr à la Magdeleine,/où vient l'oiseau de l'air apaiser sa faim.

> Mais sus l'aubre qu'éu espalanco,
> Tu toujour quihes quauco branco

> Ounte l'ome abrama noun posque aussa
> la man,
> Bello jitello proumierenco
> E redoulènto e vierginenco,
> Bello frucho madalenenco
> Ounte l'aucèu de l'èr se vèn leva la fam.

> Yet on that ravaged tree Thou savest
> oft
> Some little branch inviolate aloft,
> Tender and airy up against the blue,
> Which the rude despoiler cannot win
> unto:
> Only the birds shall come and banquet
> there,
> When, at St. Magdalene's, the fruit is
> fair.

> Moi, je la vois, cette branchette,/ et sa fraîcheur provoque mes désirs!/Je vois, au (souffle des) brises, s'agiter dans le ciel/ son feuillage et ses fruits immor-tels . . . /Dieu beau, Dieu ami, sur les ailes/ de notre langue provençale,/ fais que je puisse atteindre la branche des oiseaux!

> Iéu la vese, aquelo branqueto
> E sa frescour me fai lingueto!
> Iéu vese, i ventoulet, boulega dins lou
> céu
> Sa ramo e sa frucho inmourtalo . . .
> Bèu Diéu, Diéu ami, sus lis alo
> De nosto lengo prouvençalo,
> Fai que posque avera la branco dis
> aucèu!

> Methinks I see yon airy little bough:
> It mocks me with its freshness even
> now;
> The light breeze lifts it, and it waves
> on high
> Fruitage and foliage that cannot die.
> Help me, dear God, on our Provençal
> speech,
> To soar until the birds' own home I
> reach!

Lamartine was not the only French writer to be captivated by the songs of Provence's poets. In the past, a long tradition linked the two literatures—so close to, yet so distinct from one another. By the eleventh century, great poetry, full of erudition yet young and robust, was already flourishing in the southern regions of what was later France. A new song made itself heard. Possibly handed down by Arab poets, it linked up with the Platonic traditions of antiquity. The art of the poets of the *langue d'Oc* was carried round the points of the compass to Italy, Catalonia, France, Spain, Portugal, and Germania. The songbirds fell silent after the disasters of the Crusades and, in Mistral's words, the *langue d'Oc* made its home with shepherds and sailors until its revival in the last century with the poetry of the Félibrige.

This revival of Provençal poetry aroused a friendly response in many French writers. If Lamartine's praise enraged Sainte-Beuve—"Are you the man they dared compare with Homer?"—his rage is a mere sign of frustration. Though Barbey d'Aurevilly thought it necessary to regret that Mistral did not look "more like a shepherd or more typically native of Provence," he still acknowledged the greatness of the poem. But the writer who understood Félibrige best of all was Stéphane Mallarmé. "You who are one of the diamonds of the Milky Way," he wrote to Mistral, wishing that he could live in Avignon, on the banks of the Rhône, in the midst of his friends the poets of Provence.

No doubt Mallarmé's friendship for Mistral scarcely fits in with the idea that most of Mallarmé's admirers have of Provençal poetry and of *Mirèio* in particular. What a strange fate this work had—although passionately admired, it was sometimes judged ironically or even with an irritation verging on hostility. Admit-

tedly, this hostility is almost solely confined to France. Even though men as different as Lamartine, Barbey d'Aurevilly, Emile Zola, Ernest Renan, Alphonse Daudet, Anatole France, Mallarmé, Barrès, and Maurras considered it a great work, even ranking among the greatest, it is in France, and virtually in France alone, that its detractors are to be found. For too many Frenchmen, *Mirèio* is only a "regionalistic" poem, the last offshoot of an outmoded art.

These detractors of Provençal poetry, however, are all admirers of Provençal art—be it that of the Avignon school at the end of the Middle Ages, a plastic reflection of the civilization of the troubadours, or the art of Cezanne and Van Gogh, corresponding to the Provençal revival during the last century. No doubt they are unable to feel that they are in the presence of a national art which can be expressed equally well in poetry and in painting, putting before us one and the same art of living. This national art belongs to a nation with no frontiers, a nation that has never existed but exists nevertheless beyond the world of appearances, as it were in an invisible world. To understand it and grasp it in its unity, its continuity over more than a thousand years, we have to be able to discover what, at the end of his life, Mistral called "the pure symbol."

This "pure symbol" or, as Mistral himself defined it, "this mirage of glory and victory—which, in the depths of the transient centuries—reveals a flash of Beauty to us," does, however, have one of the major features of any true nation that actually exists in flesh and blood. It has a language. This language—Provençal—is one of the ingredients that make up the beauty of this Provençal poetry. But, for present-day Frenchmen, the main problem arising from the existence of the Provençal language is bilingualism. A century ago, when *Mirèio* was created,

Provençal writers were already all bilingual and most of them, starting with Mistral, translated their works into French themselves. At present, all those who understand Provençal also know French. This is a rare phenomenon in our day, although we are living in a polyglot age—but polyglot only for buying and selling, acting or giving orders, for we seem to have lost the sense of cultural bilingualism which, throughout the centuries, was the basic requirement of all living humanism.

An ability to think and listen in two languages, to understand the world through two different tongues marked all the great periods of Western cultural history. Latin poets understood Greek ones; Dante knew Provençal—so well, in fact, that he used it to write a few tercets of his *Divine Comedy*. In the Middle Ages every educated man knew Latin and his own national language, whether French, Flemish, German, or English. In the seventeenth and eighteenth centuries, French had taken the place of Latin as an international means of communication. Countless other examples could be quoted from all over the world, recalling the importance of the Chinese language and Chinese poetry for Japanese poets, or that of Sanskrit for Indian poets, or the fact that Solomos, founder of modern Greek poetry, first wrote in Italian before adopting everyday spoken Greek and making it a new standard language.

The French should consider themselves very fortunate in that the force of circumstances and the natural interplay of the chance events of history have placed them in a position for which the greatest humanists, the loftiest and most truly human minds have always striven—the ability to understand life and its poetry through two mother tongues, and to gain insight into the world through the use of two languages, just as we look at it through our two eyes. This is the position today of the admirers of *Mirèio,* who can hear her speak her mother tongue and understand her as Lamartine did when Mistral brought the "young girl from Provence" to his home.

But language is only a means to an end, a "way" as they say in the east. What is important is what *Mirèio* teaches us. This fifteen-year-old girl is wiser than the philosophers of our day, who know everything but have turned their backs on wisdom. She takes us into a country with no frontiers, where creatures have made a pact with the creation that surrounds them. Here, more than anywhere else, we can learn that civilizations are mortal—but we learn too that they cannot disappear. In this world of the "pure symbol," something eternal blossoms afresh with each metamorphosis, as did the language of Provence itself: there is always a new beginning.

André Chamson, historian and novelist, is a member of the Académie Française and holder of the Grand Croix of the French Legion of Honor.
Translated by Annie Jackson.

THE 1904 PRIZE

By GUNNAR AHLSTRÖM

The way in which Frédéric Mistral was nominated for the Prize was neither lyrical nor inspiring: it was the result of a conspiracy on the part of some university scholars, particularly the Germans.

"I do not know what this great Nobel Prize consists of for which my name has been put forward by German Provençalists—another thing that I did not know about," wrote Mistral to Gaston Paris on January 19, 1901. He knew that forces were at work to gain a Prize for his poetry; he also knew that they came from across the Rhine. There was, of course, a good deal of real enthusiasm in this German interest in the Provençal revival—an old language was being transformed into living literature. But the Germans, at the same time, demoted France to the level of a folk pastoral, comparable to the Germans' notion of industrial Sweden, which they regarded as an open-air museum where Dalecarlians in national costume sing their village ballads. We catch a glimpse of *Realpolitik* behind a condescending sentimentality. There is a belief that rivals can be ruled by dividing them, by arousing disruptive particularism within their frontiers. This foreshadows World War I, when the Germans tried with all their might to encourage the Gaelic revolt in Ireland. And even later, during Hitler's war, was there not open speculation about na-tionalism in Brittany and Scottish separatism?

Edward Koschwitz, Professor of Romance Language and Literature at the University of Marburg, introduced himself by correspondence to the Nobel Committee and organized an offensive by a whole group of colleagues in German universities. Mistral's candidacy was supported by a flood of recommendations from professors of Romance languages at Jena, Freiburg, Breslau, the German University in Prague, and Geneva University. With equal zeal testimonials were collected from the Athenaeum at Forcalquier and the Escolo de Lar in Aix, "showing how greatly the poet is loved in his own province." No natural discretion held Koschwitz back. With a good grace of dubious tact he poached on the preserves of the Académie Française—if they had remembered Mistral in time, they would never have proposed Sully-Prudhomme for the 1901 Prize, he stated with the self-assurance of someone who knows all there is to know about the matter.

Mistral was amazed at all this fuss. He knew that people were working for him, but he had no illusions. "This time," he wrote jocularly in March 1901, "the bird's branch is a little too high up and, besides, surely everyone must live?" Imbued with this wisdom, he did not share the indignation of his propagandists when the Prize was awarded to Sully-Prudhomme. On the contrary, as a good Frenchman, he was able to welcome the award to a fellow countryman. The next year it was Mommsen's turn and, in 1903, Björnson's. Each year Mistral's name had been put forward by various Scandinavian scholars and Romanists. *Mirèio* and *Calendau* were no longer the exclusive domain of scholars, and the band of admirers grew. Sweden, with her own provincial culture finding ample expression in her literature, was well able to understand a poet of Mistral's genre. He did, in fact, soon become a personal favorite of the influential permanent secretary, C. D. af Wirsén. In the summer of 1904 the Nobel Committee decided to propose Mistral.

But with the first autumn frosts an unfortunate shadow was cast on these efforts, one of those ridiculous accidents that may sometimes influence the world of literature. A translation of *Mirèio* appeared in Sweden in September. It was so bad that some of it was like a parody and, worst of all, its author was a member of the Committee. There were some fears that the Swedish public might judge the masterpiece on the basis of its translation which, in view of the translator's official position, might be thought to correspond exactly with the Academy's idea of Mistral. These considerations called for caution. At its meeting in November, the Academy decided to divide the 1904 Prize in half, with the Spanish writer José Echegaray sharing it with Mistral. This Solomonic judgment would make it possible to honor two Romance writers and provide an elegant way of admitting Spain to the Nobel community.

Mistral no doubt appreciated the Academy's reasons for the award. They praised "the fresh originality and true inspiration of his poetic production, which faithfully reflects the natural spirit of his people." The poet expressed his thanks to the Academy on November 23 in Provençal: "The material value of this great award will help me, through subsidies and foundations, to continue to work for the Provençal revival to which I have dedicated my writings and my life, and for the preservation of all our best folk traditions. But the worldwide renown of the Nobel Prize will have an incomparable effect, for the benefit and glorification of our Provençal language." Mistral ended with a magnificent gesture, worthy of a good Provençal, sending a kiss of kinship to the grandson of Marshal Bernadotte: "As a Provençal and a southern Frenchman, I am delighted to receive a favor from a country whose ruling dynasty has a few drops of Béarn blood—Provençal blood —in its veins."

Because of his age, Mistral was unable to attend the ceremony in Stockholm, and he sent no formal acceptance speech.

Translated by Annie Jackson.

Theodor Mommsen

1902

"The greatest living master of the art
of historical writing, with special
reference to his monumental work,
The History of Rome"

Illustrated by DECARIS

PRESENTATION ADDRESS

By C. D. AF WIRSÉN

PERMANENT SECRETARY
OF THE SWEDISH ACADEMY

THE SECOND PARAGRAPH of the Nobel statutes states that "Literature" should include not only belles-lettres, "but also other writings that in form or content show literary value." This definition sanctions the award of the Nobel Prize for Literature to philosophers, writers on religious subjects, scientists, and historians, provided that their work is distinguished by artistic excellence of presentation as well as by the high value of its content.

The Swedish Academy this year had to make its choice among many brilliant names that have been suggested. In giving the Prize to the historian Theodor Mommsen, whose name had been proposed by eighteen members of the Royal Prussian Academy of Sciences, it has selected one of the most celebrated among them.

A bibliography of Mommsen's published writings, compiled by Zangemeister on the occasion of his seventieth birthday, contains nine hundred and twenty items. One of Mommsen's most important projects was editing the *Corpus Inscriptionum Latinarum* (1867–1959), a Herculean task despite the assistance of many learned collaborators, for not only did Mommsen contribute to each of the fifteen volumes but the organization of the total work is his lasting achievement. A veritable hero in the field of scholarship, Mommsen has done original and seminal research in Roman law, epigraphy, numismatics, the chronology of Roman history, and general Roman history. Even an otherwise prejudiced critic admitted that he can speak with equal authority on an Iapygian inscription, a fragment of Appius Caecus, and agriculture in Carthage. The educated public knows him chiefly through his *Römische Geschichte* (*History of Rome*, 1854–55, 1885), and it is this monumental work in particular that induced the Swedish Academy to award the Nobel Prize to him.

[235]

The work began to appear in 1854; volume four has not yet been published, but in 1885 he brought out volume five, a masterly description of the state of the provinces under the Empire, a period so close to our own that the descriptions could be made to apply to more recent fields of activity which are mentioned in the Nobel statutes and which one can use as a starting point in assessing the total work of the writer. Mommsen's *Römische Geschichte,* which has been translated into many languages, is distinguished by its thorough and comprehensive scholarship as well as its vigorous and lively style. Mommsen combines his command of the vast material with acute judgment, strict method, a youthful vigor, and that artistic presentation which alone can give life and concreteness to a description. He knows how to separate the wheat from the chaff, and it is difficult to decide whether one should give higher praise and have more admiration for his vast knowledge and the organizing power of his mind or for his intuitive imagination and his ability to turn carefully investigated facts into a living picture. His intuition and his creative power bridge the gap between the historian and the poet. Mommsen felt this relationship when in the fifth volume of his Roman history he said that imagination is the mother not only of poetry but also of history. Indeed, the similarities are great. Ranke's detached objectivity is reminiscent of Goethe's calm greatness, and England did right in burying Macaulay in the poets' corner of Westminster Abbey.

In a few bold strokes Mommsen has drawn the character of the Roman people and shown how the Roman's obedience to the state was linked to the obedience of son to father. With extraordinary skill he has unrolled the huge canvas of Rome's development from slight beginnings to world rule. He has shown how with the growth of the Empire new tasks outgrew the old and stubbornly preserved constitution; how the sovereignty of the *comitia* gradually became a fiction, only incidentally realized by demagogues for their own purposes; how the Senate took care of public affairs in an honorable manner, but how the old aristocratic oligarchy that had once served its purpose failed to meet new demands; how a frequently unpatriotic capitalism abused its powers in political speculations; and how the disappearance of the free peasant led to disastrous consequences for the commonwealth.

Mommsen also has demonstrated how the frequent change of consuls hampered the unified and consistent conduct of wars, which led to the prolongation of military commands; how at the same time the generals became increasingly independent and how Caesarism became a necessity for many reasons but especially because of the lack of institutions commensurate with the needs of the actual Empire; and how absolutism in many cases would have caused less hardship than the oligarchic rule. False grandeur vanishes before the uncompromising eye of the historian, the wheat is separated from the chaff and, like his admired Caesar, Mommsen has a clear eye for practical needs and that freedom from illusions which he praised in the conquerors of Gaul.

Various critics have objected that Mommsen is sometimes carried away by his genius for subjective passionate judgments, especially in his frequently unfavorable remarks concerning the last partisans of dying freedom and the opponents of Caesar, and concerning those who wavered between the parties during those hard times. Objections, perhaps not always totally unjustified, have been raised to Mommsen's admiration of the power of genius even where it breaks the law, as well as to his statement that in history, which has no trials for high treason, a revolutionary can be a farsighted and praiseworthy statesman. On the other hand, it must be emphasized that Mommsen never glorifies brute power, but extols that power which serves the high goals of the state; and one has to record his firmly stated conviction that "praise that is corrupted by the genius of evil sins against the sacred spirit of history." It has also been remarked that Mommsen occasionally applies to ancient conditions modern terms that cannot fully correspond to them (*Junkertum,* the Roman Coblenz, *Camarilla, Lanzknechte, Marschälle, Sbirren,* etc.). But this method of stressing the similarities between historical phenomena of different ages is not a product of Mommsen's imagination but of his learning, which has at its disposal many analogues from various periods of history. If it adds too much color to the narrative, it also adds freshness.

Mommsen, by the way, is not a historical materialist. He admires Polybius, but he blames him for overlooking the ethical powers of man, and for having a too mechanical *Weltanschauung.* Concerning C. Gracchus, the inspired revolutionary whose measures he sometimes praises and sometimes blames, he says that every state is built on sand unless the ruler and the governed are tied together by a common morality. A healthy family life is to him the core of the nation. He severely condemns the curse of the Roman system of slavery. He has seen how a people that still has energy can be morally strengthened by disaster, and there is a pedagogical truth in his words that just as Athens' freedom was born out

[237]

of the flames with which the Persians ravaged the Acropolis, so today the unity of Italy resulted from the conflagration that the Gauls caused in Rome.

Learned, lively, sarcastic, and versatile, Mommsen has shed light on the domestic and foreign affairs of Rome, her religion, literature, law, finances, and customs. His descriptions are magnificent; no reader can forget his accounts of the battles of Lake Trasimene, Cannae, Aleria, and Pharsalus. His character sketches are equally lively. In sharp and clear outlines we see the profiles of the "political incendiary," C. Gracchus; of Marius in his last period "when insanity became a power and one plunged into abysses to avoid giddiness"; of Sulla, in particular, an incomparable portrait that has become an anthology piece; of the great Julius Caesar, Mommsen's Roman ideal; of Hannibal, Scipio Africanus, the victor of Zama—not to mention the lesser figures whose features have been drawn clearly by the master's hand.

With regard to these portraits the historian Treitschke has said that *Römische Geschichte* is the finest historical work of the nineteenth century and that Mommsen's Caesar and Hannibal must cause enthusiasm in every young man, every young soldier.

One finds in Mommsen a curious combination of qualities. He is profoundly learned, a sober analyst of sources; yet he can be passionate in his judgments. He describes in great detail and with profound knowledge the inner workings of government and the complexities of economics; but at the same time his battle scenes and character sketches are brilliant. He is perhaps above all an artist, and his *Römische Geschichte* is a gigantic work of art. Belles-lettres, that noble flower of civilization, receives the last mention in Nobel's will; Mommsen will always be counted among its prime representatives. When he delivered the first volume of his *Römische Geschichte* to the publisher, he wrote, "the labor has been immense," and on the fiftieth anniversary of his doctorate he spoke fervently of the boundless ocean of scholarship. But in his completed work the labor, however great it may have been, has been obliterated as in any true work of art which receives its own form from nature. The reader treads on safe ground, unmolested by the surf. The great work stands before our eyes as if cast in metal.

In his inaugural address in Cambridge, Lord Acton justly called Mommsen one of the greatest writers of the present, and from this point of view especially Mommsen deserves a great *literary* prize. The most recent German edition of *Römische Geschichte* has just appeared. There are no changes. The work has retained its freshness; it is a monument which, though it may not possess the soft beauty of marble, is as perennial as bronze. The scholar's hand is visible everywhere, but so is the poet's. And, indeed, Mommsen did write poetry in his youth. The *Liederbuch dreier Freunde (Songbook of Three Friends)* of 1843 is witness that he might have become a servant of the muses if, in his own words, circumstances had not brought it about that "what with folios and with prose/not every bud turned out a rose." Mommsen the historian was a friend of Theodor Storm and an admirer of Mörike; even in advanced years he translated works by the Italian poets Carducci and Giacosa.

Arts and sciences have often shown the capacity to keep their practitioners young in spirit. Mommsen is both a scholar and an artist, and at eighty-five he is young in his works. Even in old age, as late is 1895, he made valuable contributions to the Proceedings of the Prussian Academy of Sciences.

The medal of the Nobel Prize for Literature depicts a young man listening to the inspirations of the muses. Mommsen is an old man, but he possesses the fire of youth, and one rarely realizes as clearly as when reading Mommsen's *Römische Geschichte* that Clio was one of the muses. That example of pure history aroused our enthusiasm when we were young; it has kept its power over our minds, as we learn when we reread it now in our older days. Such is the power of historical scholarship if it is combined with great art.

For the above reasons we are sending today a homage from the country of Erik Gustaf Geijer to Theodor Mommsen.

There was no formal Acceptance Speech by Mommsen.

THE HISTORY OF ROME

By THEODOR MOMMSEN

Edited by Dero A. Saunders *and* John H. Collins

[Excerpt]

X
Joint Rule of Pompey and Caesar

Among the democratic chiefs who from the time of Caesar's consulship were recognized almost officially as the joint rulers of the commonwealth, in the public view Pompey clearly occupied the first place. It was before him, whom the Optimates called "the private dictator," that Cicero prostrated himself in vain. Against him were directed the sharpest sarcasms of Bibulus, and the most envenomed conversational arrows in the private chambers of the opposition.

This was only to be expected. According to the facts before the public, Pompey was indisputably the first general of his time, while Caesar was a dexterous political leader and orator of undeniable talents, but notoriously unwarlike and indeed of effeminate temperament. Such opinions had long been current, and it could not be expected that the highborn rabble would trouble itself to discover the real state of affairs and abandon established platitudes because of obscure feats of heroism on the Tagus. Caesar obviously played the part of a mere adjutant who executed for his chief the work which Flavius, Afranius, and other less capable instruments had attempted unsuccessfully.

Even his governorship did not seem to change this situation. Afranius had but recently occupied a quite similar position without thereby acquiring any special importance. In previous years several provinces at once had repeatedly been placed under one governor, and often far more than four legions had been united in one hand. As matters were again quiet beyond the Alps and the German prince Ariovistus was recognized by the Romans as a friend and neighbor, there was no prospect of conducting a war of any moment there. It was natural to compare Pompey's position under the Gabinio-Manilian laws with that which Caesar had obtained by the Vatinian, and the comparison was all to Caesar's disadvantage. Pompey ruled over nearly the whole Roman empire, Caesar over two provinces. Pompey had the soldiers and the treasures of the state almost absolutely at his disposal, while Caesar had only the sums assigned to him and an army of 24,000 men. Pompey himself could choose the time of his retirement, while Caesar's command was given to him for a limited though long period. Pompey, in short, had been entrusted with the most important undertakings by sea and land; Caesar was sent north to watch over the capital from upper Italy and insure that Pompey might rule it undisturbed.

But when Pompey was appointed by the coalition to be ruler of the capital, he undertook a task far exceeding his powers. Pompey understood nothing about ruling except how to command. The waves of agitation in the capital were simultaneously swelled by past and future revolutions. The problem of ruling such a city—quite comparable to the Paris of the nineteenth century—without an armed force was infinitely difficult, and for that stiff and stately soldier altogether insoluble. As a result, matters soon reached such a pitch that friends and foes, both equally inconvenient to him, could do as they pleased so far as he was concerned. After Caesar's departure the coalition still ruled the destinies of the world, but not the streets of the capital.

The Senate, too, which still carried on a sort of nominal government, allowed matters to take their natural course, partly because the coalition's sympathizers in that body lacked instructions from the regents, partly because the angry opposition kept aloof out of indifference or pessimism, but chiefly because the whole aristocratic class began to feel, if not to understand, its utter impotence. For the moment there was nowhere in Rome any determined government, any real authority. Men were living in an interregnum between the ruin of the aristocratic and the rise of the military rule. As the Roman commonwealth has illustrated the different political principles more purely than any other state in ancient or modern times, so it exhibited political anarchy with unenviable clarity.

It is a strange coincidence that in the same years when Caesar was creating beyond the Alps a work for the ages, there was enacted in Rome one of history's most extravagant political farces. The new regent of the commonwealth did not rule, but shut himself up in his house and sulked in silence. The former half-deposed government likewise did not rule

but sighed, sometimes privately amid the confidential circles of the villas, sometimes in chorus in the senate house. That section of the citizens who still yearned for freedom and order was disgusted with the reign of confusion, but utterly lacking leaders or counsel it maintained a passive attitude, not only avoiding political activity, but keeping as far aloof as possible from the political Sodom.

On the other hand the rabble never had a merrier arena. The number of little great men was legion. Demagoguery became quite a trade, with its professional insignia—the threadbare mantle, the shaggy beard, the long streaming hair, the deep bass voice—and not infrequently its rich rewards. For declamations the tried tricks of the theater were much in demand. Greeks and Jews, freedmen and slaves, were the most regular attenders and the loudest shouters in the public assemblies, where frequently only a minority of those voting consisted of citizens constitutionally entitled to do so.

The real power lay with the armed bands, the battalions of anarchy recruited by adventurers of rank from gladiatorial slaves and blackguards. Their possessors had from the outset been numbered mostly among the popular party; but since the departure of Caesar, who alone understood how to lead and control the democrats, all discipline had crumbled and every partisan practiced politics on his own. Even now these men fought with most pleasure under the banner of freedom; but strictly speaking, they were neither of democratic nor of antidemocratic views. They inscribed on the indispensable banner first the name of the people, then that of the Senate or of a party chief. Clodius, for instance, fought or professed to fight in turn for the ruling party, for the Senate, and for Crassus. The leaders of these bands kept to their colors only in the persecution of their personal enemies—as in the case of Clodius against Cicero and Milo against Clodius—where their partisan position served merely as an instrument in private feuds. We might as well seek to set a charivari to music as to write the history of this political witches' revel; nor is it of any moment to enumerate all the murders, besiegings of houses, acts of incendiarism and other scenes of violence within the capital, or to reckon up how often the gamut was traversed from hissing and shouting to spitting and trampling and thence to throwing stones and drawing swords.

The principal performer in this rascally theater was Publius Clodius, whose services the regents had already used against Cato and Cicero. Left to himself, this influential, talented, energetic, and truly noteworthy partisan pursued during his tribunate an ultrademocractic policy. He gave the citizens free grain, restricted the right of the censors to stigmatize immorality, and prohibited the magistrates from obstructing the comitial machinery by religious formalities. He set aside the limits which shortly before had been imposed on the right of association for the purpose of checking the political gangs, and he reestablished the "street-clubs," which with their almost military street-by-street setup were nothing else than a formal organization of the whole free and slave proletariat of the capital. Of course these exertions in behalf of freedom did not exclude a traffic in decrees of the citizenry. Like Caesar himself, Caesar's ape did a thriving business in governorships and other posts great and small, and sold the sovereign rights of the state to subject kings and cities.

Pompey looked on all these things unmoved, but if he did not perceive how seriously he thus compromised himself, his opponent did. Clodius had the cheek to dispute with the regent of Rome on a trifling question of sending back a captive Armenian prince, and the dispute soon became a formal feud which revealed Pompey's utter helplessness. The head of the state sought to meet the partisan with his own weapons, only wielded with far less dexterity. Having been tricked by Clodius regarding the Armenian prince, he offended him in turn by releasing Clodius' enemy Cicero from exile, and thus converted his opponent into an implacable foe. If the gangs of Clodius made the streets unsafe, the victorious general likewise set slaves and pugilists to work. In the street battles which ensued the general naturally was worsted by the demagogue, and Cato was kept almost constantly under siege in his garden by Clodius and his comrades. Not the least remarkable feature of this strange spectacle was that the regent and the rogue vied in courting the favor of the fallen government. Pompey, partly to please the Senate, permitted Cicero's recall, while Clodius on the other hand declared the Julian laws null and void, and called on Marcus Bibulus publicly to testify to their having been unconstitutionally passed.

Naturally no positive result could come from this dark imbroglio, for its most distinctive character was its utter pointlessness. Even a man of Caesar's genius had to learn by experience that agitation was completely worn out, and that the way to the throne no longer lay through demagoguery. It was nothing more than a historical makeshift if now, in the interregnum between republic and monarchy, some whimsical fellow dressed himself in the prophet's mantle and staff which Caesar had laid aside, and parodied the great ideals of Gaius Gracchus. The so-called party from which this democratic agitation proceeded had so little substance that afterwards it did not even play a part in the decisive struggle.

It cannot even be said that this anarchy kindled among neutral citizens a desire for a strong government based on military power. Quite apart from the fact that such neutral citizens were chiefly to be found outside Rome, and thus were not directly affected by the rioting in the capital, everyone who could be so influenced had already been thoroughly converted to the principle of authority by former experiences, especially the Catilinarian conspiracy. Those who were really alarmed were far more apprehensive of the gigantic crisis accompanying the overthrow of the constitution, than of the mere continuance of superficial anarchy in the capital. Its only noteworthy result was the painful position of Pompey due to the attacks of the Clodians, which had a material share in determining his further steps.

Much as Pompey hated taking the initiative, on this occasion he was compelled by the change of his position towards both Clodius and Caesar to depart from his previous inaction. The disgraceful situation to which Clodius had reduced him at length must arouse even his sluggish nature to hatred and anger. But far more important was the change which took place in his relations with Caesar. Of the two regents, Pompey had utterly failed in the functions which he had undertaken, while Caesar had the skill to turn his official position to an account which left all calculations and all fears far behind. Without troubling much about permission, Caesar had doubled his army by levies in his southern province inhabited mainly by Roman citizens. Instead of keeping watch over Rome from Northern Italy, he had crossed the Alps with this army, crushed in the bud a new Cimbrian invasion, and within two years (58-57 B.C.) had carried the Roman arms to the Rhine and the Channel.

In the face of such facts the aristocratic tactics of ignoring and disparaging him were scarcely suitable. He who had often been scoffed at as effeminate was now the idol of the army, the celebrated victory-crowned hero, whose fresh triumphs outshone the faded laurels of Pompey, and to whom even the Senate as early as 57 B.C. accorded far greater honors than had ever fallen to Pompey. Pompey's relation to his former adjutant was precisely that of the latter towards him after the Gabinio-Manilian laws. Caesar was now the hero of the day and the master of the most powerful Roman army; Pompey was an ex-general who had once been famous.

It is true that no open collision had yet occurred between father-in-law and son-in-law, but every political alliance is inwardly broken when the relative power proportions of the parties are materially altered. While the quarrel with Clodius was merely annoying, the change in the position of Caesar involved a very serious danger for Pompey. Just as Caesar and his confederates had formerly sought a military support against him, he now found himself compelled to seek a military support against Caesar. This required laying aside his haughty privacy and coming forward as a candidate for some extraordinary magistracy, which would enable him to match or exceed the power of the governor of the two Gauls.

His tactics, like his position, were exactly those of Caesar during the Mithradatic war. To balance the military power of a superior but still remote adversary by obtaining a similar command, Pompey required in the first instance the official machinery of government. A year and a half ago this had been absolutely at his disposal. The regents then ruled the state both through the comitia, which absolutely obeyed them as the masters of the street, and through the Senate, which was energetically overawed by Caesar. As representative of the coalition in Rome and as its acknowledged head, Pompey could doubtless have obtained from the Senate and from the citizens any decree he wished, even if it were against Caesar's interest. But the awkward quarrel with Clodius had cost Pompey the command of the streets, and he could not expect to carry a proposal in his favor in the popular assembly. Things were not quite so unfavorable for him in the Senate; but even there it was doubtful whether after such long and fatal inaction he still held the majority firmly enough in hand to procure the decree he needed.

The position of the Senate also, or rather of the nobility generally, had meanwhile undergone a change. From the very fact of its complete abasement it drew fresh energy. In the coalition of 60 B.C. various things had come to light for which the times were by no means yet ripe. The exit of Cato and Cicero (which public opinion unerringly referred to the regents, however much they kept in the background and even professed to lament it) and the marriage relationship between Caesar and Pompey suggested, with disagreeable clarity, monarchical banishments and family alliances. The larger public too, which stood more aloof from political events, observed the foundations of the future monarchy coming more and more distinctly into view.

From the moment it became clear that Caesar's object was not a modification of the republican constitution, but that the question was the life or death of the republic, many of the best men who had hitherto supported the popular party and honored Caesar as its head must inevitably have passed over to the opposite side. It was no longer only in salons and country houses that men talked of the "three dynasts" and the "three-headed monster." The dense crowds of people listened to Caesar's consular orations without a sound, and not a hand stirred to applaud when the democratic consul entered the theater. But they hissed when one of the tools of the regents showed himself in public, and even staid men applauded when an actor uttered an anti-monarchic sentence or an allusion against Pompey. When Cicero was banished, it is said that twenty thousand citizens, mostly of the middle classes, put on mourning after the Senate's example. "Nothing is now more popular," remarks a letter of this period, "than hatred of the popular party."

The regents dropped hints that through such opposition the equites might easily lose their new special places in the theater, and the populace its free grain. People therefore became somewhat more guarded in expressing their displeasure, but the feeling remained the same. The lever of money was applied with better success. Caesar's gold flowed in streams. Apparently rich men whose affairs were in disorder, influential ladies who were financially embarrassed, insolvent young nobles, merchants and bankers in difficulties, all either went in person to Gaul with the view of drawing from the fountainhead, or applied to Caesar's agents in the capital; and Caesar rarely rejected any outwardly respectable man, though he avoided dealing with vagabonds who were utterly lost. In addition Caesar undertook considerable building in the capital, by which men of all ranks from consular down to common porter were able to profit, and also expended immense sums for public amusements. Pompey did the same on a more limited scale, building the capital's first theater of stone, and celebrating its dedication with a magnificence never before seen.

Such measures naturally influenced a number of men who were inclined towards opposition, especially in the capital, and reconciled them somewhat to the new order of things. But the core of the opposition was not to be reached by this system of corruption. Every day showed more and more clearly how deep the existing constitution was rooted in the people, and how little the politically neutral groups, especially in country towns, were inclined to favor monarchy or even simply to suffer its coming.

If Rome had had a representative constitution, the discontent of the citizens would have found its natural expression in the elections, and would have grown in force by such expression. Under existing circumstances nothing was left for the constitutionalists but to place themselves under the Senate, which, degraded though it might be, was still the representative and champion of the legitimate republic. Thus it transpired that the Senate, now that it had been overthrown, suddenly found at its disposal an army far larger and more faithful than when in its power and splendor it overthrew the Gracchi and under the protection of Sulla's sword restored the state.

The aristocracy felt this, and began to bestir itself afresh. Just then Marcus Cicero, after having bound himself not only to join the do-nothing faction in the Senate but also to work with all his might for the regents, had secured their permission to return. Although Pompey in this matter only made an incidental concession to the oligarchy, intending first to play a trick on Clodius, and second to acquire in the fluent consular a tool rendered pliant by sufficient blows, Cicero's return was seized as an opportunity for republican demonstrations just as his banishment had been a demonstration against the Senate. With all possible solemnity, and protected against the Clodians by the band of Titus Annius Milo, the two consuls at the Senate's behest submitted a proposal to the citizens to permit Cicero's return, and the Senate urged all supporters of the constitution to be present for the vote. An unusual number of worthy men, especially from the country towns, gathered in Rome on the day of the voting (August 4, 57 B.C.). Cicero's journey from Brundisium to the capital gave occasion for a series of similar manifestations of public feeling. The new alliance between the Senate and the constitutionally minded citizens was thus publicly proclaimed, and helped not a little to revive the shaken courage of the aristocracy.

Pompey's helplessness in the presence of these daring demonstrations, as well as the undignified and almost ridiculous position which he had assumed in his fight with Clodius, discredited both him and the coalition. Thus the section of the Senate which adhered to the regents was left demoralized and helpless by his singular ineptitude, and could not prevent the republican-aristocratic party from regaining complete ascendency in the Senate. This party's game was still by no means hopeless for a courageous and dexterous player. It now had what it had not possessed for a century—firm popular support. If it trusted the people and itself, it might attain its objective in the shortest and most honorable way. Why not attack the regents openly and avowedly? Why should not an eminent and resolute man at the head of the Senate cancel the extraordinary powers as unconstitutional and summon the republicans of Italy to arms against the tyrants? It was possible perhaps in this way once more to restore the rule of the Senate. The republicans would thus be playing a bold game, but perhaps in this case (as often) the most courageous resolution might have been at the same time the most prudent.

Since the indolent aristocracy of this period was scarcely capable of so simple and bold a resolution, there was another and perhaps surer way, or at any rate one better adapted to the character and nature of these constitutionalists: they might work to set the two regents at odds, and thereby ultimately attain to the helm themselves. The relations between the two rulers had become altered and relaxed, now that Caesar's preponderant power had compelled Pompey to seek a new position of command. It was probable that if he obtained it, a rupture would occur in one way or another and give rise to a struggle between them. If Pompey was unsupported his defeat was scarcely doubtful, and the constitutional party would then find itself ruled by one master instead of two. But if the nobility employed against Caesar the same means by which he had won his previous victories, and made an alliance with the weaker competitor, then the victory— given a general like Pompey, and an army such as that of the constitutionalists— would probably fall to the coalition. To settle matters with Pompey after the victory, judging from his proven political incapacity, could not be an especially difficult task.

The course of events thus naturally suggested an understanding between Pompey and the republican party. Whether such an understanding could be reached, and what shape the confused relations of the two regents and the aristocracy were to assume, came up for discussion in the autumn of 57 B.C., when Pompey proposed that the Senate entrust him with extraordinary official power. He once more based his proposal, as eleven years earlier, on the price of bread in the capital, which had again (as just before the Gabinian law) reached an oppressive height. Whether it had been forced up by manipulation, as Clodius sometimes charged to Pompey and sometimes to Cicero, and these in turn charged to Clodius, cannot be determined. The continuance of piracy, the emptiness of the public chest, and the negligent and disorderly supervision of the grain distribution were already quite sufficient by themselves to produce scarcities of bread in a great city dependent almost solely on overseas supplies. Pompey's plan was to get the superintendence of all matters relating to grain throughout the empire, and, to this end, to secure on the one hand the unlimited disposal of the Roman state-treasure, and on the other hand an army and fleet, as well as a command which was superior in each Roman province to that of the governor. In short, he sought an improved edition of the Gabinian law, to which the conduct of the pending Egyptian war would naturally have been added as the conduct of the Mithradatic war was added to the pirate roundup.

However much the opposition to the new dynasts had gained ground, when the proposal was discussed in 57 B.C. the majority of the Senate was still under the constraint of the terror excited by Caesar. It obsequiously accepted the project in principle on the motion of Marcus Cicero, who was expected to give (and gave) this first proof of the pliancy which exile had taught him. But in settling the details very material changes were made in the original plan, which the tribune Gaius Messius had submitted. Pompey obtained neither a free hand with the treasury, nor legions and ships of his own, nor even an authority superior to that of the governors. The senators contented themselves with granting him considerable sums, fifteen adjutants, and full proconsular power in all affairs relating to grain supply throughout the Roman dominions for the next five years. This decree, moreover, would have to be confirmed by the citizenry.

There were many reasons which led to this alteration, almost equivalent to a rejection, of the original plan. Even the most timid must surely hesitate to invest Caesar's colleague not merely with equal but with superior authority in Gaul itself. There was the concealed opposition of Pompey's hereditary enemy and reluctant ally Crassus, to whom Pompey himself largely attributed the failure of his plan. The republican opposition in the Senate was hostile to any decree which even nominally enlarged the authority of the regents. Finally, and most important, there was the incompetence of Pompey himself, who even when compelled to act could not make himself acknowledge his own actions, but chose always to bring forward his design incognito by means of friends, while he himself in his well-known modesty declared his willingness to be content with even less. No wonder that they took him at his word, and gave him less.

Pompey was nevertheless glad to have found at least a serious employment, and above all a fitting pretext for leaving the capital. He succeeded, moreover, in providing it with ampler and cheaper grain supplies, although not without the provinces severely feeling the reflex effect. But he had missed his real object. The proconsular title, which he had a right to bear in all the provinces, remained an empty name so long as he had no troops of his own. Accordingly he soon afterwards had a second proposition made to the Senate, that it should charge him with restoring the expelled king of Egypt, if necessary by force of arms. But the more evident became his urgent need of the Senate, the less respectfully were his wishes received. It was immediately discovered in the Sibylline oracles that it was impious to send a Roman army to Egypt, whereupon the pious Senate almost unanimously resolved to avoid armed intervention. Pompey was already so humbled that he would have accepted the mission even without an army. But in his incorrigible dissimulation he left this also to be requested only by his friends, and he spoke and voted for sending another senator. Of course the Senate rejected a proposal which wantonly risked a life so precious to his country; and the ultimate issue of the endless discussions was the resolution not to interfere in Egypt at all.

These repeated repulses which Pompey met in the Senate (and still worse, had to accept without retaliation) were naturally regarded by the public as so many victories for the republicans and defeats for

the regents. Accordingly, the tide of republican opposition was always on the increase. Already the elections for 56 B.C. had gone but partly for the dynasts. Caesar's candidates for the praetorship, Publius Vatinius and Gaius Alfius, had failed, while two decided adherents of the fallen government, Gnaeus Lentulus Marcellinus and Gnaeus Domitius Calvinus, had been elected, the former as consul and the latter as praetor. For 55 B.C. the consulship was sought by Lucius Domitius Ahenobarbus, whose election it was difficult to prevent owing to his influence in the capital and his colossal wealth, and who clearly would not be content with a concealed opposition.

The comitia thus rebelled, and the Senate chimed in. The latter solemnly deliberated over an opinion which Etruscan soothsayers of acknowledged wisdom had furnished upon request respecting certain signs and wonders. The celestial revelation announced that through dissension among the upper classes the whole power over the army and treasury threatened to pass to one ruler, and the state was faced with loss of freedom (the gods seemed to point primarily at the proposal of Gaius Messius). The republicans soon descended from heaven to earth. The law as to the domain of Capua and the other laws issued by Caesar as consul had been constantly described by them as null and void, and an opinion had been expressed in the Senate as early as 57 B.C. that it was necessary to cancel them on account of their irregularity. Then, on April 6, 56 B.C., the consular Cicero proposed in a full Senate that the Campanian land distribution be debated on May 15.

It was the formal declaration of war, and all the more significant because it came from one of those men who only show their colors when they think that they can do so with safety. Evidently the aristocracy felt that the moment had come for beginning the struggle not with

Pompey against Caesar, but against the regency generally. What would further follow might easily be seen. Domitius made no secret that he intended as consul to propose to the citizens the immediate recall of Caesar from Gaul. An aristocratic restoration was at work, and with the attack on the colony of Capua the nobility threw down the gauntlet to the regents.

Caesar, although receiving detailed daily accounts of events in the capital, and, when military considerations allowed, watching their progress from as nearby as possible, had not up to then openly interferred. But now war had been declared against his colleague and especially against him; he was compelled to act, and he acted quickly. He happened to be in the neighborhood, for the aristocracy had not even found it advisable to delay the rupture until he had crossed the Alps. Early in April of 56 B.C. Crassus left the capital to make the necessary arrangements with his more powerful colleague. He found Caesar in Ravenna, from whence both proceeded to Luca. There they were joined by Pompey, who had departed from Rome soon after Crassus, ostensibly for the purpose of procuring supplies of grain from Sardinia and Africa. The most noted adherents of the regents, such as Metellus Nepos the proconsul of Hither Spain, Appius Claudius the propraetor of Sardinia, and many others, followed them. A hundred and twenty lictors and upwards of two hundred senators were counted at this conference, a new monarchical Senate in contradistinction to the republican.

In every respect the decisive voice lay with Caesar. He used it to re-establish and consolidate the existing joint rule on a new basis of more equal distribution of power. The governorships of most importance from a military point of view, next to that of the two Gauls, were assigned to his two colleagues, the two Spains to Pompey, Syria to Crassus. These offices were to be secured to them by decree of the people for five years (54-50 B.C.), with suitable military and financial support. On the other hand Caesar demanded the prolongation of his command, which expired with the year 54 B.C., to the close of 49 B.C., as well as the prerogative of increasing his legions to ten and of making the state pay for the troops he arbitrarily levied. Pompey and Crassus were promised a second consulship for the next year (55 B.C.) before they departed for their governorships, while Caesar reserved the right to administer the supreme magistracy a second time after the end of his governorship in 48 B.C., when the ten years' interval legally required between two consulships should have elapsed. The military support which Pompey and Crassus needed all the more urgently in the capital, now that Caesar's legions originally intended for this purpose could not be withdrawn from Transalpine Gaul, was to be found in new legions they were to raise for the Spanish and Syrian armies, but were not to despatch from Italy until they found it convenient to do so.

The main questions were thus settled, and such subordinate matters as the tactics to be followed against the opposition in the capital, the regulation of the candidacies for the ensuing years, etc., did not long detain them. The great master of mediation composed with his wonted ease the personal differences which stood in the way of an agreement, and compelled the most refractory elements to act in concert. An understanding befitting colleagues was re-established, externally at least, between Pompey and Crassus. Even Publius Clodius was induced to keep himself and his pack quiet, and to give no further annoyance to Pompey—not the least marvelous feat of the mighty magician.

The circumstances reveal that this

whole settlement proceeded not from a compromise among independent and rival regents meeting on equal terms, but solely from the good will of Caesar. Pompey appeared at Luca in the painful position of a powerless refugee who comes to ask aid from his opponent. Whether Caesar chose to dismiss him and declare the coalition dissolved, or to receive him and let the league continue just as it stood, Pompey was in either case politically annihilated. If he did not in this case break with Caesar, he became the powerless dependent of his confederate. If on the other hand he did break with Caesar and, which was not very probable, effected even now a coalition with the aristocracy, the last-minute alliance between opponents concluded under pressure of necessity was so little formidable that Caesar need hardly put himself out to avert it. A serious rivalry on the part of Crassus with Caesar was utterly impossible.

It is difficult to say what motives induced Caesar to surrender his superior position and to grant voluntarily the second consulate and a military command—concessions which he had refused his rival even at the consummation of the league in 60 B.C., and which the latter had since (with the evident intent of being armed against Caesar) vainly striven to attain without Caesar's help and even against his will. To be sure, it was not Pompey alone that was placed at the head of an army, but also Pompey's old enemy and Caesar's long-time ally Crassus; and undoubtedly Crassus obtained his respectable military position merely as a counterpoise to Pompey's new power. Nevertheless, Caesar lost greatly when his rival exchanged his former powerlessness for an important command.

It is possible that Caesar did not yet feel himself sufficiently master of his soldiers to lead them confidently in a war against the established government, and was therefore anxious not to be forced into civil war now by being recalled from Gaul. But whether civil war came or not depended at the moment far more on the aristocracy of the capital than on Pompey. This would have been at most a reason for Caesar not breaking openly with Pompey, so that the opposition might not be emboldened by this breach, but not a reason for conceding what was conceded. Purely personal motives may have contributed to the result. It may be that Caesar recollected how he had once stood in a similar position before Pompey, and had been saved from destruction only by Pompey's (pusillanimous, it is true, rather than magnanimous) retirement. It is probable that Caesar hesitated to break the heart of his beloved daughter who was sincerely attached to her husband, for in his soul there was room for much besides the statesman.

But the decisive reason was doubtless the consideration of Gaul. Caesar (as distinct from his biographers) regarded the subjugation of Gaul not as an incidental enterprise useful for gaining the crown, but as one on which depended his country's external security and internal reorganization—in short, its future. That he might complete this conquest undisturbed, and not be obliged to take on at that moment the settlement of Italian affairs, he unhesitatingly gave up his superiority over his rivals and granted Pompey sufficient power to settle matters with the Senate and its adherents.

This was a grave political blunder, if Caesar had no other object than to become king of Rome as quickly as possible. But the ambition of that rare man was not confined to the vulgar aim of a crown. He had the boldness to prosecute side by side, and to complete, two equally vast labors—the arranging of the internal affairs of Italy, and the winning of new and fresh soil for Italian civilization.

These tasks of course interfered with each other, and his Gallic conquests hindered much more than helped him on his way to the throne. Postponing the Italian revolution until 48 B.C., instead of settling it in 58 B.C., bore bitter fruit for him. But as statesman as well as general Caesar was that kind of daring player who, confident of himself and despising his opponents, gave always great and sometimes extravagant odds.

It was now the turn of the aristocracy to wage war as boldly as they had declared it. But there is no more pitiable spectacle than cowardly men who have the misfortune to take a bold resolution. They had simply exercised no foresight at all. It seemed to have occurred to nobody that Caesar would possibly stand his ground, or that even now Pompey and Crassus would again combine with him more closely than ever. This seems incredible, but it becomes intelligible when we glance at the leaders of the constitutional opposition in the Senate. With Cato still absent, the most influential man in the Senate was Marcus Bibulus, the hero of passive resistance, the most obstinate and stupid of all consulars. The aristocracy had taken up arms, only to lay them down as soon as the adversary merely put his hand to the sheath.

The mere news of the conferences in Luca sufficed to suppress all thought of serious opposition and to bring the mass of the timid—that is, the immense majority of the Senate—back to their duty as subjects, which in an unhappy hour they had abandoned. There was no further talk of the scheduled discussion to consider the validity of the Julian laws. The legions raised by Caesar on his own behalf were charged to the public chest by senatorial decree. The attempts, while arranging for the next consular provinces, to take away one or both Gauls from Caesar by decree were rejected by the Senate near the end of May, 56 B.C.

Thus the corporation did public penance. In secret the individual lords, one after another, thoroughly frightened at their own temerity, came to make their peace and vow unconditional obedience —none more quickly than Marcus Cicero, who repented too late of his perfidy, and with regard to the most recent period of his life clothed himself with titles of "honor" which were more appropriate than flattering. ("*Me asinum germanum fuisse*"—"I have been a complete ass.") Of course the regents agreed to be pacified. They refused nobody pardon, for there was nobody worth making an exception over. How suddenly the tone in aristocratic circles changed, after the resolutions of Luca became known, may be seen by comparing the pamphlets given forth by Cicero shortly before with that which he caused to be issued as public evidence of his repentance and his good intentions.

The regents could thus arrange Italian affairs at their pleasure and more fully than before. Italy and the capital obtained what amounted to a garrison (although not assembled in arms) and one of the regents as commandant. Of the troops levied for Syria and Spain by Crassus and Pompey, those destined for the East took their departure. But Pompey caused the two Spanish provinces to be administered by his lieutenants with the garrison already there, while he furloughed the officers and soldiers of the legions nominally raised for dispatch to Spain, and remained himself with them in Italy.

Doubtless the tacit public resistance increased, the more clearly men perceived that the regents were working to end the old constitution and, with as much gentleness as possible, to accommodate the existing government and administration to the forms of monarchy. But they submitted, because they were obliged to submit. First, all the more important matters, particularly those relating to military affairs and external relations, were disposed of without consulting the Senate, sometimes by decree of the people and sometimes at the mere good pleasure of the rulers. The arrangements agreed on at Luca regarding the military command of Gaul were submitted directly to the citizens by Crassus and Pompey, those relating to Spain and Syria by the tribune of the people Gaius Trebonius, and in other instances the more important governorships were frequently filled by decree of the people. Caesar had already shown that the regents did not need any consent to increase their troops at pleasure, nor did they hesitate to borrow troops. Caesar, for instance, received support from Pompey for the Gallic war, and Crassus from Caesar for the Parthian war. The Transpadanes, who possessed under the existing constitution only Latin rights, were treated by Caesar during his administration practically as full citizens of Rome.

While formerly the organization of newly acquired territories had always been managed by a senatorial commission, Caesar organized his extensive Gallic conquests according to his own judgment, and, without having received any further powers, founded colonies such as Novum-Comum (Como), with 5,000 colonists. Piso conducted the Thracian, Gabinius the Egyptian, Crassus the Parthian war, without consulting the Senate, and without even the usual reports to that body. In like manner triumphs and other marks of honor were accorded without the Senate being asked about them.

Obviously this did not arise from a mere neglect of forms, which would be still less understandable since in the great majority of cases no senatorial opposition was to be expected. On the contrary, it was a well-calculated design to cut off the Senate from military arrangements and high policy, and to restrict it to financial questions and internal affairs. Even opponents plainly discerned this and protested against this conduct of the regents so far as they could, by means of senatorial decrees and criminal actions. While the regents thus in the main set aside the Senate, they still made some use of the less dangerous popular assemblies, though taking care that the lords of the street should not obstruct the plans of the lords of the state. In many cases, however, they dispensed even with this empty shadow, and employed openly autocratic forms.

The humbled Senate had to submit to its position whether it would or not. The leader of the compliant majority continued to be Marcus Cicero. He was useful for his lawyer's talent of finding reasons, or at any rate words, for everything; and there was a genuine Caesarian irony in employing the man, by means of whom mainly the aristocracy had conducted their demonstrations against the regents, as the mouthpiece of servility. Accordingly the regents pardoned him for his brief desire to kick against the pricks, having previously assured themselves of his complete submissiveness. His brother had been obliged to become an officer in the Gallic army, thus also becoming a hostage. Pompey had compelled Cicero himself to accept a nominal deputy position under him, which furnished a means for politely banishing him at any moment. Clodius had doubtless been instructed to leave him meanwhile at peace, but Caesar no more discarded Clodius on account of Cicero than he discarded Cicero on account of Clodius; thus the great savior of his country, and the equally great hero of liberty, entered into an antechamber rivalry for whose illustration there was unfortunately no Roman Aristophanes.

Not only was the same rod, which already had once descended on him so severely, kept in suspense over Cicero's head; golden fetters were also laid upon him. Amid his serious financial embarrassment, the interest-free loans of Caesar, and the joint overseership of those buildings which occasioned the circulation of enormous sums in the capital, were in a high degree welcome to him. Many an immortal oration was nipped in the bud by the thought of Caesar's agent, who might present a bill to him after the close of the sitting. Consequently he vowed "in future to ask no more after right and honor, but to strive for the favor of the regents," and "to be as flexible as an earlap." They used him accordingly as what he was good for, an advocate. In this capacity he had on various occasions to defend his very bitterest foes at a higher bidding, especially in the Senate, where he often served as the organ of the dynasts and submitted the proposals "to which others probably consented, but not he himself." Indeed, as recognized leader of the party of spinelessness, he even attained a certain political importance. The regents dealt with the other members of the governing corporation accessible to fear, flattery, or gold in the same way as they had dealt with Cicero, and succeeded in keeping them on the whole in subjection.

Certainly there remained a section of their opponents who at least kept to their colors, and who were neither to be terrified nor won over. The regents had become convinced that exceptional measures, such as those once used against Cato and Cicero, did their cause more harm than good, and that it was a lesser evil to tolerate an inconvenient republican opposition than to convert their opponents into martyrs. Therefore they allowed Cato to return near the end of 56 B.C., and thenceforward both in the Senate and in the Forum, often at the peril of his life, he offered a continuous opposition to the regents which was doubtless honorable, but unhappily was at the same time ridiculous.

The regents allowed him, in the debate on the proposals of Trebonius, to push matters once more to a hand-to-hand conflict in the Forum, and to submit to the Senate a proposal that the proconsul Caesar should be given over to the Usipetes and Tencteri on account of his perfidious conduct toward those barbarians. They were patient when Marcus Favonius, Cato's Sancho Panza, after the Senate had adopted the resolution to charge the legions of Caesar to the state-chest, sprang to the door of the senate house and proclaimed to the streets the danger to the country; when the same person in his scurrilous fashion called the white bandage which Pompey wore round his weak leg a displaced diadem; when the consular Lentulus Marcellinus, on being applauded, called out to the assembly to make diligent use of this privilege of expressing their opinion now while they were still allowed to do so; when the tribune of the people Gaius Ateius Capito consigned Crassus, with all the formalities of the theology of the day, publicly to the evil spirits on the occasion of his departure for Syria.

These were, on the whole, vain demonstrations of an irritated minority. Yet the little party from which they issued was to this degree important, that on the one hand it fostered and gave the watchword to the republican opposition fermenting in secret, and on the other hand now and then dragged the majority of the Senate (which cherished at bottom quite the same sentiments with reference to the regents) into isolated actions against them. For even the majority felt the need of giving vent to their suppressed indignation, at least sometimes and in subordinate matters, especially (after the manner of those who are reluctantly servile) by exhibiting their resentment towards the great foes in rage against the small. Wherever it was possible, a gentle blow was administered to the instruments of the regents. Thus Gabinius was refused the thanksgiving festival that he asked, and Piso was recalled from his province. Thus mourning was put on by the Senate, when the tribune of the people Gaius Cato hindered the elections for 55 B.C. as long as the consul Marcellinus, who belonged to the constitutional party, was in office. Even Cicero, however humbly he always bowed before the regents, issued an equally envenomed and insipid pamphlet against Caesar's father-in-law.

But these feeble signs of opposition by the senatorial majority, and the ineffectual resistance of the minority, show only the more clearly that the government had now passed from the Senate to the regents as it had once passed from the citizens to the Senate. The Senate was already not much more than a monarchical council of state also employed to absorb the antimonarchical elements. "No man," the adherents of the fallen government complained, "is of the slightest account except the three. The regents are all-powerful, and they take care that no one shall remain in doubt about it. The whole Senate is virtually transformed and obeys the dictators; our generation will not live to see a change of things." They were living in fact no longer under the republic, but under monarchy.

But if the guidance of the state was at the absolute disposal of the regents, there remained still a political domain separated in some measure from the government proper, which was more easy to defend and more difficult to conquer—the field of ordinary magisterial elections, and that of the jury courts. It is clear that the latter do not fall directly under politics, but everywhere, and above all in Rome, partly reflect the spirit of the times. The elections of magistrates were certainly a part of the government of the state. But since at this time the state was administered substantially by extraordinary magistrates or by men wholly without title, and even the supreme magistrates, if they belonged to the antimonarchical party, were not able in any tangible way to influence the state machinery, the ordinary magistrates more and more resembled mere puppets. When in fact even those who were most disposed to opposition described themselves frankly and correctly as powerless ciphers, their elections therefore sank into mere demonstrations. Thus, after the opposition had already been wholly dislodged from the proper field of battle, hostilities might nevertheless be continued in the field of elections and of processes.

The regents spared no pains to become victors in this field also. As to the elections, they had already settled at Luca the lists of candidates for the next years, and they left no means untried to carry the candidates agreed upon there. They expended their gold primarily for the purpose of influencing the elections. A great number of soldiers were dismissed annually on furlough from the armies of Caesar and Pompey to take part in the voting at Rome, and Caesar himself was wont to guide and watch over the election campaigns from as near a point in Upper Italy as possible.

Yet the object was but very imperfectly attained. For 55 B.C. Pompey and Crassus were indeed elected consuls, in agreement with the arrangements at Luca, and Lucius Domitius, the only candidate of the opposition who persevered, was set aside. But this had been effected only by open violence, on which occasion Cato was wounded and other extremely scandalous incidents occurred. In the next consular elections, despite all the exertions of the regents, Domitius was actually elected, and Cato also now prevailed in the race for the praetorship, which Caesar's tool Vatinius had won the previous year to the scandal of the whole citizenry. At the elections for 53 B.C. the opposition succeeded in so indisputably convicting the regency candidates (along with others) of the most shameful electioneering intrigues that the regents, on whom the scandal recoiled, could not do otherwise than abandon them.

These repeated and severe defeats of the dynasts in the elections may be traceable in part to the unmanageableness of the rusty machinery, to the incalculable accidents of the polling, to the opposition at heart of the middle classes, and to the various private considerations that interfere in such cases and often strangely clash with those of party. But the main cause lies elsewhere. The elections were at this time essentially in the power of the different clubs into which the aristocracy had grouped themselves. The system of bribery was organized by them on the most extensive scale and with the utmost care. The same aristocracy which was represented in the Senate also ruled the elections. But while in the Senate it yielded grudgingly, here it worked and voted, in secret and secure from all reckoning, wholeheartedly against the regents. That the nobility's influence in this field was by no means broken by the strict law against electioneering intrigues, which Crassus as consul in 55 B.C. caused to be confirmed by the citizens, is proved by the elections of the succeeding years.

The jury courts caused equally great difficulty to the regents. As they were then composed, the decisive voice lay chiefly with the middle class, though the senatorial nobility was also influential. The setting of a high property qualification for jurymen under a law proposed by Pompey in 55 B.C. is a remarkable proof that the opposition to the regents had its center in the middle class proper, and that the great capitalists showed themselves as usual more compliant. Nevertheless the republican party was not yet deprived of all hold in the courts, and it was never weary of directing political impeachments, not indeed against the regents themselves, but against their prominent instruments. This warfare of prosecutions was waged the more keenly since by custom the duty of accusation belonged to the senatorial youth, and, as may readily be conceived, there was more of republican passion, fresh talent, and bold delight in attack to be found among these youths than among the older members of their order.

On the whole, therefore, in the sphere of the popular elections and of the jury courts it was the regents who fared worst. The controlling factors here were less tangible, and therefore more difficult to be terrified or corrupted, than the direct organs of government and administration. The holders of power encountered here, especially in the popular elections, the tough energy of a close oligarchy grouped in cliques, which is by no means finally disposed of when its rule is overthrown, and which is the more difficult to vanquish the more covert its action. They also encountered, especially in the jury courts, the repugnance of the middle classes towards the new monarchical rule. Thus they suffered in both quarters a series of defeats. The election victories of the opposition had, it is true, merely the value of demonstrations, since the regents possessed and employed the means of practically annulling any magistrate whom they disliked. However, the criminal trials in which the opposition secured condemnations deprived them, in a way keenly felt, of useful auxiliaries. As things stood, the regents could neither set aside nor adequately control the popular elections and the jury courts; and the opposition, however much it felt itself constrained even here, maintained to a certain extent the field of battle.

It proved, moreover, a still more difficult task to encounter the opposition in another field, to which it turned with greater zeal the more it was dislodged from direct political action. This was literature. Even the judicial opposition was also a literary one, and indeed preeminently so, for the orations were regularly published and served as political pamphlets. The arrows of poetry hit their mark still more rapidly and sharply. The lively youth of the high aristocracy, and still more energetically perhaps the cultivated middle class in the Italian country towns, waged the war of pamphlets and epigrams with zeal and success. There fought side by side on this field the genteel senator's son Gaius Licinius Calvus (82–48 B.C.), who was as much feared as an orator and pamphleteer as a versatile poet, and the muncipals of Cremona and Verona, Marcus Furius Bibaculus (102– c.20 B.C.) and Quintus Verleius Catullus (87 to about 54 B.C.), whose elegant and pungent epigrams flew swiftly and surely like arrows through Italy.

An oppositional tone prevails throughout the literature of these years. It is full of indignant sarcasm against the "great Caesar," "the unique general," against the affectionate father-in-law and son-in-law who ruin the whole globe in order to let their dissolute favorites parade the spoils of the long-haired Celts through the streets of Rome, to furnish royal banquets with the booty of the farthest isles of the west, and as rich rivals to supplant honest youths at home in the favor of their mistresses. There is in the poems of Catullus and the other fragments of the literature of this period something of that fervor of personal and political hatred, of that republican agony overflowing in riotous humor or stern despair, which are more prominently and powerfully apparent in Aristophanes and Demosthenes.

The most sagacious of the three rulers at least saw well that it was as impossible to despise this opposition as to suppress it by word of command. So far as he could, Caesar rather tried personally to win over the more notable authors. Cicero himself had his literary reputation to thank in

large part for the respectful treatment which he received especially from Caesar. But the governor of Gaul did not disdain to conclude a special peace even with Catullus himself, through the intervention of his father who had become personally known to him in Verona; and the young poet, who had just heaped upon the powerful general the bitterest and most personal sarcasms, was treated with the most flattering distinction. In fact, Caesar was gifted enough to meet his literary opponents on their own field and to publish (as an indirect way of repelling manifold attacks) a detailed report on the Gallic wars, which set forth with happily assumed naïveté the necessity and constitutional propriety of his military operations.

But it is freedom alone that is absolutely and exclusively poetical and creative; it and it alone is able, even in its most wretched caricature and with its dying breath, to inspire fresh enthusiasm. All the sound elements of literature were, and remained, antimonarchical. If Caesar himself could venture on this field without proving a failure, the reason was merely that even now he still cherished at heart the magnificent dream of a free commonwealth, although he was unable to transfer it either to his adversaries or to his adherents. Practical politics was not more absolutely controlled by the regents than literature by the republicans.

It became necessary to take serious steps against this opposition, which though powerless was becoming ever more troublesome and audacious. The condemnation of Gabinius at the end of 54 B.C. apparently tipped the scale. The regents agreed to introduce a dictatorship, though only a temporary one, and by means of this to carry new coercive measures especially concerning the elections and the jury courts. Pompey, as the regent on whom primarily devolved the government of Rome and Italy, was

charged with the execution of this resolve. Accordingly, it was marked by his
characteristic awkwardness in resolution
and action, as well as his singular incapacity to speak out frankly even where he
would and could command.

Toward the close of 54 B.C. the demand for a dictatorship was hinted to the
Senate, though not by Pompey himself.
Its ostensible ground was the continuance
of the system of clubs and bands in the
capital, which by acts of bribery and violence certainly exercised the most pernicious pressure on the elections as well as
on the jury courts, and kept the city in a
perpetual state of disturbance. We must
allow that this rendered it easy for the
regents to justify their exceptional measures. But, as may well be conceived, even
the servile majority shrank from granting
what the future dictator seemed to shrink
from asking openly. When the unparalleled agitation regarding the elections for
the consulship of 53 B.C. led to the most
scandalous scenes, so that the elections
were postponed a full year beyond the
fixed time and took place only after a
seven months' interregnum in July of 53,
Pompey found in this state of things the
desired occasion for indicating distinctly
to the Senate that the dictatorship was the
only means of cutting, if not of loosing,
the knot. Even then, however, the decisive word of command was not spoken.
Perhaps it would have remained long
unuttered had not the most audacious
partisan of the republican opposition,
Titus Annius Milo, stepped into the field
at the consular elections for 52 B.C. as a
candidate opposing the regency's choices,
Quintus Metellus Scipio and Publius
Plautius Hypsaeus, both of whom were
closely connected with Pompey personally and thoroughly devoted to him.

Milo, endowed with physical courage,
with a certain talent for intrigue and for
contracting debt, and above all with an
ample amount of native assurance which

had been carefully cultivated, had made
himself a name among the political adventurers of the day. He was the greatest
bully in his trade next to Clodius, and
naturally therefore at deadly odds with
the latter. As this latter Achilles of the
streets had been acquired by the regents
and with their permission was again playing the ultrademocrat, the Hector of the
streets became as a matter of course an
aristocrat! The republican opposition,
which now would have concluded an alliance with Catiline himself, readily acknowledged Milo as their legitimate
champion in all riots. In fact, the few
successes which they achieved in this field
of battle were the work of Milo and his
well-trained band of gladiators. So Cato
and his friends in return supported the
candidacy of Milo for the consulship.
Even Cicero could not avoid recommend-
ing one who had been his enemy's enemy
and his own protector during many years;
and as Milo himself spared neither
money nor violence, his election seemed
certain.

For the regents this would have been
not only a new and keenly felt defeat but
also a real danger, for the bold partisan
would surely not allow himself as consul
to be reduced to insignificance so easily
as Domitius and the other opposition re-
spectables. It happened that this Achilles
and Hector accidentally encountered
each other not far from the capital on the
Appian Way, and a fray arose between
their respective bands, in which Clodius
himself received a sword cut on the
shoulder and was compelled to take refuge in a neighboring house. This had occurred without orders from Milo. However, as the matter had gone so far and as
the storm now had to be encountered in
any case, the whole crime seemed to Milo
more desirable and less dangerous than
the half. Therefore he ordered his men to
drag Clodius forth from his lurking place
and to put him to death.

The street leaders of the regents' party —the tribunes Titus Munatius Plancus, Quintus Pompeius Rufus, and Gaius Sallustius Crispus—saw in this occurrence a golden opportunity to thwart the candidacy of Milo and carry the dictatorship of Pompey. Since the dregs of the populace, especially the freedmen and slaves, had lost in Clodius their patron and future deliverer, the requisite excitement was easily aroused. After the bloody corpse had been exhibited at the orators' platform in the Forum and the appropriate speeches had been made, the riot broke out.

The seat of the perfidious aristocracy was apparently destined as the funeral pile of the great liberator, for the mob carried the body to the senate house and set the building on fire. Thereafter the multitude proceeded to Milo's house, keeping it under siege till his band drove off the assailants by discharges of arrows. They then passed on to the houses of Pompey and his consular candidates, saluting the former as dictator and the latter as consuls, and thence to the house of the interrex Marcus Lepidus, on whom devolved the conduct of the consular elections. When the latter, as his duty dictated, refused to make the immediate arrangements for the elections which the clamorous multitude demanded, he was kept under siege in his house for five days.

But the instigators of these scandalous scenes had overacted their part. Certainly their lord and master sought to employ this favorable episode not merely to set aside Milo, but also to seize the dictatorship. However, he wished to receive it from the Senate, not from a mob of bludgeon-men. Pompey brought up troops to put down the anarchy in the capital, which had become intolerable to everybody. At the same time he now demanded what he had hitherto requested, and the Senate complied. It was merely an empty subterfuge that on the proposal of Cato and Bibulus the proconsul Pompey, retaining his former offices, was nominated as "consul without colleague" instead of dictator.

Thus in legal possession of full power, Pompey proceeded energetically against the republican party which was powerful in the clubs and the jury courts. The existing enactments as to elections were repeated and enforced by a special law, while another one, retroactive to 70 B.C., increased the penalties hitherto imposed. Still more important was the enactment that the governorships, by far the more important and especially the more lucrative half of official life, should be conferred on the consuls and praetors only after a waiting period of five years. Such an arrangement of course could only take effect after four years, which made the filling of the governorships during that period substantially dependent on special decrees of Senate, and thus in turn practically on the person or group ruling the Senate at the moment.

The jury commissions were left in existence, but limits were put to the right of counter-plea, and (perhaps still more important) freedom of speech in the courts was limited; for both the number of the advocates and the length of speeches were restricted by setting a maximum, and the prevailing bad practice of adducing character witnesses in favor of the accused, in addition to the witnesses as to the facts, was prohibited. The obsequious Senate further decreed, on Pompey's suggestion, that the nation had been endangered by the quarrel on the Appian Way. Accordingly, a special commission was appointed for all crimes connected with it, the members of which were directly nominated by Pompey. An attempt was also made to give the office of censor a serious importance once more, and thereby to purge the deeply disordered citizenry of the worst rabble.

All these measures were adopted under pressure of the sword. In consequence of the Senate's declaration that the country was in danger, Pompey called to arms the men capable of service throughout Italy and made them swear allegiance for all contingencies. An adequate and trustworthy corps was temporarily stationed at the Capitol, and at every stirring of opposition Pompey threatened armed intervention. During the proceedings at the trial regarding Clodius' murder a guard was stationed, contrary to all precedent, over the place of trial itself.

The scheme for reviving the censorship failed, because among the servile majority of the Senate no one possessed sufficient moral courage and authority even to become a candidate. On the other hand Milo was condemned by the jurymen (on April 8, 52 B.C.), and Cato's candidacy for the consulship the following year was frustrated. The literary opposition received through the new judicial ordinance a blow from which it never recovered, for the dreaded forensic eloquence was thereby driven from the field of politics, and thus felt the restraints of monarchy. Of course, opposition had not disappeared either from the minds of the great majority of the nation or even wholly from public life: to effect that end the popular elections, the jury courts, and literature must have been not merely restricted, but annihilated. Indeed, in these very transactions Pompey by his unskilfulness and perversity helped the republicans to gain even under his dictatorship several triumphs which he felt severely.

The special measures which the rulers took to strengthen their power were of course officially characterized as enactments made on behalf of public tranquility and order, and every citizen who did not desire anarchy was described as substantially concurring in them. But Pompey pushed this transparent fiction so far that instead of putting safe partisans on the special commission for investigating the recent tumult, he chose the most respectable men of all parties, even including Cato. He also applied his influence over the court primarily to maintain order, and to make it impossible for his adherents as well as for his opponents to indulge in the disturbances customary in the courts of this period.

This neutrality of the regent was recognizable in the verdicts of the special court. The jurymen did not venture to acquit Milo himself. However, most of the subordinate defendants belonging to the republican opposition were acquitted, while condemnation inexorably befell those who had aided Clodius (or in other words the regents) including not a few of Caesar's and Pompey's own most intimate friends—even Hypsaeus, his candidate for the consulship, and the tribunes of the people Plancus and Rufus, who had directed the riot in Pompey's interest.

That Pompey did not prevent their condemnation, in the interest of appearing impartial, was one specimen of his folly. A second was that in unimportant matters he violated his own laws to favor his friends, for example appearing as a character witness in the trial of Plancus, and in fact protecting from condemnation several accused persons such as Metellus Scipio who were closely connected with him. As usual, here also he wished to accomplish opposite things. In attempting to satisfy simultaneously the duties of the impartial regent and of the party chief, he fulfilled neither the one nor the other, being justly regarded by public opinion as a despot, and with equal justice by his adherents as a leader who either could not or would not protect his followers.

But although the republicans were still stirring and were even refreshed by an isolated success here and there, chiefly through the blunders of Pompey, the regency's objective in proposing the dictatorship was largely attained, the reins were drawn tighter, the republican party was humbled, and the new monarchy was strengthened. The public began to reconcile itself to the latter. When Pompey recovered from a serious illness, his restoration was celebrated throughout Italy with the accompanying demonstrations of joy which are usual on such occasions in monarchies. The regents showed themselves satisfied. On August 2, 52 B.C., Pompey resigned his dictatorship and shared the consulship with his friend Metellus Scipio.

XI
Rupture Between the Joint Rulers

Even before Pompey's temporary assumption of the political dictatorship, however, the ruling triumvirate had been reduced to a simple partnership by the death of Crassus in one of the fateful campaigns of Roman history. The conference at Luca in 56 B.C. had given Crassus the governorship of Syria, together with an army thought sufficient to regulate affairs in the East. When he arrived in Syria early in 54 B.C. he found that hostilities had already begun with the Parthians, partly because of Pompey's failure to arrange a workable peace with the Parthian state. But even Crassus' burning ambition to become a great conqueror did not prevent him from pausing for months in Asia Minor to despoil a few rich temples and carry out other lucrative schemes, and not until 53 B.C. did he lead his army into the field.

Crassus made the fatal decision to march his army straight across the desert to reach the Parthian forces reportedly poised for flight. This error was matched by an equally significant tactical decision by the Parthians, to dispense entirely with their infantry in favor of heavily armored

cavalry. In two successive desert battles at Carrhae and Sinnaca the Roman army of 40,000 was utterly destroyed, less than one-fourth escaping death or capture; and among the slain was Crassus. This signal proof that a well-led Asiatic army on the right terrain was more than a match for the hitherto invincible legions seemed to shake the Roman supremacy throughout the East. But political dissension among the Parthians, plus better Roman leadership in a theater of war quite different from the uncharted desert, enabled the Romans to turn back the Parthian invasion of western Asia Minor and once again stabilize the Roman rule there.

In Rome, meanwhile, the volcano of revolution was again whirling upward its clouds of stupefying smoke. The Romans began to have no longer a soldier or a denarius to be employed against the public foe, no longer a thought of the destinies of nations. One of the most dreadful signs of the times was that the huge national disaster of Carrhae and Sinnaca gave the politicians of that day far less concern than the wretched tumult on the Appian road in which, a couple of months after Crassus, Clodius the partisan leader perished; but it is easily conceivable and almost excusable. The breach between the two regents, long felt as inevitable and often announced as near, was now assuming a terrifying immediacy. Like the boat of the ancient Greek mariners' tale, the Roman ship of state now found itself between two great rocks moving towards each other. Its crew, expecting at any moment the crash of collision, was paralyzed by nameless dread as they were borne deeper into the whirlpool; and all eyes were fastened there as no one gave a glance to the right or the left.

After Caesar had at the conference of Luca made considerable concessions to

Pompey, and the regents had thus placed themselves substantially on an equal footing, their relation was not without the outward appearance of durability—so far as a division of the monarchical power can ever be lasting. It was another question whether the regents, at least for the present, were determined to keep together and mutually to acknowledge without reservation their rank as equals. That this was the case with Caesar, insofar as he had acquired the interval necessary for the conquest of Gaul at the price of equalization with Pompey, has been already set forth. But Pompey was hardly ever, even provisionally, a true partner in the joint enterprise. His was one of those mean and petty natures towards which it is dangerous to practice generosity. To his paltry spirit it appeared certainly a point of prudence to supplant at the first opportunity his reluctantly acknowledged rival, and his mean soul thirsted after retaliation on Caesar for the humiliation which he had suffered through Caesar's indulgence.

But while it is probable that Pompey, in keeping with his dull and sluggish nature, never formally consented to let Caesar assume an equal rank, yet the design of breaking up the alliance doubtless grew upon him little by little. At any rate the public, which usually saw through Pompey's views and intentions better than he did himself, could not be mistaken in thinking that with the death of the beautiful Julia (who died in the bloom of womanhood in the autumn of 54 B.C., and was soon followed to the tomb by her only child) the personal tie between her father and her husband was broken. Caesar attempted to reestablish these ties by asking for himself the hand of Pompey's only daughter, and offered Octavia, his sister's grand-daughter, who was now his nearest relative, in marriage to his fellow regent. But Pompey left his daughter to her existing husband Faustus

Sulla, the son of Lucius Sulla, and he himself married the daughter of Quintus Metellus Scipio.

The personal breach had unmistakably begun, and it was Pompey who drew back his hand. The populace expected that a political breach would soon follow; but the understanding continued for a time to exist, at least in public affairs. The reason was that Caesar did not wish publicly to dissolve the relation before completing the conquest of Gaul, and Pompey did not wish to dissolve it before the governing authorities and Italy were entirely humbled by his receipt of the dictatorship. It is novel but understandable that under these circumstances the regents supported each other. After the near-disaster of Aduatuca in Gaul in 54 B.C., Pompey lent Caesar one of his Italian legions that had been dismissed on furlough, while Caesar granted his consent and his moral support to Pompey in the repressive measures which the latter took against the stubborn republican opposition.

Only after Pompey had procured at the beginning of 52 B.C. the undivided consulship and an influence in the capital outweighing that of Caesar, and after all the men capable of bearing arms in Italy had tendered their military oath to him personally and in his name, did he resolve to break formally with Caesar as soon as possible. The design quickly became quite apparent. That the prosecutions which followed the tumult on the Appian Way landed with harsh and unerring severity on Caesar's old democratic partisans might perhaps pass as mere awkwardness. That the new law against electioneering intrigues, which was retroactive to 70 B.C., included also the dubious proceedings in Caesar's campaign for the consulship might likewise be nothing more, although not a few Caesarians thought that they perceived in it a definite design.

But people could no longer shut their

eyes, however willing they might be to do so, when Pompey did not select as his consular colleague his former father-in-law, as was fitting under the circumstances and was demanded in many quarters, but chose his new father-in-law Scipio, a puppet wholly dependent on him. Still less could they ignore it when Pompey got the governorship of the two Spains continued to him for five more years (that is, to 45 B.C.), plus a considerable sum appropriated from the state chest for the payment of his troops—not only without securing for Caesar a like prolongation of command and a similar grant of money, but even while laboring to effect Caesar's recall before the end of the agreed-upon term.

These encroachments were unmistakably calculated to undermine Caesar's position and eventually overthrow him. The moment could not be more favorable. Caesar had conceded so much to Pompey at Luca only because Crassus and his Syrian army would necessarily, in the event of any rupture with Pompey, be thrown into Caesar's scale; for Crassus, who since Sulla's day had been deeply hostile to Pompey and almost as long politically and personally allied with Caesar, and whose peculiar character would have made him content with being the new king's banker, could always be counted on by Caesar, who could have no apprehension at all of seeing Crassus confronting him as an ally of his enemies. The catastrophe of June of 53 B.C., by which Crassus and his army perished in Syria, was therefore a terribly severe blow for Caesar also. A few months later the national insurrection in Gaul, just when it had seemed completely subdued, blazed up more violently than ever, and Caesar for the first time was pitted against an equal opponent in the Arvernian king Vercingetorix.

Once again fate had been working for Pompey. Crassus was dead, all Gaul was

in revolt, Pompey was practically dictator of Rome and master of the Senate. What might have happened if now, instead of merely intriguing against Caesar, he had compelled the citizens or the Senate to recall Caesar at once! But Pompey never understood how to take advantage of fortune. He heralded the breach clearly enough: already in 52 B.C. his acts left no doubt about it, and in the spring of the following year he openly expressed his intention to break with Caesar. But he did not make the break, and allowed months to slip away unemployed.

But however Pompey might delay, the crisis was incessantly urged on by the force of circumstances. The impending war was not a struggle between republic and monarchy (for that had been virtually decided years before) but a struggle between Pompey and Caesar for the possession of the crown of Rome. However, neither of the pretenders could have profited by uttering this plain truth, which would merely have driven into the opposing camp all those respectable citizens who desired the continuance of the republic and believed in its possibility. The old battle cries of Gracchus and Drusus, Cinna and Sulla, worn and meaningless as they were, still remained good enough for watchwords in the struggle of the two generals contending for the sole rule; and though for the moment both Pompey and Caesar ranked themselves officially with the so-called popular party, it was a foregone conclusion that Caesar would inscribe on his banner the people and democratic progress, Pompey the aristocracy and the legitimate constitution.

Caesar had no choice. He had from the outset been an earnest democrat. The monarchy as he envisioned it differed more in outward form than in reality from the Gracchan government of the people; and he was too magnanimous and too profound a statesman to conceal his colors and to fight under any other flag than his own. The immediate advantage which this battle cry brought to him was doubtless trifling: it was confined mainly to the circumstance that he was thereby relieved of the inconvenience of directly naming the kingly office, and thus alarming his own adherents and the mass of the lukewarm by that detested word. The democratic banner yielded little further positive gain, since the ideals of Gracchus had been rendered infamous and ridiculous by Clodius. Where was there now (with the possible exception of the Transpadanes) any important group which would have been induced by democratic battle cries to take part in the struggle?

This state of affairs would have decided Pompey's part in the impending struggle, even if it had not been self-evident that he could enter it only as the general of the legitimate republic. Nature had destined him above all men to be a member of an aristocracy, and nothing but accident and selfish motives had carried him into the democratic camp as a deserter. That he should now revert to his Sullan traditions was not merely fitting, but in every way advantageous. Threadbare as was the democratic cry, the conservative slogan could not but have the more potent effect if it proceeded from the right man. Perhaps the majority, at any rate the best of the citizens, belonged to the constitutional party; and its numerical and moral strength might well influence powerfully, perhaps decisively, the impending struggle of the pretenders.

All that was lacking was a leader. Marcus Cato, its present head, fulfilled the functions of leadership (as he understood them) amid daily peril to his life and perhaps without hope of success. His fidelity to duty deserves respect, but to be the last at a forlorn post is commendable in the soldier, not in the general. He lacked the skill either to organize or to bring into

timely action the powerful reserve which had sprung up almost spontaneously in Italy for the party of the overthrown government. For good reason he had never made any pretension to military leadership, on which everything ultimately depended. If instead of this man, who knew not how to act either as party chief or general, a leader of the political and military stature of Pompey should raise the banner of the existing constitution, the citizens of Italy would necessarily flock towards it in crowds, that under it they might help to fight against the kingship of Caesar if not for the kingship of Pompey.

To this was added another consideration at least as important. It was characteristic of Pompey, even when he had formed a resolve, not to be able to find his way to its execution. While he knew perhaps how to conduct war but certainly not how to declare it, the Catonian party, although assuredly unable to conduct it, was able and most willing to supply grounds for the war against the impending monarchy. According to Pompey's intention, he would keep himself aloof and in his peculiar way now talk as though he would immediately depart for his Spanish provinces, now make preparations as though he would set out to take over the command on the Euphrates. Meanwhile the legitimate governing board, the Senate, was to break with Caesar, declare war against him, and entrust the conduct of it to Pompey. Then, yielding to the general desire, he was to come forward as the protector of the constitution against demagogic-monarchical plots, as an upright man and champion of the existing order of things against the profligates and anarchists, as the duly installed general of the Senate against the Imperator of the street, and so once more save his country.

Thus Pompey gained by the alliance with the conservatives a second army (in addition to his personal adherents) and a suitable war manifesto—advantages, to be sure, which were purchased at the high price of combining with those who were in principle opposed to him. Of the countless evils involved in this coalition, the only immediate one (though a very grave one) was that Pompey surrendered the power of commencing hostilities against Caesar when and how he pleased, and made himself dependent on all the accidents and caprices of an aristocratic corporation.

Thus the republican opposition, after having been obliged for years to play the mere spectator with no more voice than a whisper, was now brought back onto the political stage by the impending rupture between the regents. It consisted primarily of the men rallied round Cato, who were resolved in any case to struggle for the republic and against the monarchy, and the sooner the better. The pitiful outcome of the attempt made in 56 B.C. had taught them that by themselves they were in a position neither to conduct war nor even to begin it. It was known to everyone that while the entire Senate was with a few isolated exceptions averse to monarchy, the majority would restore the oligarchic government only if it might be restored without danger—in which case there would be a long time to wait.

Faced by the regents on the one hand, and on the other by this indolent majority which above all things desired peace at any price, and which was averse to any decided action and most of all to a rupture with one or other of the regents, the only possible way for Cato's group to restore the old rule lay in a coalition with the less dangerous of the rulers. If Pompey acknowledged the oligarchic constitution and offered to fight for it against Caesar, the republican opposition must recognize him as its general, and in alliance with him compel the timid majority to a declaration of war. That Pompey was scarcely earnest in his fidelity to the constitution could indeed escape nobody.

But undecided as he was in everything, he had by no means arrived at Caesar's clear and firm conviction that the first business of the new monarch must be to sweep away once and for all the oligarchic lumber. In any event the war would train a really republican army and really republican generals. After the victory over Caesar there would be more favorable prospects of setting aside not merely one of the monarchs, but the monarchy itself. Desperate as was the cause of the oligarchy, Pompey's offer to become its ally was the most favorable arrangement possible for it.

The alliance between Pompey and the Catonian party was concluded with comparative rapidity. Already during the dictatorship of Pompey a remarkable rapprochement had taken place between them. His whole behavior in the Milonian crisis, his abrupt repulse of the mob that offered him the dictatorship, his distinct declaration that he would accept this office only from the Senate, his unrelenting severity against all disturbers of the peace and especially against the ultrademocrats, the surprising complaisance with which he treated Cato and those who shared Cato's views, appeared as much calculated to please the men of order as to offend Caesar. On their side Cato and his followers, instead of combating with their wonted sternness the proposal to confer the dictatorship on Pompey, had made it their own with but trifling changes of form, so that Pompey received the undivided consulship primarily from the hands of Bibulus and Cato.

While the Catonian party and Pompey had thus at least a tacit understanding as early as the beginning of 52 B.C., the alliance was in effect formally concluded when the consular elections for 51 B.C. went not to Cato himself, but (along with an insignificant man belonging to the Senate majority) to one of Cato's most decided adherents, Marcus Claudius

Marcellus. Marcellus was no furious zealot and still less a genius, but a steadfast and strict aristocrat, just the right man to declare war if war was to be begun with Caesar. Under the circumstances this election, so surprising after the recent repression of the republican opposition, can hardly have occurred without the consent or at least the tacit permission of the regent of Rome. Slowly and clumsily, as was his wont, but steadily Pompey moved toward the rupture.

On the other hand it was not Caesar's intention to fall out with Pompey at this moment. He could not indeed seriously desire to share the ruling power permanently with any colleague, least of all with a second-rater like Pompey. Beyond doubt he had long resolved after the conquest of Gaul to take the sole power for himself, if need be by force of arms. But a man like Caesar, in whom the officer was thoroughly subordinate to the statesman, could not fail to perceive that regulating the political organism by force of arms also disorganizes it deeply and often permanently. Therefore he could not but seek to solve the difficulty, if at all possible, without open civil war. And even if civil war were unavoidable, he could not wish to be driven to it when the rising of Vercingetorix in Gaul, imperiling all that had been obtained, occupied him without interruption from the winter of 53-52 B.C. to the winter of 52-51 B.C., and when Pompey and the constitutional party were dominant in Italy.

Accordingly he sought to preserve relations with Pompey and to attain, by peaceful means if at all possible, to the consulship for 48 B.C. that had already been promised to him at Luca. If after a conclusive settlement of Celtic affairs he should then be placed at the head of the state, the decided superiority which he held over Pompey even more as a statesman than as a general might enable him to outmaneuver the latter in the senate

house and in the Forum without special difficulty. Perhaps it was possible to find for his awkward, vacillating, and arrogant rival some sort of honorable and influential position where he might be content to sink into obscurity. The repeated attempts of Caesar to keep himself related to Pompey by marriage may have been designed to pave the way for such a solution, and to settle the old quarrel through the succession of offspring inheriting the blood of both competitors. The republican opposition would then remain without a leader and therefore probably quiet, and peace would be preserved.

If this should not be successful, and if there should be (as was certainly possible) a necessity for resorting to arms, Caesar would as consul in Rome dispose of the compliant majority of the Senate. He could then impede or perhaps frustrate the coalition of the Pompeians and the republicans, and conduct the war far more suitably and more advantageously than if now as proconsul of Gaul he gave orders to march against the Senate and its general. Certainly the success of this plan depended on Pompey being good-natured enough to let Caesar still obtain the consulship for 48 B.C. assured to him at Luca. But even if it failed, it would have the advantage that Caesar had given practical and repeated evidence of the most yielding disposition. On the one hand time would thus be gained for attaining his objectives in Gaul, while on the other his opponents would be left with the odium of initiating the rupture and consequently the civil war—which was of the utmost importance for Caesar with respect to the majority of the Senate and the mercantile party, and even more with regard to his own soldiers.

On these views he acted. To be sure, through new levies in the winter of 52-51 B.C. he increased the number of his legions to eleven, including the one borrowed from Pompey. But at the same time he expressly and openly approved of Pompey's conduct during the dictatorship and the restoration of order in the capital, rejected the warnings of officious friends as calumnies, reckoned every day by which he succeeded in postponing the conflict a gain, overlooked whatever could be overlooked and bore whatever could be borne. He adhered immovably only to one decisive demand: that when his governorship expired at the end of 49 B.C. he should have his second consulship, permissible under the law and promised to him by his colleague.

This demand became the battlefield of the diplomatic war which now began. If Caesar were compelled either to resign his office of governor before the last day of December, 49 B.C., or to postpone the assumption of the consulship in the capital beyond January 1st, there would be a gap between the governorship and the consulate when he would be without office and consequently liable to criminal impeachment—which according to law could not be brought against one who was in office. In such event the public had good reason to prophesy for him the fate of Milo, because Cato had for long been ready to impeach him and Pompey was a more than doubtful protector.

To attain that object Caesar's opponents had a very simple device. According to the election laws every candidate for the consulship was obliged to appear personally before the presiding magistrate for his name to be inscribed in the official list of candidates before the election— that is, half a year before entering an office. It had probably been taken for granted in the conferences at Luca that Caesar would be released from this obligation, which was purely formal and was very often dispensed with. But the decree to that effect had not yet been issued, and, as Pompey now controlled the official machinery, Caesar depended in this respect on the good will of his rival.

Pompey incomprehensibly abandoned this completely secure position of his own accord. With his consent and during his dictatorship the personal appearance of Caesar was dispensed with by a tribunician law. However, when the new election laws were issued soon afterwards, the obligation of candidates to appear personally was repeated in general terms, and no exception was added in favor of those exempted by earlier legislation. Strictly speaking, the privilege granted to Caesar was canceled by the later general law. Caesar complained, and the requisite clause was subsequently added but not confirmed by special decree of the people, so that this enactment by mere insertion could only by looked on *de jure* as null and void. Where Pompey, therefore, might have simply stuck to the law, he preferred first to make a spontaneous concession, then to recall it, and lastly to cloak this recall in a most disloyal manner.

While in this way the shortening of Caesar's governorship was attempted indirectly, the regulations as to governorships issued at the same time sought the same object directly. The ten years for which the governorship had been granted to Caesar, in the last instance through the law proposed by Pompey himself together with Crassus, ran according to the usual mode of reckoning from March 1, 59 B.C., to the last day of February, 49 B.C. However, according to the earlier practice, the proconsul or propraetor had the right of taking over his provincial post immediately after the termination of his consulship or praetorship. Thus the successor of Caesar was to be nominated not from the urban magistrates of 50 B.C., but from those of 49 B.C., who therefore could not take over before January 1st, 48 B.C. So far Caesar still had during the last ten months of the year 49 B.C. a right to his command, not on the ground of the Pompeio-Licinian law, but according to the old rule that a command with a set term still continued after its expiration until the arrival of the successor. But now the new legislation of 52 B.C. granted the governorships not to the outgoing consuls and praetors, but to those who had served five or more years ago. This interval between the civil magistracy and the command, instead of the previous immediate sequence, made it no longer difficult to fill every legally vacant governorship immediately, so that the change of command for the Gallic provinces could take place on March 1, 49 B.C., instead of January 1 of 48 B.C.

The pitiful dissimulation and procrastinating artifice of Pompey are mixed in these arrangements in a remarkable manner with the wily formalism and the constitutional erudition of the republican party. Years before these legal weapons could be used they had been duly prepared, on the one hand to compel Caesar, by sending his successors, to resign his command on the day when his term under Pompey's own law expired (that is, on March 1), and on the other hand, if Caesar declined to resign, to enable the Senate to treat as null and void any votes cast for him in the elections. Caesar, not in a position to hinder these moves in the game, kept silent and let things take their own course.

Gradually the slow constitutional procedure unfolded itself. According to custom the Senate had to deliberate on the governorships of the year 49 B.C., so far as they went to former consuls, at the beginning of 51 B.C., and so far as they went to former praetors, at the beginning of 50 B.C. That earlier deliberation gave the first occasion to discuss the nomination of new governors for the two Gauls in the Senate, and thus the first occasion for open collision between the constitutional party supported by Pompey and the senatorial supporters of Caesar. The consul Marcus Marcellus 'accordingly

introduced a proposal to give the two Gallic provinces as of March 1, 49 B.C., to the two consulars who were to be provided with governorships for that year.

The long-repressed indignation burst forth in a torrent once the sluice was opened, and everything that the Catonians were meditating against Caesar came forth in open discussion. For them it was a settled point that the right granted Caesar by exceptional law to announce his candidacy for the consulship *in absentia* had been canceled by a subsequent decree of the people, and that the reservation inserted in the latter was invalid. The Senate should in their opinion instruct this magistrate, now that the subjugation of Gaul was completed, to discharge immediately the soldiers who had served out their time. The cases where Caesar had bestowed citizenship rights and established colonies in Upper Italy were described by them as unconstitutional. In confirmation of this view Marcellus ordained that a respected senator of the Caesarian colony of Comum, who was entitled to lay claim to Roman citizenship even if his city had only Latin rights, should receive the punishment of scourging, which was admissible only in the case of noncitizens.

Caesar's supporters (among whom the most notable was Gaius Vibius Pansa, formerly an officer in Caesar's army and now tribune of the people) affirmed in the Senate that both equity and the state of Gallic affairs demanded not only that Caesar should not be recalled ahead of time, but that he should be allowed to retain the command along with the consulship. Beyond doubt they pointed out that a few years earlier Pompey had in the same way combined the Spanish governorships with the consulship; that even at the present time, besides the important office of superintending the supply of food to the capital, he held the supreme command in Italy in addition to the Spanish; and that in fact all the men of Italy capable of bearing arms had been sworn in by him and had not yet been released from their oath.

The process began to take shape, but by no means rapidly. The majority of the Senate, seeing the breach approaching, allowed no sitting capable of issuing a decree to take place for months, and further months were lost through the solemn procrastination of Pompey. At length the latter broke the silence and ranged himself, in his usual reserved and vacillating fashion but plainly enough, on the side of the constitutional party against his former ally. He summarily rejected the demand of the Caesarians that their master should be allowed to combine the consulship and the proconsulship. This demand, he added with blunt coarseness, seemed to him no better than if a son should offer to flog his father. He also approved in principle the proposal of Marcellus, insofar as he too declared that he would not allow Caesar directly to attach the consulship to the proconsulship.

However, he also hinted (although without making any binding declaration on the point) that they would perhaps grant Caesar admission to the elections for 49 B.C. without requiring a personal appearance, as well as the continuance of his governorship at the utmost to November 13, 49 B.C. But in the meantime the incorrigible procrastinator consented to the postponement of the nomination of successors to the last day of February, 50 B.C., which Caesar's representatives had asked probably on the ground of a clause of the Pompeio-Licinian law forbidding senatorial discussion of successors before the beginning of a magistrate's last year of office.

To this end the decrees of the Senate were issued on September 29, 51 B.C. The filling of the Gallic governorships was placed on the agenda for March 1, 50 B.C. But already the Senate was attempting to break up the army of Caesar (just as had formerly been done by decree of the people with the army of Lucullus) by inducing his veterans to apply to the Senate for their discharge. Caesar's supporters canceled these decrees, as far as they constitutionally could, by their tribunician veto. But Pompey distinctly declared that the magistrates were bound unconditionally to obey the Senate, and that intercessions and similar antiquated formalities would produce no change.

The aristocratic party, whose organ Pompey now made himself, thus betrayed its intention, in the event of a victory, of revising the constitution to remove everything which had even the semblance of popular freedom. Indeed, this was doubtless the reason why it did not avail itself of the comitia at all in its attacks against Caesar. The coalition between Pompey and the constitutional party was thus formally proclaimed, and sentence was evidently already passed on Caesar, with the date of its issuance simply postponed. The elections for the following year proved thoroughly adverse to him.

During these party maneuvers of his antagonists preparatory to war, Caesar had succeeded in quelling the Gallic insurrection and restoring peace in the whole subject territory. As early as the summer of 51 B.C., under the convenient pretext of defending the frontier but obviously because the legions in Gaul began to be unnecessary there, he moved one of them to northern Italy. He could not avoid perceiving now, if he had not earlier, that he would not be able to avoid drawing the sword against his fellow citizens. Nevertheless, as it was highly desirable to leave the legions for a further time in barely pacified Gaul, he still sought to procrastinate; and being well acquainted with the Senate majority's extreme love of peace, he did not abandon the hope of still restraining them from declaring war despite the pressure from Pompey.

He did not even hesitate to make great sacrifices, if only he might for the present avoid open variance with the supreme governing board. In the spring of 50 B.C. the Senate upon Pompey's suggestion requested that Pompey and Caesar each furnish a legion for the impending Parthian war, and in accordance with this resolution Pompey demanded back from Caesar the legion lent to him some years before, so as to send it also to Syria. Caesar complied with the double demand, because neither the opportuneness of the senatorial decree nor the justice of Pompey's demand could in themselves be disputed, and keeping within the bounds of the law and of formal loyalty was more important to Caesar than a few thousand soldiers. The two legions came without delay and placed themselves at the disposal of the government. However, instead of sending them to the Euphrates, the latter kept them at Capua in readiness for Pompey; and the public once more had the opportunity of comparing Caesar's conciliatory efforts with his opponent's perfidious preparation for war.

For the discussions with the Senate Caesar had succeeded in purchasing not only one of the two consuls of the year, Lucius Aemilius Paullus, but above all the tribune of the people Gaius Curio, probably the most eminent among the many outstanding profligates of this epoch. He was unsurpassed in refined elegance, in fluent and clever oratory, in dexterity of intrigue, and in that energy which in the case of vigorous but vicious characters bestirs itself only the more powerfully amid the pauses of idleness. He was also unsurpassed in the dissoluteness of his life, in his talent for borrowing (his debts were estimated at 60,000,000 sesterces) and in his moral and political want of principle. He had previously offered himself to be bought by Caesar and had been rejected. The talent which he thereafter displayed in his attacks on

Caesar induced the latter to buy him up: the price was high, but the commodity was worth the money.

In the first months of his tribunate Curio had played the independent republican, and thundered against both Caesar and Pompey. He cashed in with rare skill on the apparently impartial position which this gave him, when in March of 50 B.C. the proposal for filling the Gallic governorships for the next year came up anew for discussion in the Senate. He expressed complete approval of the decree, but asked that it should at the same time be extended to Pompey and his extraordinary commands. His arguments—that a constitutional state of things could be brought about only by doing away with all exceptional positions, that Pompey as merely entrusted by the Senate with the proconsulship could still less than Caesar refuse obedience to it, and that the removal of but one of the two generals would only increase the danger to the constitution—carried complete conviction to superficial politicians and to the public at large. Further, Curio's declaration that he intended to prevent any one-sided proceedings against Caesar by the veto constitutionally belonging to him met with much approval in and out of the Senate.

Caesar at once consented to Curio's proposal and offered to resign his governorship and command at any moment, provided Pompey would do the same. (He might safely do so, for Pompey without his Italo-Spanish command was no longer formidable.) Pompey for that same reason could not avoid refusing. His reply—that Caesar must first resign, and that he meant speedily to follow the example thus set—was still more unsatisfactory in that he did not even specify a definite date for his retirement. Again the decision was delayed for months, as Pompey and the Catonians, perceiving the dubious humor of the majority of the

Senate, did not venture to bring Curio's proposal to a vote. Caesar employed the summer in pacifying the regions which he had conquered, in holding a great review of his troops on the Scheldt, and in making a triumphal march through the province of North Italy, which was entirely devoted to him. Autumn found him in Ravenna, the southern frontier town of his province.

At length the vote on Curio's proposal could no longer be delayed, and it yielded a signal defeat of the party of Pompey and Cato. By a margin of 370 to 20 the Senate resolved that the proconsuls of Spain and Gaul should both be called upon to resign, and with boundless joy the good citizens of Rome heard the glad news of Curio's achievement. Pompey was thus recalled by the Senate no less than Caesar; but while Caesar was ready to comply with the command, Pompey flatly refused obedience. The presiding consul Gaius Marcellus, cousin of Marcus Marcellus and like the latter belonging to the Catonian party, addressed a severe lecture to the servile senatorial majority; it was certainly vexatious to be beaten in their own camp, and beaten by a phalanx of poltroons. But where was victory to come from under a leader who, instead of bluntly dictating his orders to the senators, resorted in his later years once more to the instructions of a professor of rhetoric, that with rekindled eloquence he might encounter the youthful vigor and brilliant talents of Curio?

The coalition, thus defeated in the Senate, was in a most painful position. The Catonian section, which had undertaken to push matters to a rupture and to carry the Senate along with them, now saw their vessel vexingly stranded on the sandbanks of the indolent majority. Their leaders had to listen to the bitterest reproaches from Pompey. He pointed out emphatically and with entire justice the dangers of the seeming peace; and though

it depended on himself alone to cut the knot by rapid action, his allies knew very well that they could never expect this from him, and that it was for them to fulfill their promise of bringing matters to a crisis. After the champions of the constitution and of senatorial government had already declared the constitutional rights of the citizens and of the tribunes of the people to be meaningless formalities, they now found themselves driven by necessity to treat the constitutional decisions of the Senate itself in a similar manner and, as the legitimate government would not let itself be saved with its own consent, to save it against its will. This was nothing new; both Sulla and Lucullus had been obliged to carry every energetic resolution conceived in the interest of the government with a high hand irrespective of it, just as Cato and his friends now proposed to do. The machinery of the constitution was in fact utterly obsolete, and the Senate was now (as the comitia had been for centuries) nothing but a worn-out wheel slipping constantly out of its track.

It was rumored in October of 50 B.C. that Caesar had moved four legions from Transalpine into Cisalpine Gaul and stationed them at Placentia. This transfer of troops was within the prerogative of the governor; Curio moreover proved to the Senate the utter groundlessness of the rumor; and that body rejected the proposal of the consul Gaius Marcellus to give Pompey orders to march against Caesar on the strength of it. Yet Marcellus, in concert with the two consuls elected for 49 B.C. who likewise belonged to the Catonian party, by virtue of their own official authority requested the general to put himself at the head of the two legions stationed at Capua, and to call the Italian militia to arms at his discretion. A more casual authorization for beginning a civil war can hardly be conceived, but people had no longer time to trouble over such secondary matters, and Pompey accepted the mission. The military preparations began, and Pompey left the capital in December of 50 B.C. in order personally to forward them.

Caesar had completely attained his object of putting the onus for starting the civil war on his opponents. He had, while himself keeping on legal ground, compelled Pompey to declare war, and to declare it not as representative of the legitimate authority, but as general of an openly revolutionary minority of the Senate which had overawed the majority. This result was not to be reckoned of slight importance, although the masses were not deceived for a moment as to the fact that the war concerned other things than questions of formal law. Now that war had been declared, it was to Caesar's interest to strike as soon as possible. His opponents were just beginning to mobilize, and even the capital was not occupied. In ten or twelve days an army three times as strong as Caesar's troops in Upper Italy could be collected at Rome; but it might not be impossible to surprise the undefended city, or even perhaps by a rapid winter campaign to seize all Italy, and thus preempt the best resources of his opponents before they could be brought to bear.

The sagacious and energetic Curio, who after resigning his tribunate had immediately gone to Caesar at Ravenna, vividly represented this state of affairs to his master—though Caesar hardly needed convincing that longer delay now could only by injurious. However, to forestall any complaints by his antagonists he had brought no troops to Ravenna itself. Thus he could do nothing for the present but order his whole force to set out posthaste; and he had to wait till at least the one legion stationed in Upper Italy reached Ravenna. Meanwhile he sent a communication to Rome which by its extreme submissiveness still further compromised his

opponents in public opinion, and perhaps even, by his show of hesitation, tempted them to slacken their preparations against him.

In this communication Caesar dropped all the counterdemands which he formerly made on Pompey, and offered both to resign the governorship of Transalpine Gaul, and to dismiss eight of his ten legions, at the term fixed by the Senate. He declared himself content if the Senate would grant him either the governorship of Cisalpine Gaul and Illyria with one legion, or that of Cisalpine Gaul alone with two, not until his accession to the consulship, but only until after the close of the consular elections for 48 B.C. Thus he consented to those proposals which at the beginning of the discussions the senatorial party and even Pompey himself had pronounced satisfactory, and showed himself ready to remain in a private position between his election to the consulship and his accession to office.

Whether Caesar was in earnest in these astonishing concessions; whether he had confidence that he would be able to win against Pompey even after granting so much; or whether he reckoned that his opponents had already gone too far to find in these conciliatory proposals more than a proof that Caesar regarded his own cause as lost—can no longer be determined with certainty. The likelihood is that Caesar committed the fault of playing too bold a game, rather than the worse fault of promising something he did not intend to perform. If, strangely enough, his proposals had been accepted, he would probably have made good his word.

Curio undertook once more to represent his master in the lion's den. In three days he made the journey from Ravenna to Rome. When the new consuls Lucius Lentulus and Gaius Marcellus the younger assembled the Senate for the first time on January 1, 49 B.C., Curio delivered in a full meeting the letter addressed by the general to the Senate. In Curio's absence, the leadership of the Caesarian party in Rome had devolved upon the tribunes Marcus Antonius [Mark Antony], well known to the city gossip-chroniclers as Curio's friend and accomplice in all his follies, but also as a brilliant cavalry officer in the Egyptian and Gallic campaigns, and Quintus Cassius, Pompey's former quaestor. Both insisted on the immediate reading of the dispatch. The grave and clear words in which Caesar set forth, with all the irresistible force of truth, the imminence of civil war, the general wish for peace, the arrogance of Pompey, and his own yielding disposition; the proposals for compromise whose moderation doubtless surprised his own partisans; the distinct declaration that this was the last time that he should offer his hand for peace—all these made the deepest impression.

In spite of the dread inspired by the numerous soldiers of Pompey who flocked into the capital, the sentiment of the majority was so unmistakable that the consuls did not dare to let it find expression. Regarding Caesar's renewed proposal that both generals resign their commands simultaneously, regarding all the conciliatory suggestions in his letter, and regarding the proposal made by Marcus Caelius Rufus and Marcus Calidius that Pompey be urged to depart immediately for Spain, the consuls refused to permit a vote—as in their capacity of presiding officers they were entitled to do. Even the proposal to defer a decision until the Italian levy was called up and could protect the Senate—made by Marcus Marcellus, who although a vehement partisan was simply not so blind to military realities as his party—was not allowed to be brought to a vote. Pompey let it be known through his usual mouthpiece, Quintus Scipio, that he was determined to take up the cause of the Senate now or never, and

that he would let it drop if they delayed longer. The consul Lentulus said flatly that even the decision of the Senate was no longer controlling, and that if it should persevere in its cowardice, he would himself act and with his powerful friends take the necessary steps.

Thus overawed, the majority decreed what was commanded. Caesar was ordered at a definite and not distant day to give up Transalpine Gaul to Lucius Domitius Ahenobarbus, and Cisalpine Gaul to Marcus Servilius Nonianus, and to dismiss his army, failing which he should be regarded a traitor. When the tribunes of Caesar's party made use of their right of veto against this resolution, not only were they (as they at least asserted) threatened in the senate house itself by the swords of Pompeian soldiers, and forced, in order to save their lives, to flee in slaves' clothing from the capital: the sufficiently overawed Senate also treated their constitutional interferences as an attempt at revolution, declared the country in danger, and in the usual forms called the whole citizenry to take up arms and all magistrates faithful to the constitution to place themselves at the head of the armies.

Now it was enough. When Caesar was informed by the tribunes who had fled to his camp of the reception which his proposals had met in the capital, he called together the soldiers of the thirteenth legion, which meanwhile had arrived from its cantonments near Tergeste (Trieste) at Ravenna, and unfolded before them the state of things. It was not merely the man of genius versed in the knowledge of men's hearts, whose brilliant eloquence shone forth in this gripping crisis of his own and the world's destiny. It was not even the generous and victorious commander-in-chief addressing soldiers whom he himself had called to arms, and who for eight years had followed his banners with daily increasing enthusiasm.

There spoke, above all, the energetic and consistent statesman, who had now for nine-and-twenty years defended the cause of freedom in good times and bad; who had braved for it the daggers of assassins and the executioners of the aristocracy, the swords of the Germans and the waves of the unknown ocean, without ever yielding or wavering; who had torn to pieces the Sullan constitution, overthrown the rule of the Senate, and furnished the defenseless and unarmed democracy with protection and arms by means of the struggle beyond the Alps. And he spoke not to the Roman public, whose republican enthusiasm had been long burnt down to ashes and dross, but to the young men from the towns and villages of Northern Italy, who still felt freshly and purely the mighty influence of the thought of civic freedom; who were still capable of fighting and dying for ideals; who had themselves received for their country in a revolutionary way from Caesar the citizenship which the Roman government had refused; whom Caesar's fall would leave once more at the mercy of the fasces, and who already possessed practical proofs of how the oligarchy proposed to use these against the Transpadanes.

Such were the listeners before whom such an orator pointed out the thanks which the nobility were preparing for the general and his army in return for the conquest of Gaul; the contemptuous setting aside of the comitia; the overawing of the Senate; the sacred duty of protecting with armed hand the tribunate of the people wrested five hundred years ago by their fathers arms in hand from the nobility, and of keeping the ancient oath, which their ancestors had sworn for themselves as for their children's children, that they would man by man stand firm even unto death for the tribunes of the people. And when he, the leader and general of the popular party, summoned

the soldiers of the people, now that conciliatory means had been exhausted and concession had reached its utmost limits, to follow him in the last, the inevitable, the decisive struggle against the equally hated and despised, equally perfidious and incapable, and in fact ludicrously incorrigible aristocracy, not an officer or a soldier could hold back. The order was given for the march. At the head of his vanguard Caesar crossed the narrow brook separating his province from Italy, which the constitution forbade the proconsul of Gaul to pass. When after nine years' absence he trod once more the soil of his native land, he trod at the same time the path of revolution. "The die was cast."

XII
Civil War: Brundisium, Ilerda, and Dyrrhachium

Arms were thus to decide which of the two men who had jointly ruled Rome was to be its first sole ruler. Let us see what were Caesar's and Pompey's comparative resources for waging the impending war.

Caesar's power rested primarily on the unlimited authority which he enjoyed in his own party. If the ideas of democracy and of monarchy met together in it, this was not the result of an accidentally formed coalition which might be accidentally dissolved. On the contrary, the very nature of a democracy without a representative constitution demanded that democracy and monarchy should find their highest and ultimate expression in Caesar. In political as in military matters the first and the final decision lay with Caesar. However highly he honored any serviceable instrument, it remained an instrument still. In his own party Caesar was surrounded not by confederates but by military-political adjutants, who as a rule had risen from the army, and who as soldiers were trained never to ask the reason why but unconditionally to obey. For this reason, at the outbreak of the civil war only one of Caesar's officers and soldiers refused him obedience; and the fact that that one was the foremost of all serves simply to confirm this view of Caesar's relation to his adherents.

Titus Labienus had shared all Caesar's troubles of the dark times of Catiline as well as all the luster of the Gallic conquest. He had regularly held independent command, and frequently led half the army. As the oldest, ablest, and most faithful of Caesar's adjutants, he was also beyond question highest in position and honor. As late as 50 B.C. Caesar had entrusted to him the supreme command in Cisalpine Gaul, partly to put this confidential post into safe hands and partly to highlight the views of Labienus in his campaign for the consulship. But from this very position Labienus entered into communication with the opposite party, moved to Pompey's headquarters when hostilities began in 49 B.C., and fought through the whole struggle with unparalleled bitterness against his old friend and master.

We are not sufficiently informed either as to the character of Labienus or as to the special circumstances of his changing sides. In the main, however, his case certainly presents nothing but further proof of the fact that a military chief can rely far more confidently on his captains than on his marshals. To all appearances Labienus was one of those persons in whom military efficiency is combined with utter incapacity as statesmen. Consequently, if they unfortunately choose or are compelled to take part in politics, they exhibit those strange paroxysms of giddiness of which the history of Napoleon's marshals supplies so many tragicomic examples. He may well have felt himself entitled to rank alongside Caesar as the second chief

of the democracy, and the rejection of his claim may have sent him over to the opposing camp. His case illustrated for the first time the gravity of the evil, that Caesar's treatment of his officers as mere adjutants did not permit the rise of men fitted to undertake a separate command, while at the same time he urgently needed such men amid the easily foreseeable spread of the struggle throughout the empire. But this disadvantage was far outweighed by that unity of leadership which was the primary condition of success, and a condition which could be preserved only at such a cost.

This unity of leadership acquired its full power through the efficiency of its instruments, first of all the army. It still numbered nine legions of infantry, or at the most 50,000 men. All of these, however, had faced the enemy, and two-thirds had served in all the campaigns against the Celts. The cavalry consisted of German and Noric mercenaries, whose usefulness and trustworthiness had been proved in the war against Vercingetorix. Eight years of the most varied warfare against the Celtic nation (which was brave, although militarily quite inferior to the Italian) had given Caesar the opportunity of organizing his army as he alone knew how to organize it.

The whole efficiency of the soldier presupposes physical vigor. In Caesar's levies more regard was had to the strength and activity of the recruits than to their means or morals. But the serviceableness of an army, like that of any other machine, depends above all on the ease and quickness of its movements; and the soldiers of Caesar attained a perfection rarely reached and probably never surpassed in their constant readiness for immediate departure and in their rapidity of marching. Courage, of course, was valued above everything. Caesar practiced with unrivaled mastery the art of stimulating *esprit de corps,* so that the eminence accorded to particular soldiers and divisions appeared desirable even to those who were lower in the hierarchy of valor. He weaned his men from fear by often—where it could be done without serious danger—keeping his soldiers ignorant of an approaching battle, allowing them to meet the enemy unexpectedly.

But obedience was on a parity with valor. The soldier was required to do what he was bidden without asking why. Many an aimless fatigue was imposed on him solely as training in the difficult art of blind obedience. The discipline was strict but not harassing. It was exercised with unrelenting vigor when the soldier was in the presence of the enemy. At other times, however, especially after victory, the reins were relaxed; and if an otherwise efficient soldier then wished to indulge in perfumery or deck himself with elegant arms and the like, or even if he were guilty of outrages or irregularities of a very questionable kind—provided only his military duties were not immediately affected—the foolery and the crime were allowed to pass, and the general lent a deaf ear to the complaints of the provincials on such points. Mutiny, on the other hand, was never pardoned in the instigators or even in the guilty corps itself.

But the true soldier ought to be capable, brave, and obedient willingly and spontaneously, and it is the privilege of gifted natures alone to impel the animated machine which they govern to a joyful service by means of example and of hope, and especially by the consciousness of being turned to suitable use. As the officer who demands valor from his troops must himself have looked danger in the face, Caesar even when general found opportunity of drawing his sword and using it like the best. Moreover, in activity and fatigue he was constantly far more demanding of himself than of his soldiers.

Caesar also took care that victory, whose fruits are doubtless primarily for the general, should arouse the hope of personal gain in his soldiers. We have already mentioned that he knew how to arouse enthusiasm in his soldiers for the democratic cause, so far as the times still permitted enthusiasm, and that the political equalization of the Transpadane country (the native land of most of his soldiers) with Italy proper was one of the announced objects of the struggle. Of course material recompense was not wanting, both special rewards for distinguished feats of arms and general rewards for every efficient soldier. The officers had their portions, the soldiers received presents, and the most lavish gifts were promised for the triumph.

Above all, Caesar as a true commander understood how to awaken in every single component, large or small, of the mighty machine the consciousness of its suitable application. The ordinary man, destined for service, is ever willing to be an instrument if he feels that a master guides him. Everywhere and at all times the eagle eye of the general rested on the whole army, rewarding and punishing with impartial justice, and directing the action of each toward the good of all. There was no experimenting or trifling with the sweat and blood of the humblest; but for that very reason, where necessary, unconditional devotion even to death was required.

Without allowing each individual to see the whole plan of action, Caesar yet permitted each to catch such glimpses of the political and military connection of things that he might be recognized—even idealized—by his soldiers as a statesman and a general. He treated his soldiers throughout not as equals, but as men entitled to demand and able to endure the truth, who had to trust the assurances of their general without thinking of deception or listening to rumors; as comrades through long years of warfare and victory, among whom hardly any one was not known to him by name and in the course of so many campaigns had not formed a more or less personal relation to the general; as good companions, with whom he talked and dealt confidentially with the cheerful elasticity peculiar to him; as followers, to requite whose services and to avenge whose wrongs and death he regarded as a sacred duty.

Perhaps there never was an army which was so perfectly what an army ought to be—a machine able and willing for its ends, in the hand of a master who transfers to it his own elasticity. Caesar's soldiers were, and felt themselves, a match for a tenfold superior force—in connection with which it should not be overlooked that under the Roman tactics, intended solely for hand-to-hand conflict and especially for combat with the sword, the practiced Roman soldier showed far greater superiority over the novice than is the case today.

But still more than by superiority of valor the adversaries of Caesar were humbled by the unswerving fidelity of the soldiers for their general. It is perhaps without a parallel in history that when the general summoned his soldiers to follow him into a civil war, with the single exception of Labienus no Roman officer or soldier deserted him. His opponents' hopes for extensive desertion were thwarted as ignominiously as were their earlier attempts to break up his army. Labienus himself appeared in the camp of Pompey with a band of Celtic and German horsemen, but without a single legionary. Indeed, the soldiers, as if to show that the war was quite as much their affair as their general's, agreed among themselves that for the duration they would forgo their pay, which Caesar had promised to double on the outbreak of the civil war, and would meanwhile support their poorer comrades from the general means. In addition, every

subaltern officer equipped and paid a trooper out of his own purse.

While Caesar thus had certain essentials—unlimited political and military authority and a trustworthy army ready for the fight—his power only extended over a very limited space. It was based essentially on the province of Upper Italy. This region was not merely the most populous Italian district, but was also devoted to the democratic cause as its own. The feeling which prevailed there is shown by the conduct of a division of recruits from Opitergium, which not long after the outbreak of the war in Illyrian waters, surrounded on a wretched raft by the war vessels of the enemy, allowed themselves to be shot at all day until sunset without surrendering, when the survivors put themselves to death with their own hands during the following night. It is easy to conceive what might be expected of such a population. As they had already granted Caesar the means of more than doubling his original army, so after the war's outbreak numerous recruits presented themselves for the ample levies that were immediately instituted.

In Italy proper, on the other hand, the influence of Caesar was not even remotely comparable to that of his opponents. Although he had the skill by dexterous maneuvers to put the Catonian party in the wrong, and had sufficiently commended the justice of his cause to all who sought a pretext either to remain neutral, like the majority of the Senate, or to embrace his side, like his soldiers and the Transpadanes, the mass of the citizenry naturally did not allow themselves to be misled. When the commandant of Gaul put his legions in motion against Rome, they regarded Cato and Pompey as the defenders of the legitimate republic and Caesar as the democratic usurper, despite all legalistic explanations. Moreover, people in general expected from the nephew of Marius, the son-in-law of Cinna, and the ally of Catiline a repetition of the Marian and Cinnan horrors and a realization of Catiline's intended saturnalia of anarchy. To be sure, Caesar certainly gained allies through this expectation, for the political refugees immediately put themselves at his disposal in a body, the ruined men saw in him their deliverer, and the lowest rabble were thrown into a ferment on the news of his advance. But such friends are more dangerous than foes.

In the provinces and the dependent states Caesar had even less influence than in Italy. Transalpine Gaul as far as the Rhine and the Channel obeyed him, and the colonists of Narbo as well as the Roman settlers in Gaul were devoted to him. But in the Narbonese province itself the constitutional party had numerous adherents, and even the newly conquered regions were far more a burden than a benefit to Caesar in the impending civil war. In fact, for a good reason he used no Celtic infantry at all in that war, and but little cavalry. In the other provinces, and in the neighboring partly or wholly independent states, Caesar had indeed attempted to procure support, had lavished rich presents on the princes, had caused great buildings to be erected in various towns, and had granted them financial and military assistance. But not much had been gained by such means, and the relations with the German and Celtic princes along the Rhine and the Danube —particularly the connection with the Noric king Voctio, so important for the recruiting of cavalry—were probably the only such ties of any importance to him.

While Caesar thus entered the struggle only as commandant of Gaul, without other essential resources than efficient adjutants, a faithful army, and a devoted province, Pompey began it as *de facto* head of the Roman commonwealth, in full possession of all the resources of the legitimate government of the great Roman empire. But while his political and military position was far more considerable, it was also far less definite and firm. The unity of leadership which automatically went with Caesar's position was inconsistent with the nature of a coalition; and although Pompey, too much of a soldier to deceive himself as to its importance, attempted to force it on the coalition and had himself nominated by the Senate as sole and absolute generalissimo by land and sea, yet the Senate itself could not be set aside politically nor hindered from an occasional and therefore doubly injurious interference with the military command. The recollection of twenty years' war waged between Pompey and the constitutional party with envenomed weapons on both sides; the mutual and ill-concealed feeling that the first consequence of victory would be a rupture between the victors; the well-justified contempt which each entertained for the other; the pitiful number of respectable and influential men in the ranks of the aristocracy, and the intellectual and moral inferiority of almost all who took part in the struggle—all these together produced among Caesar's opponents a reluctant and refractory cooperation which contrasted sadly with the harmonious and compact action on the other side.

While all the disadvantages attending the coalition of naturally hostile powers were thus felt in unusual degree by Caesar's antagonists, this coalition was still a formidable power. It alone commanded the sea, all ports, all ships of war, and all the materials for equipping a fleet. The two Spains—the home of Pompey's power just as the two Gauls were the home of Caesar's—were faithful to their master and under able and trustworthy administrators. All the other provinces except for the two Gauls were governed by recently appointed men who were safely under the influence of Pompey and the active Senate minority. The protectorates all took decisive part against Caesar and in favor of Pompey. The most important princes and cities had the closest personal relations with Pompey by virtue of his manifold activities.

As for Italy, the great majority of the citizens were, as already noted, opposed to Caesar—especially, of course, the whole aristocracy with its very considerable following, but also in nearly equal degree the great capitalists, who could not hope in the event of a thorough reform of the commonwealth to preserve their partisan jury courts and their monopoly of extortion. Of equally antidemocratic sentiments were the small capitalists, the landholders and generally all classes that had anything to lose; but in these groups the cares of the next rent term and of sowing and reaping outweighed, as a rule, every other consideration.

The army at Pompey's disposal consisted chiefly of the Spanish troops, seven wholly trustworthy legions inured to war, to which might be added the weak and scattered forces in Syria, Asia, Macedonia, Africa, Sicily, and elsewhere. In Italy there were under arms at the outset only the two legions recently transferred by Caesar, whose effective strength did not amount to more than 7,000 men. Their trustworthiness was also more than doubtful, because, levied in Cisalpine Gaul and being old comrades-in-arms of Caesar, they were highly indignant at the unbecoming intrigue by which they had been made to change camps, and they recalled with longing their general who had magnanimously paid them on their departure the presents which were promised to every soldier for the triumph. But apart from the Spanish troops who might arrive in Italy the following spring either by land via Gaul or by sea, the men of the three legions still remaining from the levies of 55 B.C. as well as the Italian levy

sworn to allegiance in 52 B.C. could be recalled from their furlough. Including these, the number of troops at Pompey's disposal in Italy, without counting the seven legions in Spain and those scattered in other provinces, amounted to ten legions or about 60,000 men.

Thus it was no exaggeration at all when Pompey asserted that he had only to stamp his foot to cover the ground with armed men. It is true that a brief interval was required to render these soldiers available, but the arrangements for this purpose as well as for organizing the new levies ordered by the Senate were already everywhere in progress. Immediately after the decisive decree of the Senate on January 7, 49 B.C., in the dead of winter the most eminent aristocrats set out to hasten the calling up of recruits and the preparation of arms. The lack of cavalry was much felt, as they had been accustomed to rely wholly on the provinces, especially the Celtic ones, for this arm. To make at least a beginning, three hundred gladiators belonging to Caesar were taken from the fencing schools of Capua and mounted. However, the step met with such general disapproval that Pompey disbanded this troop and levied in its place 300 horsemen from the mounted slave herdsmen of Apulia.

The state treasury, being at its usual low ebb, was supplemented from the local treasuries and even from the temple treasures of the municipalities.

Under these circumstances the war opened at the beginning of January, 49 B.C. Of troops capable of marching Caesar had not more than a legion—5,000 infantry and 300 cavalry—at Ravenna, which by highway was some 240 miles from Rome. Pompey had two weak legions—7,000 infantry and a small squadron of cavalry—under the orders of Appius Claudius at Luceria, from which the highway distance to the capital was about the same. The other troops of Caesar, not counting the raw divisions still being formed, were stationed half on the Saône and Loire, the other half in Belgica, while Pompey's Italian reserves were already arriving from all sides at their rendezvous. Long before even the first of Caesar's Transalpine divisions could arrive in Italy, a far superior army would surely be ready to receive it.

It seemed folly, with a band the size of Catiline's and for the moment without any effective reserve, to assume the aggressive against a superior and hourly increasing army under an able general; but it was a folly in the spirit of Hannibal. If the beginning of the struggle were postponed till spring, the Spanish troops of Pompey would assume the offensive in Transalpine and his Italian troops in Cisalpine Gaul; and Pompey, a match for Caesar in tactics and his superior in experience, was a formidable antagonist in such an ordered campaign. For the moment, however, accustomed as he was to operate slowly and surely with superior masses, Pompey might be disconcerted by a wholly improvised attack. And while the suddenness of the war and the toil of a winter campaign could not greatly distress Caesar's thirteenth legion, after its severe trials in Gaul, these same burdens might well disorganize the Pompeian corps consisting of old soldiers of Caesar or of ill-trained recruits still in the course of formation.

Accordingly Caesar advanced into Italy. Two highways led south at that time from the Romagna: the Aemilio-Cassian, from Bononia over the Apennines to Arretium and Rome; and the Popillio-Flaminian, which led from Ravenna along the coast of the Adriatic to Fanum, where one branch ran westward through the Furlo pass to Rome, another southward to Ancona and thence onward to Apulia. On the former Marcus Antonius advanced as far as Arretium, on the latter Caesar himself pushed forward. Re-

sistance was nonexistent: the aristocratic recruiting officers had no military skill, their bands of recruits were not yet soldiers, and the inhabitants of the country towns were only anxious to avoid a siege. When Curio with 1,500 men approached Iguvium, a couple of thousand Umbrian recruits assembled there took flight at the mere word of his approach, and similar results on a small scale took place everywhere.

Caesar had to choose whether he would march against Rome, only 130 miles from his cavalry at Arretium, or against the legions encamped at Luceria. He chose the latter plan, to the boundless consternation of the enemy. Pompey received the news of Caesar's advance at Rome, and seemed at first disposed to defend the capital; but when the tidings arrived of Caesar's entrance into the Picenian territory and of his first successes there, he ordered Rome's evacuation. A panic, augmented by the false report that Caesar's cavalry had reached the gates, came over the world of quality. The senators, warned that every one remaining in the capital would be treated as Caesar's accomplice, streamed through the gates in crowds. The consuls so totally lost their senses that they did not even secure the treasury; and when Pompey urged them to fetch it, for which there was still time, they replied that they deemed it safer if first he occupied Picenum.

All was perplexity. Consequently, a great council of war was held in Teanum Sidicinum, at which Pompey, Labienus, and both consuls were present. First, Caesar's proposals of accommodation were again submitted. Even now he declared himself ready to dismiss his army, hand over his provinces to his successors, and become a candidate in the regular way for the consulship, provided Italy were disarmed and Pompey departed for Spain. The answer was that if Caesar immediately returned to his province, they would procure the disarming of Italy and the departure of Pompey by a senatorial decree to be duly passed in the capital.

Perhaps this reply was intended not as a transparent deceit but as an acceptance; in reality, however, it was the opposite. The personal conference which Caesar desired with Pompey the latter had to decline, to avoid provoking still more the constitutional party's distrust by the appearance of a new coalition with Caesar. As for the management of the war, it was agreed in Teanum that Pompey should take the command of the troops stationed at Luceria, on whom everything depended notwithstanding their untrustworthiness; that he should advance with these into Picenum, his own and Labienus' native country; and that he should personally call the general levy there to arms (as he had done thirty-five years ago) and attempt at the head of the faithful Picentine cohorts and the veterans formerly under Caesar to halt the enemy's advance.

Everything thus depended on whether Picenum held out until Pompey could come to its defense. Already Caesar's reunited army had penetrated into it along the coast road by way of Ancona. Here, too, preparations were in full swing. In the northernmost Picenian town, Auximum, a considerable band of recruits was collected under Publius Attius Varus. However, at the urging of the municipality Varus evacuated the town even before Caesar appeared, and a handful of Caesar's soldiers dispersed the troop not far from Auximum after a brief conflict—the first in the war. In like manner soon afterwards Gaius Lucilius Hirrus evacuated Camerinum with 3,000 men, and Publius Lentulus Spinther quit Asculum with 5,000. The men, thoroughly devoted to Pompey, for the most part willingly abandoned their houses and farms and followed their leaders over the frontier. But the district itself was already lost

when the officer sent by Pompey for the initial defense, Lucius Vibullius Rufus— no genteel senator, but a soldier experienced in war—arrived there. He had to content himself with taking the six or seven thousand recruits away from the incapable recruiting officers, and conducting them to the nearest rendezvous.

The appointed meeting place for the levies of the Albensian, Marsian and Paelignian territories was Corfinium, and there were assembled nearly 15,000 recruits from the most warlike and trustworthy regions of Italy, the flower of the constitutional army still in course of formation. Vibullius arrived there several days before Caesar, and there was nothing to prevent him from immediately obeying Pompey's instructions and conducting the rescued Picenian recruits together with those assembled at Corfinium to join the main army in Apulia. But the commandant in Corfinium was Lucius Domitius, Caesar's designated successor in Transalpine Gaul and one of the most narrow-minded and stubborn Roman aristocrats. He not only refused to comply with Pompey's orders, but also prevented Vibullius from departing with the men from Picenum. So firmly did he believe that Pompey only delayed from obstinacy, and must necessarily come to his relief, that he made no serious preparations for a siege, and did not even gather into Corfinium the bands of recruits quartered in surrounding towns.

Pompey, however, did not appear, and for good reason. While he might perhaps use his two untrustworthy legions as a reserve for the Picenian general levy, he could not oppose Caesar with them alone. A few days later, on February 14, Caesar arrived, having been joined in Picenum by the twelfth legion and near Corfinium by the eighth, both from beyond the Alps. Besides these, three new legions had been formed partly from Pompeians who had been captured or had presented themselves voluntarily, and partly from the recruits that were being levied everywhere. Thus Caesar before Corfinium already headed an army of 40,000 men, half of whom had seen service.

So long as Domitius hoped for Pompey's arrival he prepared to defend the town. But when Pompey's letters had at length undeceived him, he resolved not to persevere at the forlorn post (which would have rendered the greatest service to his party) nor even to capitulate, but rather, while informing the common soldiers that relief was close at hand, to escape with his officers of quality the following night. Yet he could not even carry this pretty scheme into effect, for the confusion of his behavior betrayed him. When part of the men began to mutiny, the Marsian recruits wished to fight against the mutineers, believing such infamy on the part of their general to be impossible. They too were obliged reluctantly to recognize the truth of the accusation, whereupon the whole garrison arrested its staff and handed it, themselves, and the town over to Caesar on February 20. The corps of 3,000 at Alba, and 1,500 recruits assembled in Tarracina, thereupon laid down their arms as soon as Caesar's patrols of horsemen appeared; a third division of 3,500 men in Sulmo had previously been compelled to surrender.

Pompey had given up Italy as soon as Caesar occupied Picenum. However, he wished to delay his embarkation to the last moment to save as much of his force as possible. Accordingly he set out slowly for Brundisium, the nearest seaport. Thither came the two legions of Luceria and such recruits as Pompey had been able hastily to collect in the deserted Apulia, as well as the troops raised by the consuls and other commissioners in Campania. There also gathered a number of political fugitives, including the most respected senators and their families. The

embarkation began, but the vessels at hand would not in one trip carry the whole multitude, which still amounted to 25,000 persons. No course remained but to divide the army, of which the larger part set out on March 4. With the smaller remainder (some 10,000 men) Pompey awaited at Brundisium the return of the fleet; for however desirable Brundisium might be for an eventual reinvasion of Italy, the place could not be held permanently against Caesar.

Meanwhile Caesar arrived and the siege began. Caesar attempted first to close the mouth of the harbor against the returning fleet by moles and floating bridges. But Pompey armed the trading vessels in the harbor, and managed to prevent the closing until the fleet appeared. Then Pompey, with great dexterity and in spite of the vigilance of the besiegers and the hostility of the inhabitants, managed to evacuate every last soldier from the town unharmed and transport them to Greece. Caesar's further pursuit, like the siege, failed for want of ships.

Thus, in a two-month campaign without a single serious engagement, Caesar had so broken up an army of ten legions that less than the half of it had with great difficulty escaped in a confused flight across the sea. The whole Italian peninsula, including the capital with the state chest and all the stores accumulated there, had fallen to the victor. The beaten party had reason to bewail the terrifying rapidity, sagacity, and energy of the "monster."

But it may be questioned whether Caesar gained or lost by his conquest of Italy. Militarily, no doubt, considerable resources were both denied his opponents and rendered available for him. Even in the spring of 49 B.C. his army embraced, in consequence of the levies instituted everywhere, a considerable number of new legions in addition to the nine old ones. On the other hand, however, it now became necessary not only to establish a considerable garrison, but also to take measures against the closing of the overseas traffic contemplated by his opponents, and against the famine which consequently threatened the capital. Thus Caesar's already amply complex military task was complicated further still.

Financially, it was certainly important that Caesar had the good fortune to seize the state treasury in the capital. But the principal sources of income and particularly the revenues from the East were still in the hands of his enemies, and the greatly increased demands of the army and the new obligation to provide for the starving population of the capital meant that the considerable sums which were found quickly melted away. Caesar soon found himself compelled to appeal to private credit, but since it seemed that he could not possibly depend long on this resource, extensive confiscations were generally anticipated as the next step.

Still more serious political difficulties were created by the conquest of Italy. Fear of an anarchical revolution was universal among the propertied classes. Friends and foes saw in Caesar a second Catiline, Pompey believing or pretending to believe that Caesar had been driven to civil war by the impossibility of paying his debts. While this was patently absurd, Caesar's antecedents were in fact anything but reassuring, and still less reassuring was the aspect of the retinue around him. Individuals of the most questionable reputation, notorious personages like Quintus Hortensius, Gaius Curio, and Marcus Antonius (the latter was the stepson of the Catilinarian Lentulus, who was executed on the orders of Cicero) were its most prominent members. The highest posts were bestowed on men who had long ceased even to reckon up their debts, and who not only kept dancing-girls—which others did also—but appeared publicly

with them. Was there any wonder that even grave and politically impartial men expected amnesty for all exiled criminals, canceling of creditor's claims, comprehensive mandates of confiscation, proscription, murder—nay, even a plundering of Rome by the Gallic soldiery?

But in this respect the "monster" deceived his foes as well as his friends. As soon as Caesar occupied the first Italian town, Ariminum, he prohibited all common soldiers from appearing armed within the walls, and the country towns, whether friendly or hostile, were protected from all injury. When the mutinous garrison surrendered Corfinium late in the evening, Caesar disregarded every military consideration by postponing the town's occupation until the following morning solely to avoid abandoning the citizens to the nocturnal invasion of his exasperated soldiers. The common soldiers among Caesar's prisoners, presumably indifferent to politics, were incorporated into his own army; the officers were not merely spared but freely released without distinction and without the exaction of pledges, and all which they claimed as private property was promptly handed over without any strict investigation of their claims. Lucius Domitius himself was thus treated, and even the money and baggage which Labienus had left behind was sent after him to the enemy's camp.

Despite his painful financial embarrassment, the immense estates of his opponents were not touched. Indeed, Caesar preferred to borrow from friends, rather than stir up the possessors of property even by exacting the formally admissible but practically antiquated land tax. The victor regarded only the less difficult half of his task as solved with the victory: it could be consolidated, according to his own expression, only by the unconditional pardon of the vanquished. Accordingly, during the whole march from Ravenna to Brundisium he incessantly renewed his efforts to bring about a personal conference with Pompey and a tolerable compromise.

But if the aristocracy had previously refused to listen to any reconciliation, their unexpected and disgraceful emigration raised their wrath to madness, and the wild threats of the defeated contrasted strangely with the victor's moderation. The communications from the emigrants' camp to their friends in Italy were full of projects for confiscations and proscriptions, for purifying the Senate and the state, compared with which the Sullan restoration was child's play, and which even the moderates of their own party heard with horror.

This contrast between the frantic passion of impotence and the wise moderation of power produced its effect. The whole group more concerned with material than political interests threw itself into Caesar's arms. The country towns idolized "the uprightness, the moderation, the prudence" of the victor; and even opponents conceded that these demonstrations of respect were sincere. The great capitalists the tax farmers, and the jurymen showed no special desire, after the shipwreck of the constitutional party in Italy, to entrust themselves further to the same pilots. Capital came out of hiding, and "the rich lords resorted again to their daily task of writing their rent rolls."

Even the great majority of the Senate, at least numerically speaking—for few of the nobler and more influential senators were included—had disregarded the orders of Pompey and the consuls by staying in Italy, some even in the capital itself; and they acquiesced in Caesar's rule. His moderation, well calculated even in its apparent excess, attained its object by partly allaying the trembling anxiety of the propertied classes. This was doubtless an incalculable gain for the future, for the prevention of anarchy—and the

scarcely less dangerous fear of anarchy—was indispensable to the future reorganization of the commonwealth.

But at the moment this moderation was more dangerous for Caesar than renewing the Cinnan and Catilinarian fury would have been: while it did not convert enemies into friends, it converted friends into enemies. Caesar's Catilinarian adherents were indignant at being denied murder and pillage, and these audacious and desperate personages, some of them men of talent, would likely prove cross and intractable. The republicans, on the other hand, were neither converted nor propitiated by the conqueror's leniency. According to the Catonian party's creed, duty towards what they called their fatherland superseded every other consideration; even one who owed freedom and life to Caesar remained duty bound to take up arms or at least to plot against him. The lukewarm constitutionalists were no doubt willing to accept peace and protection from the new monarch. Nevertheless, they ceased not to curse both monarchy and monarch at heart.

The more clearly the change of the constitution became manifest, the more distinctly the great majority of the citizens—both in the capital with its keener taste for political excitement, and among the more energetic country population—awoke to a consciousness of their republican sentiments. The friends of the constitution in Rome reported truthfully to their brethren in exile that all classes and all persons at home favored Pompey. The discontent among these circles was increased by the moral pressure which the more notable and decided emigrants exercised over the humbler and more lukewarm multitude. The conscience of the honorable man smote him for staying in Italy, while the half-aristocrat fancied himself among the plebeians if he did not go into exile, or even if he took his seat in the Caesarian Senate of nobodies. The victor's extreme clemency gave increased political importance to this silent opposition. Since Caesar abstained from terrorism, it seemed as if his secret opponents could show their dislike for his rule without much risk.

Thus Caesar soon experienced remarkable treatment at the hands of the Senate. He had begun the struggle to liberate the overawed Senate from its oppressors. This done, he wished to obtain Senate approval of his acts, and full powers for continuing the war. For this purpose the tribunes belonging to his party convoked the Senate on April 1. The meeting was fairly well-attended, but the more notable of the senators remaining in Italy were absent, including even Marcus Cicero, the former leader of the servile majority, and Caesar's own father-in-law Lucius Piso.

Still worse, those present were cool to Caesar's proposals. When he spoke of full power to continue the war, one of the only two consulars present, Servius Sulpicius Rufus, a timid man who desired nothing but a quiet death in bed, suggested that Caesar would deserve well of his country if he abandoned the thought of carrying the war to Greece and Spain. When Caesar thereupon requested the Senate at least to transmit his peace proposals to Pompey, there was no opposition to the request itself, but the threats of the emigrants had so terrified the neutrals that no one was found to carry the olive branch.

Thus, through the aristocracy's disinclination to help build the monarch's throne, and through the same inertness which Caesar had shortly before used to frustrate Pompey's legal nomination as generalissimo in the civil war, he too was now thwarted in a like request. Other impediments also arose. Caesar wished to be named as dictator, in order to regularize his position in some kind of way. But his wish was not granted because constitu-tionally such a magistrate could only be appointed by one of the consuls, and the attempt of Caesar to buy the consul Lentulus (whose disordered finances made him a good prospect) proved a failure.

Furthermore, the tribune of the people Lucius Metellus lodged a protest against all Caesar's acts, and threatened to protect personally the public chest when Caesar's men came to empty it. Caesar could not avoid ordering the inviolable person pushed aside as gently as possible. Otherwise, however, he continued to abstain from all violent steps. He declared to the Senate (just as the constitutional party had done shortly before) that he had desired to regulate matters legally with the help of the supreme authority, but since this help was refused he could dispense with it.

Without more ado about the Senate and legal formalities, he gave the temporary administration of the capital to the praetor Marcus Aemilius Lepidus as city prefect, and made the necessary arrangements for the administration of the provinces that obeyed him. Even amid the din of the gigantic struggle, and despite Caesar's lavish promises, it still made a deep impression on the multitude when they first saw in their free Rome the monarch wielding a monarch's power and breaking open the treasury doors with his soldiers. But the time had passed when popular feelings determined the course of events. The decision lay with the legions, and a few hurt feelings more or less were unimportant.

Caesar hastened to resume the war, for he intended to maintain the offensive to which he owed his initial successes. The position of his antagonist was singular. After the original plan of invading the two Gauls simultaneously from Italy and Spain had been frustrated by Caesar's initiative, Pompey had intended to go to Spain. There he had a very strong position. The army, amounting to seven legions, included a large number of Pompey's veterans, and years of fighting in the Lusitanian mountains had hardened both soldiers and officers. Among its captains Marcus Varro was simply a celebrated scholar and a faithful partisan; but Lucius Afranius had fought with distinction in the East and in the Alps, and Marcus Petreius, the conqueror of Catiline, was an officer as dauntless as he was able. While in the Further province Caesar still had various adherents from the time of his governorship, the more important province of the Ebro was attached by ties of veneration and gratitude to Pompey, who twenty years before had commanded there during the Sertorian war, and after the war's end had organized it anew.

After the Italian disaster Pompey could have done nothing better than proceed to Spain with the rescued remnant of his army, and then advance at the head of his whole force to meet Caesar. But unfortunately he had, in the hope of saving the troops in Corfinium, tarried in Apulia so long that he was compelled to embark from nearby Brundisium instead of from the Campanian ports. Why, as master of the sea and Sicily, he did not revert to his original plan cannot be determined. Whether the short-sighted and distrustful aristocracy showed no desire to entrust themselves to the Spanish troops and population, the fact is that Pompey remained in the East, and Caesar might choose to attack either the army being organized in Greece under Pompey's own command, or that ready for battle under his lieutenants in Spain. Caesar decided for the latter, and as soon as the Italian campaign ended had collected on the lower Rhone nine of his best legions, 6,000 cavalry—partly men picked by Caesar himself in the Celtic cantons, partly German mercenaries—and a number of Iberian and Ligurian archers.

But his opponents had also been active.

Lucius Domitius had proceeded from Corfinium—as soon as Caesar had released him—with his attendants and with Lucius Vibullius Rufus to Massilia (Marseilles), and had actually induced that city to declare for Pompey and to refuse passage to Caesar's troops. Of the Spanish legions the two least trustworthy were left behind under the command of Varro in the Further province, while Afranius and Petreius set out with the five best, reinforced by 40,000 Spanish infantry and 5,000 Spanish cavalry. Their objective, in accordance with Pompey's orders transmitted by Vibullius, was to close the Pyrenees against the enemy.

Meanwhile Caesar arrived in Gaul and, as the siege of Massilia still detained him, he immediately dispatched most of his troops on the Rhone—six legions and the cavalry—along the great road via Narbo (Narbonne) to Rhodes in order to reach the Pyrenees first. The movement was successful. When Afranius and Petreius arrived at the passes, they found them already occupied by the Caesarians. They then took up a position at Ilerda (Lerida) between the Pyrenees and the Ebro, a town lying twenty miles north of the Ebro on the right bank of one of its tributaries, the Sicoris (Segre), which was crossed by only one solid bridge hard by Ilerda. South of Ilerda the mountains which adjoin the left bank of the Ebro approach close to the town; to the northward there stretches on both sides of the Sicoris a level plain commanded by the hill on which the town is built.

For an army which had to submit to a siege it was an excellent position. But the defense of Spain, once the line of the Pyrenees had been lost, could only be undertaken in earnest behind the Ebro; and as no secure communication was established between Ilerda and the Ebro, and no bridge existed over the latter stream, the retreat from the temporary to the true defensive position was not sufficiently secured. The Caesarians established themselves above Ilerda in the delta between the Sicoris and the Cinga (Cinca) rivers, which join below Ilerda. But the attack began in earnest only after Caesar arrived in the camp on June 23. Under the walls of the town the struggle was maintained with equal exasperation and valor on both sides and with frequent alternations of success. However, the Caesarians did not attain their object—to establish themselves between the Pompeian camp and the town and thereby capture the stone bridge. Consequently their communications with Gaul depended solely on two bridges hastily thrown over the Sicoris about eighteen or twenty miles upstream, as the river at Ilerda itself was too considerable to be bridged.

The floods resulting from the melting snows swept away these temporary bridges. As there were no vessels for crossing the highly swollen rivers, and the restoration of the bridges was temporarily impracticable, the Caesarian army was confined to the narrow space between the Cinga and the Sicoris; while the left bank of the Sicoris, and with it the road by which the army communicated with Gaul and Italy, were exposed almost undefended to the Pompeians, who passed the river partly by the town bridge and partly by swimming on skins in the Lusitanian fashion. It was the season shortly before harvest, when the old produce was almost used up and the new was not yet gathered; and the narrow strip between the two streams was soon denuded of food. In the camp actual famine prevailed (a modius of wheat cost 50 denarii) and dangerous diseases broke out; whereas on the left bank there were accumulated provisions and varied supplies, as well as troops of all sorts—reinforcements of cavalry and archers from Gaul, officers and soldiers from furlough, foraging parties returning—totalling 6,000 men. The

Pompeians attacked this mass with superior force and drove it with great loss to the mountains, while the Caesarians on the right bank were obliged to remain passive spectators of the unequal conflict.

The communications of the army were thus in the hands of the Pompeians. In Italy the reports from Spain suddenly ceased, and the suspicious rumors which began to circulate were not far from the truth. Had the Pompeians followed up their advantage energetically they could not have failed either to wipe out the mass crowded on the left bank of the river, which was scarcely capable of resistance, or at least to drive it back towards Gaul and occupy this bank so completely that not a man could cross the river without their knowledge. But both points were neglected. The isolated bands were pushed aside with loss, but neither destroyed nor completely beaten back. and the prevention of the crossing of the river was left substantially to the river itself.

Thereupon Caesar formed his plan. He ordered portable boats of a light wooden frame and osier work lined with leather, like those used in the Channel by the Britons and subsequently by the Saxons, to be prepared in camp and transported in wagons to where the bridges had stood. On these frail barks the other bank was reached unopposed and the bridge reestablished without much difficulty. The road connecting with it was thereupon quickly cleared, and the eagerly expected supplies conveyed to the camp. Caesar's happy idea thus rescued the army from its immense peril. Then the Caesarian cavalry, which far surpassed the enemy's in efficiency, began to scour the country on the left bank of the Sicoris. The most considerable Spanish communities between the Pyrenees and the Ebro, and even several south of the Ebro, passed over to Caesar's side.

The supplies of the Pompeians were

sharply reduced by Caesar's foraging parties and the defection of the neighboring communities. They resolved to retire behind the line of the Ebro, and began hastily to form a bridge of boats over the Ebro below the mouth of the Sicoris. Caesar sought to cut off the retreat of his opponents over the Ebro and to detain them in Ilerda; but so long as the enemy held the bridge at Ilerda and he had neither ford nor bridge there, he could neither distribute his army over both banks of the river nor invest Ilerda. His soldiers therefore worked day and night to lessen the river's depth by canals drawing off the water, so that the infantry could wade across. But the preparations of the Pompeians were finished sooner than those of the Caesarians. When the former began their march towards the Ebro along the left bank of the Sicoris, the canal project seemed not far enough advanced to permit an infantry crossing. Therefore Caesar ordered only his cavalry to pass the stream and, by clinging to the enemy rear, to detain and harass them.

But when Caesar's legions saw in the gray morning light the enemy's columns which had been retiring since midnight, they discerned with the sure instinct of veterans the strategic importance of this retreat, which would compel them to follow their antagonists into distant regions filled with hostile troops. At their own request the general ventured to lead the infantry into the river, and although the water reached up to the shoulders of the men, it was crossed without accident. It was high time. If the narrow plain separating the town of Ilerda from the mountains enclosing the Ebro were once traversed and the Pompeians entered the mountains, their retreat to the Ebro could no longer be prevented. Notwithstanding the constant cavalry attacks which greatly delayed their march, they had already approached within five miles of the mountains when, having been on the

march since midnight and unspeakably exhausted, they abandoned their original plan of crossing the whole plain in one day and pitched their camp. Here the infantry of Caesar overtook them in the evening and encamped opposite to them during the night. The nocturnal march which the Pompeians had at first contemplated was abandoned from fear of night cavalry attacks. On the following day also both armies remained immovable, occupied only in reconnoitering the country.

Early on the third morning Caesar's infantry began a movement through the pathless mountains alongside of the road, that they might turn the enemy's position and bar the route to the Ebro. The object of the strange march, which seemed at first to turn back towards the camp before Ilerda, was not at once perceived by the Pompeian officers. When they discerned it, they sacrificed camp and baggage and advanced by a forced march along the highway to gain the crest of the ridge before the Caesarians. But it was already too late: when they came up, the compact enemy masses were already posted on the highway itself. A desperate attempt to discover other routes to the Ebro over the steep mountains was frustrated by Caesar's cavalry, which surrounded and cut to pieces the Lusitanian troops sent forth for that purpose.

Had a battle taken place between the Caesarians and the Pompeian army—which was utterly demoralized with the enemy cavalry in its rear and the infantry in front—the issue was scarcely doubtful, and the opportunity for fighting presented itself several times. But Caesar made no use of it, and with some difficulty restrained the impatient eagerness of his confident soldiers. In any event the Pompeian army was strategically lost, and Caesar wished to avoid weakening his army and further envenoming the bitter feud by useless bloodshed. The day after he had succeeded in cutting off the Pompeians from the Ebro, the soldiers of the two armies had begun to fraternize and to negotiate respecting surrender. Indeed, the terms asked by the Pompeians, especially as to the sparing of their officers, had already been conceded by Caesar when Petreius with his escort consisting of slaves and Spaniards came upon the negotiators and caused all the Caesarians whom he could reach to be put to death. Nevertheless the Pompeians who had come to Caesar's camp were sent back unharmed, and he persevered in seeking a peaceful solution.

Ilerda, where the Pompeians still had a garrison and considerable supplies, now became the point which they sought to reach; but with the hostile army in front and the Sicoris between them and the fortress, they marched without coming nearer to their object. Their cavalry became gradually so afraid that the infantry had to take them into the center and legions had to be set as the rear-guard. The procuring of water and forage became more and more difficult, and they had to kill the beasts of burden which could no longer be fed. At length the wandering army was formally inclosed between the Sicoris and the enemy's force, which drew rampart and trench around it. It attempted to cross the river, but Caesar's German horsemen and light infantry anticipated it by occupying the opposite bank.

No bravery or fidelity could now delay the inevitable capitulation, which occurred on August 2, 49 B.C. Caesar granted to officers and soldiers their lives and liberty and the property they still retained, plus restoring what had been already taken from them, the full value of which he undertook personally to repay to his own soldiers. While he had compulsorily enrolled in his army the recruits captured in Italy, he honored these old legionaries of Pompey by the promise that no one should be compelled to serve under Caesar against his will. He required only that each should give up his arms and go home. Accordingly about a third of the soldiers, who were natives of Spain, disbanded at once, while the Italians were discharged on the borders of Transalpine and Cisalpine Gaul.

On the breaking up of his army Hither Spain fell into the power of the victor. In Further Spain, where Marcus Varro held the chief command for Pompey, it seemed to him advisable when he learned of the disaster of Ilerda that he should throw himself into the insular town of Gades, carrying thither for safety the considerable sums collected by confiscating the treasures of the temples and the property of prominent Caesarians, the substantial fleet he had raised, and the two legions entrusted to him. But on the mere rumor of Caesar's arrival the most notable towns of the province (such as Corduba, Carmo, and Gades itself), long attached to Caesar, drove away the Pompeian garrisons or induced them to revolt. One of Varro's two legions also set out of its own accord for Hispalis, and passed over to Caesar's side along with the town. When at length even Italica closed its gates against Varro, he resolved to capitulate. About the same time Massilia also submitted.

The year 49 B.C. also saw two further Caesarian successes and one major defeat. The capture of Sardinia by Quintus Valerius and of Sicily by Gaius Curio helped forestall the starvation of Italy which Pompey was planning by naval blockade. But Curio's further expedition to Africa came to grief, after some initial successes, when he and his forces were surrounded and wiped out by the army of Pompey's ally, King Juba of Numidia.

How far these events of 49 B.C. interfered with Pompey's general plan of campaign, and particularly what part in that plan was assigned to the important Spanish corps after the loss of Italy, can only be determined by conjecture. That Pompey intended to come by way of Africa and Mauretania to the aid of his army in Spain was simply a romantic and beyond doubt groundless rumor circulating in the camp at Ilerda. More likely he still kept to his earlier plan of attacking Caesar from both sides in Transalpine and Cisalpine Gaul even after losing Italy, and meditated a combined attack at once from Spain and Macedonia. The Spanish army was presumably meant to remain on the defensive at the Pyrenees till the fully organized Macedonian army was ready to march. Then both would have started simultaneously and joined forces either on the Rhone or on the Po, while the fleet, it may be conjectured, would have attempted a landing in Italy proper.

On this supposition Caesar apparently prepared himself to meet an attack on Italy. One of his ablest officers, the tribune Marcus Antonius, commanded there with propraetorian powers. The southeastern ports of Sipus, Brundisium, and Tarentum, where a landing might first be expected, received a garrison of three legions. Besides this Quintus Hortensius, the degenerate son of the well-known orator, collected a fleet in the Tyrrhenian Sea, and Publius Dolabella a second fleet in the Adriatic, partly to support the defense of Italy and partly to transport the intended expedition to Greece. In the event of a Pompeian land penetration into Italy, Marcus Licinius Crassus, the eldest son of Caesar's old colleague, was to conduct the defense of Cisalpine Gaul, and Marcus Antonius' younger brother that of Illyricum.

But the expected attack was long in coming. Not until midsummer of 49 B.C. did the conflict begin in Illyria. There Caesar's lieutenant Gaius Antonius with his two legions was on the island of Cu-

ricta (Veglia in the gulf of Quarnero), and Caesar's admiral Publius Dolabella with forty ships lay in the narrow arm of the sea between this island and the mainland. Pompey's admirals in the Adriatic, Marcus Octavius with the Greek division of the fleet and Lucius Scribonius Libo with the Illyrian, attacked Dolabella's squadron, destroyed all his ships, and cut off Antonius on his island. To rescue him, a corps under Basilus and Sallustius came from Italy and the squadron of Hortensius from the Tyrrhenian Sea.[7]But neither the former nor the latter was able to effect anything in the presence of the far superior enemy fleet.

The legions of Antonius had to be abandoned to their fate. Provisions came to an end, the troops became troublesome and mutinous. Except for a few divisions which succeeded in reaching the mainland on rafts, the corps, still fifteen cohorts strong, laid down their arms and were conveyed to Macedonia to be incorporated into the Pompeian army, while Octavius was left to complete the subjugation of the undefended Illyrian coast. The Dalmatae, the most powerful tribe in these regions, the important insular town of Issa (Lissa), and other townships embraced the party of Pompey. But the adherents of Caesar maintained themselves in Salonae (Spalato) and Lissus (Alessio); and the former town not merely sustained with courage a siege which reduced it to extremities, but made so effective a sally that Octavius raised the siege and sailed off to Dyrrhachium to pass the winter.

The success achieved in Illyricum by the Pompeian fleet, though not inconsiderable, had little influence on the campaign as a whole. Moreover, it appears miserably small when we consider that Pompey's land and naval activity during the whole eventful year of 49 B.C. was confined to this single feat of arms, and that from the East, where the general, the

Senate, the second great army, the principal fleet, the immense military and still more extensive financial resources of the republicans were united, no intervention at all took place in the crucial struggle in the West. The scattering of the forces in the eastern empire, the general's method of never operating except with superior masses, his cumbrous and tedious movements, and the discord of the coalition may perhaps partly explain (though not excuse) the inactivity of his land forces. But that the fleet, which commanded the Mediterranean without a rival, should have thus done nothing to influence the course of affairs—nothing for Spain, next to nothing for Massilia, nothing to defend Sardinia, Sicily, Africa, or, if not to reoccupy Italy, at least to obstruct its supplies —gives some inkling of the well-nigh inconceivable confusion and perversity which must have prevailed in the Pompeian camp.

The net result of this campaign was corresponding. Caesar's offensive against Spain was completely successful, that against Sicily and Africa partly so. Pompey's plan of starving Italy was thwarted mainly by the capture of Sicily, and his general plan of campaign was frustrated completely by the destruction of the Spanish army, while in Italy only a very small portion of Caesar's defensive arrangements had met any test. Notwithstanding the painful losses in Africa and Illyria, Caesar came out of the first year of the war decisively victorious.

However, if nothing material was done from the East to hinder Caesar's subjugation of the West, efforts at least were made towards political and military consolidation during the ignominious respite. The great rendezvous of Caesar's opponents was Macedonia. There headed Pompey himself and the mass of the emigrants from Brundisium. There also came the other refugees from the West—Marcus Cato from Sicily, Lucius Domitius from Massilia, and especially a number of the best officers and soldiers of the broken Spanish army, headed by its generals Afranius and Varro.

In Italy emigration gradually became among the aristocrats a question not merely of honor but also of fashion, and it obtained a fresh impulse through the unfavorable accounts of Caesar's position before Ilerda. Not a few of the lukewarm and the political trimmers went over by degrees, even Marcus Cicero at last persuading himself that he did not adequately discharge his duty as a citizen by writing a dissertation on concord. The Senate of emigrants at Thessalonica, where official Rome pitched its interim abode, numbered nearly 200 members, including many venerable old men and almost all the consulars.

But emigrants indeed they were. This Roman Coblenz was a pitiful spectacle of high pretensions and paltry performances, with unseasonable reminiscences and still more unseasonable recriminations, political perversities and financial embarrassments. It was a matter of little moment that, while the old structure was crumbling, they were painstakingly watching over every ornamental scroll and speck of rust in the constitution. After all, it was simply ridiculous when the genteel lords had pangs of conscience about calling their deliberative assembly "the Senate," and cautiously entitled it "the three hundred," or when they launched tedious investigations as to whether a curiate law could be legitimately enacted beyond the ring-wall of Rome.

Far worse traits were the indifference of the lukewarm and the narrow stubbornness of the ultras. The former would neither act nor keep silent. If asked to perform some definite task for the common good, with the inconsistency of the weak they regarded the suggestion as a malicious attempt to compromise them, and either did not do what was ordered or

did it halfheartedly. At the same time, of course, with their know-it-all attitude after it was too late and their over-wise impracticalities, they perpetually hindered those who were acting. Their daily work consisted of criticizing, ridiculing, and bemoaning every occurrence great or small, and in unnerving and discouraging the multitude by their own sluggish hopelessness.

While these displayed the prostration of weakness, the ultras blatantly exhibited the exaggeration of action. They made no attempt to conceal that the price of any peace negotiation was Caesar's head. Every attempt towards peace, which Caesar continued to make, was tossed aside without examination, or used only to cover insidious attempts on the lives of Caesar's envoys. That Caesar's declared partisans had forfeited life and property was a matter of course, but the neutrals fared little better. Lucius Domitius, the bumbler of Corfinium, gravely proposed in council that the senators who had fought in Pompey's army should decide whether those who had remained neutral, or had emigrated but not entered the army, should be acquitted, fined, or punished by the forfeiture of life and property. Another of these ultras formally charged Lucius Afranius with corruption and treason for his defective defense of Spain.

Among these deep-dyed republicans political theory assumed almost the character of a religious faith. Accordingly, they detested Pompey, his personal adherents, and their own more lukewarm partisans still more, if possible, than their open opponents, displaying all the dull obstinacy of hatred that characterizes orthodox theologians; and they were mainly to blame for the numberless and bitter quarrels which distracted the emigrant army and Senate. Nor did they confine themselves to words. Marcus Bibulus, Titus Labienus, and others of this clique

carried out their theory by causing captured officers or soldiers of Caesar's army to be executed en masse—which, it may be assumed, did not make Caesar's troops fight less fiercely. If the counterrevolution in favor of the republic, for which all the elements existed, did not break out in Italy during Caesar's absence, the reason in the opinion of Caesar's discerning opponents lay chiefly in the general dread of the unbridled fury of the republican ultras after the restoration.

The better men in the Pompeian camp were in despair over this frantic behavior. Pompey, himself a brave soldier, spared the prisoners as far as he could. But he was too pusillanimous and in too awkward a position to prevent or even to punish all such atrocities as a commander-in-chief should. Marcus Cato, the only man who at least carried moral consistency into the struggle, attempted with more energy to check such proceedings. He induced the emigrant Senate to prohibit by special decree the pillage of subject towns and the killing of a citizen except in battle. The able Marcus Marcellus had similar views. No one, indeed, knew better than Cato and Marcellus that the extreme party would carry out their ghastly threats, if necessary defying all the decrees of the Senate. If even now the ultras could not be tamed despite all considerations of prudence, people might expect after their victory a reign of terror from which Marius and Sulla themselves would have recoiled in horror. We can understand why Cato professed himself more afraid of the victory than of the defeat of his own party.

Military preparation in the Macedonian camp was in the hands of Pompey as commander-in-chief. His position, always anomalous, had become still worse through the unfortunate events of 49 B.C. In the eyes of his partisans he was mainly to blame for this result. This judgment was in many respects unjust. Much of the misfortune endured was chargeable to the perversity and insubordination of his lieutenants, especially Lucius Domitius and the consul Lentulus. From the moment Pompey took charge of the army he had led it with skill and courage, and had saved very considerable forces from the debacle. That he was not a match for Caesar's superior genius—a fact now recognized by all—could not fairly be made a matter of reproach. But results alone decided men's judgment. Trusting in Pompey the constitutional party had broken with Caesar, and the pernicious consequence of this breach recoiled upon Pompey. While no attempt was made to change the supreme command, owing to the notorious military incapacity of all the other chiefs, confidence in the commander-in-chief was paralyzed.

These painful consequences of the defeats were heightened by the injurious influences of the emigration. Among the refugees were a number of efficient soldiers and capable officers, especially those from the former Spanish army. But the number who came to serve and fight was small, while the number of generals of quality who called themselves proconsuls and Imperators with as good title as Pompey, and of genteel lords who endured active military service more or less reluctantly, was alarmingly great. These introduced the capital's mode of life into the camp, with no benefit to the army. The tents of such grandees were graceful bowers, the ground elegantly covered with fresh turf, the walls clothed with ivy; silver plate stood on the table, and the winecup often circulated even in broad daylight. Those fashionable warriors formed a singular contrast with Caesar's daredevils, who ate coarse bread and, lacking that, devoured even roots, and who swore that they would rather chew the bark of trees than flee from the enemy.

Moreover, Pompey's actions were hampered by the necessity of consulting with a senatorial governing board personally hostile to him, and this embarrassment was sharply increased when the Senate of emigrants took up its abode almost in his very headquarters, displaying there all the venom of the emigrants in its sittings. And finally, there was nowhere any man of mark who could throw his own weight into the scale against these preposterous doings. Pompey himself was intellectually far too second-rate, and far too hesitating, awkward, and reserved. Marcus Cato would have had the requisite moral authority, plus the good will to support Pompey with it. But Pompey, instead of seeking his aid, jealously kept him in the background, and preferred (for instance) to commit the highly important chief command of the fleet to that totally incapable Marcus Bibulus.

While Pompey thus handled his political position with characteristic perversity, outdoing himself to worsen an already bad situation, on the other hand he devoted himself with commendable zeal to organizing the considerable but scattered forces of his party. The flower of his force was composed of the troops brought from Italy. From these, supplemented by the Illyrian prisoners of war and the Romans domiciled in Greece, five legions were formed. Three others came from the East—the two Syrian legions made up of the remains of Crassus' army, and one formed out of the two weak legions hitherto stationed in Cilicia.

Nothing prevented the withdrawal of these corps of occupation. On the one hand the Pompeians had an understanding with the Parthians, and might even have had an alliance if Pompey had not indignantly refused the price they demanded for it—cession of the Syrian province which Pompey had added to the empire. On the other hand Caesar's plan of dispatching two legions to Syria, and inducing the Jews once more to revolt by means of the prince Aristobulus kept a prisoner in Rome, was frustrated partly by the death of Aristobulus and partly by other causes. New Pompeian legions were also raised, one from the veteran soldiers settled in Crete and Macedonia, and two from the Romans of Asia Minor. To all these were added 2,000 volunteers, derived from the remains of the Spanish select corps and other similar sources, and the contingents of subject allies. The cavalry (except for a noble guard, more respectable than militarily important, formed from the young aristocracy of Rome, and the Apulian slave herdsmen whom Pompey had mounted) consisted exclusively of contingents from Roman provinces and protectorates and totaled some 7,000 men.

Finally, Pompey's fleet was very considerable. It consisted partly of the Roman transports brought from Brundisium or subsequently built, partly of the war vessels of the king of Egypt, of the Colchian princes, of the Cilician dynast Tarcondimotus, of the cities of Tyre, Rhodes, Athens, Corcyra, and generally of all the Asiatic and Greek maritime states. It numbered nearly 500 sail, of which the Roman vessels formed a fifth. Immense stores of food and military supplies were accumulated in Dyrrhachium. The warchest was well filled, for the Pompeians possessed the principal sources of revenue and turned to their own account the resources of the satellite princes, the senators of distinction, the tax farmers, and generally of the whole Roman and non-Roman population within their reach. Every device that the reputation of the legitimate government and the much renowned protectorship of Pompey over kings and peoples could put in motion in Africa, Egypt, Macedonia, Greece, Western Asia and Syria was applied for the protection of the Roman republic. The title "King of Kings" given to Pompey in his camp, and the report which circulated in

Italy that Pompey was arming the Getae, Colchians, and Armenians against Rome, could hardly be called exaggerations.

Altogether, Pompey commanded an army of 7,000 cavalry and eleven legions (of which, it is true, five at most could be described as veteran) and a fleet of 500 sail. The temper of the soldiers, for whose provisioning and pay Pompey gave adequate care, and to whom the most abundant rewards were promised after victory, was consistently good, and in several of the most efficient divisions even excellent. However, much of the army consisted of new recruits whose training, however zealously pressed, still took time. As a whole the force was imposing, but of a somewhat motley character.

The commander-in-chief's plan was that the army and fleet should be fully mobilized by the winter of 49–48 B.C. along the coast and in the waters of Epirus. The admiral Bibulus had already arrived with 110 ships at his new headquarters, Corcyra. On the other hand the land army, whose headquarters during the summer had been at Berrhoea on the Haliacmon, had not yet arrived, but was moving slowly along the great highway from Thessalonica toward the west coast to the future headquarters at Dyrrhachium. The two legions which Metellus Scipio was bringing up from Syria wintered at Pergamus in Asia, and were expected in Europe only toward the spring. In fact, all their movements were proceeding so leisurely that for the moment the ports of Epirus were guarded, except for the fleet, merely by their own civic defenses and the levies of the adjoining districts.

It thus remained possible for Caesar, despite the Spanish war, to take the offensive also in Macedonia, and he at least was not slow to act. He had long ago ordered the collection of war vessels and transports in Brundisium, and there he sent the greater portion of his select troops after the Spanish victory and the fall of Massilia. The unparalleled exertions which Caesar thus required from his soldiers thinned their ranks more than conflict had done, and the mutiny of one of the four oldest legions, the ninth, on its march through Placentia indicated the dangerous temper of the army. But Caesar's presence of mind and personal authority gained the mastery, and nothing impeded the embarkation from this quarter.

However, the want of ships which had prevented the pursuit of Pompey in March of 49 B.C. threatened to frustrate this expedition also. The war vessels which Caesar had ordered built in the Gallic, Sicilian, and Italian ports were not yet ready, or at any rate not on the spot. His Adriatic squadron had been destroyed the previous year at Curicta, and he found at Brundisium not more than twelve ships of war and scarcely transports enough to carry at once a third of the twelve legions and 10,000 cavalry intended for Greece. The considerable enemy fleet dominated the Adriatic and especially all the mainland and island harbors on its eastern coast.

Under these circumstances it is a question why Caesar did not march through Illyria, a route which obviated any naval threat and was also shorter for his troops, most of whom came from Gaul, than the route by Brundisium. It is true that Illyria was rugged and poor, but it was traversed by other armies soon afterward, and this obstacle can hardly have daunted the conqueror of Gaul. Perhaps he feared that during the troublesome march through Illyria Pompey might convey his whole force over the Adriatic to Italy, thereby changing places with Caesar—though such a rapid response was scarcely to be expected from his slow-moving antagonist. Perhaps Caesar originally favored the maritime route on the theory that his fleet could meanwhile be brought to respectable strength, and,

when after returning from Spain he learned the true situation in the Adriatic, it was too late to change his plan. Perhaps—and in view of Caesar's quick and decisive temperament it is even highly probable—he found himself irresistibly tempted by the fact that the still-undefended Epirote coast would certainly be covered by the enemy in a few days, and a bold stroke might thwart once more his antagonist's whole plan.

Whatever his reasoning, on January 4th of 48 B.C. Caesar set sail from Brundisium with six legions, greatly thinned by toil and sickness, and 600 horsemen. It was a counterpart to his foolhardy Britannic expedition, but at least the first throw was fortunate. The coast of Epirus was reached in the middle of the Acroceraunian (Chimara) cliffs, at the little-frequented roadstead of Paleassa (Paljassa). The transports were seen both from the harbor of Oricum (creek of Avlona) where a Pompeian squadron of eighteen sail was lying, and from the headquarters of the hostile fleet at Corcyra; but the first group considered itself too weak, and the second was not ready to sail, so that Caesar's initial force landed without hindrance. While the vessels at once returned to bring over the second, Caesar that same evening scaled the Acroceraunian mountains. His first successes were as great as the enemy's surprise. The Epirote militia offered no resistance, the important seaports of Oricum and Apollonia along with a number of smaller towns were taken, and Dyrrhachium, the chief Pompeian arsenal filled with supplies but only feebly garrisoned, was in the utmost danger.

The rest of the campaign did not measure up to this brilliant beginning. Bibulus subsequently made up for some of his negligence by redoubling his exertions. He not only captured and burned nearly thirty of the returning transports, but also established along the whole occupied coast a most careful watch, despite the inclement season of the year and the necessity of bringing everything for the guardships, even wood and water, from Corcyra. In fact, his successor Libo (for Bibulus soon succumbed to the unwonted fatigues) even blockaded the port of Brundisium for a time until lack of water dislodged him from the little island facing it which he had seized. As a result, the second part of the army could not be brought over to Caesar, nor did he succeed in capturing Dyrrhachium. Pompey learned through one of Caesar's peace envoys of his plan to invade the Epirote coast, and thereupon accelerated his march to reach that important arsenal in the nick of time.

Caesar's situation was critical. Although he extended his range in Epirus as far as his slight strength permitted, the subsistence of his army remained difficult and precarious, while the enemy's mastery of the sea and its possession of the stores at Dyrrhachium gave him plenty of everything. With an army presumably little above 20,000 strong he could not challenge Pompey with at least twice that number. He had to deem himself fortunate that Pompey did not immediately force a battle, but went methodically to work and took up winter quarters between Dyrrhachium and Apollonia on the right bank of the Apsus, facing Caesar on the left, in order that after his eastern legions arrived in the spring he might overwhelm the enemy.

Thus months passed. If the arrival of better weather, which brought the enemy strong reinforcements plus the free use of his fleet, found Caesar still in the same position he was surely lost, with his weak band wedged in among the rocks of Epirus between the immense fleet and the trebly superior land army of the enemy; and already the winter was drawing to a close. His sole hope still depended on his transport fleet. It was hardly to be hoped

that it could steal or fight its way through the blockade, but after the first voluntary foolhardiness this second gamble was mandatory. How desperate Caesar regarded his situation is shown by his scheme—when the fleet still did not come —to sail alone in a fishing boat across the Adriatic to Brundisium to fetch it. The plan was only abandoned because no mariner could be found to undertake the daring voyage.

But his personal appearance was not needed to induce his faithful lieutenant in Italy, Marcus Antonius, to make a last effort to save his master. Once more the transport fleet, with four legions and 800 horsemen on board, sailed from Brundisium, and fortunately a strong south wind carried it past Libo's galleys. But the same wind which saved the fleet also blew it past the camps of Caesar and Pompey to the north of Dyrrhachium towards Lissus, which town fortunately still adhered to Caesar. When it sailed past Dyrrhachium the Rhodian galleys started in pursuit, and hardly had Antonius' ships arrived at Lissus when the enemy's squadron appeared. But just at this moment the wind suddenly veered, and drove the pursuing galleys partly back into the open sea and partly on the rocky coast. Through the most marvellous good fortune the landing of the second convoy had also been successful.

Antonius and Caesar were still some four days' march from each other, separated by Dyrrhachium and the whole enemy army. But Antonius fortunately made the perilous march around Dyrrhachium and joined Caesar, who had gone to meet him, on the right bank of the Apsus. Pompey, after vainly attempting to prevent the junction and to force Antonius' corps to fight alone, took up a new position at Asparagium on the river Genusus (Skumbi), which flows parallel to the Apsus between the latter and the town of Dyrrhachium, and there remained

once more immovable. Caesar felt himself now strong enough to give battle, but
Pompey declined it. On the other hand
Caesar with his fast-marching infantry
deceived his adversary, just as at Ilerda,
by getting between the enemy's camp and
its base at Dyrrhachium.

The chain of the Graba Balkan, which
stretches from east to west on the Adriatic and ends in the narrow tongue of
land at Dyrrhachium, sends off a lateral
branch in a southwesterly direction some
fourteen miles east of Dyrrhachium. This
branch then turns crescent-like towards
the sea, and with the main chain encloses
a small plain extending round a cliff on
the seashore. Here Pompey now took up
his camp, and, although Caesar's army
kept the land route to Dyrrhachium
closed against him, his fleet kept in constant communication with the town and
he was amply and easily supplied from it.
Among the Caesarians, notwithstanding
strong detachments scouring the back
country, and despite all the general's exertions to organize a system of transport
and thereby a regular supply, there was
such scarcity that flesh, barley, and even
roots very frequently had to take the
place of the customary wheat.

As his phlegmatic opponent still did
not act, Caesar sought to occupy the
heights which enclosed the plain held by
Pompey, in order at least to hinder the
enemy's superior cavalry and to operate
with more freedom against Dyrrhachium,
and if possible to compel his opponent
either to fight or sail away. Nearly half of
Caesar's troops were detached to the interior, and it seemed almost quixotic for
the rest to attempt virtually to besiege an
army perhaps twice as strong, concentrated in position, and resting on the sea
and the fleet. Yet Caesar's veterans by infinite exertions surrounded the Pompeian
camp with a chain of posts sixteen miles
long. To this inner line was afterward
added a second outer one, to protect

against attacks from Dyrrhachium and
against attempts to turn their position, so
easily executed with the aid of the fleet.

Pompey attacked portions of these entrenchments more than once with a view
to breaking the enemy line if possible,
but he did not attempt to prevent the investment by a battle. Instead he constructed entrenchments around his own
camp, connecting them by lines. Both
sides sought to push forward their
trenches as far as possible, and the earth-
works advanced but slowly amid constant
conflicts. At the same time skirmishes
took place on the opposite side of Caesar's camp with the garrison of Dyrrhachium. Caesar hoped to seize the fortress
with the help of some of its garrison, but
was prevented by the enemy fleet. There
was incessant fighting at different points
—on one of the hottest days at six places
simultaneously—and as a rule the tried
valor of the Caesarians had the advantage. Once, for instance, a single cohort
maintained itself in its entrenchments
against four legions for several hours
until support came up. No notable success was achieved by either side, yet the
effects of the investment gradually became oppressive to the Pompeians. The
stopping of the rivulets flowing down
from the heights compelled them to be
content with poor and scanty wellwater.
Still more troublesome was the lack of
fodder for the horses, which the fleet
could not supply adequately. Numbers
died, and it was no use to transport them
by water to Dyrrhachium since fodder
was also lacking there.

Pompey could not delay much longer
freeing himself from his disagreeable position. He was informed by Celtic desert-
ers that the Caesarians had failed to build
a cross-wall along the beach between
their two chains of entrenchments 600
feet apart, and on this he formed his
plan. While Caesar's inner line was attacked by legions from the camp, and the

outer line by light troops landed from the sea beyond the enemy's entrenchments, a third division landed in the space between the two lines and attacked the embattled defenders in the rear. The entrenchment next to the sea was taken, and its garrison fled in wild confusion. With difficulty Marcus Antonius, the commander of the next trench, succeeded in limiting the Pompeian advance; but apart from the considerable loss, the entrenchment along the sea remained in enemy hands and the line was broken.

Caesar the more eagerly seized the opportunity soon afterward of attacking with the bulk of his infantry a Pompeian legion which had incautiously become isolated. But it resisted valiantly, and as the battleground was intersected by mounds and ditches, Caesar's right wing along with the cavalry missed its way. Instead of supporting the left in attacking the Pompeian legion, it got into a narrow trench that led from one of the old camps towards the river. Pompey, who came up hastily with five legions to aid his troops, found the two enemy wings separated and one of them in a forlorn position. A panic seized the Caesarians at his advance, and all plunged into disorderly flight. That the matter ended with merely the loss of 1,000 of Caesar's best soldiers, and not the complete defeat of his army, was due simply to the fact that Pompey also could not freely deploy his forces on the broken ground, and to the further fact that from fear of a stratagem he at first held back his troops.

Even so, these days were fraught with mischief for Caesar. Not only had he endured the most serious losses and surrendered at one blow his entrenchments, the result of four months of gigantic labor; the recent engagements had put him back exactly where he started. Pompey's elder son Gnaeus had in a bold attack partly burnt and partly carried off Caesar's few ships of war in the port of Oricum, and soon afterward had set fire to the transport fleet left behind in Lissus. Thus all possibility of reinforcement by sea from Brundisium was lost. The pent-up Pompeian cavalry now poured over the adjacent country and threatened to make the already difficult task of provisioning Caesar's army utterly impossible. Caesar's daring enterprise of mounting an offensive without ships, against an enemy in command of the sea and resting on his fleet, had totally failed. In the present theater of war he found himself facing an impregnable defensive position, and unable to attack effectively either Dyrrhachium or the hostile army. Pompey alone could now choose the most favorable circumstances to attack an antagonist already wrestling with grave problems of supply.

XIII
Civil War: Pharsalus and Thapsus

The war had reached a crisis. Hitherto Pompey had, to all appearances, played the game of war without a particular plan, adjusting his defense to the exigencies of each attack; nor was this to be censured, for protracting the war enabled him to harden his recruits, bring up his reserves, and make fuller use of his superior Adriatic fleet. Caesar was beaten both tactically and strategically. True, this defeat did not have the effect which Pompey might reasonably expect; the soldierly energy of Caesar's veterans prevented an immediate break-up of the army by hunger and mutiny. But it seemed to depend solely on Pompey, by judiciously following up his victory, to reap its full fruits.

It was up to Pompey to take the aggressive, and he was resolved to do so. He had three different ways of rendering his victory fruitful. The first and simplest was to assail the vanquished army and, if it departed, to pursue it. Secondly, Pompey might leave Caesar himself and his best troops in Greece and cross in person with the main army to Italy (as he had long been preparing to do) where the feeling was decidedly republican, and where Caesar's forces, after the departure of the best troops and their commander for Greece, would not be of much moment. Lastly, the victor might turn inland, effect a junction with the legions of Metellus Scipio, and attempt to capture Caesar's troops stationed in the interior. These latter had, immediately after the arrival of the second convoy from Italy, sent strong detachments to Aetolia and Thessaly to procure supplies, and had ordered two legions under Gnaeus Domitius Calvinus to advance on the Egnatian highway towards Macedonia, to intercept and if possible defeat in detail Scipio's force advancing on the same road from Thessalonica.

Calvinus and Scipio had already approached within a few miles of each other when Scipio suddenly turned southward. Then, rapidly crossing the Haliacmon (Inje Karasu) and leaving his baggage there under Marcus Favonius, he penetrated into Thessaly to attack Caesar's legion of recruits under Lucius Cassius Longinus, engaged in subduing the countryside. But Longinus retired over the mountains toward Ambracia to join the detachment under Gnaeus Calvisius Sabinus sent by Caesar to Aetolia; and Scipio could only send his Thracian cavalry in pursuit, for Calvinus threatened his reserve left under Favonius on the Haliacmon with the same fate which he had intended for Longinus. So Calvinus and Scipio met on the Haliacmon, and encamped opposite each other for a considerable time.

Pompey might choose among these plans, while Caesar had no choice. After the unfortunate engagement at Dyrrha-

chium he retreated toward Apollonia, and Pompey followed. The march from Dyrrhachium to Apollonia, along a difficult road crossed by several rivers, was no easy task for a defeated army pursued by the enemy; but the dexterous leadership of their general and the indestructible marching energy of the soldiers compelled Pompey after four days to give up the pursuit as useless. He now had to decide between the Italian expedition and the march into the interior. However attractive the former might seem, and though various voices urged it, he preferred not to abandon Scipio's corps, especially since he hoped by this march to lay hands on the corps of Calvinus.

Calvinus at the moment was on the Egnatian road at Heraclea Lyncestis between Pompey and Scipio, and further distant from Caesar than from the great Pompeian army. Moreover, he knew nothing of the events at Dyrrhachium and of his perilous position, since after Caesar's defeat the whole countryside inclined to Pompey and Caesar's messengers were everywhere seized. Not until the enemy's main force was a few hours away did Calvinus learn the true state of affairs from the enemy's advanced posts themselves. A quick departure southward towards Thessaly averted his imminent destruction, and Pompey had to be content with liberating Scipio from his position of peril.

Caesar had meanwhile arrived unmolested at Apollonia. Immediately after the disaster at Dyrrhachium he had resolved to transfer the struggle from the coast into the interior, to get beyond the reach of the enemy's fleet—the ultimate cause of his previous failure; the march to Apollonia had only been intended to place his wounded in safety and to pay his soldiers there, where his depots were stationed. This done, he set out for Thessaly, leaving garrisons behind in Apollonia, Oricum, and Lissus. Calvinus' corps had likewise started towards Thessaly, where Caesar could also more easily join forces with the two legions of reinforcements under Quintus Cornificius coming from Italy, this time overland through Illyria.

Ascending by difficult paths in the valley of the Aous and crossing the mountain chain which separates Epirus from Thessaly, Caesar arrived at the Peneus. Calvinus was likewise directed thither, and the junction of the two armies, thus accomplished by the shortest and least exposed route, took place at Aeginium not far from the source of the Peneus. The first Thessalian town (Gomphi) before which the united army arrived closed its gates. It was quickly stormed and given up to pillage, and the other terrified towns of Thessaly submitted as soon as Caesar's legions merely appeared. Amid these marches and conflicts, and with the help of the supplies—albeit not too ample —which the region afforded, the traces and recollections of past calamitous days gradually vanished.

The victories of Dyrrhachium had thus borne little immediate fruit for the victors. Pompey's unwieldy army and numerous cavalry had not been able to follow his nimble enemy into the mountains; Caesar like Calvinus had escaped from pursuit, and the two stood securely united in Thessaly. Perhaps it would have been best if Pompey had now embarked straightway for Italy, where success was scarcely doubtful. But only a division of the fleet departed for Sicily and Italy. In the coalition camp the war was regarded as so completely won at Dyrrhachium that it only remained to seek out and capture the defeated army. Their former overcaution was succeeded by still less-justified arrogance. They ignored the fact that they had, strictly speaking, failed in the pursuit; that they had to encounter a refreshed and reorganized army in Thessaly; and that there was grave risk in leaving the sea, renouncing the support of the fleet, and following their antagonist to a battlefield of his choice. They were simply resolved at any price to fight with Caesar, and therefore to get at him as soon as possible and by the most convenient way. Cato took command of the garrison of eighteen cohorts at Dyrrhachium, and the 300 ships of war at Corcyra. Pompey and Scipio proceeded by different routes to the lower Peneus, and met at Larisa.

South of Larisa is a plain intersected by a tributary of the Peneus, the Enipeus; Caesar's army lay on the left bank of the latter stream near the town of Pharsalus, while Pompey pitched his camp opposite to Caesar on the right bank of the Enipeus along a gradual slope. Pompey's entire army was assembled, while Caesar still expected the arrival of nearly two legions now stationed under Quintus Fufius Calenus in Greece, and the two legions of Cornificius en route from Italy via Illyria. Pompey's army, numbering eleven legions (47,000 men) and 7,000 horse, was more than double Caesar's in infantry, and seven times as numerous in cavalry. Fatigue and conflicts had so decimated Caesar's troops that his eight legions numbered not over 22,000 men under arms—well under half their normal size. Pompey's victorious army, provided with a countless cavalry and ample supplies, had provisions in abundance, while Caesar's troops had difficulty keeping alive, and could only hope for better supplies from the approaching harvest. The Pompeian soldiers, who had learned in the last campaign to know war and trust their leader, were in the best of humor.

All military considerations on Pompey's side favored engaging in the decisive battle soon, since they had now confronted Caesar in Thessaly; and the emigrant impatience of the genteel officers and others with the army doubtless made such reasoning invincible in the war council. Since Dyrrhachium these lords had regarded their triumph as established fact. Already they were contending among themselves over Caesar's supreme pontificate, and sending instructions to Rome to hire houses at the Forum for the next elections. When Pompey hesitated to cross the rivulet separating the two armies, which Caesar with his much weaker force did not venture to pass, great indignation was aroused. Pompey, it was said, only delayed in order to play somewhat longer his part of Agamemnon, ruling over so many consulars and praetorians.

Pompey yielded. Caesar, under the impression that matters would not come to a battle, had just formed a plan of turning the enemy's flank, and for that purpose was about to set out towards Scotussa. But he likewise arrayed his legions for battle when he saw the Pompeians preparing to offer it on his bank.

Thus the battle of Pharsalus was fought on August 9, 48 B.C., on almost the same field where a victory over Philip of Macedonia a hundred and fifty years before had laid the foundation of Rome's dominion in the East. Pompey rested his right wing on the Enipeus, Caesar resting his left on the broken ground in front of the river. The two other wings were stationed out in the plain, covered in each case by cavalry and light troops. Pompey's plan was to keep his infantry on the defensive, while his cavalry scattered the weak enemy horse, mixed with light infantry after the German fashion, and then took Caesar's right wing in the rear. Pompey's infantry courageously sustained the first charge, and the engagement there came to a stand. Labienus likewise dispersed Caesar's cavalry after a brave but brief resistance, and deployed his force to the left with the view of turning the infantry.

But Caesar, foreseeing his cavalry defeat, had stationed behind it some 2,000 of his best legionaries. As the enemy's horsemen, driving those of Caesar before them, galloped along and around the line, they suddenly came upon this select corps advancing intrepidly against them and, rapidly thrown into confusion by the unexpected and unusual infantry attack, galloped at full speed from the field of battle. The victorious legionaries cut to pieces the now defenseless enemy archers, then rushed at Pompey's left wing and began on their part to turn it. At the same time Caesar's reserve advanced along the whole line to the attack. The unexpected defeat of the Pompeian army's best arm not only raised the courage of their opponents, but broke that of the army and above all that of the general. When Pompey, who from the outset distrusted his infantry, saw his horsemen gallop off, he rode back at once to the camp without even awaiting the outcome of the general attack ordered by Caesar. His legions began to waver and soon to retire over the brook into the camp, which was not accomplished without severe loss.

The day was thus lost and many an able soldier had fallen, but Pompey's army was still substantially intact, and his situation was far less perilous than Caesar's after the defeat at Dyrrhachium. But while Caesar had learned that fortune loves to withdraw herself at certain moments even from her favorites, in order to be won back through their perseverance, Pompey knew fortune only as the constant goddess, and despaired when she withdrew. Caesar's grander nature only developed mightier energies in the face of adversity; Pompey's inferior soul under similar pressure sank into the abyss of despondency. As once in the Sertorian war Pompey had been on the point of abandoning his post when faced by a superior opponent, so now, when he saw his legions retire over the stream, he threw from him the fatal general's scarf and rode off by the nearest route to the sea.

His discouraged and leaderless army—for Scipio, although recognized by Pompey as colleague in supreme command, was general-in-chief in name only—hoped to find protection behind the camp walls, but Caesar allowed it no rest. The obstinate resistance of the Roman and Thracian camp guard was speedily overcome, and the mass was compelled to withdraw in disorder to the heights above the camp. It attempted by moving along these hills to reach Larisa; but Caesar's troops, heeding neither booty nor fatigue and advancing by better paths in the plain, intercepted the route of the fugitives. In fact, when late in the evening the Pompeians suspended their march, their pursuers were even able to draw an entrenched line excluding them from the only water in the neighborhood.

So ended the day of Pharsalus. The enemy's army was not only defeated, but annihilated: 15,000 of the enemy lay dead or wounded on the field of battle, while the Caesarians missed only 200 men. The Pompeians who remained together, amounting still to nearly 20,000 men, surrendered the next morning. Only isolated troops (including, it is true, the officers of most note) sought a refuge in the mountains, and nine of the eleven enemy eagles were handed over to Caesar. Caesar, who on the very day of the battle had reminded his soldiers to remember the fellow citizen in the foe, did not treat the captives as did Bibulus and Labienus; nevertheless he too now found it necessary to exercise some severity. The common soldiers were incorporated in the army, fines or confiscations were inflicted on the men of better rank, and the captured senators and equites of note with few exceptions suffered death. The time for clemency was past, and the longer the civil war lasted, the more remorseless and implacable it became.

Some time elapsed before the consequences of August 9, 48 B.C., could be fully discerned. First was the passing over to Caesar's side of all those who had supported the party vanquished at Pharsalus merely as the more powerful; the defeat was so decisive that the victor was joined by everyone not willing or obligated to fight for a lost cause. All the cities, kings, and peoples who had hitherto been Pompey's vassals now recalled their naval and military contingents, and declined to receive the refugees of the beaten party. Almost the sole exceptions were the little town of Megara, which allowed itself to be besieged and stormed by the Caesarians, and King Juba of Numidia, who after his victory over Curio awaited with still greater certainty the long-expected annexation of his kingdom by Caesar, and was thus tied to the defeated party for better or worse.

Just as the protectorates submitted to the victor of Pharsalus, the tail of the constitutional party—all who had joined it halfheartedly or, like Marcus Cicero and his ilk, merely danced around the aristocracy like the witches around the Brocken—hastened to come to terms with the new monarch, who with contemptuous indulgence readily and courteously granted their petition. But the flower of the defeated party made no compromise. The aristocracy was done for, but the aristocrats could never be converted to monarchy. The highest revelations of humanity are perishable: the once-true religion may become a lie, the most blessed political system a curse. But even a dying gospel still finds confessors. If such a faith cannot move mountains like faith in the living truth, yet it remains true to itself to the end, and does not depart from the earth until it has dragged its last priests and partisans along with it, and a new generation, freed from those shadows of the dead past, rules over a world that has renewed its youth.

So was it in Rome. Into whatever abyss

of degeneracy the aristocratic rule had now sunk, it had once been a great political system. The sacred fire by which Italy had been conquered and Hannibal vanquished continued to glow, though somewhat dim and dull, in the Roman nobility so long as that nobility existed, and rendered impossible a cordial understanding between the men of the old regime and the new monarch. A large part of the constitutional party submitted outwardly, and recognized the monarchy so far as to accept pardon from Caesar and to retire as much as possible into private life—which, however, ordinarily was not done without the mental reservation of thereby preserving themselves for better days. This course was chiefly followed by the partisans of lesser note, but the able Marcus Marcellus, who had brought about the rupture with Caesar, judiciously and voluntarily banished himself to Lesbos. However, in most of the genuine aristocracy passion was more powerful than cool reflection—no doubt with the help of self-deception as to their prospects and fear of the victor's vengeance.

No one probably judged the situation with such painful clarity, free from fear or hope, as Marcus Cato. Completely convinced that after Ilerda and Pharsalus monarchy was inevitable, and courageous enough to accept that bitter truth and act upon it, he hesitated whether the constitutional party ought even to continue a war which would necessarily require sacrifices for a lost cause by many who knew not why they fought. And when he resolved to oppose the monarchy not for victory, but for a speedier and more honorable fall, he sought to draw no one into this war who chose to survive the republic's fall and accept the monarchy. He believed that so long as the republic had been merely threatened, it was his right and duty to compel the lukewarm to take part in the struggle. Now, he felt it senseless and cruel to force the individual to

share the republic's ruin. Not only did he himself discharge every one who desired to return to Italy; when the wildest of the partisans, Gnaeus Pompey the younger, insisted on executing these people and Cicero in particular, Cato alone by his moral authority prevented it.

Pompey also had no desire for peace. Had he deserved to hold the position he occupied, he might have perceived that an aspirant to a crown cannot return to the ordinary beaten track, and that there is no place left on earth for one who has failed in that aim. But Pompey was hardly too noble-minded to ask a favor which the victor would have perhaps been magnanimous enough to grant. On the contrary, he was probably too mean to do so. Whether he could not decide to trust himself to Caesar, or whether in his usual vague way, after the first impression of the disaster of Pharsalus had worn off, he began to cherish new hope, Pompey was resolved to continue the struggle and seek yet another battlefield.

Thus, despite Caesar's efforts by prudence and moderation to appease the fury of his opponents and lessen their number, the struggle went on without a break. But almost all the leading men had fought at Pharsalus; and while none were killed except Lucius Domitius Ahenobarbus, their flight scattered them in so many directions that they were unable to mount a common plan for continuing the campaign. Most of them found their way, partly through the desolate mountains of Macedonia and Illyria and partly by the aid of the fleet, to Corcyra, where Marcus Cato commanded the reserve left behind.

Here a council of war took place under the presidency of Cato, at which Metellus Scipio, Titus Labienus, Lucius Afranius, Gnaeus Pompey the younger, and others were present; but the commander-in-chief's absence and the painful uncertainty as to his fate, as well as the party's internal dissensions, prevented any common agreement, and eventually each took the course he felt most suitable for himself or for the common cause. Among the many straws to which one might cling, it was in fact highly difficult to say which one would keep above water longest.

Macedonia and Greece were lost by the battle of Pharsalus. It is true that Cato (who had immediately evacuated Dyrrhachium on the news of the defeat) still held Corcyra, and Rutilius Lupus the Peloponnesus, for the constitutional party. For a moment it seemed as if the Pompeians would make a stand at Patrae in the Peloponnesus, but the accounts of the advance of Calenus sufficed to frighten them from that quarter. There was also no serious attempt to maintain Corcyra. The Pompeian squadrons despatched to the Italian and Sicilian coasts after the victories at Dyrrhachium had achieved not unimportant successes against Brundisium, Messana and Vibo, and at Messana had burnt the whole fleet being fitted out for Caesar. However, the ships involved, mostly from Asia Minor and Syria, were recalled by their communities after Pharsalus, so that the expedition came to an end of itself.

In Asia Minor and Syria there were at the moment no troops of either party, except for the Bosporan army of Pharnaces which had taken possession, ostensibly on Caesar's behalf, of various regions belonging to his opponents. In Egypt there was still a considerable Roman army formed of the troops left behind by Gabinius, and thereafter recruited from Italian vagrants and Syrian or Cilician banditti; but the recall of the Egyptian vessels soon made it evident that the court of Alexandria had no intention of standing by the defeated party or even placing its troops at their disposal.

Somewhat more favorable prospects presented themselves in the West. In Spain, Pompeian sympathies were so strong among the population that the Caesarians had to give up their planned attack against Africa, and an insurrection seemed inevitable as soon as a leader of note appeared on the peninsula. In Africa the coalition—or rather King Juba of Numidia, who was the true regent there —had been arming unmolested since the autumn of 49 B.C.

Thus, while the whole East was lost by the coalition at Pharsalus, it might continue the war honorably perhaps in Spain and certainly in Africa; for to claim the aid of the Numidian king, who had been a subject of Rome, against revolutionary fellow citizens was no act of treason, though doubtless a painful humiliation. Those who gave up right or honor in this conflict of despair might move outside the law and commence hostilities as robbers. They might enter into alliance with independent neighboring states, and introduce the public foes into the civil strife. And finally, they might give lip service to the monarchy while seeking to restore the legitimate republic by the assassin's dagger.

That the vanquished should withdraw and renounce the new monarchy was at least a natural expression of their desperate position. The mountains and above all the sea had long been for the ancient world the asylum not only of all crime, but also of intolerable misery and of oppressed right. It was natural for Pompeians and republicans to wage a defiant war from the mountains and the sea against the monarchy of Caesar, which had ejected them, and especially natural for them to take up piracy on a grand scale with more compact organization and more definite aims. Even after the recall of the eastern squadrons they still possessed a considerable fleet, while Caesar had as yet virtually no vessels of war. Their connection with the Dalmatae, who had risen against Caesar in their own interest, plus their control over the most important seas and seaports, presented most advantageous prospects for a small-scale naval war. Sulla's hunting out of the democrats had ended in the Sertorian insurrection, a conflict waged first by pirates and then by robbers which ultimately became a serious war. So possibly, if Cato's aristocrats or Pompey's adherents showed as much spirit and fire as the Marian democracy, and if a true sea king was to be found among them, a commonwealth independent of the monarchy of Caesar and perhaps a match for it might still arise on the unconquered sea.

Far more contemptible was the idea of dragging an independent neighboring state into the Roman civil war to effect a counterrevolution. Law and conscience condemn the deserter more severely than the robber, and a victorious gang of bandits finds its way back into a commonwealth more easily than emigrants who march back with the public foe. Besides, it was scarcely probable that a restoration could be effected in this way. The only state from which support could be sought was the Parthian; and it was at least doubtful whether it would adopt the republican cause, and most improbable that it would fight for that cause against Caesar.

The time for republican conspiracies had not yet come.

While the remnant of the defeated party was thus driven helplessly about by fate, with even those determined to continue the struggle knowing not how or where to do so, Caesar, resolving and acting as quickly as ever, laid everything aside to pursue Pompey—the only opponent whom he respected as an officer, and the one whose capture would probably have paralyzed half (and perhaps the more dangerous half) of his opposition. With a few men he crossed the Hellespont, where his single bark encountered an enemy fleet destined for the Black Sea and captured the entire crews, who were stupefied by the news of Pharsalus. As

soon as the most necessary preparations were made, he then hastened to the East in pursuit of Pompey.

The latter had gone from the Pharsalian battlefield to Lesbos, whence he brought away his wife and his second son Sextus, and had sailed onward round Asia Minor to Cilicia and thence to Cyprus. He might have joined his partisans at Corcyra or in Africa; but repugnance toward his aristocratic allies and the thought of the reception which awaited him there, after the day of Pharsalus and above all after his disgraceful flight, seem to have induced him to prefer the Parthian king to Cato. While employed in collecting money and slaves from the Roman revenue farmers and merchants in Cyprus, and in arming a band of 2,000 slaves, he learned that Antioch had declared for Caesar and thereby closed the route to the Parthians. So he sailed instead to Egypt, where a number of his old soldiers served in the army, and where the situation and rich resources of the country would allow him time and opportunity to reorganize the war.

In Egypt, after the death of Ptolemy Auletes his children, Cleopatra, about sixteen years of age, and Ptolemy Dionysus, about ten, had jointly ascended the throne as consorts according to their father's will. But soon the brother, or rather his guardian Pothinus, had driven the sister out and compelled her to seek a refuge in Syria, whence she made preparations to get back to her paternal kingdom. Ptolemy and Pothinus with the whole Egyptian army were at Pelusium to protect the eastern frontier against her, when Pompey cast anchor at the Casian promontory and requested permission to land. The Egyptian court, long informed of the disaster at Pharsalus, was about to refuse when the king's tutor Theodotus pointed out that Pompey would then probably employ his connections in the Egyptian army to instigate rebellion, and that it would be safer, and also more politic towards Caesar, if they used this opportunity to do away with Pompey. Political reasonings of this sort were potent arguments among statesmen of the Hellenic world.

Achillas, the general of the royal troops, and some of Pompey's former soldiers went in a boat to his vessel, inviting him to come to the king and, as the water was shallow, to enter their barge. As he was stepping ashore, the military tribune Lucius Septimius stabbed him from behind under the eyes of his wife and son, who were compelled to watch the murder from the deck of their ship without the means of rescue or revenge. Thus on September 28, 48 B.C., the very same day on which thirteen years before he had entered the capital in triumph over Mithradates, the man who for a generation had been called the Great, and who for years had ruled Rome, died on the inhospitable Casian shore by the hand of one of his old soldiers.

A good officer, but otherwise limited in both intellect and heart, for thirty years fate had with superhuman constancy allowed him to shine in solving a series of easy tasks. He had been permitted to pluck all laurels planted and fostered by others, and had been presented with every opportunity for obtaining the supreme power—only to reveal an example of spurious greatness without parallel in history. Of all pitiful parts, the most pitiful is to pass for more than one really is; it is the inevitable fate of monarchy, for scarcely once in a thousand years does a man arise who is a king not merely in name but in fact. If this disproportion between appearance and reality had not been so marked in Pompey, one might gravely reflect that it was indeed he who was in a certain sense the first of the series of Roman monarchs.

When Caesar followed Pompey's trail into the roadstead of Alexandria, it was all over. With deep agitation he turned away when the murderer brought to his ship the head of the man who had been his son-in-law and for long years his colleague, and whom he had come to Egypt to capture alive. The dagger of the rash assassin conceled the question of how Caesar would have dealt with a captive Pompey. But while humane sympathy, which still found a place alongside ambition in Caesar's great soul, enjoined that he should spare his former friend, his interest also required that he demolish Pompey otherwise than by execution. For twenty years Pompey had been the acknowledged ruler of Rome, and a dominion so deeply rooted does not perish with the ruler's death. The death of Pompey did not break up the Pompeians, but merely replaced an aged, incapable, and worn-out chief with his sons Gnaeus and Sextus, both young and active and the second a man of decided capacity. Thus hereditary pretendership attached itself at once to the newly founded hereditary monarchy like a parasite, and it was very doubtful whether by this change Caesar did not lose more than he gained.

Caesar now had nothing further to do in Egypt, and both Romans and Egyptians expected him to apply himself immediately to the subjugation of Africa and to the huge task of organization awaiting him after victory. But Caesar was faithful to his custom of regulating matters once and for all while on the spot. Being firmly convinced that no resistance was to be expected either from the Roman garrison or the Egyptian court, and being moreover in urgent pecuniary embarrassment, he landed in Alexandria with the two amalgamated legions (numbering 3,200 men and 800 Celtic and German cavalry) and took up his quarters in the royal palace. There he proceeded to collect the necessary funds and to regulate the Egyptian succession, ignoring the saucy remark of Pothinus that Caesar should not neglect his own important affairs for such petty matters.

But a storm was secretly brewing. Alexandria like Rome was a cosmopolitan city, hardly inferior to the latter in numbers, and far superior to it in commercial spirit, skill of handicraft, and a taste for science and art. Its citizens had a lively sense of their own national importance; and if there was no political feeling, there was at least a turbulent spirit which induced them to riot in the streets as regularly and heartily as today's Parisians. One may therefore conceive their feelings when they saw the Roman general ruling in the palace of the Lagids and their kings accepting the award of his tribunal. Pothinus and the boy-king, both of whom resented the peremptory demand for the payment of old favors as well as the intervention in the throne dispute (which could only redound in favor of Cleopatra), ostentatiously sent the treasures of the temples and the gold plate of the king to be melted at the mint in order to satisfy the Roman demands. With increasing indignation the Egyptians—who were pious to the point of superstition, and who rejoiced in the world-renowned magnificence of their court as if it were their own possession—beheld the bare walls of their temples and the wooden cups on the table of their king.

The Roman army of occupation, essentially denationalized by its long abode in Egypt and many intermarriages with Egyptian women, and which moreover numbered many former Pompeians and runaway Italian criminals and slaves in its ranks, was also indignant at Caesar, who had obliged it to suspend its action on the Syrian frontier, and at his handful of haughty legionaries. The tumult at the landing, when the multitude saw the Roman axes carried into the old palace, and the numerous assassinations of his soldiers in the city, had shown Caesar the immense danger to his small force in the presence of that exasperated multitude. But it was difficult to depart at this season because of the prevailing northwest winds, and the attempt to embark might easily bring the outbreak of the insurrection. Besides, it was not Caesar's nature to leave without finishing his work.

Accordingly he ordered reinforcements from Asia at once, and meanwhile made a show of the utmost self-possession. Never was there greater gaiety in his camp than at Alexandria; and while the beautiful and clever Cleopatra was not sparing of her charms in general, and least of all towards her judge, Caesar also appeared to value most his victories won over beautiful women. It was a merry prelude to near-disaster. Led by Achillas and, as was afterwards proved, at the secret orders of the king and his guardian, the Roman army of occupation appeared unexpectedly in Alexandria. As soon as the citizens saw that it had come to attack Caesar, they made common cause with the soldiers.

With a presence of mind which partly atoned for his earlier foolhardiness Caesar hastily collected his scattered men, seized the king and his ministers, and entrenched himself in the royal residence and the adjoining theater. There being no time to save the war fleet stationed in the principal harbor immediately in front of the theater, he ordered that it be set on fire and that Pharos, the island with the lighthouse commanding the harbor, be occupied by means of boats. Thus at least a restricted position for defense was secured, and the way kept open for supplies and reinforcements. At the same time orders were issued to the commandant of Asia Minor as well as to the nearest subject countries, the Syrians and Nabataeans, the Cretans and the Rhodians, to send troops and ships in all haste to Egypt.

Meanwhile the insurrection, now led by the princess Arsinoë and her confidant the eunuch Ganymedes, had free range throughout Egypt and in most of the capital. In the streets of the later there was daily fighting, but Caesar was unsuccessful in gaining freer scope and breaking through to the fresh-water lake of Marea which lay behind the town, where he could have provided himself with water and forage. At the same time, the Alexandrians were unable to deprive the besieged of all drinking water; for when the Nile canals in Caesar's part of the town had been spoiled by introducing salt water, drinkable water was unexpectedly found in wells dug on the beach.

As Caesar could not be overcome by land, the besiegers exerted themselves to destroy his fleet and cut him off from his sea-borne supplies. The island with the lighthouse, and the mole connecting this with the mainland, divided the harbor into western and eastern halves, which were in communication with each other through two arched openings in the mole. Caesar commanded the island and the eastern harbor, while the mole and the western harbor were held by the citizens; and, as the Alexandrian fleet had been burnt, his vessels sailed freely in and out. The Alexandrians, after having vainly attempted to introduce fire-ships from the western into the eastern harbor, equipped with the remnant of their arsenal a small squadron, and with this blocked the way of Caesar's vessels when these were towing in a fleet of transports with a legion that had arrived from Asia Minor; but the excellent Rhodian mariners of Caesar mastered the enemy.

Not long afterwards, however, the citizens captured the lighthouse island, and from that point totally closed the narrow and rocky mouth of the eastern harbor for larger ships. Thus Caesar's fleet was compelled to remain in the open roads before the eastern harbor, and his communication with the sea hung only on a weak thread. Caesar's fleet, attacked in

that roadstead repeatedly by the superior naval force of the enemy, could neither shun the unequal conflict, since the loss of the lighthouse island closed the inner harbor against it, nor yet withdraw, for losing the roadstead would have cut Caesar off from the sea. Though the brave legionaries supported by the skilled Rhodian sailors consistently triumphed in these conflicts, the Alexandrians renewed and augmented their naval armaments with unwearied perseverance. The besieged had to fight as often as it pleased the besiegers, and a single victory for the later would have left Caesar totally hemmed in and probably lost.

It was imperative to recover the lighthouse island. A double attack, made by boats from the harbor side and by the war vessels from the seaboard, recaptured both the island and the lower part of the mole. Caesar ordered the attack stopped at the mole's second arch opening, and at that point closed the mole from the city by a transverse wall. But when a violent conflict arose around the entrenchers, the Roman troops left undefended the part of the mole adjoining the island. An Egyptian force landed there unexpectedly, attacked in the rear the Roman soldiers and sailors crowded on the mole at the transverse wall, and drove the whole mass in wild confusion into the sea. Roman ships rescued some, but most—including about 400 soldiers and a still larger number of sailors—were drowned. The general himself was obliged to seek refuge in his ship, and when this sank from overloading, he had to save himself by swimming to another. But the severe loss was amply compensated by recovery of the lighthouse island, which together with the mole as far as the first arch opening remained in Caesar's hands.

At last the longed-for relief arrived. Mithradates of Pergamum, an able warrior of the school of King Mithradates of Pontus (whose natural son he claimed to be), led a motley army by land from Syria—Ityraeans of the prince of the Libanus, Bedouins of Jamblichus, Jews under their leader Antipater, and contingents of the petty chiefs and communities of Cilicia and Syria. From Pelusium, which Mithradates had the good fortune to occupy the day he arrived, he took the great road toward Memphis with the view of crossing the Nile before it divides into its many mouths in the Delta. During this movement his troops received substantial support from the Jewish peasants who were settled in large numbers in this part of Egypt.

The Egyptians, headed by the young king Ptolemy (whom Caesar had released in the vain hope of quenching the insurrection), dispatched an army to detain Mithradates on the Nile's farther bank. This army fell in with the enemy beyond Memphis at the so-called Jews'-camp, between Onion and Heliopolis. Nevertheless Mithradates, trained in Roman-style maneuvering and encamping, succeeded in fighting his way to the opposite bank at Memphis. Caesar, as soon as he received word of the relieving army's arrival, conveyed part of his troops in ships to the end of the lake of Marea west of Alexandria, and marched round this lake and up the Nile to meet Mithradates advancing down the river.

The junction took place without enemy hindrance. Caesar then followed the retreating king into the Delta, and, notwithstanding the deep canal in front of the Egyptian vanguard, overthrew it at the first onset and immediately stormed the Egyptian camp. It lay at the foot of a rise between the Nile—from which only a narrow path separated it—and marshes difficult of access. Caesar ordered the camp assailed simultaneously from the front and from the flank on the path along the Nile, while a third detachment was to ascend unseen the heights behind the camp. The victory was complete. The camp was taken, and those Egyptians who did not fall to the sword were drowned in attempting to escape to the fleet on the Nile. In one of the overladen boats, the young king also disappeared beneath the waters of his native stream.

Immediately after the battle Caesar advanced at the head of his cavalry from the land side straight into the part of the capital occupied by the Egyptians. In mourning attire, with the images of their gods in their hands, the enemy received him and sued for peace; and the legionaries left behind, when they saw him return as victor, welcomed him with boundless joy. The fate of the city, which had ventured to thwart his plans and which had brought the master of the world within a hairsbreadth of destruction, lay in Caesar's hands. But he was too much of a ruler to be vengeful, and dealt with the Alexandrians as with the citizens of Massilia. Pointing to their devastated city deprived of its granaries, its world-renowned library, and other important public buildings through the burning of the fleet, he exhorted the inhabitants to cultivate earnestly the arts of peace alone, and to heal the wounds which they had inflicted on themselves.

For the rest, he contented himself with granting the Jews of Alexandria the rights enjoyed by the Greek population, and with replacing the Roman army of occupation, which at least nominally obeyed the kings of Egypt, by a formal garrison composed of the two besieged legions plus a third which afterwards arrived from Syria, under a commander chosen by himself. He purposely selected for this position of trust a man whose birth made it impossible for him to abuse it—Rufio, an able soldier but the son of a freedman. Cleopatra and her younger brother Ptolemy obtained the sovereignty of Egypt under the Roman protection. The princess Arsinoë was carried off to Italy, to prevent her from serving again as a pretext for revolt by the Egyptians, who in Oriental fashion were as devoted to their dynasty as they were indifferent towards individual dynasts. Cyprus again became a part of the Roman province of Cilicia.

This insignificant Alexandrian insurrection, of slight importance compared with the world-shaking events then taking place in the Roman state, had nonetheless a momentous influence in that it compelled the one man who was everything, and without whom nothing could be settled, to forgo his proper tasks for October of 48 B.C. to March of 47 in order to fight alongside Jews and Bedouins against a city rabble. The results of personal rule began to appear. The monarchy had arrived, but the monarch was absent and the wildest confusion reigned everywhere. For the moment the Caesarians were, like the Pompeians, without leadership. Everywhere matters were decided partly by the ability of the individual officers but most of all by accident.

Indeed, matters were in a serious state in Africa, where the constitutional party had ruled absolutely from the start of the civil war. Until the battle of Pharsalus, King Juba had been the *de facto* ruler there. He had vanquished Curio, and his flying horsemen and numberless archers were the main strength of the army. Beside him the Pompeian governor Varus played so subordinate a role that he even had to deliver the Roman captives from Curio's army to the king, and look on while they were executed or transported into the interior.

After the battle of Pharsalus a change took place. Except for Pompey, no leader of the defeated party thought of flight to the Parthians. As little did they attempt to hold the sea with their united resources; the efforts of Marcus Octavius in Illyrian waters were isolated and without permanent success. The great majority of republicans and Pompeians headed for Africa, where alone an honorable and constitutional warfare might still be waged against the usurper. There gradually gathered the fragments of the army scattered at Pharsalus, the troops that had garrisoned Dyrrhachium, Corcyra, and the Peloponnesus, and the remains of the Illyrian fleet. There met the second commander-in-chief Metellus Scipio, Pompey's two sons Gnaeus and Sextus, the republican political leader Marcus Cato, and the able officers Labienus, Afranius, Petreius, and Octavius.

If the resources of the emigrants had diminished, their fanaticism had if possible even increased. Not only did they continue to murder their prisoners, and even Caesar's officers under flag of truce: King Juba, who combined the partisan's exasperation with the fury of the half-barbarous African, even laid down the maxim that the citizens of every community suspected of sympathizing with the enemy should be exterminated and their town burnt—a theory applied in practice against some unfortunate townships. In fact, it was solely due to Cato's energetic intervention that the flourishing provincial capital Utica, which like Carthage of old had long been eyed jealously by the Numidian kings, did not meet the same fate, and that only precautionary measures were taken against its citizens, who were not unjustly accused of Caesarian leanings.

As neither Caesar nor any of his lieutenants made the smallest move against Africa, the coalition had ample time to reorganize politically and militarily. First, it was necessary to fill the post of commander-in-chief left open by Pompey's death. King Juba was not disinclined to retain the position which he had held in Africa up to the battle of Pharsalus. Indeed, he bore himself no longer as a Roman vassal but as an ally or even as a protector, and took it upon himself, for example, to coin Roman silver money with his name and device. He even proposed to be the sole wearer of purple in the camp, and suggested that the Roman commanders lay aside their purple mantle of office. Metellus Scipio also demanded the supreme command because Pompey had recognized him on an equal footing, though more because Pompey was his son-in-law than on military grounds. A like demand was raised by Varus as provincial governor—self-nominated, it is true—since the war was to be waged in his province. And lastly, the army desired for its leader the propraetor Marcus Cato.

Obviously the army was right. Cato was the only man with the requisite devotion, energy, and authority for the difficult office. If he was no military man, it was infinitely better to appoint a nonmilitary man who understood how to listen to reason and make his subordinates act, than an officer of untried capacity like Varus or one of tried incapacity like Metellus Scipio. But the decision fell at length on this same Scipio, and it was Cato himself who mainly determined that decision.

He did so not because he felt unequal to such a task, or because his vanity found satisfaction in declining rather than accepting. Still less was it because he loved or respected Scipio, with whom he was at odds personally, and who despite his notorious inefficiency had attained influence merely through being Pompey's father-in-law. He did it simply and solely because in his obstinate legal formalism he chose to let the republic founder according to law rather than save it in an irregular way. When after the battle of Pharsalus he met Marcus Cicero at Corcyra, he had offered to hand over the Corcyran command to the latter—who still held the rank of general from his Cilician administration—as the ranking officer according to the letter of the law. By this readiness he had driven almost to despair the unfortunate advocate, who

now cursed his military laurels a thousand times; but he also astonished all men of the least perspicacity.

The same principles were applied now when something more was at stake. Cato weighed the question of the new commander-in-chief as if the matter involved a field at Tusculum, and adjudged it to Scipio. By this sentence both his own and Varus' candidacy were set aside. But it was also he alone who resisted with energy the claims of King Juba, and made him feel that the Roman nobility came to him not as a suppliant might approach a Parthian king, beseeching aid at the hands of a protector, but as men entitled to command and require aid from a subject. In view of the state of the Roman forces in Africa Juba could not avoid lowering his claims to some extent, although the weak Scipio agreed that his troops should be paid from the Roman treasury, and that the province of Africa should be ceded to him in the event of victory.

Alongside the new commander-in-chief the Senate of the "three hundred" again emerged. It established itself in Utica, replenishing its thinned ranks by admitting the wealthiest and most esteemed men of the equestrian order.

Military preparations were energetically pushed, chiefly through the zeal of Cato, and every man capable of arms, even freedmen and Libyans, was enrolled in the legions. So many hands were withdrawn from agriculture that many of the fields were untended, but the result was certainly imposing. The heavy infantry numbered fourteen legions, of which two were already raised by Varus, eight others formed partly from the refugees and partly from provincial conscripts, and four were legions of Juba armed in the Roman manner. The heavy cavalry, consisting of Celts and Germans who came with Labienus and sundry others incorporated in their ranks, was 1,600 strong without counting Juba's cavalry squadron equipped in Roman style. The light troops consisted of mounted bowmen, a host of archers on foot, and innumerable Numidians riding without bridle or rein and armed merely with javelins. To these might be added Juba's 120 elephants and the fleet of 55 sail commanded by Publius Varus and Marcus Octavius.

The urgent want of money was somewhat remedied through self-taxation by the Senate, which was the more productive since the richest African capitalists had been induced to enter it. Grain and other supplies were accumulated in immense quantities in defensible fortresses, while at the same time open townships were swept as clean of stores as possible. The absence of Caesar, the troublesome temper of his legions, and the ferment in Spain and Italy gradually raised men's spirits, and fresh hopes of victory began to replace the recollection of the Pharsalian defeat.

The time Caesar lost in Egypt nowhere revenged itself more severely than here. Had he proceeded to Africa immediately after Pompey's death, he would have found a weak, disorganized, and frightened army under hopelessly divided leaders. Now, owing especially to Cato's energy, there was in Africa an army equal in size to that defeated at Pharsalus, led by generals of note, and under a regulated superintendence.

An evil star seemed to preside over this African expedition of Caesar. Even before embarking for Egypt he had made certain preparatory arrangements in Spain and Italy looking toward the African war, but all these had yielded nothing but mischief. From Spain, according to Caesar's arrangement, the governor of the southern province Quintus Cassius Longinus was to cross with four legions to Africa and, after joining forces with King Bogud of West Mauretania, was to advance with him toward Numidia and

the Roman province of Africa. But that army destined for Africa included a number of native Spaniards and two former Pompeian legions; Pompeian sympathies also prevailed in the province, and the unskilful and tyrannical behavior of the Caesarian governor was not suited to allay them. A formal revolt took place, with troops and towns taking part for or against the governor. Those who had risen against Caesar's lieutenant were on the point of openly displaying the Pompeian banner, and Pompey's elder son Gnaeus had already embarked for Spain to capitalize on this favorable development, when the disavowal of the governor by the most respectable Caesarians and the interference of the commander of the northern province suppressed the insurrection in the nick of time.

Gnaeus Pompey, who had lost time en route in vainly attempting to establish himself in Mauretania, came too late. Gaius Trebonius, whom Caesar sent to Spain to relieve Cassius in the fall of 47 B.C., met with absolute obedience everywhere, but amid these blunders nothing was done from Spain against the republicans in Africa. Indeed, because of these complications King Bogud of West Mauretania, who as Caesar's ally might at least have hindered King Juba, had been called away with his troops to Spain.

Still more serious were the disturbances among the troops collected at Caesar's orders in southern Italy for transporting to Africa. They were mainly the old legions which had founded Caesar's throne in Gaul, Spain, and Thessaly. Their spirit had not been improved by victories, and had been utterly disorganized by long repose in Lower Italy. The almost superhuman demands which the general had made on them, whose effects were only too apparent in their fearfully thinned ranks, left even in these men of iron a secret rancor which required only time and quiet to set in ferment. The only man with influence over them had been absent and almost unheard-of for a year. Their commanding officers were far more afraid of the soldiers than the soldiers of them, and overlooked in the conquerors of the world every outrage and every breach of discipline.

When the orders to embark for Sicily arrived, requiring the soldier to exchange the luxurious ease of Campania for a third campaign certainly as difficult as those of Spain and Thessaly, the reins, too long relaxed and now too suddenly tightened, snapped asunder. The legions refused to obey till the promised presents were paid to them, scornfully repulsed the officers sent by Caesar, and even threw stones at them. An attempt to extinguish the incipient revolt by increased promises not only had no success, but the soldiers set out in masses to demand fulfillment of the promises from the general in the capital. Several officers who attempted to restrain them were slain.

It was a formidable danger. Caesar ordered the gates occupied by the few soldiers who were in the city, to ward off at least for the moment the justly feared pillage, and suddenly appeared among the furious bands demanding to know what they wanted. They exclaimed: "Discharge!" In a moment the request was granted. Caesar added that regarding the presents promised to his soldiers at his triumph, as well as the lands which he had not promised but had destined for them, they might apply to him on the day when he and the other soldiers celebrated their triumph. In the triumph itself they could not participate, having been previously discharged.

The mutineers were not prepared for this turn of events. Convinced that they were essential for the African campaign, they had demanded their discharge only so that, if it were refused, they might attach their own conditions to further service. Half shaken in their belief as to their own indispensability; too awkward to bring the negotiation back to the proper channel; shamed by Caesar's fidelity to his word even toward soldiers who had forgotten their allegiance, and by his generosity which even now granted more than he had ever promised; deeply affected at the prospect of being mere civilian spectators of the triumph of their comrades; shocked at being no longer called "comrades" but "citizens," a form of address which from his mouth sounded so strangely, destroying in one blow the whole pride of their past soldierly career; and besides all this, under the spell of the man whose presence had an irresistible power—the soldiers stood mute and lingering awhile, till from all sides a cry arose to be permitted again to be called Caesar's soldiers. Caesar, after allowing himself to be sufficiently entreated, granted the permission, but the ringleaders in the mutiny had their triumphal presents reduced by a third. History knows no greater psychological masterpiece, nor one more completely successful.

This mutiny harmed the African campaign, at least by considerably delaying its start. When Caesar arrived at Lilybaeum, the port of embarkation, the ten legions destined for Africa were far from ready, and the experienced troops were farthest behind. However, hardly had six legions (five were newly formed) arrived together with the necessary war vessels and transports, when Caesar put to sea with them.

The enemy fleet, which because of the prevailing autumn gales was drawn up on the beach of an island in front of the bay of Carthage, did not oppose the passage. But the same storms scattered Caesar's fleet, and when he availed himself of the opportunity of landing not far from Hadrumetum (Susa), he could disembark only some 3,000 men, mostly recruits, and 150 horsemen. His attempt to capture Hadrumetum, strongly occupied by the enemy, miscarried, but Caesar possessed himself of two seaports near each other, Ruspina (Monastir near Susa) and Little Leptis. Here he entrenched himself; but his position was so insecure that he kept his cavalry in the ships, and the ships provisioned with water and ready for sea, in order to re-embark instantly if he were attacked by a superior force. This, however, was not necessary, for just at the right time the ships driven out of their course arrived.

The very next day Caesar, whose army suffered from want of grain because of the activities of the Pompeians, undertook with three legions an expedition into the interior. But on the march he was attacked not far from Ruspina by the corps which Labienus had brought up to dislodge Caesar from the coast. As Labienus had only cavalry and archers, and Caesar almost nothing but infantry, the legions were quickly surrounded and exposed to the enemy's missiles without being able to retaliate or attack successfully. No doubt the deploying of the entire line relieved once more the flanks, and spirited charges saved the honor of their arms. But a retreat was unavoidable, and had Ruspina not been so near, the Moorish javelin might have done the work of the Parthian bow at Carrhae.

Caesar, now fully convinced of the difficulty of the impending war, did not again expose his untried soldiers, disheartened by the new mode of fighting, but awaited the arrival of his veterans. The interval was employed in providing a counterpoise to the enemy's crushing superiority in long-range weapons. The use of men from the fleet as light horsemen or archers availed little, but Caesar succeeded in mobilizing against Juba the Gaetulian pastoral tribes wandering on the southern slope of the Atlas mountains toward the Sahara. The blows of the Mar-

ian and Sullan period had reached even these peoples, and their indignation against Pompey, who had made them subordinate to the Numidian kings, rendered them from the outset favorably inclined to the heir of the mighty Marius of whose Jugurthan campaign they still had a lively recollection. The Mauretanian kings, Bogud in Tingis and Bocchus in Iol, were Juba's natural rivals and to a certain extent long since in alliance with Caesar. Further, there still roamed in the border region between the kingdoms of Juba and Bocchus the last of the Catalinarians, Publius Sittius, who eighteen years before had transformed himself from a bankrupt Italian merchant into a leader of Mauretanian freebooters, and since then had acquired both a name and a body of retainers amid the Libyan quarrels. Bocchus and Sittius together fell on Numidia, occupying the important town of Cirta; and their attack, as well as that of the Gaetulians, compelled King Juba to send part of his troops to his southern and western frontiers.

Caesar's situation, however, continued amply unpleasant. His army was crowded into a space of six square miles, and though the fleet conveyed grain, the want of fodder was as keenly felt by Caesar's cavalry as by that of Pompey before Dyrrhachium. The light troops of the enemy, notwithstanding all Caesar's exertions, remained so immeasurably superior that it seemed almost impossible for him to invade the interior even with veterans. If Metellus Scipio had abandoned the coast towns, he might perhaps have achieved a victory like those which the Parthians won over Crassus and Juba over Curio, and he could at least have endlessly protracted the war. Every consideration suggested this plan of campaign. Even Cato, although far from a strategist, counseled its adoption, and offered at the same time to lead a corps to Italy and call the republicans to arms—which amid the utter confusion there might very well have met with success. But Cato could only advise, and the commander-in-chief Scipio decided that the war should be fought along the coast.

This was a blunder not only because they thereby abandoned a sure-fire strategy, but also because much of their own army, as well as the civilian populace in the new theater of hostilities, was in a dangerous mood. The fearfully strict recruitment, the seizure of supplies, the devastation of the smaller townships, and the general feeling that they were being sacrificed for an already lost alien cause had exasperated the native population against the republicans; and the acts of terror against any community merely suspected of indifference had raised this exasperation to bitter hatred. The African towns which could declared for Caesar, and desertion spread among the numerous Gaetulians and Libyans serving in the light troops and even in the legions of the republicans. But Scipio persevered with all the obstinacy of folly. He marched his entire force from Utica to Ruspina and Little Leptis, furnished Hadrumetum to the north and Thapsus to the south with strong garrisons, and in concert with Juba, who likewise appeared before Ruspina with all his troops not required to defend his frontier, offered battle repeatedly to the enemy.

Caesar, however, was determined to wait for his veteran legions. As one after another arrived, Scipio and Juba lost their desire for a pitched battle, and Caesar could not compel one because of his marked inferiority in light cavalry. Nearly two months passed in skirmishing near Ruspina and Thapsus, devoted chiefly to establishing outposts and discovering the concealed store-pits common in the country. Caesar, compelled by the enemy's horse to keep to the heights or to cover his flanks by entrenchments, gradually accustomed his soldiers to the new mode of fighting during this laborious and protracted warfare. Friend and foe hardly recognized the brilliant general in this cautious tactician who trained his men carefully and often in person; and they became almost puzzled by his masterly skill in delay.

At last Caesar, having received his final reinforcements, made a lateral movement towards Thapsus. Scipio had strongly garrisoned this town, thereby committing the blunder of offering his opponent an easy point of attack. He soon committed a second and less excusable one of attempting to rescue Thapsus, thus giving battle on ground where the infantry would be decisive. Immediately along the shore opposite Caesar's camp the legions of Scipio and Juba appeared, their front ranks ready for fighting while the rear were occupied in forming an entrenched camp. At the same time the garrison of Thapsus prepared for a sally.

Caesar's camp guard sufficed to repulse the latter. His veteran legions, correctly judging the enemy from their disorderly array, compelled a trumpeter to sound the attack while the enemy entrenching was still going on, and even before the general gave the signal. The whole line advanced headed by Caesar himself, who, when he saw his men attack without waiting for his orders, galloped forward to lead them. The right wing, in advance of the other divisions, frightened the elephants opposed to it (this was the last great battle in which these animals were employed) by throwing bullets and arrows, so that they wheeled round on their own ranks. The covering force was cut down, the enemy left wing broken, and the whole line overthrown. The defeat was the more destructive since the new enemy camp was not yet ready and the old one somewhat distant. Both were successively captured almost without resistance.

The mass of the defeated army threw

away their arms and sued for quarter, but Caesar's soldiers were no longer those who had readily refrained from battle before Ilerda and honorably spared the defenseless at Pharsalus. The habit of civil war and the rancor left by the mutiny asserted themselves terrifyingly at Thapsus. If the hydra which they fought always put forth new energies, if the army hurried from Italy to Spain to Macedonia to Africa, if the longed-for repose never came, the soldier not unreasonably charged this state of affairs to Caesar's unseasonable clemency. Swearing to remedy the general's neglect, he ignored the pleas of his disarmed fellow citizens as well as the commands of Caesar and his officers. The fifty thousand corpses that covered the battlefield of Thapsus— including several Caesarian officers known as secret opponents of the new monarchy, who were cut down by their own men— showed how the soldier procures his own repose. The victorious army's dead on that April 6th of 46 B.C. numbered no more than fifty.

The battle of Thapsus ended the African struggle as completely as Pharsalus a year and a half before had terminated that in the East. Cato as commandant of Utica convoked the Senate, set forth the state of affairs, and asked those assembled to decide whether to yield or defend themselves to the last man, urging only that all resolve and act together. The more courageous view found several supporters, who proposed to free all slaves capable of bearing arms. However, Cato rejected this as an illegal encroachment on private property, and suggested instead a patriotic appeal to the slave owners. But this fit of resolution soon passed over, and the assembly, now composed largely of African merchants, agreed to capitulate. When Faustus Sulla and Lucius Afranius arrived in Utica with a strong division of cavalry from the field of battle, Cato still made an attempt

to hold the town through them. But he indignantly rejected their demand to wipe out the untrustworthy citizens of Utica, choosing to let the last stronghold fall undefended into the hands of the monarch rather than profane the republic's dying moments by such a massacre.

After he had, partly by his authority and partly by liberal largesses, checked so far as he could the fury of the soldiery against the unfortunate Uticans; after he had with touching solicitude furnished the means for flight to those who preferred not to trust Caesar's mercy, and to those who wished to remain the opportunity for capitulating under the most tolerable conditions; and after having thoroughly satisfied himself that he could render to no one any further aid, he retired to his bedchamber and plunged his sword into his breast.

Few of the other fugitive leaders escaped. The cavalry that fled from Thapsus encountered the bands of Sittius, and were cut down or captured by them. Their leaders Afranius and Faustus were delivered up to Caesar, and were slain in a tumult by his veterans when he did not order their immediate execution. Metellus Scipio with the fleet of the defeated party fell into the power of the cruisers of Sittius and, when they were about to lay hands on him, stabbed himself. King Juba, not unprepared for such an issue, had resolved to die in a way which he felt befitted a king, and had readied an enormous funeral pyre in the market place of Zama which was intended to consume himself, his treasures, and the dead bodies of the entire citizenry of the town. But the inhabitants, showing no desire to become mere decorations at his funeral rites, closed the city gates against the king when he appeared, accompanied by Marcus Petreius.

King Juba, one of those natures that become savage amid a life of dazzling and insolent enjoyment, and concoct even out of death an intoxicating feast, resorted with his companion to one of his country houses. There, after a copious banquet, he challenged Petreius to fight him to death in single combat. But the conqueror of Catiline himself suffered death at the hand of the king, who thereupon caused himself to be stabbed by one of his slaves. The few men of eminence who escaped, such as Labienus and Sextus Pompey, followed the latter's elder brother to Spain and sought, like Sertorius before them, a last refuge as robbers and pirates in the shores and mountains of that still half-conquered land.

Caesar regulated the affairs of Africa without resistance. As Curio had already proposed, the kingdom of Massinissa was broken up, with the most eastern portion united with the kingdom of Bocchus, while the faithful Bogud was rewarded with considerable gifts. Cirta and the surrounding district, hitherto held under Juba's supremacy by the prince Massinissa and his son Arabion, were conferred on Publius Sittius, so that he might settle his half-Roman bands there. But at the same time this district, plus by far the largest and most fertile portion of Juba's kingdom, was united as "New Africa" with the older province of Africa. Thus the empire undertook the defense of the country against the roving desert tribes, instead of entrusting it (like the republic) to a dependent king.

The struggle of Pompey and the republicans against the monarchy thus ended, after four years, in the complete victory of the new monarch. Doubtless the monarchy could be dated not from the battles of Pharsalus and Thapsus, but from the moment when Pompey and Caesar had established their joint rule and overthrown the previous aristocratic constitution. Yet it was only those bloody baptisms of August 9, 48 B.C., and April 6, 46 B.C., that set aside the joint rule so different from absolute dominion, and

conferred recognition and status on the new monarchy. Risings of pretenders and republican conspiracies might provoke new commotions, perhaps even new revolutions and restorations. But the five-hundred-year-old continuity of the republic had been broken, and throughout the Roman empire monarchy had acquired the legitimacy of established fact.

That the constitutional struggle was at an end was proclaimed by Marcus Cato when he fell on his sword at Utica. For many years he had been the foremost defender of the legitimate republic against its oppressors, continuing the struggle long after he had abandoned any hope of victory. But now the struggle itself had become impossible. The republic which Lucius Brutus had founded was dead, never to be revived; what on earth were the republicans to do now? When the treasure was carried off the sentinels were thereby relieved; and who could blame them if they departed? There was more nobility, and above all more judgment, in Cato's death than there had been in his life.

Cato was anything but a great man. But with all that shortsightedness, that perversity, that dry prolixity, and those spurious phrases which have stamped him for all time as the ideal of unreflecting republicanism and the favorite of all who make it their hobby, he was yet the only man who honorably and courageously championed the great doomed system in its last struggle. Just because the shrewdest lie feels itself inwardly annihilated by the simple truth, and because the dignity and glory of human nature ultimately depend not on shrewdness but on honesty, Cato has played a greater part in history than many men of far superior intellect. It only heightens the tragic significance of his death that he was himself a fool; indeed, it is just because Don Quixote is a fool that he is a tragic figure. And it is a moving fact that on this vast stage, where so many great and wise men had moved and acted, the fool was destined to give the epilogue.

He did not die in vain. That the last republican departed as the first monarch came was the fearfully striking protest of the republic against the monarchy, a protest which ripped aside all the so-called constitutional character of Caesar's monarchy, and exposed its shibboleth of the reconciliation of parties as a hypocritical screen behind which despotism flowered. The unrelenting warfare of political plots and literary accusations which the ghost of the republic waged against the monarchy for centuries, from Cassius and Brutus down past Thrasea and Tacitus, was the legacy of the dying Cato to his enemies.

This republican opposition drew from Cato its whole attitude—stately, transcendental in its rhetoric, pretentiously rigid, hopeless, and faithful unto death. Accordingly, it began immediately after his death to worship as a saint the man who in his lifetime was not infrequently a laughingstock and a scandal. But the greatest mark of respect was the involuntary homage paid by Caesar, when he made an exception to the contemptuous clemency with which he was wont to treat all his opponents. In the case of Cato alone, Caesar pursued him even beyond the grave with that energetic hatred which practical statesmen are wont to feel towards antagonists who oppose them on the ground of principles which they regard as equally dangerous and impracticable.

XIV

The Old Republic and the New Monarchy: I

The new monarch of Rome, the first ruler over the whole Graeco-Roman civilization, Gaius Julius Caesar, was in his fifty-sixth year (he was probably born on July 12, 102 B.C.) when the battle at Thapsus, the last in a long chain of momentous victories, placed in his hands the power to decide the world's future. Few men have had their elasticity so thoroughly tested as Caesar, sole creative genius of Rome and the last produced by the ancient world, which accordingly followed the path he marked for it until its sun was set. Sprung from one of Latium's oldest noble families, tracing back its lineage to the heroes of the Iliad and the kings of Rome, he spent his boyhood and young manhood like the typical genteel youth of that epoch. He had tasted both the sweet and the bitter in the cup of fashionable life, had recited and declaimed, had attempted literature and verses in his idle hours, had pursued love affairs of every sort, and had learned all the mysteries of shaving, curls, and ruffles pertaining to the dandyism of the day, as well as the still more mysterious art of always borrowing and never paying.

But the flexible steel of that nature was proof against even these dissipations, for Caesar maintained unimpaired both his bodily vigor and his elasticity of mind and heart. In fencing and riding he was a match for any of his soldiers, and his proficiency at swimming saved his life at Alexandria. The incredible rapidity of his journeys, usually made at night for the sake of gaining time (in sharp contrast to Pompey's procession-like slowness), astonished his contemporaries and was not the least among the causes of his success.

The mind was like the body. His remarkable intuitive powers revealed themselves in the precision and practicality of all his arrangements, even regarding situations which he himself had not seen. His memory was matchless, and he could easily carry on several occupations simultaneously with equal self-possession. Although a gentleman, a man of genius, and a monarch, he had still a heart. All his life he cherished the purest veneration for his mother Aurelia, his father having died early. To his wives and above all to his daughter Julia he displayed an honorable affection, which was not without influence even on political affairs. He maintained warm and faithful relations with the ablest and most excellent men of his time, high and low, each after his kind. As he never abandoned any of his partisans after the unfeeling manner of Pompey, but adhered to his friends unswervingly through good times and bad, several of these, such as Aulus Hirtius and Gaius Matius, even after his death gave noble testimonies of their attachment to him.

If in so harmoniously organized a nature any one aspect stands out, it is that he disdained everything theoretical or ideological. Caesar was of course a man of passion, for without passion there is no genius; but his passion was never stronger than he could control. Song and love and wine had taken lively possession of his spirit in the season of his youth, but they did not penetrate to the core of his nature. Literature occupied him long and earnestly; but while Alexander could not sleep for thinking of the Homeric Achilles, Caesar in his sleepless hours mused on the inflections of Latin nouns and verbs. He made verses, as everybody then did, but they were weak. On the other hand, he was interested in astronomy and natural science. While wine continued to be Alexander's destroyer of care, the temperate Roman, after the revels of his youth were over, avoided it entirely.

Around him, as around all those whose youth has felt the dazzling luster of woman's love, fainter gleams continued ever to linger. Even in later years he had love adventures and successes with women, and retained a certain foppishness in his appearance—or, to speak more correctly, a pleasing consciousness of his own manly beauty. He carefully covered his baldness, which he felt keenly, with the laurel chaplet that he wore in public in later years; and he would doubtless have traded some of his victories for the return of his youthful locks. But however much he enjoyed the society of women, he allowed them no measure of influence over him. Even his much-censured relation to Cleopatra only served to mask a political weakness.

Caesar was thoroughly a realist and a man of sense; and whatever he undertook was pervaded and guided by the cool sobriety which is the most characteristic mark of his genius. To this he owed the power of living energetically in the present, undisturbed either by recollection or by expectation; to this he owed the capacity of acting at any moment with fullest vigor, and of applying his whole genius even to the smallest enterprise; to this he owed the many-sided power , with which he grasped and mastered whatever understanding can comprehend and will can compel; to this he owed the self-possessed ease with which he dictated his writings as well as projected his campaigns; to this he owed the "marvelous serenity" which remained steadily with him through good and evil days; to this he owed his complete independence, uninfluenced by favorite, by mistress, or even by friend.

As a result of this clarity of judgment Caesar never formed illusions regarding the power of fate and the ability of man; in his case the friendly veil was lifted which conceals the inadequacy of man's works. Prudently as he laid his plans and considered all possibilities, he never forgot that in all things fortune (that is to say, accident) must bestow success. With this may be connected the circumstance that he so often played a desperate game, especially again and again risking his person with daring indifference. As occasionally the most sagacious men enter into a pure game of hazard, so Caesar's rationalism at some points made contact with mysticism.

Such gifts could not fail to produce a statesman. From early youth, accordingly, Caesar was a statesman in the truest sense, with the highest aim which a man is allowed to set for himself—the political, military, intellectual, and moral regeneration of his own deeply decayed nation, and of the still more deeply decayed Hellenic nation joined to his own. The hard school of thirty years' experience changed his views as to how this aim might be reached, but his aim itself remained constant both in time of hopeless humiliation and of unlimited power, both when as demagogue and conspirator he stole toward it by paths of darkness, and when as joint ruler and then as sole monarch he worked at his task before the eyes of the world.

All the permanent measures that Caesar set in motion at the most scattered times take their places in the great building plan. Therefore we cannot properly speak of his isolated achievements, for he did nothing isolated. With justice men admire the inimitable simplicity of Caesar the author, and the unique purity and beauty of his language. With justice the greatest masters of war have praised Caesar the general, who with a singular disregard for routine and tradition always discerned the mode of warfare by which the given enemy could be conquered, and which was thus the right one; who with prophetic certainty found the proper means for every end; who after defeat stood ready for battle like William of Orange, and invariably ended the campaign with victory; who managed the rapid movement of masses—that element of warfare which distinguishes military genius from mere ordinary ability—with unsurpassed perfection, and found the means of victory not in massive forces but in the celerity of their movements, not in long preparation but in rapid and daring action even with inadequate means.

But all these were with Caesar mere secondary matters. He was no doubt a great orator, author, and general, but he became each of these merely because he was a consummate statesman. The soldier especially played in him an altogether subsidiary part, and it is one of his principal distinctions from Alexander, Hannibal, and Napoleon that he began his public life not as an officer but as a politician. He had originally intended to reach his object, like Pericles and Gaius Gracchus, without the use of force, and for eighteen years as leader of the popular party he confined himself exclusively to political plans and intrigues. Then, reluctantly convinced at the age of forty that military support was necessary, he had put himself at the head of an army.

It was therefore natural that he should ever remain more statesman than general —just like Cromwell, who also transformed himself from opposition leader into military chief and democratic king, and who in general, little as the prince of Puritans seems to resemble the dissolute Roman, is yet in his development, his objectives, and his achievements perhaps the closest to Caesar of all modern statesmen. Even in his mode of warfare this improvised generalship is apparent. Just as Napoleon's campaigns against Egypt and England clearly exhibit the artillery lieutenant who had risen to command, so Caesar's similar enterprises betray the demagogue transformed into a general. A dyed-in-the-wool officer would hardly have been prepared, for political reasons not altogether compelling, to ignore military considerations as Caesar did on several occasions, most strikingly in his landing in Epirus. Several of his acts are therefore censurable from a military viewpoint; but what the general loses, the statesman gains.

The statesman's task is as universal as was Caesar's genius. He undertook the most varied things, but all without exception bore on the one great object to which he faithfully and consistently devoted himself, and he never preferred one aspect of this great activity to another. A master of the art of war, he did his utmost to avert civil strife and, when it nevertheless began, to earn laurels with the least possible spilling of blood. Although the founder of a military monarchy, he was uniquely successful in preventing the formation of a hierarchy of marshals or a government of praetorians. If he had a preference for any one form of service to the state, it was for the sciences and arts of peace rather than for those of war.

The most remarkable peculiarity of his action as a statesman was its perfect harmony. In reality, all the conditions for this most difficult of human functions were united in Caesar. A thorough realist, he never allowed the images of the past to disturb him. For him nothing was of value in politics but the living present and the law of reason—just as in his grammarian's role he ignored historical and antiquarian research, recognizing nothing but the living language and the rule of symmetry. A born ruler, he governed the minds of men as the wind drives the clouds, and compelled the most heterogeneous natures to his service—the plain citizen and the rough subaltern, the genteel matrons of Rome and the fair princesses of Egypt and Mauretania, the brilliant cavalry officer and the calculating banker.

His talent for organization was marvelous. No statesman ever compelled alliances, no general ever collected an army, out of such unyielding and refractory elements, and kept them together with the firmness that Caesar displayed in cementing his coalitions and his legions. Never did a regent judge his instruments, and assign to each its appropriate place, with so acute an eye.

He was monarch, but he never played the king. Even when absolute lord of Rome he deported himself like the party leader, pliant and smooth, easy and charming in conversation, complaisant towards everyone, seeming to wish nothing more than to be the first among his peers. Caesar entirely avoided the blunder into which so many similar men have fallen, of carrying into politics the military tone of command. However much occasion his disagreeable relations with the Senate gave for it, he never resorted to outrages such as that of the eighteenth Brumaire. Caesar was monarch, but he was never seized with the giddiness of the tyrant. He is perhaps the only one among the earth's great who in large matters and small never acted from impulse or caprice, but always according to his duty as ruler, and who might look back on his life and doubtless find erroneous calculations to deplore, but no false step of passion to regret. There is nothing in Caesar's life even remotely comparable to those aberrant excesses, such as the murder of Clitus or the burning of Persepolis, which the history of Alexander records.

He is, in sum, perhaps the only great man who preserved to the end the statesman's touch for discriminating between the possible and the impossible, and was not broken by that most difficult task for greatly gifted natures—the task of recognizing, when on the pinnacle of success, its natural limits. What was possible he performed, never ignoring the possible good for the sake of the impossible better, never disdaining at least to provide palliatives for evils that were incurable. But when he recognized that fate had spoken, he always obeyed. Alexander on the Hyphasis, Napoleon at Moscow, turned back because they had to, and were indignant at destiny for granting merely limited successes even to its favorites. Caesar turned back voluntarily on the Thames and on the Rhine; and even on the Danube and the Euphrates he thought not of world conquest, but merely of practical frontier regulation.

Such was this unique man, so easy and yet so infinitely difficult to describe. His whole nature is transparent clarity, and tradition preserves more copious information about him than about any of his peers in the ancient world. Our conceptions of such a person may well vary in shallowness or depth, but they cannot be truly different. The grand figure has exhibited the same essential features to every inquirer of the least discernment, and yet no one has succeeded in reproducing it to the life. The secret lies in its perfection. As a man no less than as a historical figure, Caesar occupies a position where the great contrasts of existence meet and balance. Of mighty creative power and yet at the same time of the most penetrating judgment; no longer a youth and not yet an old man; of the highest energy of will and the highest capacity of execution; filled with republican ideals and at the same time born to be a king; a Roman in the deepest essence of his nature, and yet called to reconcile and combine in himself as well as in the outer world the Roman and Hellenic cultures— Caesar was the entire and perfect man.

Accordingly, we miss in him more than in any other historic figure what are called characteristic features, which are in reality mere deviations from the natural course of human development. What in Caesar passes for such at first glance is seen, on closer observation, to be the peculiarity not of the individual but of the epoch. His youthful adventures, for instance, were common to all his more gifted contemporaries of like position, and his unpoetical but strongly logical temperament was the temperament of Romans in general. It was also part of Caesar's humanity that he was completely controlled by considerations of time and place; for there is no abstract humanity, and the living man cannot but occupy a place in a given nationality and culture. Caesar was a perfect man just because more than any other he placed himself amid the currents of his time, and because more than any other he epitomized the essential peculiarity of the Roman nation—practical aptitude as a citizen. His Hellenism was only the Hellenism which had long been intimately blended with the Italian nation.

In this very circumstance, however, lies the difficulty, perhaps the impossibility, of depicting Caesar to life. As the artist can paint everything save consummate beauty, so the historian, when once in a thousand years he encounters perfection, can only be silent. For normality is doubtless capable of being described, but only by the negative notion of the absence of defect. Nature's secret, whereby she combines normality and individuality in her most finished productions, is beyond expression. We can only deem fortunate those who beheld this perfection, and gain some faint conception of it from the reflected luster which rests imperishably on the creations of so great a nature.

True, these also bear the stamp of the times. The Roman hero stood beside his youthful Greek predecessor not as an equal but as a superior, but meantime the world had grown old and faded. Caesar's course was no longer, like that of Alexander, a joyous marching toward an infinitely remote goal. He built on and with ruins, and was content to establish himself as securely as possible within the ample yet limited scope assigned to him. With reason, therefore, the dreamers of succeeding ages have passed over the unpoetical Roman, while investing Alexander with the golden luster of poetry and the rainbow hues of legend. But with equal reason the political life of nations has for two thousand years reverted again and again to the lines which Caesar drew; and the fact that the peoples to whom the world belongs still designate their highest monarchs by his name is at once deeply significant and a source of shame.

If the old and totally vicious state of things was to be expunged and the commonwealth renovated, it was necessary first of all that the country be effectively pacified and the rubbish of the recent catastrophe cleared away. In this work Caesar adopted the principle of reconciling the existing parties—or, to put it more correctly (for where irreconcilable antagonisms exist we cannot speak of real reconciliation) the principle that the arena where the nobility and the people had hitherto contended was to be abandoned by both parties, which were to meet together on the ground of the new monarchical constitution.

First of all, therefore, the older quarrels of the republican past were regarded as finished forever. While Caesar ordered that Sulla's statues, which had been thrown down by the mob on the news of the battle of Pharsalus, should be re-erected, thus recognizing that history alone should sit in judgment on that great man, at the same time he canceled the last of Sulla's exceptional laws, recalled the exiles banished during the Cinnan and Sertorian troubles, and restored the children of the outlaws to eligibility to office. In like manner all those were restored who early in the recent catastrophe had lost their Senate seats or their civil rights through sentence of the censors or political processes, especially through impeachments based on the exceptional laws of 52 B.C. Only those who had killed for money remained under attainder (as was reasonable), and Milo, the most daring henchman of the senatorial party, was excluded from the general pardon.

Far more difficult than the settlement of these past questions was the treatment of the existing parties, Caesar's own democratic adherents and the overthrown aristocracy. It was understandable that the former should be, if possible, still less sat-

isfied than the latter with Caesar's conduct after victory and with his summons to abandon the old political arena. Caesar himself doubtless desired the same general outcome that Gaius Gracchus had contemplated, but the objectives of the Caesarians were no longer those of the Gracchans. The Roman popular party had gradually been driven from reform to revolution, from revolution to anarchy, from anarchy to a war against property. They celebrated among themselves the memory of the reign of terror, and now adorned Catiline's tomb, as formerly that of the Gracchi, with flowers and garlands. They had placed themselves under Caesar's banner because they expected him to succeed where Catiline had failed.

But as it speedily became plain that Caesar had no intention of following Catiline's course, and that the most which debtors might expect was some alleviation of payment and modification of procedure, the indignant partisans loudly inquired, For whom had the popular party conquered? This rabble high and low, chagrined at the miscarriage of their intended Saturnalia, began first to flirt with the Pompeians, and then during Caesar's absence (from January 48 to autumn of 47 B.C.) to instigate a second civil war within the first.

The praetor Marcus Caelius Rufus, a good aristocrat and bad payer of debts, a man of some talent and much culture, and, as a vehement and fluent orator, one of Caesar's most zealous champions in the Forum, on his own responsibility proposed a law which granted debtors an interest-free respite of six years. When he was opposed in this step, he proposed a second law canceling all claims arising out of loans and current house rents; whereupon the Caesarian Senate deposed him from office.

It was on the eve of the battle of Pharsalus, when the balance seemed to incline to the side of the Pompeians. Rufus entered into communication with Milo, the old street fighter for the aristocracy, and the two contrived a counterrevolution whose banner combined the republican constitution with the cancellation of creditors' claims and the manumission of slaves. Milo left his place of exile in Massilia and called the Pompeians and the slave herdsmen to arms in the region of Thurii, while Rufus made arrangements to seize the town of Capua by armed slaves. But the latter plan was detected before its execution and frustrated by the Capuan militia. Quintus Pedius, who advanced with a legion into the territory of Thurii, scattered the plundering band there, and the fall of the two leaders put an end to the scandal.

Nevertheless, the following year (47 B.C.) a second fool, the tribune Publius Dolabella, equally insolvent but far less talented than his predecessor, reintroduced the law as to creditors' claims and house rents. Then, with his colleague Lucius Trebellius, he sought to support his view (it was the last time) with demagogic incitement. There were street riots and serious frays between the armed bands on both sides until the commandant of Italy, Marcus Antonius, ordered the military to interfere; and Caesar's early return from the East put a complete stop to the preposterous proceedings. Caesar attributed so little importance to these brainless projects that after some time he even received Dolabella again into favor. Against such a rabble, engaged not in political activity but solely in a bandit war against property, the mere existence of a strong government is sufficient; and Caesar did not deign to curry favor for his monarchy by concerning himself with alarmist apprehensions over these communists of that day.

While Caesar thus could and did leave the popular party to continue its already far-advanced disintegration, the aristocratic party possessed much greater vital-

ity. His object here was not to bring about its dissolution—which time alone could effect—but to begin and pave the way for it by a nice blend of repression and conciliation. Among minor measures, from a natural sense of propriety, Caesar avoided exasperating the fallen party by empty sarcasm. He did not celebrate a triumph over his conquered fellow citizens, and he mentioned Pompey often and always with respect, causing his overthrown statue to be put back after the senate house had been restored.

Caesar assigned the narrowest possible limits to political prosecutions. There was no inquiry into the various communications between the constitutional party and nominal Caesarians. Caesar himself threw into the fire unread the piles of papers found in the enemy's headquarters at Pharsalus and Thapsus, and spared himself and the country from political processes against suspected individuals. Further, all the common soldiers who had followed their Roman or provincial officers into the contest against Caesar came off with impunity, except for Roman citizens who had served in the army of King Juba; their property was confiscated as penalty for their treason.

Even to the officers of the conquered party Caesar had granted unlimited pardon up to the close of the Spanish campaign of 49 B.C.; but he became convinced that he had gone too far, and that the removal of at least the leaders was inevitable. He therefore set up the rule that every one who had served as an officer in the enemy's army or had sat in the opposition-senate after Ilerda forfeited his property and his political rights, and was banished from Italy for life. If he did not survive the war, his property was forfeited to the state. But those who had formerly accepted pardon from Caesar and were later found in the ranks of the enemy thereby forfeited their lives. These rules, however, were materially modified in practice. The death sentence was carried out only against a very few of the numerous backsliders. In property confiscations not only were all the estate's debts as well as widows' claims for their dowries paid off (as was reasonable), but a part of the estate was also left to the children of the deceased. Lastly, not a few of those liable to banishment and confiscation of property were pardoned entirely or got off with fines, like the African capitalists who were impressed into the senate of Utica. And even the others almost without exception had their freedom and property restored, if they could only bring themselves to petition Caesar to that effect. Indeed, several who declined to do so, such as the consular Marcus Marcellus, received pardon unasked, and ultimately in 44 B.C. a general amnesty was issued for all who were still unrecalled.

The republican opposition submitted to pardon, but it was not reconciled. Discontent with the new order and exasperation against the ruler were general. There was no further opportunity for open political resistance, and it is hardly worth noting that some opposition tribunes acquired the republican crown of martyrdom by an intervention against those who had called Caesar king. But republicanism expressed itself all the more decidedly as an inner opposition, and in secret agitation and plotting. Not a hand stirred when the Imperator appeared in public. There were abundant wall placards and sarcastic verses full of bitter and telling popular satire against the new monarchy. When a comedian ventured on a republican allusion, he was saluted with the loudest applause. Praise of Cato was the most fashionable theme of opposition pamphleteers, and their writings found a more grateful audience because literature itself was no longer free.

Indeed, Caesar even now combated the republicans on their own ground. He and his abler confidants replied to the Cato literature with Anticatones, and the republican and Caesarian scribes fought round the dead hero of Utica like the Trojans and Greeks round the body of the Trojan Patroclus. But as a matter of course the Caesarians had the worst of this conflict, where the public with its thoroughly republican feelings was judge. No course remained but to overawe the authors. On this account well-known and dangerous literary men, such as Publius Nigidius Figulus and Aulus Caecina, had more difficulty in obtaining permission to return to Italy than other exiles, while the opposition writers in Italy were subjected to a practical censorship whose restraints were all the more annoying because the punishment to be dreaded was utterly arbitrary.

The underground machinations against the new monarchy will be set forth in another connection. Here it is sufficient to say that risings of pretenders as well as of republicans were incessantly brewing throughout the Roman empire; that the flames of civil war, kindled now by Pompeians and now by republicans, again burst forth brightly at various places; and that in the capital there was perpetual conspiracy against the life of the monarch. But Caesar could not be induced by these plots even to surround himself with a permanent bodyguard, and usually contented himself with making known the detected conspiracies by public placards.

However much Caesar was wont to treat his personal safety with daring indifference, he could not conceal from himself the serious danger which this mass of malcontents represented to his creations. Yet disregarding the urgent warnings of his friends, and without deluding himself as to the implacability of the opponents to whom mercy was granted, he persevered with marvelous composure and energy in pardoning by far the greater number of them. He did so neither from the chivalrous magnanimity of a proud man, nor from the sentimental mercy of effeminacy, but from the statesmanlike consideration that vanquished parties are disposed of more quickly and less injuriously by their absorption into the state than by any attempt to wipe them out or to banish them from the commonwealth.

Caesar's high purposes required the constitutional party itself, which in fact embraced not only the aristocracy but all the elements of a free national spirit among the Italian citizenry. His schemes, which sought to renovate the antiquated state, needed the whole mass of talent, culture, and hereditary and self-acquired distinction comprehended within this party, and in this sense he may well have regarded the pardoning of his opponents as the finest reward of victory. Accordingly, the most prominent chiefs were indeed removed, but full pardon was not withheld from men of the second and third rank, especially younger men. These were not, moreover, allowed to sulk in passive opposition, but by more or less gentle pressure were made to take an active part in the new administration and to accept honors and offices from it.

As with Henry the Fourth and William of Orange, so Caesar's greatest difficulties began only after the victory. Every revolutionary conqueror learns by experience that if after vanquishing his opponents he would not remain a mere party chief like Cinna and Sulla, but would like Caesar, Henry the Fourth, and William of Orange substitute the common welfare for his own party's necessarily one-sided program, there is a point when he faces the united hostility of all parties including his own; and the purer his ideal the more this is true. The constitutionalists and the Pompeians paid homage with their lips, yet at heart hated the monarchy or at least the dynasty. The degenerate populists were in open rebellion from the mo-

ment they perceived that Caesar's goals were by no means their own. Even Caesar's personal adherents murmured when they found that their chief was establishing not a bandit state but a monarchy equal and just toward all, and that their personal gains were to be diminished by the raising up of the vanquished. This reorganization of the commonwealth was acceptable to no party, and had to be imposed on his associates no less than on his opponents.

Caesar's own position was in this sense weaker than before his victory, but what he lost the state gained. By annihilating the parties, while not simply sparing the partisans but allowing every man of talent or even merely of good family to hold office regardless of his political past, he focused on his great design the massed energies of the state; and the voluntary or compulsory participation of men of all parties in the same work imperceptibly led the nation over to the newly prepared ground. Nor was he misled by the fact that this reconciliation was for the moment only external, and that there was much less agreement about the new state of things than about hatred for Caesar. He knew well that antagonisms lose their keenness when brought into outward union, and that only thus can the statesman assist the working of time, which alone can heal such strife by laying the old generation in the grave. Still less did he inquire who hated him or meditated his assassination. Like every genuine statesman he served not for reward, nor even for the love of the people, but sacrificed the favor of his contemporaries for the blessing of posterity, and above all for the opportunity to save and renew his nation.

In describing in detail the method by which this transition from the old to the new was effected, we must first of all recollect that Caesar came to complete rather than to begin. The plan of a new political framework suited to the times, long ago projected by Gaius Gracchus, had been maintained by his adherents and successors with more or less spirit and success but ever without wavering. Caesar, from the outset almost by hereditary right the head of the popular party, had for thirty years borne its banner without ever changing or concealing his colors, and he remained the democrat even when monarch. As he accepted without limitation (except for the preposterous projects of Catiline and Clodius) the heritage of his party; as he displayed the bitterest personal hatred for the aristocracy and the genuine aristocrats; and as he retained unchanged the essential ideas of Roman democracy—alleviation of the burdens of debtors, transmarine colonization, gradual equalization of the classes comprising the state, and emancipation of the executive power from the Senate—to this extent his monarchy differed so little from the older democracy that on the contrary that democracy attained its completion and fulfilment by means of his monarchy.

For this monarchy was not an Oriental despotism, but a monarchy such as Gaius Gracchus had wished to found and Pericles and Cromwell founded—the representation of the nation by the man in whom it puts supreme and unlimited confidence. The ideas which underlay Caesar's work were not strictly new, but to him belongs their realization, which after all is the main point. To him belongs the grandeur of execution, which would probably have surprised the brilliant builder himself if he could have seen it. For it has always commanded the deepest admiration of everyone who has observed it, whether as living reality or in the mirror of history, whatever his historical epoch or political convictions, limited only by his ability to comprehend human and historical greatness.

At this point, however, it is proper to express once and for all what the historian ever tacitly assumes, and to protest against the custom—common alike to simplicity and perfidy—of using historical praise and censure as phrases of general application with no regard for circumstances. The present case involves construing the judgment of Caesar into a judgment of what is called Caesarism. It is true that history ought to instruct the present, but not in the vulgar sense, as if by simply turning over the leaves one could diagnose the ills of the present from the records of the past, and derive from these the specifics for a prescription. It is instructive only so far as observing older cultures reveals the organic conditions of civilization generally—the fundamental forces everywhere alike, the manner of their combination everywhere different—and leads and encourages men not to slavish imitation but to independent reproduction.

In this sense the history of Caesar and of Roman Imperialism, with all the unsurpassed greatness of the master worker, with all the historical necessity of the work, is in truth a sharper censure of modern autocracy than could be written by the hand of man. According to the same natural law by which the smallest organism infinitely surpasses the most artistic machine, every constitution, however defective, which expresses the free will of the majority infinitely surpasses the most brilliant and humane absolutism; for the former is capable of growth and therefore living, while the latter is what it is and therefore dead.

This law of nature demonstrates itself all the more completely in the Roman military monarchy, in that under the impulse of its creator's genius, and in the absence of all foreign pressures, that monarchy developed in purer form than in any similar state. From Caesar's time, as Gibbon has shown long ago, the Roman system had only an external coherence, repeating itself only mechanically; while internally, even under Caesar it was utterly withered and dead. If in its early stages, and above all in Caesar's own soul, the hopeful dream of combining free popular development and absolute rule was still cherished, the government of the highly gifted emperors of the Julian house soon taught men a terrible lesson in how far it was possible to hold fire and water in the same vessel.

Caesar's work was salutary and necessary not because it was or could be a blessing in itself. But given the social organization of antiquity based on slavery and utterly foreign to republican-constitutional representation, and under the organization of the urban constitution which during five hundred years had ripened into oligarchic absolutism, an absolute military monarchy was both a logical necessity and the least of evils. When the slave-holding aristocracy of Virginia and the Carolinas shall have carried matters as far as their predecessors in Sullan Rome, Caesarism will there too be legitimized at the bar of history; where it appears under other circumstances it is at once a caricature and a usurpation. But history will not deny the true Caesar his due honor, because her verdict in the presence of bad Caesars may lead fools astray and give rogues occasion for lying and fraud. She too is a Bible; and if she cannot any more than the Bible hinder the fool from misunderstanding and the devil from quoting her, she too will be able to requite them both.

The position of the new supreme head of the state appears formally, at least at the outset, as a dictatorship. Caesar took it up first after his return from Spain in 49 B.C., then laid it down again after a few days and waged the decisive campaign of the following year simply as consul. But in the autumn of that year after the battle of Pharsalus he reverted to the dictatorship and had it repeatedly

entrusted to him, at first for an undefined period, but from January 1, 45 B.C., as an annual office, and then in January or February of 44 B.C. for the duration of his life, so that in the end he pointedly dropped the earlier reservation as to laying down the office and formally expressed his life tenure in the new title of *dictator perpetuus*.

This dictatorship, both in its initial transitory and its second enduring phase, was not that of the old constitution, but the supreme office devised by Sulla. It was an office whose functions were fixed not by the constitutional ordinances regulating the supreme single magistracy, but by special decree of the people granting the holder the power to project laws and to regulate the commonwealth, an unlimited official prerogative which superseded the republican partition of powers. It was a mere elaboration of this general prerogative when the holder of power was entrusted by separate acts with the right of deciding on war and peace without consulting the Senate and the people, with the independent disposal of armies and finances, and with choosing provincial governors.

Caesar could accordingly assume prerogatives which lay outside the proper functions of the magistracy, and even outside the traditional power of the state. It appears almost as a concession on his part that he abstained from nominating the magistrates in place of the comitia, limiting himself to proposing a proportion of the praetors and of the lower magistrates, and that he had himself empowered by special decree of the people to create patricians, which was not at all permissible according to use and custom.

For other magistracies the dictatorship in effect left no room. Caesar did not himself fill the censorship, but he doubtless made full use of censorial rights, particularly the important right of nominating senators. He frequently held the consulship alongside the dictatorship, once even without colleague. But he refused to attach it permanently to his person, and he ignored the pleas for him to undertake it for a five- or even a ten-year term.

Caesar had no need to undertake the superintendence of religion, since he was already pontifex maximus. Membership in the college of augurs was conferred on him as a matter of course, along with an abundance of old and new honors, such as the title of "father of the fatherland," giving his name to the month of his birth, and other courtly manifestations which ultimately developed into outright deification. Two of these arrangements deserve to be singled out. First, Caesar was given the same personal inviolability as the tribunes of the people; and second, the title of Imperator was granted to him permanently alongside his other official designations.

Men of judgment will need no proof that Caesar intended to impose his supreme power permanently on the commonwealth, or that he chose a simple and fitting name for the new institution; for if it is a blunder to create names without power, it is scarcely less of an error to set up the substance of power without a name. Only it is not easy to determine what final shape Caesar had in mind, partly because in this period of transition it is difficult to distinguish the scaffolding from the permanent structure, and partly because his worshipful followers anticipated their master's nod and loaded him (doubtless to his disgust) with a multitude of powers and honors.

Least of all could the new monarchy act through the consulship, just because its elective character could hardly be separated from it. Moreover, Caesar obviously labored to downgrade this hitherto supreme office into an empty title, and subsequently, when he accepted it, he gave it away to persons of secondary rank before the year expired. The dictatorship came most frequently and clearly into prominence, but probably only because Caesar wished to use it in its old significance of an extraordinary presidency for surmounting extraordinary crises. On the other hand it was far from suitable for the new monarchy, for it was inherently marked with an exceptional and unpopular character, and a democratic statesman could hardly be expected to choose a permanent organizational form which had been created by the most gifted champion of the opposition.

The new name of Imperator, on the other hand, seemed in every respect a more appropriate title for the monarchy, just because in this context it was entirely new, and without apparent reason for its introduction. The new wine might not be put into old bottles. Here is a new name for the new thing, summing up most pregnantly what the democratic party had already expressed (though less precisely) in the Gabinian law as the function of its chief—the concentration and perpetuation of official power in the hands of a popular chief independent of the Senate. On Caesar's coins, especially those of the last period, we find the title of Imperator prevailing, and in Caesar's law as to political crimes the monarch seems to have been designated by this name. Thus later generations came to connect the monarchy with the name of Imperator. To give this new office both a democratic and religious sanction, Caesar probably intended to combine in it the tribunician power along with the supreme pontificate.

Unquestionably the new organization was not meant to be limited to its founder's lifetime. But Caesar did not succeed in settling the thorny problem of the succession, and it must remain moot whether he planned to institute some sort of election of a successor, such as marked the early Roman kings, or whether he wished to make the supreme office hereditary, as his adopted son subsequently claimed. It is not improbable that he had some notion of combining the two systems, and of arranging the succession (as did Cromwell and Napoleon) so that the ruler should be succeeded by his son; but if he had no son, or the son did not seem suitable, the ruler might choose his successor by adoption.

In law the new office of Imperator was based on the position which the consuls or proconsuls occupied outside Rome, so that primarily the military command, but along with it the supreme judicial and administrative power, were comprehended in it. But the Imperator's authority exceeded that of the consular-proconsular, being not only unlimited in time and space and held for life, but also operative in the capital. Unlike the consul, the Imperator could not be checked by colleagues of equal power, and all the restrictions gradually imposed on the original supreme power did not apply to the Imperator.

In a word, this new office of Imperator was nothing else than the re-establishment of the old kingship; for it was those very limitations of power as regards time, place, colleagues, and the co-operation of the Senate or the community which distinguished the consul from the king. Hardly a trait of the new monarchy is lacking from the old: the union of the supreme military, judicial, and administrative authority in the hands of the prince; religious leadership of the commonwealth; the right of issuing ordinances with binding power; the reduction of the Senate to an advisory council; the revival of the patriciate and of the city praefecture.

But still more striking than these analogies is the internal similarity of the ancient Roman monarchy of Servius Tullius and the monarchy of Caesar. If those old kings of Rome with all their plenitude of power had yet been rulers of a free community and protectors of the commons against the nobility, Caesar too had not come to destroy liberty but primarily to break the intolerable yoke of the aristocracy. Nor need it surprise us that Caesar, anything but a political antiquarian, went back five hundred years to find the model for his new state. Since the highest office of the Roman commonwealth had always remained a kingship restricted by a number of special laws, the idea of the regal office itself had by no means become obsolete. At various periods and from very different sides—in the decemviral power, in the Sullan regency, and in Caesar's own dictatorship—the regal power had in fact recurred during the republic. Indeed, by a certain logical necessity, whenever exceptional powers seemed needed there emerged, as distinct from the usual limited *imperium*, the unlimited *imperium* which was simply nothing else than the regal power.

Lastly, surface considerations also recommended this recurrence to the former kingly position. Mankind has infinite difficulty in achieving new creations, and therefore cherishes established forms as sacred heirlooms. Accordingly Caesar judiciously connected himself with Servius Tullius, just as subsequently Charlemagne connected himself with Caesar, and Napoleon attempted at least to connect himself with Charlemagne. He did so not covertly and secretly, but like his successors in the most open manner possible. Indeed, the very object of this connection was to find a clear, national, and popular form of expression for the new state. From ancient times there stood on the Capitol the statues of those seven kings, whom the conventional history of Rome was wont to bring on the stage; Caesar ordered his own to be erected beside them as the eighth. He appeared publicly in the costume of the old kings of

Alba. In his new law as to political crimes, the principal departure from the law of Sulla was that alongside and on a level with the collective community was placed the Imperator, as the living personal expression of the people. In the formula used for political oaths the genius of the Imperator was added to the Jupiter and Penates of the Roman people. The outward badge of monarchy was, according to the universal view of antiquity, the image of the monarch on the coins; from the year 44 B.C. the head of Caesar appears on those of the Roman state.

There could accordingly be no complaint that Caesar left the public in the dark as to his view of his position. As distinctly and as formally as possible, he came forward as king of Rome. It is conceivable (although not probable, and in any case unimportant), that he intended to designate his office not by the new title of Imperator but by the old one of King. Even in his lifetime many of his enemies and friends were of the opinion that he intended to have himself expressly so nominated. Indeed, several of his most vehement adherents suggested in different ways and at different times that he should assume the crown—most strikingly Marcus Antonius, when as consul he offered the diadem to Caesar before all the people in February of 44 B.C.

But Caesar rejected all these proposals at once. If at the same time he took steps against those who used these incidents to stir republican opposition, it by no means follows that he was not sincere in his rejection. The assumption that he encouraged these invitations, in order to prepare the multitude for the unfamiliar spectacle of the Roman diadem, utterly misjudges the mighty power of the sentimental opposition with which Caesar had to reckon. This opposition could not be rendered more compliant, but on the contrary gained strength from the fact that Caesar himself recognized its power. It

may have been the uncalled-for zeal of his followers that occasioned these incidents. It may also be that Caesar permitted or even suggested the scene to Antonius, to bring the inconvenient gossip to a sharp halt by a refusal before the eyes of the citizens, a refusal which was inserted at his command in the state calendar and which therefore could hardly be revoked. The probability is that Caesar appreciated both the value of a convenient title as well as the popular prejudice which focuses on the names of things regardless of their essence. Thus he was resolved to avoid the name of king—tainted with an ancient curse, and connoting to the Romans of his time the despots of the East rather than their own Numa and Servius —and to appropriate the substance of the regal office under the title of Imperator.

But whatever title he gave himself in his thoughts, the sovereign ruler was there, and accordingly the court gathered itself at once with its usual accompaniments of pomp, insipidity, and emptiness. Caesar appeared in public not in the consular robe bordered with purple stripes, but in the all-purple robe regarded by antiquity as the proper regal attire. Seated on his golden chair, and without rising from it, he reviewed the solemn procession of the Senate. The festivals commemorating his birthday, his victories, and his vows filled the calendar. When Caesar came to the capital, his principal servants marched forth in troops to escort him over a considerable distance. To be near him began to be of such importance that rents rose in the quarter of the city where he dwelt. Personal interviews with him became so difficult, because of the multitude of individuals soliciting audience, that Caesar often found it necessary to communicate in writing even with his intimate friends, and persons of the highest rank sometimes had to wait for hours in his antechamber.

People felt, more clearly than Caesar liked, that they no longer approached a fellow citizen. There arose a monarchical aristocracy, to a remarkable degree both new and old, which sprang from the idea of overshadowing the aristocracy of the oligarchy by that of royalty, the nobility by the patriciate. The patrician body still existed, although without important privileges as an order, in the guise of a tight aristocratic guild. But as it could receive no new families it had dwindled away over the centuries, and by Caesar's time no more than fifteen or sixteen patrician clans still survived. Caesar, himself sprung from one of them, received by popular decree the right of creating new patrician families, thus establishing, in contrast to the republican nobility, a new patrician aristocracy which met all the requisites of a monarchical privileged order—the charm of antiquity, complete dependence on the government, and total insignificance. On all sides the new sovereignty revealed itself.

Under a monarch thus practically unlimited there was little room for a constitution, and still less for continuing the old commonwealth based on legal cooperation of the citizens, the Senate, and the several magistrates. Caesar reverted completely to the old tradition: the citizen-assembly remained alongside the king the supreme expression of the sovereign people's will; the Senate reverted to its original function of advising the ruler when requested; and the ruler again concentrated in his person the whole executive authority, with no independent official by his side any more than was true of the ancient kings.

For legislation the democratic monarch adhered to the primitive Roman maxim that the people alone, in concert with the king convoking them, had the power to regulate the commonwealth; and Caesar had his enactments regularly sanctioned by decree of the people. To be sure, the energy and authority, half-moral and half-political, which the yea or nay of those old warrior assemblies had carried could not again be instilled into the so-called comitia of this period. The co-operation of the citizens in legislation, which under the old constitution had been extremely limited but real and living, was under the new one a mere shadow. Thus there was no need of special restrictive measures against the comitia, many years' experience having shown that every government—oligarchical as well as the monarchical—easily kept on good terms with this formal sovereign. These Caesarian comitia were practically important only in so far as by retaining in principle the sovereignty of the people they constituted a protection against absolutism. But at the same time Caesar also revived the other maxim of the old state law, that the command of the sole magistrate is unconditionally valid so long as he holds office, and that while legislation no doubt belongs only to the king and the citizens in concert, the royal edict is equivalent to law at least till the abdication of its author.

While the democratic king thus conceded to the community at least a formal share of sovereignty, it was by no means his intention to divide his authority with the previous governing body, the Senate. Caesar's Senate was to be (in a quite different way from the later Senate of Augustus) merely a supreme state council with which he consulted as to laws, and in whose name the more important administrative ordinances might be issued; for cases in fact occurred where senatorial decrees were issued unbeknownst to any of the senators who were recorded as present at their preparation.

There were no serious legal obstacles to reducing the Senate to its original deliberative position, which it had overstepped more *de facto* than *de jure*. However, it was necessary for Caesar to protect himself from practical resistance, for the Roman Senate was as much the focus of the opposition to Caesar as the Attic Areopagus was to Pericles. Chiefly for this reason the number of senators, which had normally amounted at most to six hundred and had been greatly reduced by the recent crises, was raised by extraordinary supplement to nine hundred. At the same time, to keep it at least up to this mark, the number of quaestors to be nominated annually—that is, members annually admitted to the Senate—was raised from twenty to forty.

The extraordinary reinforcement of the Senate was undertaken by the monarch alone, while for the annual additions he secured a permanent influence through the law that the electoral colleges were required to vote for the first twenty quaestorship candidates who were recommended by the monarch. Besides, the crown could confer the honorary rights of the quaestorship or any superior office, and thus a seat in the Senate, even to individuals not formally qualified. The extraordinary appointments naturally went in the main to adherents of the new order, and introduced, along with equites of respectable standing, various dubious and plebeian personages into the proud corporation—former senators removed by the censor or expelled because of a judicial sentence, foreigners from Spain and Gaul who to some extent had to learn their Latin in the Senate, subaltern officers who had not previously received even the equestrian ring, sons of freedmen or of men who followed dishonorable trades, and similar elements.

The exclusive circles of the nobility, who naturally took bitterest offense at this change in the composition of the Senate, saw it as an intentional corruption of the institution itself. Caesar was not capable of such a self-destructive policy, but he was as determined not to be governed by his council as he was convinced of the necessity of its existence. They might more correctly have discerned in these actions his intention to change the Senate's exclusively oligarchic character, and to make it once more what it had been in olden days—a state council representing all classes through their most intelligent elements, and not necessarily excluding the man of humble birth or even the foreigner. Just as the ancient kings introduced non-citizens, so Caesar introduced non-Italians into his senate.

While the nobility's rule was thus set aside and its existence undermined, and while the Senate in its new form was merely a tool of the monarch, autocracy took firm root in the whole administration of the state, and the executive power was concentrated in the hands of the monarch. First, the Imperator decided in person every important question. Caesar was able to carry on personal government to an extent we puny men can hardly conceive, and for more general reasons than his unparalleled rapidity and decisiveness. When we see Caesar, Sulla, Gaius Gracchus, and Roman statesmen in general displaying a capacity for work that transcends our notions of human powers, the reason lies not in any change in human nature but in the different organization of the modern household. The Roman house was a machine in which even the mental powers of the slaves and freedmen yielded their produce to the master; and a master who knew how to govern these worked as it were with countless minds. It was the *beau ideal* of bureaucratic centralization, which our countinghouse system indeed strives zealously to imitate, but still lags as far behind its prototype as the modern power of capital falls short of the power of ancient slavery.

Caesar knew how to profit by this advantage. Wherever any post demanded special confidence, we see him filling it, so far as other considerations at all permitted, with his slaves, freedmen, or followers of humble birth. His works show what such an organizing genius could accomplish with such an instrument; but how these marvelous feats were achieved in detail we have no adequate answer. Bureaucracy resembles manufacture in this respect, that the work done does not appear as that of the individual who made it, but as that of the factory in which it was produced. This much only is clear, that Caesar had no assistant who exerted a personal influence over his work or was even initiated into the whole plan. Not only was he the sole master; he also worked without skilled helpers, merely with common laborers.

In strictly political affairs Caesar avoided so far as possible any delegation of functions even as to details. Where it was inevitable, as when he needed a principal representative in Rome during his frequent absences, the person chosen was, significantly, not the monarch's legal deputy, the prefect of the city, but a confidant without official status, usually Caesar's banker, the cunning and pliant Phoenician merchant Lucius Cornelius Balbus from Gades. In administration Caesar was above all careful to take over the keys of the treasury—which the Senate had seized from the fallen kings, and through which it had established its government—and to entrust them only to servants absolutely and exclusively devoted to him. The monarch's private wealth remained, of course, strictly separate from the property of the state. But Caesar took in hand the whole financial and monetary system, and conducted it as he and other Roman grandees were wont to manage their estates. The levying of provincial taxes, and also largely the coining of money, were entrusted to the Imperator's slaves and freedmen to the exclusion of men of the senatorial order —a momentous step, from which in time

grew the important class of procurators and the "imperial household."

On the other hand, the governorships, now more than ever military commands after their financial functions had been taken over by the new imperial tax receivers, did not go to the monarch's retainers except in the case of Egypt alone. The country of the Nile, geographically isolated and politically centralized in the extreme, was better suited than any other district to break off permanently from the central power, as witness the repeated attempts by hard-pressed Italian party chiefs to establish themselves there during the recent crisis. Probably just this consideration induced Caesar not to declare the land a province, but to leave the harmless Lagid dynasty there. This is surely the reason why the command of the legions stationed in Egypt were not entrusted to a man of the Senate (or, in other words, to the former government) but was treated as a menial office like taxgathering.

In general, however, Caesar felt that Roman soldiers should not, like Oriental armies, be commanded by lackeys. The more important governorships were thus normally entrusted to exconsuls, the less important to expraetors; and the five-year interval prescribed by the law of 52 B.C. was probably set aside, so that the governorship followed hard on the heels of the term of office in Rome. On the other hand the distribution of the governorships, hitherto arranged sometimes by decree of the people or Senate, sometimes by agreement among the magistrates or by lot, passed over to the monarch. As the consuls were often induced to resign before the end of their year, to make room for replacement consuls (*consules suffecti*); as the number of praetors annually nominated was raised from eight to sixteen, with half being nominated by the Imperator (as in the case of the quaestors); and as the Imperator reserved the right of nominating titular praetors and titular quaestors—Caesar therefore never lacked a sufficient number of acceptable candidates for the governorships. Their recall was of course left to the regent's discretion, though as a rule the consular governor did not remain more than two years or the praetorian more than one year in his province.

Lastly, as for the administration of the capital city, the Imperator for a time evidently intended to entrust this also to magistrates nominated by him. He revived the old city lieutenancy of the kings, and during several absences of indefinite duration he committed the administration of the capital to one or more such lieutenants nominated by him without consulting the people. These lieutenants united in themselves all the administrative functions including even the right of coining money with their own name, although of course not with their own likeness. In 47 B.C. and in the first nine months of 45 there were neither praetors nor curule aediles nor quaestors; even the consuls were not nominated until near the end of the former year, and in the latter Caesar was consul without colleague.

This looks quite like an attempt to revive the old regal authority inside Rome, limited only by the democratic past of the new monarch: in other words, an attempt to abolish the consulship, the censorship, the praetorship, the curule aedileship, and the quaestorship, leaving only the prefect of the city during the king's absence and the tribunes and plebeian aediles appointed for protecting popular freedom. But Caesar subsequently abandoned this, neither accepting the royal title himself nor canceling those venerable names interwoven with the glorious history of the republic. The consuls, praetors, aediles, tribunes, and quaestors substantially retained their previous formal powers, but within a totally altered situation.

The foundation political idea of the republic was the identification of the Roman empire with the city of Rome, and by this token the city's magistrates were treated as magistrates of the empire. In Caesar's monarchy this view fell into abeyance. The magistrates of Rome governed thenceforth only the first among the empire's many municipalities, the consulship especially becoming a purely titular post of practical importance only because of the major governorship appended to it.

Thus the fate which the Roman community had been accustomed to visit on the vanquished now befell itself, and its sovereignty over the empire was converted into a limited communal freedom within the Roman state. Like the praetors and quaestors, the plebeian aediles were doubled in number and two new "grain aediles" (*aediles ceriales*) were added to superintend the supplies of the capital. Candidates for those offices were chosen by the community, without the restriction that marked the consuls and perhaps also the tribunes of the people and plebeian aediles. In general the ancient safeguards of popular freedom were not touched—but this, of course, did not prevent a refractory tribune of the people from being seriously interfered with and, in fact, deposed and erased from the roll of senators. As the Imperator was thus in all more important questions his own minister, as he controlled the finances by his servants and the army by his adjutants, and as the old republican offices were again converted into municipal magistracies, the autocracy was sufficiently established.

In the spiritual hierarchy Caesar made little material alteration. If the Roman state religion had served to support the ruling oligarchy, it might render the same service to the new monarchy; thus the Senate's conservative religious policy was transferred to the new king. When the conservative Varro published about this time his *Antiquities of Divine Things,* the great fundamental repository of Roman theology, he was allowed to dedicate it to the Pontifex Maximus Caesar. The faint luster still adhering to the worship of Jove shone round the newly established throne, and the old national faith became in its dying stages the instrument, however hollow and feeble, of a Caesarian papacy.

In judicial matters the old regal jurisdiction was reestablished. The king had once judged criminal and civil cases without being legally bound in the former to respect an appeal to the people for mercy, or in the latter to delegate the decision to jurymen. In like fashion Caesar claimed the right of bringing any case to his own bar, and disposing of it personally or (in his absence) through his city lieutenant. In fact we find him, quite after the manner of the ancient kings, now sitting publicly in judgment in the Forum on Roman citizens accused of high treason, now holding a judicial inquiry in his house regarding dependent kings similarly accused. Thus the only special privilege of Roman citizens seems to have consisted in the publicity of the judicial procedure. But exercise of this kingly judicial right, although Caesar discharged its duties with impartiality and care, was naturally limited to exceptional cases.

In criminal and civil cases the former republican judicial practices were substantially retained. Criminal cases were disposed of before various jury commissions competent to the crimes, civil cases partly before the court of inheritance (the *centumviri*) and partly before the single *iudices.* Judicial proceedings were supervised in the capital chiefly by the praetors, in the provinces by the governors. Even under the monarchy political crimes continued to be referred to a jury commission. The new ordinance which Caesar issued precisely specified the pun-

ishable acts, excluded all prosecution of opinions, and fixed banishment rather than death as the penalty. The jurymen were chosen not exclusively from the Senate, as the oligarchy wished, nor solely from the equestrian order, as the strict Gracchans would have desired, but on the basis of the compromise law of Cotta, with an eye to reconciling the parties. However, in line with Pompey's law of 55 B.C., the *tribuni aerarii* who came from the lower ranks of the people were set aside by the requirement that jurymen must own property of at least 400,000 sesterces. Thus senators and equites now divided the judicial functions which had so long been an apple of discord between them.

Any case might be initiated either before the king's bar or before the competent republican tribunal, the latter of course taking precedence in any conflict; but a sentence handed down by either tribunal finally disposed of the case. Even the monarch might not overturn the verdict of a qualified juryman except (as under the law of the republic) where corruption, violence, or similar circumstances warranted canceling the juryman's sentence. On the other hand, the principle that an injured person might appeal any magisterial decree to the magistrate's superior probably obtained sufficient currency as to give rise to the later imperial appellate jurisdiction. Perhaps all the magistrates, at least all the provincial governors, were regarded as subordinates of the ruler, so that any of their decrees might be appealed to him.

These innovations, even the most important of which (the general right of appeal) cannot be reckoned as an absolute improvement, by no means remedied all the evils in the Roman administration of justice. Criminal procedure cannot be sound in any slave state, since the task of proceeding against slaves lies at least *de facto* in the hands of the master. The Roman master naturally punished his slave only if the crime rendered the slave useless or disagreeable to him: slave criminals were treated somewhat like oxen addicted to goring, and, as the latter were sold to the butcher, so were the former sold to fight in the arena. But even criminal procedure against free men, which had always been partly a political process, had amid the recent disorderly generations become transformed from a grave legal proceeding into a factional fight employing favor, money, and violence.

The blame rested jointly on all parties —magistrates, jurymen, litigants, even the public as spectators. But the most incurable wounds were inflicted by the lawyers. As the parasitic plant of courtroom eloquence flourished, all ideas of right and wrong vanished, and the distinction between opinion and evidence (so difficult for the public to understand) disappeared from Roman criminal practice. "An ordinary defendant," says an experienced Roman advocate of this period, "may be accused of any crime whether he has committed it or not, and will certainly be condemned." Numerous pleadings in criminal cases have come down to us from this epoch, and hardly one of them makes even a serious attempt to define the crime and present the proof or counterproof.

That the contemporary civil procedure was in many ways likewise unsound goes without saying. It too suffered from the intrusions of party politics, as for instance in the process of Publius Quinctius in 83–81 B.C., where the most contradictory decisions were given depending on whether Cinna or Sulla had the ascendency in Rome; and the advocates, frequently nonjurists, also added abundant confusion both intentionally and unintentionally. But in the nature of such cases political considerations became involved only exceptionally, and lawyers' quibbles could not so easily erode natural ideas of

right. Accordingly, the civil pleadings handed down from this period, while not meeting our stricter tests of effectiveness, are yet far less libelous and more judicious than the contemporary speeches in criminal causes.

If Caesar retained Pompey's curb on the eloquence of advocates, or even strengthened it, nothing was lost; and much was gained when better-selected and better-superintended magistrates and juryman were nominated and the flagrant corruption and intimidation of the courts came to an end. But the sacred sense of right and the reverence for the law, which it is difficult to destroy in the minds of the multitude, is still more difficult to replace. Though the legislator did away with various abuses, he could not heal the root of the evil; and it was doubtful whether time, which cures everything curable, would in this case bring relief.

The Roman military system of this period was in nearly the same condition as that of Carthage in Hannibal's time. The governing classes furnished only officers, the subjects, plebeians, and the provincials the army. Financially and militarily the general was almost independent of the central government, and in fortune or misfortune was left substantially to himself and the resources of his province. Civic and even national spirit had vanished from the army, and *esprit de corps* alone was left as an inner bond. The army had ceased to be an instrument of the commonwealth. Politically it had no viewpoint of its own, though it was doubtless able to adopt that of the master who commanded it. Militarily, under its usual miserable leaders it degenerated into a useless rabble, but under the right general it attained a military perfection which the citizen army could never match.

The officer class especially had degenerated. The higher ranks, senators and equites, grew more and more unused to arms. Where formerly there had been a zealous competition for the posts of staff officers, now every man of equestrian rank who chose to serve was sure of a military tribuneship; several of these posts had to be filled with men of humbler origin; and any man of quality who still served sought at least to finish his term in Sicily or some other province where he was sure not to face the enemy. Officers of ordinary bravery and efficiency were stared at as prodigies, Pompey especially becoming the object of a military idolatry by his contemporaries which displayed their own unfitness. As a rule the staff gave the signal for desertion and mutiny; in spite of the culpable indulgence of the commanders, proposals for cashiering officers of rank were daily occurrences. We still possess the picture drawn (not without irony) by Caesar's own hand of the situation at his headquarters when orders were given to march against Ariovistus: of the cursing and weeping, the preparation of wills, and even the presentation of requests for furlough.

Among the soldiers no trace of the better classes could any longer be found. The general legal obligation to bear arms still existed, but the levy, if resorted to alongside of enlisting, took place in the most irregular manner. Numerous persons liable to serve were wholly passed over, while those once inducted were retained beneath the eagles for thirty years and longer. The Roman citizen-cavalry was merely a sort of mounted noble guard, whose perfumed cavaliers and exquisite highbred horses only appeared in the festivals of the capital. The so-called citizen-infantry was a troop of mercenaries swept together from the lowest ranks of the population. The subjects furnished all the cavalry and the light troops, and came to be more and more extensively employed in the infantry as well. The post of centurion, on which the efficiency of the legions essentially depended, and which according to the military constitution was to be filled by soldiers rising from the ranks, was not merely conferred as a favor, but often sold to the highest bidder. Because of the government's bad financial management and the venality and fraud of nearly all the magistrates, the payment of the soldiers was extremely defective and irregular.

The inevitable result was that the Roman armies frequently pillaged the provincials, mutinied against their officers, and ran away from the enemy. Instances occurred where considerable armies, such as the Macedonian army of Piso in 57 B.C., though undefeated were utterly ruined by such misconduct. Capable leaders such as Pompey, Caesar, and Gabinius doubtless formed able and effective, and to some extent exemplary, armies out of these materials. But these armies belonged far more to their general than to the commonwealth. The still more complete decay of the Roman navy —which had remained an object of antipathy to the Romans and had never been fully nationalized—scarcely needs mention. Here, too, everything that could be injured had been reduced to ruin under the oligarchic government.

Caesar's reorganization of the Roman military system was substantially limited to tightening and strengthening the reins of discipline, which had been relaxed under the previous negligent and incapable supervision. The system as a whole seemed to him neither to need nor to be capable of radical reform; therefore he accepted the elements of the army just as Hannibal had accepted them. His ordinance setting three years' mounted service (i.e., as an officer), or six years of service on foot, as a prerequisite for holding a municipal magistracy or sitting in the municipal council before the thirtieth year, proves indeed that he wished to attract the better classes to the army. But it also proves with equal clarity that amid the steady decline of martial spirit he felt it no longer possible to associate unconditionally the holding of an honorary office with the completion of military service. This also explains why Caesar did not try to re-establish the Roman citizen-cavalry. The levy was better arranged, the time of service regulated and shortened, but otherwise the infantry of the line continued to come chiefly from the lower orders of the Roman citizens, the cavalry and the light infantry from the subjects. It is surprising that nothing was done to reorganize the fleet.

The untrustworthy character of the cavalry compelled Caesar to adopt the innovation—which doubtless seemed hazardous to him—of enlisting hired foreigners, especially Germans. Another innovation was the appointment of adjutants of the legion (*legati legionis*). Hitherto the legions had been led by military tribunes, nominated partly by the citizens and partly by the governor concerned. Six tribunes were placed over each legion, the command alternating among these; and only as a temporary and extraordinary measure was a single commandant appointed by the general. In later times these adjutants of legions, or colonels, appear as a permanent institution, nominated no longer by the governor whom they obey but by the supreme command in Rome; and both changes seem to stem from Caesar's arrangements in connection with the Gabinian law. This important new step was inserted in the military hierarchy partly because of the need for a more energetic centralization of the command, and partly because of the lack of capable superior officers, but chiefly in order to provide a counterpoise to the governor by associating with him one or more colonels nominated by the Imperator.

The most essential change in the military system was the installation of the Imperator as a permanent military head. Superseding the previous unmilitary and incapable governing corporation, he united in his hands the whole control of the army, and thus converted a largely nominal supervision into a real and energetic supreme command. We are not properly informed as to the relation between this supreme command and the special commands hitherto omnipotent in their respective spheres. Probably the relation between the praetor and the consul, or the consul and the dictator, provided a pattern. Thus, while the governor remained the supreme military authority in his province, the Imperator was entitled to assume it for himself or his delegates at any moment; and while the governor's authority was confined to the province, that of the Imperator extended over the whole empire.

Furthermore, it is extremely probable that the nomination of military tribunes and centurions (so far as it had hitherto belonged to the governor) as well as the new adjutants passed directly into the hands of the Imperator. In like manner the arrangement of the levies, the granting of leaves of absence, and the more important criminal cases may also have devolved upon the commander-in-chief. With the regulated control by the Imperator, and with the governors' powers thus limited, there was little need to fear that the armies might become disorganized or converted into the private troops of their respective officers.

But however decided were the indications of military monarchy, and however distinctly Caesar reserved the supreme command for himself, he was nevertheless quite disinclined to base his authority on the army. No doubt he deemed a standing army necessary, but only because the state's geographical position required comprehensive regulation of the frontiers and permanent frontier garrisons. Both during the recent civil war and earlier, he had worked at the tranquilizing of Spain, and had established strong frontier defensive positions along the great African desert and on the Rhine. He also made similar plans for the regions of the Euphrates and the Danube. Above all he designed an expedition against the Parthians to avenge the defeat of Carrhae. He had scheduled three years for this war, and was resolved to settle accounts thoroughly yet cautiously with these dangerous enemies once for all. In like manner he had formed the scheme of attacking King Burebistas of the Getae (Goths), who was extending his power on both sides of the Danube, and of protecting Italy in the northeast by border districts similar to those which he had created in Gaul.

On the other hand, there is no evidence that Caesar contemplated like Alexander a career of victory extending indefinitely. It is indeed said that he had intended to march from Parthia to the Caspian to the Black Sea, and thence along its northern shores to the Danube; to annex all Scythia and Germany as far as the Northern Ocean (which according to the notions of those days was not so far from the Mediterranean); and to return home through Gaul. But no credible authority vouches for the existence of these fantastic projects. The Roman state already included a mass of barbaric elements difficult to control, and for centuries to come had more than enough to do in assimilating them. Hence such conquests, even granting their military practicability, would have been nothing but blunders far more brilliant and far worse than Alexander's Indian expedition. Judging both from Caesar's conduct in Britain and Germany, and from the conduct of those who became his political heirs, it is highly probable that Caesar (like Scipio Aemilianus) called on the gods not to increase the empire but to preserve it. His schemes

of conquest apparently restricted themselves to a stabilization of the frontier—measured, it is true, on his own great scale—which should secure the line of the Euphrates and replace the fluctuating and militarily useless boundary of the empire on the northeast by establishing and rendering defensible the line of the Danube.

If it is merely probable that Caesar ought not to be designated a world conqueror in the same sense as Alexander and Napoleon, it is quite certain that his design was not to found his new monarchy primarily on the army. He did not seek to place the military authority above the civil, but to incorporate it into, and as far as possible subordinate it to, the civil commonwealth. The invaluable pillars of a military state, those old and far-famed Gallic legions, were honorably dissolved just because of the incompatibility of their *esprit de corps* with a civil commonwealth, and their glorious names were perpetuated only in newly founded urban communities. The soldiers who were allotted land by Caesar on their discharge were not, like those of Sulla, settled together in quasi-military colonies of their own, but, especially in Italy, were isolated as much as possible and scattered throughout the peninsula. Only in the case of the Campanian land remaining for disposal was it impossible to avoid a concentration of the old soldiers of Caesar.

The difficult task of keeping the soldiers of a standing army within the civil community was attacked in various ways. The former arrangement merely prescribing certain years of service, which might be interrupted by temporary discharge, was retained, which occasioned a faster turnover in the army. Soldiers who had served out their terms were regularly settled as agricultural colonists. And perhaps most important, the army was kept away from Italy and centers of civil and political life, and directed toward what Caesar considered the soldier's only proper place—that is, on the frontier, where he might ward off the foreign foe.

The true criterion of a military state—the development of a privileged corps of guards—is not to be found with Caesar. Although a special bodyguard for the general on active duty had long existed, under Caesar this fell completely into disuse. His praetorian cohort seems to have consisted essentially of orderlies rather than a select corps, and consequently was never an object of jealousy to the troops of the line. Even less as king than as general would Caesar tolerate a bodyguard. Although well aware of the lurking assassins who constantly beset him, he rejected the Senate's proposal to create a select guard, soon dismissed the Spanish escort which he had used at first in the capital, and contented himself with the retinue of lictors traditional for Roman supreme magistrates.

However much of his and his party's ideal—to found a Periclean government in Rome not on the sword but on the confidence of the nation—Caesar had been obliged to abandon in the struggle, he continued to strive against the idea of a military monarchy with an energy almost without parallel in history. This too was certainly an impracticable ideal, and the only instance in which the earnest longing of that vigorous mind was more powerful than its clear judgment. The government which Caesar had in mind was not only by necessity highly personal, and thus as likely to perish with its author as the creations of Pericles and Cromwell. Amid the deep disorganization of the nation, it was incredible that even for his lifetime the eighth king of Rome would succeed like his seven predecessors in ruling his fellow citizens merely through law and justice; and it was equally improbable that he would again successfully incorporate the standing

army, which in the last civil war learned its power and unlearned its obedience, as a controllable part of civil society.

Anyone who has calmly considered the extent to which respect for law had disappeared from top to bottom of Roman society must regard the former hope as almost a dream. If with the Marian military reform the soldier had generally ceased to be a citizen, the Campanian mutiny and the battlefield of Thapsus showed with painful clarity what kind of support the army now lent to the law. Even the great democrat could scarcely hold in check the powers which he had unchained. At his signal thousands of swords still flew from the scabbard, but they were no longer equally ready at that signal to return to the sheath.

Fate is mightier than genius. Caesar sought to restore the civil commonwealth, and became the founder of the military monarchy which he abhorred. He overthrew the regime of aristocrats and bankers only to put a military regime in its place, and the commonwealth continued as before to be tyrannized and exploited by a privileged minority. And yet it is a privilege of the highest natures thus creatively to err. The brilliant failures of great men to achieve their ideals form the best treasures of nations. It was Caesar's work that the Roman military state did not become a police state till after the lapse of several centuries; it is due to him that the Roman emperors, however little they otherwise resembled the great founder of their sovereignty, mainly employed the soldier not against the citizen but against the public foe, and esteemed both nation and army too highly to set the latter as constable over the former.

The regulation of financial matters was of slight difficulty, because of the empire's immense magnitude and the absence of any extensive public borrowing. If the state had been in constant financial embarrassment, the fault was not chargeable to inadequate revenues, which in recent years had immensely increased. To the earlier estimated income of 200,000,-000 sesterces, 85,000,000 more were added by the creation of the provinces of Bithynia-Pontus and Syria. This increase, along with the other new or augmented sources of income (especially the constantly increasing yield of the taxes on luxuries), far outweighed the loss of rent from the Campanian public lands. Besides, immense windfalls had been brought into the treasury through Lucullus, Metellus, Pompey, Cato and others.

The cause of the state's financial embarrassments lay partly in increased ordinary and extraordinary expenditures, partly in poor management. Under the former head, the distribution of grain in the capital claimed almost exorbitant sums. Through its extension by Cato in 63 B.C. the yearly expenditure for that purpose amounted to 30,000,000 sesterces, and after 58 B.C., when the nominal price hitherto paid was abolished, it swallowed up a fifth of the state revenues. The military budget also had risen through the need for new garrisons in Cilicia, Syria, and Gaul. The extraordinary expenditures included the great cost of the navy, on which, for example, five years after the great pirate roundup of 67 B.C., 34,000,000 sesterces were expended at once. In addition, very considerable sums were consumed in wars and warlike preparations, such as 18,000,000 sesterces paid to Piso merely for outfitting his Macedonian army, 24,000,000 sesterces annually to Pompey for the maintenance and pay of the Spanish army, and similar sums to Caesar for the Gallic legions.

But considerable as were these demands, the Roman treasury would probably have been able to meet them had not its once efficient administration been affected by the universal laxness and dishonesty of the age. The treasury often had to suspend payments merely through failure to collect its outstanding claims. The two quaestors placed over it—young men annually changed—contented themselves at best with inaction; while the permanent staff, once so justly esteemed for its integrity, now perpetuated the worst abuses, more especially since such posts had come to be bought and sold.

As soon, however, as the financial threads were concentrated in the cabinet of Caesar, new life and stricter order at once pervaded all the wheels and springs of that great machine. The two innovations of Gaius Gracchus that ate like a gangrene into the Roman financial system—the leasing of the direct taxes, and the distribution of grain—were partly abolished and partly revised. Caesar, unlike his predecessor, did not seek to hold the nobility in check by the great capitalists and the populace of the capital, but to set them aside and to deliver the commonwealth from all parasites of whatever rank.

Therefore in these two important questions he followed Sulla rather than Gaius Gracchus. The leasing system was continued for indirect taxes, for which it was very old and (under the Roman financial maxim which Caesar retained inviolable, that tax collection should at any cost be kept simple and manageable) absolutely could not be dispensed with. But the direct taxes were thenceforth universally made either taxes in kind to be supplied directly to the state, as in the case of the African and Sardinian deliveries of grain and oil, or converted, like the revenues of Asia Minor, into fixed money payments whose collection was entrusted to the tax districts themselves.

The grain distribution in the capital had hitherto been regarded as a profitable prerogative of the community which ruled, and which therefore had to be fed by its subjects. Caesar set aside this infamous principle, but it could not be overlooked that only these largesses protected a multitude of destitute citizens from starvation. To this extent Caesar retained them. Under the Sempronian law as reaffirmed by Cato every citizen settled in Rome could legally claim free bread grain, and the list of recipients had risen to 320,000. This number was reduced, by excluding all individuals otherwise provided for, to 150,000, which was fixed once and for all as the maximum. At the same time the list was revised annually, so that places vacated by removal or death might be again filled by the most needy applicants.

By thus converting a political privilege into a provision for the poor, a unique moral and historical principle came into being. Civil society but slowly and gradually perceives its interdependence of interests. In earlier antiquity the state protected its members from the public enemy and the murderer, but it need not protect its helpless fellow citizens from a worse enemy, want. Greek civilization first developed, in the Solonian and post-Solonian legislation, the principle that the community was obligated to provide for its invalids and indeed for its poor generally. Caesar first transformed a restricted Greek municipal practice into an organic state institution, and converted what had been a burden and a disgrace for the commonwealth into the first of those institutions, now as countless as they are beneficial, where the depth of human compassion contends with the depth of human misery.

In addition to these fundamental reforms a thorough revision of income and expenditures took place. Not a few communities and even whole districts were exempted from taxation, either indirectly by receiving the Roman or Latin franchise, or directly by special privilege. Still more communities had their taxes lowered; and Asia, the most oppressed province of all, was not only granted direct taxation but had also a third of these remitted. New revenues, as from the communities subdued in Illyria and especially in Gaul—the latter alone paid 40,000,000 sesterces per year—were fixed throughout on a low scale.

On the other hand, various towns such as Little Leptis in Africa had their taxes raised as a penalty for their wartime conduct. The very lucrative Italian harbor-tolls so recently abolished were instituted all the more readily, in that this tax fell primarily on luxuries imported from the East. To these new or revived sources of ordinary income were added the extraordinary sums which accrued as a result of the civil war: the booty collected in Gaul; the stock of cash in the capital; the treasures taken from the Italian and Spanish temples; the sums raised in the shape of of forced loans, compulsory presents, or fines from dependent communities and rulers; the pecuniary penalties imposed by judicial sentence, or simply by sending an order to pay, on individual wealthy Romans; and above all things the proceeds from the estates of defeated opponents.

How productive were these extraordinary sources may be seen from the fact that the African capitalists who sat in the opposition-Senate were fined 100,000,000 sesterces, while 70,000,000 more were received from the sale of Pompey's property. This course was necessary because the power of the beaten nobility rested in great measure on their colossal wealth, and could be effectually broken only by imposing on them the costs of the war. But Caesar somewhat mitigated the odium of the confiscations by channeling their proceeds solely to the state. Unlike Sulla, who overlooked any act of fraud in his favorites, Caesar rigorously exacted the purchase price even from his most faithful adherents, such as Marcus Antonius.

Expenditures were lowered first of all

by considerably restricting the distribution of grain. The supply to the poor of the capital, as well as the kindred supply of oil newly introduced by Caesar for the Roman baths, was in great part supported by contributions in kind from Sardinia and especially from Africa, and was thus kept wholly or largely separate from the state treasury. On the other hand regular military expenditures were increased partly by augmenting the standing army, and partly by raising the legionary's pay from 480 to 900 sesterces annually.

Both these latter steps were in fact indispensable. There was a total want of any real frontier defense, whose prerequisite was a considerable increase of the army. Doubling the soldier's pay was doubtless employed by Caesar to attach his soldiers firmly to him, but it was introduced permanently for a very different reason. The former pay of 1⅓ sesterces per day had been fixed in very ancient times, when money had an altogether different value than in Caesar's day. In a period when day laborers in the capital earned an average of 3 sesterces, it could be retained only because the soldier entered the army chiefly for the sake of the perquisites, largely illicit, of military service. The first precondition to a serious reform in the military system, and to ending those irregular gains of the soldier which mainly burdened the provincials, was a suitable increase in pay; and fixing it at 2½ sesterces may be regarded as a necessary and beneficial step, despite the great burden thereby imposed on the treasury.

It is difficult to conceive of the extraordinary expenses which Caesar undertook voluntarily or otherwise. The wars themselves consumed enormous sums, and similar amounts were required to fulfil the promises which he had been obliged to make during the civil war. It was a bad example, and one unhappily not soon forgotten, that every common soldier received 20,000 sesterces for his participation, and every citizen in the capital 300 sesterces for his nonparticipation. But Caesar, having once pledged his word, was too much of a king to break it. Besides, he satisfied innumerable demands of honorable liberality, and put immense sums into building, which had been shamefully neglected during the last years of the republic. The cost of his buildings in the capital, executed partly during the Gallic campaigns and partly afterwards, was reckoned at 160,000,000 sesterces. The net result of Caesar's financial administration is expressed in the fact that, while he fully met all equitable claims, nevertheless by March of 44 B.C. 700,-000,000 sesterces lay in the public treasury and 100,000,000 in his own—a sum ten times that in the treasury in the republic's palmiest days.

But difficult as it was, the task of breaking up the old parties and furnishing the new commonwealth with an appropriate constitution, an efficient army, and well-ordered finances was not the hardest part of Caesar's work. Real regeneration of the Italian nation required a reorganization that would transform all parts of the great empire—Rome, Italy, and the provinces. Let us endeavor here also to delineate the old state of things, as well as the beginnings of a new and more tolerable time.

The good stock of the Latin nation had long since wholly disappeared from Rome. By its very nature, a capital loses its municipal and even its national stamp more quickly than any subordinate community. There the upper classes speedily withdraw from urban public life, in order to find their home in the state as a whole rather than in a single city. There are inevitably concentrated the foreign settlers, the fluctuating population of travelers for pleasure or business, the mass of the indolent, lazy, criminal, financially and morally bankrupt (and for that very reason cosmopolitan) rabble. All this applied preeminently to Rome. The rich Roman frequently regarded his town house merely as a lodging. When the urban municipal offices were converted into imperial magistracies, when the civic assembly became the governing assembly of the empire, and when smaller self-governing tribal or other associations were not tolerated within the capital, then all true community life ceased for Rome. From all the empire people flocked to Rome for speculation, for debauchery, for intrigue, for training in crime, or even to hide there from the eye of the law.

While these evils arose partly from the very nature of a capital, they were accompanied by others more accidental and perhaps still more grave. There has perhaps never existed a great city so thoroughly lacking means of support as Rome. Importation on the one hand, and home manufacture by slaves on the other, made any free industry impossible from the outset. The radical evil pervading all the societies of antiquity—slavery —showed its consequences most conspicuously in the capital. Nowhere were such masses of slaves accumulated as in the city palaces of the great families or the wealthy upstarts. Nowhere were the peoples of three continents mingled as in Rome's slave population—Syrians, Phrygians and other half-Hellenes with Libyans and Moors, Getae and Iberians with the mounting influx of Celts and Germans. The demoralization inseparable from the absence of freedom, and the terrible inconsistency between formal and moral right, were far more glaringly apparent in the partially or wholly cultivated city slave than in the rural serf who tilled the field in chains like a fettered ox.

Still worse than the slave masses, however, were those who had been *de jure* or simply *de facto* released from slavery—a mixture of mendicant rabble and rich parvenus, no longer slaves and not yet citi-zens, economically and even legally dependent on their masters, but with the pretensions of free men. These freedmen were drawn above all toward the capital, where various profits could be had and where retail trade as well as the minor handicrafts were almost wholly in their hands. Their influence on elections is well known, and their leading part in the street riots is evident from the ordinary signal by which these were virtually proclaimed by the demagogues—the closing of shops and places of business.

The government not only did nothing to counteract this corruption, but even encouraged it from selfish policy. The judicious law which prohibited individuals condemned for a capital offense from dwelling in the city was winked at by the negligent police. The urgently needed supervision of popular associations was at first neglected, and afterwards was even forbidden as an unwarranted restriction of popular freedom. The public festivals had so increased that the seven ordinary ones alone—the Roman, the Plebeian, those of the Mother of the Gods, of Ceres, of Apollo, of Flora, and of Victoria—lasted altogether sixty-two days; and to these were added the gladiatorial games and numerous other extraordinary amusements. The duty of providing grain at low prices—unavoidable with such a proletariat living wholly from hand to mouth—was treated with the most unscrupulous frivolity, and the fluctuations in the price of bread grain were incredible. These grain distributions formed as it were an official invitation to every citizen proletarian who was destitute of food and disinclined to work to move to the capital.

The bad seed yielded a corresponding harvest. The political system of clubs and bands, and the religious worship of Isis and similar pious extravagances, had their roots in this state of things. People constantly faced want, and not unfrequently utter famine. Nowhere was life less secure than in the capital, whose sole unique trade was murder professionally prosecuted by banditti. Luring the prospective victim to Rome was the preliminary to assassination, and no one ventured into the countryside near the capital without an armed retinue.

The city's outward condition corresponded to this inward disorganization, and seemed a keen satire on the aristocratic government. Nothing was done to regulate the Tiber, except that the single bridge was rebuilt of stone at least as far as the Tiber-island. No more was done toward leveling the city of the Seven Hills, except perhaps where rubbish accumulation effected some improvement. The wretchedly kept streets were crooked, narrow, and steep, the footpaths small and ill-paved. The ordinary houses, poorly built of brick to a giddy height, were constructed mostly by speculative builders for the account of small proprietors, by which means the former became enormously rich while the latter were reduced to beggary. Like isolated islands amid this dreary sea rose the splendid palaces of the rich, which pre-empted the space for smaller houses just as their owners pre-empted the rights of lesser men in the state. The marble pillars and Greek statues of these palaces formed a striking contrast to the decaying temples, whose images were still in great part carved of wood.

Official supervision of streets, of river banks, of fires, or of building was almost unknown. If the government troubled itself at all about the frequent floods, conflagrations, and collapses, it was only to ask the state theologians for their advice on the true meaning of such signs and wonders. If we try to imagine a London with the slave population of New Orleans, with the police of Constantinople, with the nonindustrial character of modern Rome, and the political ferment of Paris in 1848, we can get some idea of the republican glory whose departure the sulky letters of Cicero and his associates deplore.

Caesar sought to help rather than deplore. Rome remained, of course, a cosmopolitan city. Any attempt to give it a specifically Italian character would not only have been impracticable, but also would not have suited Caesar's plan. Just as Alexander found an appropriate capital for his Graeco-Oriental empire in the Hellenic, Jewish, Egyptian and above all cosmopolitan city of Alexandria, so the capital of the new Romano-Hellenic empire, situated between East and West, was to be not an Italian community but the denationalized capital of many nations. For this reason Caesar tolerated the worship of the newly introduced Egyptian gods alongside Father Jove, and even allowed the Jews to practice their strange foreign ritual in the capital. However offensive was the motley mixture of Rome's parasitic population, he nowhere opposed its extension. Rather, at his popular festivals he caused dramas to be performed not only in Latin and Greek but also in other languages, presumably Phoenician, Aramaic, Syrian, and Spanish.

But if Caesar consciously accepted the existing fundamental character of the capital, he yet worked energetically to improve the lamentable and disgraceful conditions prevailing there. Unhappily, the basic evils were the most difficult to eradicate. Caesar could not abolish slavery, and it must remain an open question whether he might eventually have attempted at least to limit the number of slaves in the capital, as he undertook in another field. As little could he create a free industry in Rome. Yet his great building program partly remedied the lack of employment there, and offered the proletariat a source of small but honorable gain.

At the same time Caesar labored energetically to shrink the free proletariat. The constant influx brought to Rome by the grain distribution was materially restricted, if not wholly stopped, by converting this distribution into a provision for a fixed number of the poor. The ranks of the existing proletariat were thinned by the tribunals instructed to proceed rigorously against the rabble, and also by comprehensive transmarine colonization. Of the 80,000 colonists whom Caesar sent overseas in his few years of rule, a great majority must have come from the capital's proletariat. Indeed, most of the Corinthian settlers were freedmen. Though freedmen were traditionally excluded from any urban honorary office, Caesar opened the senate house to them in his colonies, doubtless to encourage emigration by the better-situated freedmen.

This emigration must have been more than a mere temporary arrangement. Caesar, convinced like every sensible man that the proletariat's misery could really be remedied only by a well-regulated system of colonization, and put in a position to realize it to an almost unlimited extent, must have intended to continue the process by keeping open a constant means of abating a constantly recurring evil. Measures were also taken to limit the market fluctuations of the most important means of subsistence in the capital. The reorganized and liberally administered state treasury furnished the means for this purpose, and two new magistrates, the grain aediles, were charged with supervising the contractors and the markets of the capital.

The club system was checked by constitutional change more effectually than was possible through prohibitive laws, since the corruption and violence of the electioneering automatically ended along with republican elections and the republic itself. Moreover, the combinations which grew up under the Clodian law were broken up, and the whole system of association was placed under supervision of the government. Except for the ancient guilds and associations, the religious unions of the Jews, and other specially exempted categories, for which a simple intimation to the Senate seems to have sufficed, permission to organize a permanent society with fixed dues and meetings was made a concession to be granted by the Senate, and, as a rule, doubtless only with the monarch's consent.

To this was added a stricter policing and administration of justice. The laws, especially as regards violence, were strengthened, and the irrational republican law which permitted the convicted criminal to avoid a part of his penalty by self-banishment was set aside. Caesar's detailed police regulations are in great part still preserved; they include regulations requiring house proprietors to put the streets into repair and pave the footpath in its whole breadth with hewn stones, as well as appropriate enactments regarding the movement of litters and wagons, which were allowed to move freely through the capital's narrow streets only in the evening and at night. Supervision of the police remained as before chiefly in the hands of four aediles, each of whom now superintended a distinctly marked-off police district.

Lastly, public building in the capital received from Caesar, who combined in himself the Roman and the organizer's love of building, a stimulus which not merely put to shame the mismanagement of recent times, but also left the best efforts of the Roman aristocracy as far behind as Caesar's genius surpassed the honest talents of the Marcii and Aemilii. Caesar excelled his predecessors not merely by the extent of his buildings and the magnitude of his expenditures, but by a genuine statesmanly perception of the public good. Instead of building temples and other splendid structures, as did his successors, he relieved the market place of Rome, where the citizen-assemblies, the chief courts, the exchange, and the daily traffic of both business and idleness still were crowded together, by constructing a new place of assembly, the Saepta Julia in the Campus Martius, a new courthouse, and the Forum Julium, between the Capitol and the Palatine.

But these achievements were but the first steps toward a complete remodeling of Rome. Projects were already formed for a new senate house, for a new magnificent bazaar, for a theater to rival that of Pompey, for a public Latin and Greek library modeled on that recently destroyed at Alexandria (the first institution of its sort in Rome), and for a temple of Mars intended to surpass all earlier rivals in riches and glory. Still more brilliant was the idea of draining the Pomptine marshes, and altering the lower course of the Tiber by leading it through a new channel to an adequate artificial harbor. By this gigantic plan the capital's most dangerous enemy, malaria, would be banished; the extremely limited building space would be vastly enlarged; and the city would at the same time obtain a safe seaport, so long and painfully needed. It seemed as if the Imperator could remove mountains and rivers, and contend with nature herself.

However, much as Rome gained in commodiousness and magnificence by the new order of things, its political supremacy was irretrievably lost through that very change. The idea that the Roman state should coincide with the city had indeed gradually become preposterous, but the maxim was so central to the Roman republic that it could not perish before the republic itself. Only in Caesar's new state was it completely set aside (except perhaps for some legal fictions), and the capital was placed on a level with other municipalities. Indeed, Caesar—here as always endeavoring not merely to regulate the thing, but also to call it by its right name—issued his Italian municipal ordinance both for the capital and for other urban communities. The Rome of the imperial period, just because it was incapable of a living as a community, was essentially inferior to other major municipalities. Republican Rome was a den of robbers, but it was also the state; the Rome of the monarchy, although beginning to embellish itself with all the glories of three continents and to glitter in gold and marble, was nothing more than a royal residence appended to a poorhouse —in other words, a necessary evil.

XV

The Old Republic and the New Monarchy: II

While Caesar's only object in the capital was to get rid of palpable evils by massive police action, it was far more difficult to remedy the deep economic disorganization. Its radical misfortunes were those already noted—the disappearance of the agricultural and the unnatural increase of the mercantile population. The reader will not fail to remember the wretched state of Italian agriculture. Despite the most earnest attempts to check the annihilation of small holdings, farm husbandry was no longer the predominant economy in any Italian region in this period, except perhaps for the Apennine and Abruzzi valleys.

As for the management of estates, there is no material difference between the Catonian system already described and that pictured for us by Varro, except that the latter shows the traces for better or for worse of the progress of city life on a great scale in Rome. "Formerly," says Varro, "the barn on the estate was larger than the manorhouse; now it is wont to be the reverse." In Tusculum and Tibur, on the shores of Tarracina and Baiae, where the old Latin and Italian farmers had sown and reaped, there now rose in barren splendor the villas of Roman nobles, some covering the space of a fair-sized town with their gardens and aqueducts, fresh and salt water ponds for breeding and keeping river and marine fish, nurseries of snails and slugs, game preserves for hares, rabbits, stags, roes, and wild boars, and aviaries containing even cranes and peacocks.

But the luxury of a great city also enriches many an industrious hand, and supports more poor than philanthropy. Those noble aviaries and fishponds were of course a very costly indulgence. The system was carried to such an extent that the stock of a pigeon house was valued at 100,000 sesterces. A methodical system of fattening had sprung up, and manure from the aviaries became important in agriculture. A single bird-dealer was able to furnish at once 5,000 fieldfares at three denarii each, a single fish-breeder 2,000 *muraenae;* and the fishes left behind by Lucius Lucullus brought 40,000 sesterces. As may readily be conceived, under such circumstances any one who followed this occupation industriously and intelligently might earn very large profits on little capital. A small bee-breeder of this period sold from his one-acre thyme-garden near Falerii an average of 10,000 sesterces worth of honey each year.

The rivalry among growers of fruit went so far that the marble-lined fruit-chamber in elegant villas was often fitted out as a dining room, with fine fruit acquired by purchase sometimes exhibited there as homegrown. At this period the cherry from Asia Minor and other foreign fruit trees were first planted in Italy. The vegetable gardens, the beds of roses and violets in Latium and Campania, yielded rich produce, and the "market for

dainties" by the side of the Via Sacra, where fruits, honey, and chaplets were sold, played an important part in the life of the capital.

Generally the management of estates, worked on the planter system, had reached an economic level scarcely to be surpassed. The valley of Rieti, the region round the Fucine lake, the districts on the Liris and Volturnus, and indeed Central Italy in general, were in the most flourishing condition. Even certain branches of industry, which were suitable adjuncts to an estate cultivated by slaves, were taken up by intelligent landlords, and under favorable circumstances inns, weaving factories, and especially brickworks were constructed on the estate. The Italian producers of wine and oil not only supplied the Italian market but also carried on a considerable export trade.

A homely professional treatise of this period compares Italy to a great fruit garden; and a contemporary poet pictures his beautiful native land as a place where well-watered meadows, luxuriant grain fields, and pleasant vine-covered hills are fringed by the dark line of the olive trees, where the "ornament" of the land, smiling in varied charms, cherishes the loveliest gardens in its bosom and is itself wreathed round by food-producing trees. These descriptions, evidently faithful pictures of the landscape daily presented to the eye of the poet, transplant us into the most flourishing districts of Tuscany and Terra di Lavoro.

It is true that pastoral husbandry, which for reasons formerly explained was always spreading especially in southern and southeastern Italy, was in every respect a backward step; but it too participated in the general progress of agriculture. Much was done for improvement of breeds, and asses for breeding brought 60,000, 100,-000, and even 400,000 sesterces. The solid Italian husbandry of this period, when the general development of intelligence and abundance of capital rendered it fruitful, achieved far more brilliant results than the old system of small cultivators could ever have done. It was even carried beyond the bounds of Italy, for the Italian agriculturist reared cattle and even cultivated grain on large tracts in the provinces.

Alongside this estate husbandry unnaturally prospering over the ruin of the small farmers, private banking also assumed enormous proportions, as the Italian merchants vying with the Jews spread over all the provinces and protectorates of the empire. However, to demonstrate how all capital ultimately flowed to Rome, it will be sufficient to point to the single fact that in the money market of the capital the regular rate of interest at this time was six per cent—cheaper by a half than it was on an average elsewhere in antiquity.

Out of this economic system, based both in its agrarian and mercantile aspects on masses of capital and on speculation, there arose a most fearful maldistribution of wealth. The often-used and often-abused phrase of a nation of millionaires and beggars applies perhaps nowhere so aptly as to Rome at the end of the republic. The essential maxim of the slave state—that the rich man who lives on his slaves is necessarily respectable, while the poor man who lives by his own labors is necessarily vulgar—has perhaps never again been recognized with such terrible precision as the principle underlying all public and private intercourse. There was no middle class in our sense, as indeed no such class can exist in any fully developed slave state. What appears to be a middle class is composed of those rich business men and landholders who are so uncultivated, or so highly cultivated, as to stay within their own sphere and keep aloof from public life. Of the men of business—a class among whom numerous freedmen and other upstarts

were often seized with the giddy fancy of playing the man of quality—there were not many who showed so much judgment.

A model of this sort was Titus Pomponius Atticus, frequently mentioned in accounts of this period. He acquired an immense fortune partly through estate farming in Italy and Epirus, partly from money transactions throughout Italy, Greece, Macedonia, and Asia Minor. But at the same time he remained the simple man of business, refusing to be seduced into soliciting office or even into monetary transactions with the state. Equally remote from avaricious niggardliness or the prodigal and burdensome luxury of his time (his table, for instance, was maintained at a daily cost of 100 sesterces), he contented himself with an easy existence including the charms of both country and city life, the pleasures of intercourse with the best society of Rome and Greece, and all the enjoyments of literature and art.

More numerous and more solid were the Italian landholders of the old type. Contemporary literature preserves the description of one such rural nobleman, Sextus Roscius, who was murdered amid the proscriptions of 81 B.C. His wealth, estimated at 6,000,000 sesterces, is mainly invested in his thirteen landed estates; he manages it in person systematically and with enthusiasm; he seldom or never comes to the capital, and when he does, his clownish manners contrast not less with those of the polished senator than his hosts of uncouth rural slaves with the elegant domestic slaves of the capital. Far more than the circles of the cosmopolitan nobility, and the mercantile lords at home everywhere and nowhere, these landlords and their country homes preserved the discipline and manners as well as the pure and noble language of their fathers.

This landlord class was regarded as the

flower of the nation. The speculator who has made his fortune, and who aspires to ultimate respectability, buys an estate and seeks, if not to become a squire himself, at any rate to rear his son with that view. We find traces of this landlord class wherever a national movement appears in politics, and wherever literature puts forth any fresh growth. From it the patriotic opposition to the new monarchy drew its best strength; to it belonged Varro, Lucretius, Catullus; and nowhere perhaps is the comparative freshness of this landlord-life more clearly revealed than in the graceful Arpinate introduction to the second book of Cicero's treatise *De Legibus*—a green oasis amidst the fearful desert of that equally empty and voluminous writer.

But the cultivated class of merchants and the vigorous order of landlords were far overshadowed by the two classes that gave the society its tone—the mass of beggars and the world of quality. We have no figures to indicate precisely the relative proportions of poor and rich in this epoch, yet we may again recall the expression of a Roman statesman some fifty years earlier, that the number of solidly rich families among the Roman citizens did not number 2,000. The body of citizens had changed since then, but the clear indications are that the disproportion between poor and rich had remained at least as great. The impoverishment of the multitude shows itself only too plainly in the grain distributions and army enlistments. The corresponding increase of riches is expressly attested by an author of this generation, when, speaking of the Marian period, he describes an estate of 2,000,000 sesterces as "riches according to the circumstances of that day"; and the statements which we find as to individual wealth support the same conclusion. The very rich Lucius Domitius Ahenobarbus promised four acres of land out of his own property to each of

twenty thousand soldiers. Pompey's estate amounted to 70,000,000 sesterces, that of Aesopus the actor to 20,000,000. Marcus Crassus, the richest of the rich, possessed 7,000,000 sesterces at the outset of his career, and at its close, after spending enormous sums, 170,000,000.

The effect of such poverty and such riches was on both sides an economic and moral disorganization outwardly different, but at bottom the same. If the common man was saved from starvation only by the state, it was the necessary consequence of this mendicant misery (although it also reciprocally appears as a cause of it) that he addicted himself to the beggar's laziness and the beggar's good cheer. The Roman plebeian was fonder of looking at the theater than of working, and the taverns and brothels were so frequented that the demagogues found it to their special interest to win over the proprietors of such establishments.

The gladiatorial games, which both revealed and fostered the worst demoralization of ancient times, had become so flourishing that a lucrative business was done in the sale of the programs for them. This age introduced the horrible innovation whereby the life or death of the vanquished gladiator depended not on the law of duel or on the pleasure of the victor, but on the caprice of the onlooking public; and according to its signal the victor either spared or transfixed his prostrate antagonist. The trade of fighting had so risen, or freedom had so fallen in value, that the intrepidity and emulation lacking on the battlefields of this age were universal in the arena, where the law of the duel required that every gladiator allow himself to be stabbed mutely and without shrinking. In fact, free men not unfrequently sold themselves to contractors for board and wages as gladiatorial slaves. The plebeians of the third century B.C. also suffered want and famine, but they did not sell their freedom; and still less would the jurists of that period have approved as lawful the equally immoral and illegal contract of such a gladiatorial slave "to let himself be chained, scourged, burnt or killed without opposition, if the laws of the institution should so require."

In the world of quality such things did not occur, but at base it was hardly different, and least of all better. The aristocrat boldly competed with the proletarian in indolence: if the latter lounged on the pavement, the former lay in bed till late in the day. Extravagance was as unbounded as it was tasteless. It was lavished on politics and on the theater, of course to the corruption of both. The consular office was purchased at an incredible price—in the summer of 54 B.C. the first voting-division alone was paid 10,000,000 sesterces. And any pleasure a cultured man might take in the drama was spoiled by the mania for decoration.

Rents in Rome appear to have averaged four times as high as in the country-towns, and a house in the capital once sold for 15,000,000 sesterces. The house of Marcus Lepidus (consul in 78 B.C.), which at the time of Sulla's death was the finest in Rome, a generation afterwards was not even in the first hundred Roman palaces. We have already mentioned the extravagance in country houses, one of which brought 4,000,000 sesterces, chiefly because of its fishpond. A fashionable grandee now needed at least two villas —one in the Sabine or Alban mountains near the capital, and a second in the vicinity of the Campanian baths—and preferably also a garden immediately outside Rome. Still more irrational than these palaces were the palatial sepulchres, several of which still attest how lofty a pile of masonry the rich Roman needed in order to die in style.

Fanciers of horses and dogs too were not wanting, 24,000 sesterces being a not uncommon price for a showy horse. The rich also indulged in fine furniture, such as tables of African cypress-wood costing 1,000,000 sesterces; in dresses of purple stuffs or transparent gauzes accompanied by an elegant adjustment of their folds before the mirror (the orator Hortensius is said to have brought a damage suit against a colleague because he ruffled his dress in a crowd); and in precious stones and pearls, which in this period first took the place of the far more beautiful and artistic ornaments of gold. It was already utter barbarism, when at Pompey's triumph over Mithradates the image of the victor appeared wrought wholly of pearls, and when the sofas and the shelves in the dining hall were silver-mounted and even the kitchen utensils were made of silver. In a similar spirit the collectors of this period took out the artistic medallions from old silver cups, to set them anew in vessels of gold.

There was also no lack of luxury in travelling. "When the governor travelled," Cicero tells us of a Sicilian governor, "which of course he did not in winter, but only at the beginning of spring— not the spring of the calendar but the beginning of the season of roses—he had himself conveyed, as was the custom with the kings of Bithynia, in a litter with eight bearers, sitting on a cushion of Maltese gauze stuffed with rose leaves, with one garland on his head and a second twined round his neck, applying to his nose a little smelling-bag of fine linen, with minute meshes, filled with roses; and thus he had himself carried even to his bedchamber."

But no luxury flourished more than the coarsest of all—the luxury of the table. The whole arrangement and life of the villa ultimately revolved around dining. There were not only different dining rooms for winter and summer, but dinner was served in the picture gallery, in the fruit-chamber, in the aviary, or on a platform erected in the deer park, around which, when the bespoken "Orpheus" appeared in theatrical costume and blew his flourish, the duly-trained roes and wild boars congregated. Amid all this care bestowed on decoration, the reality was by no means forgotten. Not only was the cook a graduate in gastronomy, but the master himself often acted as the instructor of his cooks. The roast had long ago been overshadowed by marine fishes and oysters, but now the Italian river-fishes were utterly banished from good tables, and Italian delicacies and wines were looked on as almost vulgar. Even at the popular festivals three foreign wines—Sicilian, Lesbian, and Chian—were distributed in addition to Italian Falerian, while a generation before it had been sufficient even at great banquets to send round Greek wine once. In the cellar of the orator Hortensius were found 10,000 jars of foreign wine, at 33 quarts each. It was no wonder that Italian winegrowers began to complain of the competition from the Greek islands.

No naturalist could ransack land and sea more zealously for new animals and plants than the epicures of that day ransacked them for new culinary dainties. The practice of the guest taking an emetic after a banquet, to avoid the consequences of the varied fare set before him, no longer created surprise. Debauchery of every sort became so systematic and aggravated that it found its professors, who earned a livelihood by instructing the youth of quality in the theory and practice of vice.

There is no need to dwell longer on this confused picture, so monotonous in its variety, especially since the far-from-original Romans confined themselves to an exaggerated and stupid copy of Helleno-Asiatic luxury. But Plutus devours his children as well as Kronos. The competition for these worthless objects of fashionable longing so forced up prices that those who swam with the stream saw the most colossal estate melt away, and even those who only joined in what was most necessary saw their inherited and firmly established wealth rapidly undermined. The race for the consulship was the usual road to ruin for noble houses, but much the same applies to the games, the great buildings, and all those other pleasant but expensive pursuits.

The princely wealth of that period was surpassed only by its still more princely liabilities. Around 62 B.C. Caesar owed 25,000,000 sesterces, after deducting his assets. Marcus Antonius owed 6,000,000 sesterces at the age of twenty-four, and 40,000,000 fourteen years afterwards. Curio owed 60,000,000, Milo 70,000,-000. That the extravagant habits of the Roman world of quality rested solely on credit is shown by the fact that the monthly interest rate once rose suddenly from four to eight per cent, through the borrowing of different competitors for the consulship. Insolvency, instead of leading in due time to a meeting of creditors or at any rate to a liquidation which might at least clear up matters, was ordinarily prolonged by the debtor as much as possible. Instead of selling his property and especially his landed estates, he continued to borrow and to present the semblance of riches till the crash only became the worse, and the winding-up yielded a result as in Milo's case, where the creditors obtained something like four per cent.

Amid this rapid transition from riches to ruin and this systematic swindling, nobody of course profited so much as the cool banker who knew when to give or refuse credit. Debtor-creditor relations thus reverted almost to the point where they had stood during the worst of the social crises of the third century B.C. The nominal owners held their lands virtually at the sufferance of their creditors. The debtors were either in servile subjection to their creditors, so that the humbler of them appeared like freedmen in the creditor's train, and those of higher rank spoke and voted even in the Senate at the nod of their creditor lord; or they threatened to declare war on property itself, to intimidate their creditors or get rid of them by conspiracy and civil war. On such relations was based the power of Crassus. Out of them arose the insurrections of Cinna, and still more definitely those of Catiline, of Coelius, and of Dolabella, closely resembling the Hellenic world's battles of a century before between those who had and those who had not. That in so rotten an economy every financial or political crisis should occasion the most dreadful confusion was merely to be expected. We need hardly mention that the usual phenomena—the flight of capital, the sudden depreciation of landed estates, innumerable bankruptcies, and an almost universal insolvency—made their appearance during the civil war just as during the Social and Mithradatic wars.

Under such circumstances morality and family life were treated as outmoded among all ranks of society. To be poor was not merely the sorest disgrace and the worst crime, but the only disgrace and the only crime. For money the statesman sold the state, and the citizen his freedom. The officer's post and the judge's vote were to be had for money, and for money the lady of quality surrendered her person like the common courtesan. Perjury and falsification of documents had become so common that a popular poet of this age referred to an oath as "the plaster for debts." Men had so forgotten what honesty was that a person who refused a bribe was regarded not as an upright man, but as a personal foe. The criminal statistics of all times and countries will hardly furnish a parallel to the dreadful picture of crimes—so varied, so horrible, and so unnatural—which the trial of Aulus Cluentius unrolled in the bosom of one of the most respected families of an Italian country town.

But while the slime was thus accumu-

lating ever more deleteriously and deeply underneath the national life, the more smooth and glittering was the surface, overlaid with the varnish of polished manners and universal friendship. All the world interchanged visits, so that in the houses of quality it was necessary to admit the persons presenting themselves in a certain order fixed by the master or occasionally by the attendant in waiting, and to give audience only to the more notable one by one, while the rest were summarily admitted partly in groups, and partly *en masse* at the close. (This practice Gaius Gracchus, here too paving the way for the new monarchy, is said to have introduced.) The interchange of courtesy letters was as common as courtesy visits; "friendly" letters flew over land and sea between persons who had neither personal relations nor business with each other, whereas proper and formal business letters scarcely occur except where the letter is addressed to a corporation.

In like manner invitations to dinner, the customary new year's presents, and the domestic festivals were divested of meaning and almost transformed into public ceremonials. Even death did not release the Roman from obligation to his countless "neighbors," for in order to die respectably he had to provide each of them at least with a keepsake. Just as in certain circles of our mercantile world, genuine family intimacy and friendship had so totally vanished from the Rome of that day that the whole intercourse of business and acquaintance could be garnished with forms and flourishes of affections which had lost all meaning. Thus the reality gradually came to be superseded by that spectral shadow of "friendship," which holds by no means the least place among the various evil spirits brooding over the proscriptions and civil wars of this age.

Equally characteristic of the brilliant

decay of this period was the emancipation of women. Economically, women had long since made themselves independent. In the present epoch we even meet with solicitors acting specially for women, who officiously lend their aid to solitary rich ladies in managing their property and their lawsuits, impress them with their knowledge of business and law, and thereby procure for themselves ampler perquisites and legacies than other loungers on the exchange.

But it was not merely from the economic guardianship of father or husband that women felt themselves emancipated. Love intrigues of all sorts were constantly in progress. The ballet dancers (*mimae*) were easily a match for those of the present day in the variety and skill of their pursuits, and prima donnas like Cytheris pollute even the pages of history. But their virtually licensed trade was materially injured by the free art of aristocratic ladies. Liaisons in the first houses had become so frequent that only an exceptional scandal could cause any special talk, and legal action now seemed almost ridiculous. The unparalleled scandal created by Publius Clodius in 61 B.C. at the women's festival in the house of the pontifex maximus, although a thousand times worse than the occurrences which fifty years before had led to a series of capital sentences, passed wholly without punishment and almost without investigation. The watering-place season—in April, when political business was suspended and the world of quality congregated in Baiae and Puteoli—derived its chief charm from the relations licit and illicit which, along with music and song and elegant breakfasts on board or on shore, enlivened the gondola voyages.

The ladies, however, were by no means content with this domain which rightfully belonged to them. They also acted as politicians, appeared in party conferences, and took part with their money and their

intrigues in the wild machinations of the time. Any one who beheld these female statesmen performing on the stage of Scipio and Cato, and saw at their side the young fop—as with smooth chin, delicate voice, and mincing gait, with headdress and neckerchiefs, frilled robe, and women's sandals, he copied the loose courtesan—might well have recoiled in horror from this unnatural world, in which the sexes seemingly wished to change parts.

The aristocracy's ideas on divorce may be judged from the conduct of their best and most moral hero. Marcus Cato, who did not hesitate to give up his wife to a friend desirous of marrying her, nor on the death of this friend to marry the same wife a second time. Celibacy and childlessness became common, especially among the upper classes. While these had long regarded marriage as a burden shouldered only in the public interest, we now encounter even in Cato and his followers the maxim to which Polybius a century before traced the decay of Greece, that it is the duty of a citizen to keep great wealth together and therefore not to beget too many children. Where were the days when the designation "children-producer" (*proletarius*) had been a term of honor for the Roman?

In such circumstances the Latin stock in Italy diminished alarmingly, and its fair provinces were overspread partly by parasitic immigrants and partly by desolation. Much of the population of Italy flocked to foreign lands. Already the total talent and working power needed to supply Italian magistrates and Italian garrisons for the whole Mediterranean world exceeded the resources of the peninsula, especially since the elements thus sent abroad were often lost forever to the nation. The more Rome grew to be a multinationed empire, the less the governing aristocracy looked on Italy as their exclusive home; while a considerable portion of the soldiers perished in the many wars, especially in the bloody civil war, and another portion became wholly estranged from their native country by the long term of service, which sometimes lasted for a generation. In like manner a portion of the landholders and almost the whole body of merchants spent all or much of their lives out of the country, and the itinerant trading life in particular estranged the latter altogether from the mother country and from the conditions of family life.

In return for these, Italy obtained on the one hand the proletariat of slaves and freedmen, and on the other the craftsmen and traders flocking thither from Asia Minor, Syria, and Egypt, who flourished chiefly in the capital and still more in the seaport towns of Ostia, Puteoli, and Brundisium. In the largest and most important part of Italy however, there was not even a replacement by impure elements, but an absolute decline in population. Especially was this true of such pastoral districts as Apulia, the chosen land of cattle-breeding, which contemporaries call the most deserted part of Italy, and of the region around Rome, where the Campagna was annually becoming more desolate under the reciprocal action of declining agriculture and increasing malaria. Labici, Gabii, and Bovillae, once cheerful little country towns, were so decayed that it was difficult to find representatives of them for the ceremony of the Latin festival. Tusculum, although still one of the most esteemed communities of Latium, consisted almost solely of some genteel families who lived in the capital but retained their native Tusculian franchise, and had fewer citizens entitled to vote than even small communities in the interior of Italy. The stock of men capable of arms in this district, on which Rome's ability to defend herself had once mainly depended, had so totally vanished that people read with astonishment and perhaps with horror the accounts—so

fantastic in comparison with the current state of affairs—of the Aequian and Volscian wars. Matters were not so bad everywhere, especially in the other portions of Central Italy and in Campania. Nevertheless, as Varro complains, "the once populous cities of Italy" in general "stood desolate."

It is a dreadful picture, this picture of Italy under the oligarchy. There was nothing to soften the fatal contrast between the two worlds of beggary and riches. The more clearly this contrast was felt, the giddier the height of wealth and the abyss of poverty, the more frequently were individuals tossed from the bottom to the top of this hazardous world, and from top to the bottom again. The wider the chasm between the two worlds, the more completely they coincided in undermining family life (which is the germ and core of all nationality), in laziness and luxury, unsubstantial economy, unmanly dependence, corruption differing only in its price, criminal demoralization, and longing to begin the war with property.

Riches and misery in close league drove the Italians out of Italy, and filled the peninsula partly with swarms of slaves, partly with awful silence. It is a terrible picture, but not one peculiar to Italy. Wherever the government of capitalists in a slave state has fully developed, it has desolated God's fair world in the same way. As rivers glisten in different colors, but a common sewer looks everywhere the same, so the Italy of the Ciceronian epoch resembles the Hellas of Polybius and still more closely the Carthage of Hannibal's time, where in exactly similar fashion the all-powerful rule of capital ruined the middle class, raised trade and estate-farming to the highest prosperity, and ultimately led to a hypocritically whitewashed moral and political corruption of the nation. All the arrant sins of capital against nation and civilization in modern times remain as far inferior to the abominations of the ancient capitalist states as the free man, be he ever so poor, remains superior to the slave. Not until the dragonseed of North America ripens will the world again have similar fruits to reap.

These evils, under which the national economy of Italy lay prostrate, were in their deepest essence irremediable, and those capable of remedy depended largely on the people and on time. For the wisest government, like the most skilful physician, cannot give freshness to the corrupt juices of the organism, or do more in the case of deep-rooted evils than to prevent those accidents which obstruct the remedial power of nature. The peaceful energy of the new rule furnished some such preventive, for by it some of the worst excrescences were done away with, such as the pampering of the proletariat, the failure to punish crimes, and the purchase of offices. But the government could do more than simply abstain from harm. Caesar was not one of those people who refuse to embank the sea, because no dike can defy some sudden influx. It is better if a nation and its economy follow spontaneously the natural path; but seeing that they had got out of this path, Caesar applied all his energies to bring the nation back to its home and family life by special intervention, and to reform the economy by law and decree.

With a view to checking the desertion of Italy by the Italians, and to induce the world of quality and the merchants to make their homes in their native land, the term of service for soldiers was shortened; men of senatorial rank were prohibited altogether from settling outside Italy, except on public business; and other Italians of marriageable age (from the twentieth to the fortieth year) were forbidden to be absent from Italy for more than three consecutive years. In his first consulship Caesar had on founding the colony of Capua given preference to fathers

with several children. Now as Imperator he proposed special rewards for fathers of large families, while as supreme judge of the nation he treated divorce and adultery with unparalleled rigor.

He even issued a detailed law on luxury—which, among other points, cut down at least one irrational extravagance in building, that of sepulchral monuments; restricted the use of purple robes and pearls to certain times, ages, and classes, and totally prohibited it in grown-up men; fixed a maximum for table expenditures; and directly forbade a number of luxurious dishes. Such ordinances were admittedly not new, but it was new when the "master of morals" seriously insisted on their observance, stationed paid inspectors at the provision markets, and ordered that the tables of men of rank be examined and the forbidden dishes on them confiscated. It is true that these police lessons in moderation did little more than compel luxury to retire somewhat into concealment. But if hypocrisy is the homage which vice pays to virtue, under the circumstances even a semblance of propriety was an improvement not to be despised.

Caesar's measures regulating Italian monetary and agricultural relations were of a graver character and promised greater results. The first move here related to the scarcity of money and the debt crisis generally. The law called forth by the outcry as to hidden capital—that no one should have on hand more than 60,000 sesterces in gold and silver—was probably issued only to allay the public's blind indignation against the usurers. The form of publication, based on the fiction that this was merely the renewed enforcement of an earlier law, shows that Caesar was ashamed of this enactment, and it can hardly have been put into practice.

Far more serious was the treatment of pending claims for debt, whose complete remission was vehemently demanded

from Caesar by the party which carried his name. We have already mentioned that he did not yield to this demand, but two important concessions to debtors were made as early as 49 B.C. First, arrears of interest were cancelled, and interest already paid was deducted from the principal. Second, the creditor was compelled to accept the debtor's moveable and immoveable property in lieu of payment at their estimated value before the civil war.

The latter enactment was not unreasonable. If the creditor was to be looked on *de facto* as the owner of the property to the amount of the sum due him, it was proper that he should bear his share in the general depreciation. On the other hand the canceling of interest payments made or outstanding—which practically meant that creditors lost the interest itself plus an average of 25 per cent of their capital—was in fact a partial cancellation of creditors' claims, for which the democrats had clamored so vehemently. But however bad may have been the conduct of the usurers, it is not possible thereby to justify the retroactive abolition of all claims for interest.

In order at least to understand this agitation we must recollect how the democratic party stood on the question of interest. The legal prohibition against taking interest, which the old plebeian opposition had extorted in 342 B.C., had been practically disregarded by the nobility (which controlled the civil procedure by means of the praetorship) but had remained formally valid since that period. The democrats of the first century B.C., who regarded themselves as inheritors of the old agitation as to social privilege, had maintained the position of the illegality of all interest, and temporarily even had enforced that principle during the confusion of the Marian period.

It is not credible that Caesar shared his party's crude views on the interest ques-

tion. The fact that his account of the matter of liquidation mentions the surrender of the debtor's property in lieu of payment, but is silent as to the cancellation of interest, is perhaps a tacit self-reproach. But like every party leader, he could not directly repudiate the traditional maxims of his party—especially when he had to decide this question even before his departure for Epirus, rather than as the all-powerful conqueror of Pharsalus. But while he perhaps permitted rather than originated this violation of legal order and of property, it is certainly to his credit that the monstrous demand for wiping out all debts was rejected; and it may perhaps be looked on as a saving of his honor, that the debtors were far more indignant at this extremely unsatisfactory (according to their view) concession than the injured creditors, and made under Caelius and Dolabella those foolish and speedily suppressed attempts to extort by riot and civil war what Caesar had refused.

But Caesar did not confine himself to temporary help for the debtor; he did as legislator what he could to reduce the fearful power of capital. First of all, the great legal maxim was proclaimed that freedom is not a possession commensurable with property but an eternal right of man, of which the state alone, and not the debtor, is judicially entitled to deprive the criminal. It was Caesar, perhaps stimulated here also by the more humane Egyptian and Greek legislation, who introduced this principle—diametrically opposed to the earlier ordinances on bankruptcy—into the common law, where it has remained ever since.

According to earlier Roman law the debtor unable to pay became the serf of his creditor. To be sure, the Poetelian law had allowed a debtor who had become unable to pay because of temporary embarrassment, rather than genuine insolvency, to save his personal freedom by the cession of his property. Nevertheless, for the truly insolvent that principle of law, though modified in minor ways, had remained substantially unaltered for five hundred years. Direct recourse to the debtor's estate occurred only exceptionally, when the debtor had died, or had forfeited his citizenship, or could not be found. It was Caesar who first gave an insolvent the right—on which our modern bankruptcy regulations are based—of formally ceding his estate to his creditors, whether it sufficed to satisfy them or not. Thus he might save at best his personal freedom (though with diminished honorary and political rights), and begin a new financial existence in which he could be sued only for claims proceeding from the earlier period and not protected in the liquidation, if he could pay them without renewed financial ruin.

While the great democrat thus had the imperishable honor of emancipating personal freedom in principle from capital, he attempted moreover to limit the excessive power of capital by usury laws. He did not affect to disown the democratic antipathy for interest as such. For Italian money-dealing there was fixed a maximum amount of loans the individual capitalist might make, apparently proportionate to the size of his Italian landed estate, and perhaps amounting to half its value. Transgressions of this enactment were, after the procedure prescribed in the republican usury laws, treated as criminal offences and sent before a special jury commission.

If these regulations were successfully carried into effect, every Italian man of business would be compelled to become at the same time an Italian landholder, and the class of capitalists subsisting entirely on their interest would disappear wholly from Italy. Indirectly, too, the no less degraded group of insolvent landowners who practically managed their estates for their creditors was by this same means materially curtailed, inasmuch as their creditors, if they wished to keep their lending business, were compelled to buy for themselves. From this very fact besides it is plain that Caesar by no means simply wished to renew the old naive prohibition of interest, but on the contrary to allow it within certain limits.

It is quite probable, however, that he did not confine himself merely to specifying for Italy a loan maximum, but also, especially with respect to the provinces, prescribed maximum interest rates. The enactments that it was illegal to take more than 1 per cent per month, or to charge interest on arrears of interest, or to sue for arrears of interest exceeding the original loan, were (probably also after the Graeco-Egyptian model) first introduced in the empire by Lucius Lucullus in Asia Minor, and retained there by his better successors. Soon afterwards they were transferred to other provinces by edicts of the governors, and ultimately at least some of them were given the force of law in all provinces by a senatorial decree of 50 B.C. The fact that these Lucullan enactments afterwards appeared intact as imperial law, and have thus become the basis of both Roman and modern legislation as to interest, may also perhaps be traced back to an ordinance of Caesar.

Hand in hand with these efforts to limit the ascendancy of capital went Caesar's endeavors to restore agriculture to the status most advantageous for the commonwealth. For this purpose better policing and administration of justice was essential. Hitherto nobody in Italy had felt secure of his person or property: Roman *condottieri,* when their gangs were not helping to manage the politics of the capital, applied themselves to robbery in the forests of Etruria or rounded off the country estates of their paymasters by fresh acquisitions. This sort of club law was now at an end, and the change must have benefitted especially the agricultural population of all classes. Caesar's plans for public works were also of similar intent. For instance, the construction of a convenient highway from Rome through the Apennine passes to the Adriatic was designed to stimulate the internal traffic of Italy, and the lowering of the level of the Fucine lake to benefit the Marsian farmers. But Caesar also sought to benefit Italian husbandry by more direct measures. Thus, Italian graziers were required to take at least a third of their herdsmen from freeborn adults, whereby brigandage was checked and at the same time a source of gain was opened to the free proletariat.

In the agrarian question Caesar, already experienced from his first consulship, was more judicious than Tiberius Gracchus. He did not seek to restore the small farmers at any price, even including a revolution (concealed under juristic clauses) directed against property. On the contrary, like every other genuine statesman, he regarded the security of property, or what is at any rate regarded by the public as property, as the first and most inviolable of all political maxims; and only within the limits of this maxim did he seek to improve the lot of the Italian small holders, which also appeared to him as a vital question for the nation.

Even so, there was much still left for him to do. Every private right, whether it was called property or entitled heritable possession, whether traceable to Gracchus or to Sulla, was unconditionally respected by him. On the other hand Caesar, after instituting in his strictly economical fashion (which tolerated no waste or negligence even on a small scale) a general revision of Italian land titles by the revived commission of Twenty, earmarked all the public land of Italy, including a considerable portion of the estates in the hands of religious groups but legally belonging to the state,

for distribution in the Gracchan fashion insofar as it was fitted for agriculture. The Apulian summer pastures and the Samnite winter pastures belonging to the state were retained as public domain; and it was at least the design of the Imperator, if these lands should not suffice, to procure the necessary additional land by buying Italian estates with public funds.

In selecting the new farmers provision was naturally made first for veteran soldiers; thus the burden which the levy imposed on the nation was converted as far as possible into a benefit by the fact that Caesar took the proletarian as a recruit, but gave him back as a farmer. (It is noteworthy also that desolate Latin communities such as Veii and Capena seem to have been preferentially provided with new colonists.) Caesar's regulation that the new owners could not alienate their lands for twenty years was a happy medium between given full right of sale, which would have soon brought most of the distributed land back into the hands of the great capitalists, and the permanent restrictions which Tiberius Gracchus and Sulla had enacted, both equally in vain.

Lastly, while the government thus energetically applied itself to remove the diseased and strengthen the sound elements of Italian national life, the newly regulated municipal system—which had but recently developed out of the Social War alongside the state framework—was intended to give the new monarchy a fitting communal life, and to enliven again the best elements of the nation. The leading principles in the two municipal ordinances issued in 49 B.C. for Cisalpine Gaul and in 45 B.C. for Italy, the latter of which remained the fundamental law for the future, are apparently, first, the strict purifying of the urban corporations from all immoral elements, though no trace of a political police yet occurs; and second, the utmost restriction of centralization and the utmost freedom of movement in the communities, which even now were granted the right to elect their own magistrates and a definite though limited civil and criminal jurisdiction. It is true, however, that the general police enactments such as the restrictions on the right of association came into play here.

Such were the ordinances by which Caesar attempted to reform the Italian national economy. It is easy both to show their insufficiency, seeing that they allowed a multitude of evils to remain, and to prove that they operated injuriously in various respects by severely restricting freedom of dealing. It is still easier to show that the general ills of the Italian economy were incurable. But in spite of this the practical statesman will admire the work as well as the master workman. It was already no small achievement merely to recognize and grapple with the evil, where a man like Sulla had despaired of remedy and contented himself with a mere formal reorganization; and we may well conclude that Caesar's reforms achieved as much as it was given to a statesman and a Roman to achieve. He could not and did not expect them to regenerate Italy. On the contrary, he sought to attain this in a very different way, for the understanding of which it is necessary first to review the condition of the provinces as Caesar found them.

There were fourteen such provinces: seven European—Further and Hither Spain, Transalpine Gaul, Italian Gaul with Illyricum, Macedonia with Greece, Sicily, Sardinia with Corsica; five Asiatic —Asia, Bithynia and Pontus, Cilicia with Cyprus, Syria, and Crete; and two African—Cyrene and Africa. To these Caesar added three new ones by establishing the two new governorships of Lugdunese Gaul and Belgica, and by constituting Illyricum a separate province.

The misrule of these provinces by the oligarchy had reached a point which,

notwithstanding various noteworthy efforts, no other government, at least in the West, has ever attained. Certainly the responsibility for this rests not on the Romans alone. Almost everywhere before their day the Greek, Phoenician, or Asiatic rule had crushed the higher spirit and the sense of right and liberty inherited from better times. It was doubtless bad that every accused provincial was required, upon demand, to defend himself in person in Rome; that the Roman governor interfered at pleasure in the administration of justice and the management of dependent communities, pronounced capital sentences, and cancelled transactions of the municipal council; and that in case of war he treated the militia as he chose and often infamously, as when Cotta at the siege of the Pontic Heraclea assigned to the militia all the posts of danger in order to spare his Italians, and when the siege went badly, ordered the heads of his engineers to be laid at his feet. It was doubtless bad that no rule of moral or criminal law bound either the Roman administrators or their retinue, and that outrages, rapes, and murders with or without legal pretext were daily occurrences in the provinces. But these things at least were nothing new. Most men had long been accustomed to be treated like slaves, and it signified little in the long run whether a Carthaginian overseer, a Syrian satrap, or a Roman proconsul acted as the local tyrant. Almost the only thing for which the provincials still cared, their material well-being, was far less disturbed by such occurrences, which however numerous merely affected isolated individuals, than by the financial exactions which pressed heavily on all, and which had never before been prosecuted with such vigor.

In this area the Romans gave fearful proof of their old mastery of money matters. From its original modest and rational foundations, the Roman system of provincial oppression increased both in size and in corruption. The ordinary taxes became far more oppressive from their inequality and from the preposterous system of levying them than from their exorbitant level. As to the burden of quartering troops, Roman statesmen themselves expressed the opinion that a town suffered nearly as much when a Roman army took up winter quarters in it as when an enemy took it by storm. While originally the taxation had been an indemnification for the burden of military defense undertaken by Rome, with the community paying tribute thus being exempt from ordinary service, now garrison duty—as is attested in the case of Sardinia—was performed mostly by the provincials; and even in the regular armies, the whole burden of the cavalry-service, besides other duties, devolved upon them.

The extraordinary exactions—such as the deliveries of grain for little or no compensation to benefit the proletariat of the capital, the frequent and costly naval armaments and coast-defenses in order to check piracy, the task of supplying works of art, wild beasts, or other demands of the insane Roman luxury in the theatre and the chase, and the military requisitions in case of war—were as frequent as they were oppressive and incalculable. A single instance may show how far things were carried. During the three years' administration of Sicily by Gaius Verres, the number of farmers in Leontini fell from 84 to 32, in Motuca from 187 to 86, in Herbita from 252 to 120, in Agyrium from 250 to 80. Thus in four of the most fertile districts of Sicily, 59 per cent of the landholders preferred to let their fields lie fallow rather than cultivate them under such a government. And these landholders, as their small number shows and is expressly stated, were by no means small farmers, but respectable planters and in large part Roman citizens!

In the protectorates the forms of taxa-

tion were somewhat different, but the burdens were if possible still worse, since in addition to the exactions of the Romans there came those of the native rulers. In Cappadocia and Egypt, the farmer as well as the king was bankrupt, the former being unable to satisfy the tax collector, the latter his Roman creditor. To these must be added the exactions not merely of the governor himself but also of his "friends," each of whom fancied that he had as it were a draft on the governor and accordingly the right to come back from the province a made man.

The Roman oligarchy in this respect resembled a gang of robbers who carried on the plundering of the provincials in a professional and businesslike manner. Capable members of the gang worked not too nicely, for they had to share the spoil with the advocates and the jurymen, and the more they stole the more secure they were. The notion of honor in theft was already developed; the great robber looked down on the small, and the latter on the mere thief, with contempt. Any one who for a wonder had been condemned boasted of the vast sums which he was proved to have extorted. Such was the behavior in the provinces of the men whose ancestors had been accustomed to bring home nothing from their governorships but the thanks of the subjects and the approbation of their fellow citizens.

But still worse, if possible, and still less subject to any control, was the havoc committed by the Italian business men among the unhappy provincials. The richest lands and the whole commercial and monetary business in the provinces were concentrated in their hands. The estates which Italian grandees owned in overseas regions were exposed to all the misery of management by stewards, and never saw their owners, excepting perhaps for the hunting-parks which even now had begun to appear in Transalpine

Gaul with an area amounting to nearly twenty square miles.

Usury flourished as never before. The small landowners in Illyricum, Asia, and Egypt managed their estates even in Varro's time in large part practically as the debtor-slaves of their Roman or non-Roman creditors, just as the plebeians in former days had for their patrician lords. Cases occurred of capital being lent to urban communities at four per cent per month. It was not unusual for an energetic and influential man of business to get either the title of envoy given to him by the Senate or that of officer by the governor, and, if possible, to have soldiers put at his service for the better prosecution of his affairs. A case is told on credible authority where one of these honorable martial bankers prosecuted a claim against the town of Salamis in Cyprus by keeping its municipal council blockaded in the town hall, until five of the members had died of hunger.

To these two modes of oppression, each of which by itself was intolerable and which were always being better arranged to supplement each other, were added the general calamities for which the Roman government was also in considerable part at least indirectly responsible. In the various wars a large amount of capital was siphoned away from the country and a larger amount destroyed, sometimes by the barbarians and sometimes by the Roman armies. Due to the worthlessness of the Roman land and maritime police, brigands and pirates swarmed everywhere. In Sardinia and the interior of Asia Minor brigandage was endemic. In Africa and Further Spain it became necessary to fortify with walls and towers all buildings constructed outside of cities. The panaceas which the Roman governor was wont to interpose when the inevitable scarcity of money or famine occurred—the prohibition of the export of gold or grain from the province

—did not help matters. Communal affairs were almost everywhere embarrassed, in addition to the general distress, by local disorders and the frauds of public officials.

Where such grievances afflicted communities and individuals not temporarily but for generations with an inevitable, steady, and ever-growing oppression, the best regulated public or private economy could not but succumb to them, and the most unspeakable misery could not but extend over all the nations from the Tagus to the Euphrates. "All the communities," says a treatise published as early as 70 B.C., "are ruined." The same truth is specially attested as regards Spain and Narbonese Gaul, the very provinces which, comparatively speaking, were still in the most tolerable economic position. In Asia Minor even towns like Samos and Halicarnassus stood almost empty. Legal slavery seemed here a haven of rest compared with the torments to which the free provincial succumbed, and even the patient Asiatic had become, according to the descriptions of Roman statesmen, weary of life. Any one who desires to fathom the depths to which man can sink in the criminal infliction of all conceivable injustice, and in its no less criminal endurance, might gather together from the criminal records of this era the wrongs which Roman grandees could perpetrate and Greeks, Syrians, and Phoenicians could suffer. Even the statesmen of Rome publicly and frankly conceded that the Roman name was unutterably odious through all Greece and Asia; and when the citizens of the Pontic Heraclea on one occasion put to death the whole of the Roman tax collectors, the only occasion for regret was that such things did not occur oftener.

The Optimates scoffed at the new master who went in person to inspect his "farms" one after the other. In reality, the condition of the provinces demanded all the earnestness and wisdom of one of those rare men who redeem the name of king from being regarded as merely a conspicuous example of human insufficiency. The wounds inflicted had to be healed by time, but Caesar took care that they might be so healed, and that there should be no fresh inflictions.

The system of administration was thoroughly remodelled. The Sullan proconsuls and propraetors had been in their provinces essentially sovereign and subject to no control. Those of Caesar were the well-disciplined servants of a stern master, who from the very unity and life-tenure of his power sustained a more natural and more tolerable relation to the subjects than those annually changing petty tyrants. The governorships were no doubt still distributed among the two retiring consuls and the sixteen praetors; but as the Imperator directly nominated eight of the latter, and the distribution of the provinces among the competitors depended solely on him, they were in reality bestowed by the Imperator.

The functions of the governors were also practically restricted. The superintendence of justice and the administrative control of the communities remained in their hands, but their command was paralyzed by the new supreme command in Rome and its adjutants associated with the governor. The levying of taxes was probably even now committed substantially to imperial officials, so that the governor was thenceforward surrounded with an auxiliary staff which was absolutely dependent on the Imperator by virtue either of the laws of the military hierarchy or of the still stricter laws of domestic discipline. While hitherto the proconsul and his quaestor had appeared as if they were members of a gang of robbers dispatched to levy contributions, the magistrates of Caesar were present to protect the weak against the strong. Instead of the previous worse than useless

equestrian or senatorian tribunals, the proconsul and his staff had to answer for themselves at the bar of a just and unyielding monarch. The law as to extortions, which Caesar had already in his first consulate made more stringent, was applied by him against the chief commandants in the provinces with an inexorable severity going even beyond its letter; and the tax officers, if indeed they ventured to indulge in an injustice, atoned for it to their master as slaves and freedmen according to cruel domestic law of that time.

The extraordinary public burdens were reduced to the right proportion and the actual necessity, while the ordinary burdens were materially lessened. In addition to the comprehensive regulation of taxation already mentioned, the extension of the exemptions from tribute, the general lowering of the direct taxes, the limitation of the system of *decumae* to Africa and Sardinia, and the complete setting aside of middlemen in the collection of the direct taxes, were most beneficial reforms for the provincials. It cannot be proved that Caesar, after the example of one of his great democratic predecessors Sertorius, sought to free the subjects from the burden of quartering troops, or that he insisted on the soldiers erecting permanent encampments for themselves. But he was not the man to abandon the subject to the soldier, at least after he had exchanged the part of pretender for that of king. It was quite in keeping with his spirit when the heirs of his policy created such military camps, and then converted them into towns which formed rallying points for Italian civilization amid the barbarian frontier districts.

It was a task far less difficult to check official irregularities than to deliver the provincials from the oppressive ascendency of Roman capital, whose power could not be directly broken without applying remedies still more dangerous than the evil. For the time being the government could abolish only isolated abuses (as when Caesar prohibited the use of the title of state envoy for financial purposes) and meet manifest acts of violence and usury by a sharp application of the general penal and usury laws which also applied to the provinces. But a more radical cure of the evil was only to be expected from reviving the prosperity of the provincials under a better administration.

Temporary enactments to relieve the insolvency of particular provinces had been issued on several earlier occasions. Caesar himself in 60 B.C. as governor of Further Spain had assigned to creditors two-thirds of the income of their debtors in order to pay themselves from that source. Lucius Lucullus likewise when governor of Asia Minor had directly cancelled a portion of the arrears of interest which had swelled beyond measure, and had for the remaining portion assigned the creditors a fourth part of the produce of the lands of their debtors, as well as a suitable proportion of the profits accruing from house rents or slave labor. We are not expressly informed that Caesar after the civil war instituted similar general liquidations of debt in the provinces. Yet from what has just been remarked, and from what was done in the case of Italy, it can hardly be doubted that Caesar likewise directed his efforts towards this object, or at least that it formed part of his plan.

While thus the Imperator, as far as lay within human power, relieved the provincials from the oppressions of the magistrates and capitalists of Rome, it could certainly be expected that the reinvigorated government would scare off the wild border-peoples, and disperse the freebooters by land and sea, as the rising sun chases away the mist. However the old wounds might still smart, with Caesar there appeared for the sorely tortured subjects the dawn of a more tolerable

epoch, the first intelligent and humane government that had appeared for centuries, and a policy of peace which rested not on cowardice but on strength. Well might the subjects above all mourn along with the best Romans by the bier of the great liberator.

But this abolition of existing abuses was not the main objective in Caesar's provincial reform. In the Roman republic, according to the views of aristocrats and democrats alike, the provinces had been nothing but (as they were frequently called) country estates of the Roman people, to be employed and worked as such. This view now passed away. The provinces as such were gradually to disappear, in order to prepare a new and more spacious home for the renovated Helleno-Italic nation, no one of whose component parts existed merely for the sake of another, but all for each and each for all. The new existence in the renovated home, the fresher, broader, grander national life, was of itself to overcome the sorrows and wrongs of the nation for which there was no help in the old Italy.

These ideas, as is well known, were not new. The emigration from Italy to the provinces that had been going on for centuries had long since (though unconsciously on the part of the emigrants themselves) paved the way for such an extension of Italy. The first man who in a systematic way guided the Italians to settle beyond the bounds of Italy was Gaius Gracchus, creator of the Roman democratic monarchy, author of the Transalpine conquests, and founder of the colonies of Carthage and Narbo. The second Roman democratic statesman of genius, Quintus Sertorius, began to introduce the barbarous Occidentals to Latin civilization, teaching the Spanish youth of rank to wear Roman dress, and urging them to speak Latin and to acquire the higher Italian culture at the training institute founded by him in Osca. When Caesar founded his government a large Italian population, though lacking much in stability and concentration, already existed in all the provinces and protectorates. In addition to the formally Italian towns in Spain and southern Gaul, we need only recall the numerous legions of citizens raised by Sertorius and Pompey in Spain, by Caesar in Gaul, by Juba in Numidia, and by the constitutional party in Africa, Macedonia, Greece, Asia Minor, and Crete; the Latin lyre (doubtless ill-tuned) on which the town poets of Corduba as early as the Sertorian war sang the praises of the Roman generals; and the translations of Greek poetry, valued for their very elegance of language, which the earliest non-Italian poet of note, the Transalpine Publius Terrentius Varro of the Aude, published shortly after Caesar's death.

On the other hand, the interpenetration of Latin and Greek culture was as old as Rome. In the unification of Italy the conquering Latin nation had assimilated all the other conquered nationalities except the Greek, which was received just as it stood without any attempt at amalgamation. Wherever the Roman legionary went the Greek schoolmaster, no less a conqueror in his own way, followed; at an early date we find famous teachers of the Greek language settled on the Guadalquivir, and Greek as well as Latin was taught in the institute of Osca. The higher Roman culture itself was in fact nothing else than the proclamation of the great gospel of Hellenic manners and art in the Italian idiom; and the Hellene could hardly protest if the civilizing conquerors chose to proclaim it first of all in their own language to the barbarians of the West. Already the Greek everywhere (and especially where the national feeling was purest and strongest, on the frontiers threatened by barbaric denationalization) saw in Rome the protector and avenger

of Hellenism. In fact, the founding of towns by Pompey in the East resumed the beneficent work of Alexander after an interruption of centuries.

The idea of an Italo-Hellenic empire with two languages and a single nationality was not new, for otherwise it would have been a blunder. But its development from isolated projects to a firmly grasped conception, from scattered initial efforts to the laying of a firm foundation, was the work of the third and greatest of the Roman democratic statesmen.

The first and most essential condition for the political levelling of the empire was the preservation and extension of the two dominant nations, along with the absorption as rapidly as possible of the barbarian peoples (or those termed barbarian) existing by their side. In a certain sense we might name along with Romans and Greeks a third nationality, which was also omnipresent in the world of that day, and which was destined to play no insignificant part in the new state of Caesar. We speak of the Jews. This remarkable people, yielding yet tenacious, was then as now everywhere and nowhere at home, and everywhere and nowhere powerful. The successors of David and Solomon were of hardly more significance for the Jews of that age than Jerusalem for those of the present day. The nation doubtless found for its religious and intellectual unity a visible symbol in the petty kingdom of Jerusalem; but the nation itself consisted not merely of its subjects, but of the innumerable bodies of Jews scattered through the whole Parthian and Roman empires.

Especially within the cities of Alexandria and Cyrene the Jews formed special communities that were administratively and even locally distinct, not unlike the "Jews' quarters" of our towns, but with a freer position and superintended by a "master of the people" as superior judge and administrator. How numerous was the Jewish population in Rome before Caesar's time, and how closely the Jews even then kept together as fellow countrymen, is shown by the remark of an author of this period, that it was dangerous for a governor to offend the Jews in his province, because he might then certainly reckon on being hissed after his return by the populace of the capital. Even at this time the predominant business of the Jews was trade. The Jewish trader moved everywhere with the conquering Roman merchant just as he later accompanied the Genoese and the Venetian, and on all sides capital flowed into the hands of the Jewish as well as the Roman merchants.

At this period too we encounter the peculiar antipathy of the Occidentals towards this so thoroughly Oriental race and their foreign opinions and customs. This Judaism, though not the most pleasing feature of the nowhere pleasing mixture of nations which then prevailed, was nevertheless a historical fact which the statesman could neither ignore nor combat, and which Caesar, like his predecessor Alexander, with correct discernment fostered as far as possible. While Alexander's founding of Alexandrian Judaism did almost as much for the nation as King David's planning the temple of Jerusalem, Caesar also advanced the interests of the Jews in Alexandria and in Rome by special favors and privileges, protecting their peculiar worship against the Roman and Greek local priests.

These two great rulers of course did not contemplate placing the Jewish nationality on an equal footing with the Hellenic or Italo-Hellenic. But the Jew, who has not received like the Occidental the Pandora's gift of political organization, and who is substantially indifferent to the state; who is as reluctant to give up the essence of his nationality as he is ready to adapt himself to any nationality up to a certain degree—for this very reason the Jew was particularly suited for a state built on the ruins of a hundred living states and endowed from the outset with a somewhat abstract and toneddown nationality. Even in the ancient world Judaism was an effective leaven of cosmopolitanism and to that extent a specially privileged member in the Caesarian state, whose citizenship was strictly speaking world citizenship, and whose nationality was at bottom nothing but humanity.

But the Latin and Hellenic nationalities continued exclusively as the positive elements of the new citizenship. The distinctively Italian state of the republic was thus at an end; but the rumor that Caesar was purposely ruining Italy and Rome in order to transfer the center of the empire to the Greek east, and to make Ilion or Alexandria its capital, was nothing but a piece of talk (equally explicable and silly) by the angry nobility. On the contrary, in Caesar's framework the Latin nationality always remained predominant, as is indicated in the fact that he issued all his enactments in Latin, although those destined for Greek-speaking countries were also issued in Greek. In general he arranged the relations of the two great nations in his monarchy just as his republican predecessors had arranged them in the united Italy: the Hellenic nationality was protected where it existed, the Italian was extended as far as circumstances permitted, and the Italian was destined to inherit the races to the absorbed.

This last was necessary because a complete equalization of Greek and Latin elements would probably have soon occasioned the catastrophe which Byzantinism produced several centuries later. For the Greek element was not only intellectually markedly superior to the Roman, but also had hosts of Hellene and half-Hellene missionaries who had migrated compulsorily or voluntarily to Italy, and whose influence could not be overestimated. The rule of Greek lackeys over the Roman monarchs is as old as the monarchy. The first in the equally long and repulsive list of such personages is Pompey's confidential servant, Theophanes of Mytilene, who by his power over his weak master contributed probably more than any one else to the outbreak of the war between Pompey and Caesar. Not without reason was he treated with divine honors by his countrymen after his death, for he commenced the *valet de chambre* government of the imperial period.

The government accordingly had every reason not to encourage the spread of Hellenism at least in the West. If Sicily was not simply relieved of the pressure of the *decumae* but had its communities invested with Latin rights, this was presumably meant to be followed in due course by full equalization with Italy. For it must have been Caesar's design to merge into Italy this glorious island, which, though desolate at that time under the rule of predominantly Italian speculators, was by nature destined to be not so much a neighboring land as rather the finest of Italy's provinces. But otherwise the Greek element was preserved and protected wherever it existed. However political crises might tempt the Imperator to demolish the strong pillars of Hellenism in the West and in Egypt, Massilia and Alexandria were neither destroyed nor denationalized.

On the other hand the Roman element was promoted by the government through colonization and Latinizing with all vigor throughout the empire. The principle that all the soil in the provinces not ceded by special act of the government to communities or private persons was the property of the state, and that its holders had merely an heritable possession revocable at any time, no doubt originated from a bad combination of formal law and brute force. But it was inevitably necessary in order to deal expeditiously with the nations destined to destruction, and thus was retained by Caesar and raised from a democratic party-theory to a fundamental principle of monarchical law.

Gaul, of course, was the immediate arena for the extension of Roman nationality. In 49 B.C. Cisalpine Gaul obtained throughout what many of its inhabitants had long enjoyed, political equality with the mother country by the formal admission of the Transpadane communities into the Roman citizens union. Practically this province had already become completely Latinized during the forty years since the bestowal of Latin rights. The exclusives might ridicule the broad and gurgling accent of the Celtic Latin, or miss "an undefined something of the grace of the capital" in the Insubrian or Venetian who as Caesar's legionary had won by his sword a place in the Roman Forum and even in the Roman senate-house. Nevertheless, Cisalpine Gaul with its dense agricultural population was even before Caesar's time a predominantly Italian country, and remained for centuries the true asylum of Italian manners and culture. Indeed, the teachers of Latin literature found nowhere else outside the capital so much encouragement and approbation. While Cisalpine Gaul was thus substantially merged into Italy, its former place was occupied by the Transalpine province, which Caesar's conquests had converted from a frontier into an inland province, and which by location as well as climate was fitted beyond all other regions to become in due course an Italian land.

In the other non-Greek and non-Latin regions of the empire, which were still more remote from the influence of Italy and the process of assimilation, Caesar confined himself to establishing several centers of Italian civilization in order to pave the way for a future complete equalization. Such steps can be pointed out in every province except for the poorest and least important of all, Sardinia. In northern Gaul the Latin language obtained official recognition throughout, though it was not yet employed for all branches of public intercourse; and the colony of Noviodunum (Nyon) arose on Lake Leman as the most northerly town with an Italian constitution.

In Spain, at that time presumably the most densely peopled country of the Roman empire, Caesarian colonists were settled in the important Helleno-Iberian seaport town of Emporiae alongside the old population. Moreover, as recently discovered records have shown, a number of colonists probably taken predominantly from the proletariat of the capital were located in the town of Urso (Osuna), not far from Seville in the heart of Andalusia, and perhaps also in several other townships of this province. The ancient and wealthy mercantile city of Gades, whose municipal system Caesar as praetor had remodeled, obtained from the Imperator in 49 B.C. the full rights of the Italian *municipia,* thus becoming what Tusculum had been in Italy, the first extra-Italian community not founded by Rome to receive full Roman citizenship. Some years afterwards, similar rights were conferred also on some other Spanish communities, and Latin rights presumably on still more.

In Africa the project which Gaius Gracchus had initiated was now carried out. On the spot where once stood the city of the hereditary foes of Rome, 3,000 Italian colonists and a great number of the tenants on lease and sufferance in the Carthaginian territory were settled. The new "Venus-colony," the Roman Carthage, throve with amazing rapidity in its incomparably favorable location. Utica, hitherto the capital and first commercial town in the province, had already been partly compensated beforehand, apparently by the bestowal of Latin rights.

In the Numidian territory newly annexed to the empire, Cirta and other communities assigned to the Roman *condottiere* Publius Sittius for himself and his bands obtained the legal status of Roman military colonies. The stately provincial towns, which the insane fury of Juba and the desperate remnant of the constitutional party had reduced to ruins, did not revive so rapidly as they had been demolished, and many a desolate site long recalled this fatal period. But the two new Julian colonies, Carthage and Cirta, became and continued to be the centers of Afro-Roman civilization.

In desolate Greece Caesar, besides other plans such as founding a Roman colony in Buthrotum (opposite Corfu), busied himself above all with the restoration of Corinth. Not only was a considerable colony of citizens settled there, but a plan was projected for cutting through the isthmus so as to avoid the dangerous circumnavigation of the Peloponnesus and to make the whole traffic between Italy and Asia pass through the Corintho-Saronic gulf. Lastly, even in the remote Hellenic east the monarch created Italian settlements, such as those at Heraclea and Sinope on the Black Sea, where the Italian colonists shared the towns with the old inhabitants, and the important port of Berytus on the Syrian coast, which like Sinope obtained an Italian constitution. Even in Egypt a Roman station was established on the lighthouse-island commanding the harbor of Alexandria.

Through these ordinances Italian municipal freedom was widely disseminated over the provinces. The communities of full citizens—that is, all the towns of the Cisalpine province, and the citizen-colonies and *municipia* scattered in Transalpine Gaul and elsewhere—were on an equal footing with the Italian, insofar as they administered their own affairs. On the other hand the more important questions came before the Roman authorities competent to deal with them, usually the governor of the province. The formally autonomous Latin and the other emancipated communities (including all those of Sicily and of Narbonese Gaul, so far as they were not citizen-communities, and a considerable number also in the other provinces) had such broad municipal freedom that the governor was only entitled to interfere by virtue of his administrative powers. No doubt there had already been communities of full citizens within the provinces of governors, such as Aquileia and Narbo; and whole governors' provinces, such as Cisalpine Gaul, had consisted of communities with Italian constitutions. But it was politically if not legally singularly important that there was now a province as well as Italy peopled solely by Roman citizens, and that others promised to become so.

With this disappeared the first great practical distinction that separated Italy from the provinces. The second—that ordinarily no troops were stationed in Italy—was likewise in the process of disappearing. Troops were now stationed only where there was a frontier to be defended, and the commandants of the provinces in which this was not the case, such as Narbo and Sicily, were officers only in name. The formal contrast between Italy and the provinces continued certainly even now to exist, for Italy was the sphere of civil jurisdiction and of consuls and praetors, while the provinces were districts under martial law and subject to proconsuls and propraetors. But procedures under civil and martial law had long been practically coincident, and the different titles of the magistrates signified little after one Imperator was over all.

In these various municipal foundations and ordinances—which are traceable at least in plan, if not perhaps all in execution, to Caesar—a definite system is apparent. Italy was converted from the mistress of the subject peoples into the mother of the renovated Italo-Hellenic nation. The complete equalization of the Cisalpine province with the mother country was a promise and a guarantee that, in Caesar's monarchy just as in the healthier days of the republic, every Latinized district might expect to achieve equal footing alongside its elder sisters and the mother herself. On the threshold of full national and political equality with Italy stood the adjoining lands, such as the Greek Sicily and the south of Gaul, which were rapidly becoming Latinized. In a more remote stage of preparation were the other provinces of the empire, in which (just as hitherto Narbo in Southern Gaul had been a Roman colony) the great maritime cities of Emporiae, Gades, Carthage, Corinth, Heraclea in Pontus, Sinope, Berytus, and Alexandria now became Italian or Helleno-Italian communities, the centers of Italian civilization even in the Greek East and the fundamental base of the future national and political leveling of the empire.

The rule of the urban community of Rome over the shores of the Mediterranean was at an end. In its stead came the new Mediterranean state, and its first act was to atone for the two worst outrages which that urban community had perpetrated on civilization. While the destruction of the two greatest marts of commerce in the Roman dominions marked the turning-point at which the Roman protectorate degenerated into political tyranny and financial oppression, the prompt and brilliant restoration of Carthage and Corinth marked the foundation of the great new commonwealth which was to lead all the Mediterranean regions to national and political equality in a single state. Well might Caesar add to the far-famed ancient name of Corinth the new one of "Honor to Julius" (LAVS JVLI).

While the new empire was thus furnished with a national character, which doubtless lacked individuality because necessarily it was an inanimate product of art rather than a natural growth, it also needed unity in those institutions which express the general life of nations —in constitution and administration, in religion and jurisprudence, in money, measures, and weights—in all of which, of course, extensive local diversities were quite compatible with essential union. In all these departments we can only speak of the initial steps, for the completion of Caesar's monarchy was the work of the future, and all that he did was to lay the foundation for the building of centuries. But several of the lines which the great man drew can still be recognized, and it is more pleasing to follow him here than in his building on the ruins of the past.

As to constitution and administration, we have already noted the most important elements of the new unity—the transition of the sovereignty from the municipal council of Rome to the sole ruler of the Mediterranean monarchy; the conversion of that municipal council into a supreme imperial council representing Italy and the provinces; and above all, the transference of the Roman, and generally of the Italian, municipal organization to the provincial communities. This bestowal of Latin, and thereafter of Roman, rights on the communities ripe for full admission to the united state gradually of itself brought about uniform communal arrangements.

In one respect alone, however, this process could not be waited for. The new empire needed immediately an institution which should place before the government at a glance the proportions of population and property in the different communities—in other words, an improved census. First the census of Italy was reformed. According to Caesar's ordinance —which probably, indeed, only carried out the arrangements which were at least in principle adopted as a result of the Social War—when a census took place in the Roman community, there were to be simultaneously registered by the highest authority in each Italian community the name of every citizen and that of his father or manumitter, his district, his age, and his property. These lists were to be furnished to the Roman censor early enough to enable him to complete in due time the general list of Roman citizens and property.

That it was also Caesar's intention to introduce similar institutions in the provinces is attested partly by the measurement and survey of the whole empire ordered by him, partly by the nature of the arrangement itself; for it furnished the general instrument for securing the information needed for the central administration. Evidently here too Caesar intended to revert to the earlier republican practice, and to reintroduce the republican census of the empire in essentially the same way as he effected the Italian—by extending the institution of the urban censorship to all the subject communities of Italy and Sicily. This had been one of the first institutions which the torpid aristocracy allowed to drop, thus depriving the supreme administrative authority of any concept of its resources in men and money, and consequently of any possibility of effective control. The indications show irrefutably that Caesar intended to renew the general census that had been obsolete for centuries.

We need scarcely say that in religion and in jurisprudence no thorough levelling could be thought of. Yet with all toleration towards local faiths and laws, the new state needed a common worship corresponding to the Italo-Hellenic nationality and a general code of law superior to the municipal statutes. The need for them is shown by their *de facto* existence. In the field of religion men had for centuries been busy fusing together the Italian and Hellenic worships, partly by external adoption and partly by internal adjustment of their respective conceptions of the gods. Owing to the pliant formless character of the Italian deities, there had been no great difficulty in resolving Jupiter into Zeus, Venus into Aphrodite, and every essential idea of the Latin faith into its Hellenic counterpart. The Italo-Hellenic religion already existed in broad outline. How conscious men were of having gone beyond the Roman point of view towards an Italo-Hellenic quasi-nationality is shown by the distinction, made in the already mentioned theology of Varro, between the "common" gods acknowledged by Romans and Greeks alike, and the special gods of the Roman community.

As concerns criminal law, where the government interferes more directly and where judicious legislation will suffice, there was no difficulty in attaining needed uniformity for the unity of the empire. In civil law, where the initiative belongs to commercial intercourse and merely the formal shape to the legislator, the code for the united empire had been already long since developed in a natural way through commerical intercourse itself. Roman urban law was indeed still legally based on the embodiment of the Latin national law contained in the Twelve Tables. Later laws had doubtless introduced various improvements of detail, among which the most important was probably the abolition of the old inconvenient mode of commencing a lawsuit, and the substitution for it of an instruction drawn up in writing by the presiding magistrate for the single juryman. But in the main the popular legislation had only piled upon that venerable foundation an endless chaos of special laws long since in great part antiquated and forgotten, which can only be compared to the English statute-law. The attempts to impart scientific shape and system to them had certainly rendered the tortuous paths of the old civil law accessible; but no Roman Blackstone could remedy the fundamental defect that an urban code composed four hundred years earlier, with its equally diffuse and confused supplements, was now to serve as the law of a great state.

Commercial intercourse provided for itself a more thorough remedy. The lively intercourse between Romans and non-Romans had long ago developed in Rome an international private law—that is to say, a body of maxims especially relating to commercial matters. Roman judges made decisions based on these, when a case could not be decided either according to their own or any other national code, and they were thus compelled to revert to the common views of right underlying all dealings. The formation of the newer law proceeded on this basis. In the first place, as a standard for the legal dealings of Roman citizens with each other, it substituted *de facto* for the old and practically useless urban law a new code based in substance on a compromise between the national law of the Twelve Tables and the international code. The former was essentially adhered to (though of course with modifications suited to the times) in the law of marriage, family, and inheritance; whereas the international law was standard in all matters regarding property, ownership, and contracts.

Lastly, in money, measures, and weights the substantial equalization of the Latin and Hellenic systems had long been in progress. It was very ancient so far as concerned the definitions of weight and measures indispensable for trade and commerce, and in the monetary system little more recent than the introduction of silver coinage. But these older equations were not sufficient, because in the Hellenic world itself the most varied metrical and monetary systems existed side by side. It was necessary, and doubtless formed part of Caesar's plan, to introduce Roman money, Roman measures, and Roman weights everywhere in the new united empire in such a manner that they alone should be used in official intercourse, and that the non-Roman systems should be restricted to local currency or placed in specified ratio to the Roman. The action of Caesar, however, can only be discerned in two of the most important of these, the monetary system and the calendar.

The Roman monetary system was based on the two precious metals circulating side by side and in a fixed relation to each other, gold being given and taken according to weight, silver in the form of coin. But in the extensive foreign trade gold far preponderated over silver. It is uncertain whether the acceptance of Roman silver money was not even at an earlier period obligatory throughout the empire. At any rate, uncoined gold essentially performed the function of imperial money throughout Roman territory, the more so as the Romans had prohibited the coining of gold in all the provinces and protectorates. Thus the denarius had, in addition to Italy, naturalized itself *de jure* or *de facto* in Cisalpine Gaul, in Sicily, in Spain, and in various other places, especially in the West. But the imperial coinage begins with Caesar. Exactly like Alexander, he marked the foundation of the new monarchy embracing the civilized world by the fact that the only universally accepted metal obtained the first place in coinage. The scale on which the new Caesarian gold piece was immediately coined is shown by the fact that in a single treasure buried seven years after Caesar's death 80,000 of these pieces were found together, though financial speculations may have exercised a collateral influence in this respect.

As for silver money, the exclusive rule

of the Roman denarius in the West, for which the foundation had previously been laid, was finally established by Caesar when he closed the only Occidental mint that still competed with the Roman, that of Massilia. The coining of silver or copper small money was still permitted to a number of Occidental communities; three-quarter denarii were struck by some Latin communities of southern Gaul, half denarii by several cantons in northern Gaul, and copper small coins even after Caesar's time by various communes of the west. But this small money was throughout coined after the Roman standard, and its acceptance was probably obligatory only in local dealings.

Caesar, like the earlier government, does not seem to have contemplated unifying the monetary system of the East, where great masses of coarse silver money (much of it too easily debased or worn away) and to some extent even, as in Egypt, a copper coinage akin to our paper money were in circulation, and where the Syrian commercial cities would have felt severely the loss of their previous national coinage corresponding to the Mesopotamian currency. We find here subsequently the arrangement that the denarius is legal currency everywhere and is the only medium of official reckoning, while the local coins circulate within their limited range but on an unfavorable exchange rate as compared with the denarius. This was probably not introduced all at once, and in part may have preceded Caesar. But it was at any rate the essential complement to the Caesarian imperial coinage, whose new gold piece was modeled on the almost equally heavy coin of Alexander and was doubtless designed especially for circulation in the East.

Of a kindred nature was the reform of the calendar. The republican calendar, which strangely enough was still the old decemviral calendar, had come by a com-

[372]

bination of wretched mathematics and wretched administration to anticipate the true time by 67 whole days, so that the festival of Flora, for example, was celebrated on July 11 instead of April 28. Caesar finally removed this evil, and with the help of the Greek mathematician Sosigenes officially introduced the Italian farmer's year regulated according to the Egyptian calendar of Eudoxus, as well as a rational system of intercalation. At the same time the old beginning of the year on March 1 was abolished, and the date of January 1—fixed at first as the official time for changing the supreme magistrates, and therefore long since prevailing in civil life—was assumed also as commencing the calendar year. Both changes came into effect on January 1, 45 B.C., and along with them the use of the Julian calendar so named after its author, which long after the fall of the monarchy of Caesar remained the regulative standard of the civilized world and in the main is so still. By way of explanation there was added in a detailed edict a star calendar derived from the Egyptian astronomical observations and transferred—though not very skillfully—to Italy, which fixed the rising and setting of the stars named according to days of the calendar. In this domain also the Roman and Greek worlds were thus placed on a par.

Such were the foundations of the Mediterranean monarchy of Caesar. For the second time in Roman history the social question had reached a crisis whose antagonisms were actually insoluble. On the former occasion Rome had been saved by being merged into Italy, and in the new and enlarged home the old antagonisms fell into abeyance. Now Rome was once more saved by the fact that the countries of the Mediterranean were merged in it or became prepared for merging. The war between the Italian poor and rich, which in the old Italy could only end with the destruction of the nation, no longer had a battlefield or a meaning in the Italy of three continents. The Latin colonies closed the gap which threatened to swallow up the Roman community in the third century B.C.; the deeper chasm two hundred years later was filled by the Transalpine and overseas colonizations of Gaius Gracchus and Julius Caesar.

For Rome alone history not only performed miracles but repeated them, and twice cured the internal crisis, which within the state itself was incurable, by regenerating the state. There was doubtless much evil in this regeneration. As the union of Italy was accomplished over the ruins of the Samnite and Etruscan nations, so the Mediterranean monarchy built itself on the ruins of countless once living and vigorous states and tribes. But it was a corruption out of which sprang a fresh growth, part of which remains green to this day. What was pulled down were merely the secondary nationalities long since marked for destruction by the leveling hand of civilization.

Caesar, wherever he acted as a destroyer, only carried out the pronounced verdict of historical development. But he protected the germs of culture where and as he found them, in his own land as well as among the sister nation of the Hellenes. He saved and renewed the Roman type; and not only did he spare the Greek type, but with the same self-reliant genius that accomplished the regeneration of Rome he undertook also the regeneration of the Hellenes, and resumed the interrupted work of the great Alexander whose image, we may well believe, was never absent from Caesar's soul. He solved these two great tasks not merely side by side, but the one by means of the other. The two great essentials of humanity—general and individual development, or state and culture—once united in embryo in those old Graeco-Italians feeding their flocks in primeval simplicity far from the coasts and islands of the Mediterranean, had become severed when they were parted into Italians and Hellenes, and had remained apart for many centuries. Now the descendant of the Trojan prince and the Latin king's daughter created, out of a state without distinctive culture or cosmopolitan civilization, a new whole in which culture and state again met in the rich fullness of blessed maturity.

These are the outlines which Caesar drew for this work, according to which he himself labored, and according to which posterity—for many centuries confined to the paths which this great man marked out—endeavored to work generally in accordance with the intentions of the illustrious master, if not with his intellect and energy. Little was finished, much was merely begun. Whether the plan was complete, those who venture to vie in thought with such a man may decide. We observe no material defect in what lies before us. Every single stone of the building is enough to make a man immortal, yet all combine to form one harmonious whole. Caesar's reign as king of Rome was five and a half years, not half as long as Alexander's. In the intervals of seven great campaigns, which allowed him to stay no more than fifteen months altogether in the capital, he regulated the destinies of the world for the present and the future, from the establishment of the boundary line between civilization and barbarism down to the removal of the pools of rain in the streets of the capital, and yet retained time and composure enough to follow attentively the prize pieces in the theater and to confer the chaplet on the victor with improvised verses.

The rapidity and precision with which his plan was executed prove that it had long been meditated and all its parts settled in detail, but they still remain not much less wonderful than the plan itself. The outlines of the new state were defined

for all coming time, leaving to the boundless future the completion of the structure. To this extent Caesar might say that his aim was attained, and this was probably what he meant when he sometimes said that he had "lived enough." But precisely because the building was endless, as long as he lived the master restlessly added stone to stone, always with the same dexterity and elasticity busy at his work, never overturning or postponing, just as if there were for him no tomorrow but only today. Thus he worked and created as never any mortal before or since. As worker and creator, after wellnigh two thousand years he still lives in the memory of nations as the first and only Imperator Caesar.

We have reached the end of the Roman republic. After five hundred years' rule in Italy and in the countries on the Mediterranean, we have seen it brought to ruin in politics and morals, religion and literature, not through outward violence but through inward decay, thereby making room for the new monarchy of Caesar. There was in that world, as Caesar found it, much of the noble heritage of past centuries and an infinite abundance of pomp and glory, but little spirit, less taste, and least of all true delight in life. It was indeed an old world, and even the richly gifted patriotism of Caesar could not make it young again. The dawn does not return till after the night has run its course. But with him there came, to the sorely harassed peoples on the Mediterranean, a tolerable evening after the sultry noon. And when at length after a long historical night the new day dawned, and fresh, free nations commenced their race towards new and higher goals, there were among them not a few which were sprung from seed sown by Caesar, and which owed and still owe to him their national individuality.

THE LIFE AND WORKS OF
THEODOR MOMMSEN

By JÉRÔME CARCOPINO

MANY YEARS have passed since Theodor
Mommsen was awarded the Nobel Prize
for Literature by the Swedish Academy.
Only a year later, on November 1, 1903,
just twenty-nine days before his eighty-
sixth birthday, Mommsen was struck
down by apoplexy. At the time he was on
the ladder of the library in his house. The
insatiable reader was looking for a book
he wanted to consult.

If it is true that genius is merely endless patience served by a combination of
the most extraordinary and the most
rarely associated intellectual gifts, who
more than Mommsen deserves to be remembered? His work is so vast and
weighty that a whole monastery of Bene-
dictine monks might not have sufficed for
its production, and it is so solid that after
a century whole sections still stand. Second, his talents were so many and diverse
that one can never be sure that one has
really probed his nature.

For his fellow countrymen, Mommsen
is not only the great man who established
German hegemony over the history of the
Roman world. He is also the erratic but
passionate politician who was a member
of the Reichstag from 1873 to 1882, lost
his chair at Leipzig University (but was
reinstated in 1874) through his violent
radicalism, was sentenced to six months
in jail for his virulent attacks on Bismarck,

yet put all his prestige behind his persecu-
tor and sustained his ambition to use the
might of Prussia to unite Germany. And
for the scholars of the whole world, he is
the unquestioned master of antiquity, the
embodiment of Roman history.

It is chiefly this aspect of Mommsen
that will be considered in the following
pages. But it is remarkable that in his
youth nothing—except a culture that
knew no frontiers, a universal thirst for
knowledge, and a capacity for work that
was almost superhuman—presaged that
he would become the champion of
democracy in a victorious Germany or
that he would be the historian whose recognition by the Swedish Academy was
received with universal applause.

Theodor Mommsen was born at Garding, a village in Schleswig, which was
then part of Denmark, on November 30,
1817. His childhood and adolescence—
from 1821 to 1834—were spent at Odes-
sloe, a small town in Holstein, which was
also Danish at that time. It was in Holstein that he finished his studies: from
1834 to 1838 at the Christaneum College
at Altona; from 1838 to 1843 at the Danish University of Kiel. And it was from
Holstein that, without ever having set
foot on German soil, he embarked for
Italy with a scholarship from King Christian VIII of Denmark. In 1836 Momm-

sen was so fervent in his loyalty to the Danish crown that he was grievously troubled by the alarming news from Copenhagen about the health of the old king, Frederick VI.

Yet, less than thirty years later, the violent annexation of the duchies of Schleswig and Holstein to the Prussian crown was the main plank in his campaign for election at Halle. This change of face was linked with another. The future extreme democrat, whose agnosticism at times seemed almost too aggressive, had been brought up in a Christian, conformist family. His father was the assistant minister—or curate—of the Protestant communities of Garding and Odesloe. And the first manuscript written in his childish hand was a collection of prayers and pious thoughts, which twenty years later he asked his fiancée, Miss Reimer, to burn.

Very probably it was in the white-hot environment of the Albertina Fraternity at Kiel University that he both lost his faith and was converted to democracy. Yet one is surprised to find that, even at Kiel, he did not answer the call of history. Unaware of his destiny, he put down his name, not for the faculty of philosophy where history was taught, but for that of law, where he obtained his doctor's degree. It was as a professor of law that he made his career. Just as Pasteur revolutionized the medicine of his day without being a doctor, Mommsen changed the knowledge of Roman history without teaching it anywhere. In Berlin as at Leipzig in his maturity, he remained loyal to the study of law to which he had devoted his youth at Kiel; perhaps this was because it seemed to be the path that offered more promise of openings in the civil service, the courts as well as the bar.

But the wind blows whither it will. And circumstances, which favored the development of his natural aptitudes,

soon turned a budding lawyer into the gigantic historian whose stature still puts us all in the shade.

Mommsen's greatest piece of luck was beyond a doubt the environment in which he was born and bred. He never suffered penury but knew poverty, with the need to work that it involved, the self-discipline that it forced upon him, and the dignity it implied. The few simple, wholesome pastimes—swimming, rowing, and sledding—provided by the coastal town of his youth tempered the robust health he had received from nature. He grew up in the cult of duty fostered by parents who scrupulously obeyed the precepts of the Christian religion. Even after he had lost his faith he never ceased practicing the virile virtues inspired by the Gospels—physical courage, of which he offered many proofs; abhorrence of falsehood, which he expressed all too often with rugged, unsparing frankness; generosity, which led him to relieve undeserved misfortunes but never to adopt the true charity that forgives offenses and embraces the weak.

As a child, he had loved to capture dragonflies in the family orchard at Odesloe merely for the pleasure of giving them back their freedom. Later, however, it is all too true that his words were often spiteful and he was unsparing with his sarcasm on those he viewed as cowards and those who rashly dared resist his arguments and exasperated him by persisting in what he considered an error incurred through stupidity or bad faith. He certainly inherited more of his mother's energy and rigor than his father's gentleness. But it is to his father, the best teacher he ever had, that he owed an intellectual training which is equally astonishing for its breadth, depth, and precociousness.

When young Theodor left for the Christaneum at Altona he took with him the intellectual baggage he had been packed with at home—more than the best of our graduates carry nowadays. From his father he had learned Greek, which he translated with ease; Latin, which he spoke and wrote fluently; French and English; these were in addition to the German and Danish spoken in his bilingual native province. But the lessons received at home had been neither abstract nor dry. Instead, they had developed at an increasingly rapid rhythm but in a stimulating atmosphere of genuine humanism. Minister Jens Mommsen had a special love for poetry: first, of course, for that written in German but also for every other without exception. He imparted this preference to his son who was obliged to render in German verse not only the odes of Horace but also the poems of Byron, the plays of Shakespeare, the ballads of Victor Hugo, even the fables of Florian. He inoculated the boy with that rewarding vice—the love of reading.

For Theodor study became a second nature. Study first and study always, from Odesloe to Kiel and from Leipzig to Berlin, was his ruling passion. Its tyrannical demands were satisfied at the cost of efforts in which he took joy and pride, of night watches which his vigorous temperament enabled him to prolong without a trace of fatigue. At Kiel, with the utmost ease, he added two new strings to his linguistic bow: Swedish and Italian. And one is justified in saying that by then he had assimilated all that was worthwhile in the culture, both ancient and modern, of the Western world.

His fellow philologists bowed down before the prodigious learning of the law student who towered a hundred cubits above them. They simply could not understand how he found time to accumulate such a mass of facts and references in the midst of his lectures and their games and drinking bouts. In the end they discovered the secret of his immeasurable superiority: he needed practically no sleep and what he read at night doubled what he learned during the day. Mommsen was always the last in bed and the first up—a habit that stayed with him all his life. The only time I met him was by chance, in 1901 or 1902, in the rue de Richelieu between midnight and one o'clock in the morning. He was on his way back, arm in arm with one of his daughters, to the Hotel Louvois. That is where he always stopped in Paris because he only had to cross a small square, without climbing a stair or wasting a minute, to reach the manuscripts he assiduously worked on in the French National Library.

Camille Jullian in Paris and Ettore Pais in Rome both told me the same anecdote about Mommsen quite independently of each other. When they attended his lectures in Berlin he took more interest in them because they were foreigners, and occasionally he asked them to his home for private talks. But that was always at dawn or even earlier, at five o'clock in the morning. He too could have said what Edouard Herriot said to André Billy: "I sleep two hours a night. The rest of the time I read, and I remember every word I read." That colossal brain really deserved the homage paid him by Harnack: "Mommsen's waking nights illuminate our working days."

The light he shed on past centuries, which he wanted to understand and aimed at bringing back to life, issued from a source that shone with brilliant ideas and sometimes with the rays of poetry. Theodor Mommsen may have nurtured illusions about himself and been too ready to give up history. The field he had ploughed was so vast that it was bound sooner or later to overflow the limits of any special discipline he might have chosen. Inevitably his erudition—fed as it was on reality, heightened by his meditations, and illuminated by the best in European literature—led him not only to the new discoveries he squandered so recklessly, but also to the vigorous syntheses that soon made him famous.

He possessed a sense of reality that never left him and more than once turned his steps away from the beaten track toward still unknown truths. Moreover, whatever subject he took in hand, his scientific honesty made him feel such a need to study it in depth that he had perforce to deepen and broaden his horizons unceasingly. At the very start, he carried out his first researches in such a way that he soon burst through the rather narrow bounds imposed by academic convention. His first attempt was a master stroke. For his thesis in 1843, his professors at Kiel University had asked him to write down the remarks suggested by reading what they called the Law on the Scribes and Ushers. Taking no notice of the opinion then current, Mommsen went straight to the heart of the matter and shed new light on a controversial question. Faced with the evidence he produced, his judges were forced to accept his conclusions. Despite the briefness of his essay "Ad legem de scribis et viatoribus animadversiones" (Remarks on the Law of the Scribes and Ushers), and the harsh terms in which it was couched, they awarded Mommsen his Doctor's Degree summa cum laude.

In that same year, 1843, though he had no other obligation to do so than his conscience as a researcher, he extended his investigations from the scribes and ushers to all the other Roman professional groups and defined their nature in a paper entitled "De collegiis et sodaliciis Romanorum" (On the Colleges and Corporations of the Romans). In an appendix he felicitously tackled the problems raised by the discovery in 1816 of a stone on which were inscribed the statutes of the Funeral College set up by a group of devotees of Diana and Antinous at Lanuvium in 133 B.C. As a result of this, and thanks to the support he received from his professors at Kiel, he was awarded the scholarship he had requested from the King.

Thus Mommsen was able to travel to Naples and Rome in order to examine on the spot the original texts preserved in the museums there, the scope and importance of which he had so signally made clear. But from the very start, though only twenty-six years old, he had envisaged a totally different plan, whose vastness should have terrified him but in fact merely spurred him on. Under the influence of Otto Jahn, a young lecturer at Kiel University whose matured convictions confirmed his own, Mommsen had formed the opinion that a true knowledge of Roman law must be based on texts found in inscriptions executed by order of the legislators themselves. His aim was to collect not only the legal documents of Roman epigraphy but all Latin inscriptions—those he would collate in the manuscripts and ancient works north of the Alps, those contained in Italian collections, and those he would hunt out in distant lands where they were still hidden.

Theodor Mommsen did not yet see himself as the future historian of ancient Rome. But he already dreamed of becoming its epigraphist: it was a road to Damascus that opened up before him when he embarked for Italy in 1843.

The idea that now obsessed Mommsen had already been in the air for many years. It had, for instance, occurred to the members of the Académie Française. But they had neither drawn the broad outline of a practical plan nor laid the foundations of the collective organization its implementation would have required, nor—more important still—obtained the funds to finance so vast an enterprise. In Germany scholars were of different minds. Some would have liked a logical system based on the subject matter of the documents; others preferred a presentation in chronological order. Mommsen took good care not to get mixed up in their quarrels.

He took as his model Augustus Boeckh, who had divided Greek inscriptions according to their provenance. Not only had he the approval of Otto Jahn, but his plan received the support of Count Borghesi, whose experience was unique in that field at the time and who gave his advice in private letters to scholars all over Europe. In the spring of 1845, Mommsen, who in a declaration of respectful gratitude proclaimed Borghesi his one and only master, went to consult the oracle in his eyrie on the lofty peak of San Marino. With all the impudence of youth, he decided to leave aside the hesitations of established scholars. There and then he undertook the immense task of checking all known epigraphs within the vast territory of the *orbis romanus* according to the only classification that satisfied his good sense—region by region and locality by locality. It was only after such a topographical inventory had been compiled that all and sundry would be in a position, with the help of the detailed indices furnished with it, to extract the dates and data it contained.

Paying not the slightest attention to opposition, asking no help from official quarters—it would be given when success smiled on his undertaking—he won over Wigand, a Leipzig publisher who in 1852 printed two volumes of the Latin inscriptions found in the Kingdom of Naples. They were later combined to form Volume X of the famous *Corpus Inscriptionum Latinarum* (1867–1959). This revealed, as if by a flash of lightning, the model that had to be adopted. The battle

was won or, as Moritz-Haupt declared, *ex tenebris lux fact est*—out of darkness light was made.

Following in the footsteps of Mommsen, the Berlin Academy finally decided to take upon itself the honor of forming the collection of Latin inscriptions and entrusted its direction to the man whose initiative it was. Mommsen now surrounded himself with the best collaborators he could find, dividing among them the various districts where, in accordance with his method, they vied with each other in gathering an immense harvest of documentation. With a strong hand in a velvet glove, he controlled the work of his team, whose skill the German Emperor Wilhelm II justly praised in the letter of condolence he sent Mommsen's widow on November 1, 1903. That praise was all the more fervid because it was calculated to diminish subtly the part played in the collective enterprise by a lion whose claws the imperial government had felt on more than one occasion.

For himself, Mommsen reserved Apulia, Cisalpine Gaul, and the eastern provinces. He also undertook the coordination of all inscriptions, whatever their origin, previous to the death of Julius Caesar. That was the only concession he could logically make to the partisans of a chronological arrangement. That collection appeared under his responsibility and signature in 1863. It eventually formed volume one of *Corpus Inscriptionum Latinarum*. The other volumes followed at intervals, rousing the admiration of all concerned. Only volume sixteen, the last, appeared after Mommsen's death. The other fifteen, most of which comprised several in-folio tomes, were published in rapid succession under his supervision. They contain over two hundred thousand inscriptions collected from England to the Sahara and from the Atlantic to the Euphrates. As Mommsen had foreseen, the speeding up of scientific exploration everywhere in what was the ancient Roman world led to the publication of supplements which in some cases were just as thick as the original tomes.

Mommsen would be immortal even if the *Corpus Inscriptionum Latinarum* was the only publication linked with his name. But however vast that work may be, it did not satisfy its author's boundless energy. Indeed, it seems to have merely stimulated his appetite and, as it advanced, Mommsen glimpsed new fields for study. He amazed his contemporaries by the prodigious amount of his inexhaustible output.

Count Borghesi, Mommsen's oracle, had first come in contact with the formula of the Caesars' styling when he played with his father's collection of coins and medals as a child. Mommsen, who always observed the economic vicissitudes of ancient times and their effects on contemporary legislation, immersed himself in the study of numismatics. This led to the publication in 1860 of *Die Geschichte des Römischen Münzwesens* (*History of the Roman Coinage*).

When Mommsen reviewed the inscriptions on bronze tablets preserved in the Naples Museum, he came across one that was not written in Latin but in Oscan. To avoid error in reading and translating the text, he felt impelled to compare the Latin language with the other languages spoken in Italy in the past. The outcome was *Die unteritalische Dialekte* (The Dialects of Southern Italy), a work of philology published in 1850.

But that was not all. As editor of the *Corpus* he was always in search of new discoveries in the epigraphic field. Little did he care in what country they were announced, Italy, Africa, or the Far East. They were all grist for his mill. When he could not go and see them for himself, he demanded copies, photographs, and rubbings, and endeavored at once to establish the text, elucidate its obscure points, propose its publication and exegesis which, when contained in a definitive memoir, were accepted without discussion.

That is what happened to the new aqueduct of Venafrum, which, set into a wall at Venafro, had by some strange chance remained unnoticed. Mommsen had the good luck to come across it in 1846. He deciphered it, interpreted it, and attributed it to the chancery of Augustus between 14 and 11 B.C. In 1851 the Spaniards discovered fragments of the statute that Vespasian had granted the Latin colonies of Salpensa and Malaga. By 1855 Mommsen had succeeded in fitting them together, adding a commentary whose main points his successors had merely to assimilate. In 1869 a Rescript by Claudius was unearthed in the Trentino. Without a moment's hesitation Mommsen, in the review *Hermes,* established its destination and date: A.D. 46. In 1880 a petition addressed to Commodus by the peasants who cultivated his lands was discovered at Sonk-el-Khmis in Tunisia; they complained that his agent had overtaxed and molested them. Mommsen analyzed the text a year before Cagnat and Fernique published it in the *Revue Archéologique* and six years before Fustel established the conditions in which the petitioners lived. In 1903, the year of his death, Mommsen still kept a sharp eye on the epigraphic material that filled his reserves and reconstructed beyond all possible doubt the orders issued by Julius Caesar fixing living conditions in the Roman colony of Urso (now Osuna in Andalusia).

But Mommsen was quick to elude the tentacles of epigraphy whenever his curiosity was attracted to some other field. Nothing Roman was foreign to him. Whenever in his presence a problem was aired or a difficulty arose in the department where he was considered lord and master, he did his best to solve the one or overcome the other. His pupils collected in eight volumes of *Gesammelte Schriften* (Collected Writings) some two hundred miscellaneous essays, mostly in German, —which he scattered generously at the slightest provocation. None is unimportant. Some—for instance those on the recruitment of an Emperor's standing army or on the convergent interests of small farmers and big landowners—might advantageously be altered here and there, but they laid foundations and established principles that have a permanent value.

In the Collected Writings, a treasure trove of scholarship in many different shapes and forms, legal writings take pride of place. Mommsen would have approved his disciples' giving them priority: he had performed far too scrupulously his duties as professor of law to allow anyone to accuse him of forgetting the tasks they involved. Consequently, we must not be surprised to find that, in addition to all the burdens borne, without stumbling, he also managed to bring out a faultless edition of the *Corpus Juris Civilis* (1866–1870). He entrusted *Codex Justinius* to Krüger; to Schoell and, after his death, to Kroll the *Novellae*. For himself, he kept the weightiest part—the *Institutiones* and the *Digesta*. We have seen that there can be no question of remaking his *Corpus Inscriptionum Latinarum;* it would be no less hazardous to begin his *Corpus Juris Civilis* over again.

Lastly, after fulfilling his duties to the university, and swept away perhaps by his ardent patriotism, Mommsen found it an easy matter to convince the commission working on the *Monumenta Germaniae Historica* that it would be a good idea to complete that collection of medieval texts with the series of *Auctores Antiquissimi.* Comprising works dating back to the time when the Roman Empire had been brought to its knees by the barbarian invaders, it would bridge that period

between the Empire of the Caesars and the Holy Empire of the German nation and further serve to legitimate Germany's claim as the true heir to Rome. Mommsen allotted to others the majority of the authors he had selected for study— Ausonius, Claudius, Fortunatus, Saint Avitus, and even Corippus, author of the African poem *Johannis.* Needless to say, he did not spare himself and his share of the work included the three volumes of the *Chronica Minora,* the *Getica* of Jordanes, the *Variae* of Cassiodorus, and the *Liber Pontificalis,* which has been kept up to date by the Papal chancery and contains the history of the early days of the Holy See.

If at the end of his life Mommsen had been asked if he had read all the writings produced by or dealing with ancient Rome, he would have been able to reply quite truthfully in the affirmative. He had picked and successively set on his loom all the threads a historian needs to prepare his woof, and he was in a better position than anyone else in the world to weave an unbreakable web. As far as codices, inscriptions, papyri, and Latin literature were concerned, he had read, studied, and digested everything. It would have been unnatural, after so many days and years of analysis, to have persisted in postponing the hour of synthesis.

Mommsen left two big books on which he set the seal of his formidable erudition and original genius. One is his *Römisches Staatsrecht (Roman Public Law),* which provides information on the structure of the Roman government for use wherever that subject is taught. The other is his *Römische Geschichte (History of Rome),* which has won worldwide fame and almost deserves to be called a best seller. The time has come to discuss these two major works, weigh their merits, and judge their chances of survival.

In my eyes, the merits of his *Roman Public Law* seem infinite. He began it in

1876 and finished it simultaneously with his *Römisches Strafrecht* (*Roman Criminal Law*), which had started out as a separate work. It is the fruit of his maturity, in which he exploited all the codes that he had never ceased to explore as a jurist and historian. If it ever comes to be left on the shelf the reason will be that its substance has been assimilated in the works of his heirs and successors. Either directly or through others, he has been and will continue to be the inevitable companion of all those who take an interest in the institutions of ancient Rome. One might have preferred a less static composition, in which the course of political and social development would unfold gradually through the years as in a moving picture. But Mommsen confessed that, faced with a subject of such complexity and one covering so many centuries, he felt a sense of impotence even though he had taken the precaution of dividing it up piecemeal, institution by institution. Who can blame him if, to satisfy the demands of a scholarship that refuses to accept empty words, he remembered the proverb "Grasp all, lose all" and therefore deliberately gave up the idea of a chronological order whose superficial or fictitious harmony would have traduced reality. In his preface, he justified this decision, asserting that, if he described each institution in detail apparently isolated from its context, he did not lose sight of its place in the coherent, overall structure of Roman society. When dismantling the chief wheels of the constitutional machine, the various magistracies, the sovereign authority that capped them, the Senate and its *comitia,* he did not fail to note the links and interactions between the different parties, and the picture he painted seems so adequate and lifelike that one cannot imagine it in other lines and colors. Indeed, for our knowledge of ancient Rome, Mommsen's *Roman Public Law* constitutes an inestimable acquisition—what Thucydides termed an acquisition for all time.

I must admit that the same cannot be said of his *History of Rome,* which was first published in 1853. It was written effortlessly and at a gallop, if I may use the term, with all the youthful enthusiasm of an author who was not quite thirty-six years old. Its defects, whether evitable or not, are clear to see. First Mommsen seldom mentions his sources, with the result that the reader is obliged to take him at his word. There are, of course, exceptions to this rule: in some passages he deigns to defend his position in a footnote of a certain importance.

Secondly, the work is incomplete. Volume one begins, as is only right, with the Italic origins, but volume three stops at 46 B.C., with Caesar's victory over the Senate's armies in Africa and Cato's suicide at Utica. Volume four, which should have related the vicissitudes of the Empire, never saw the day and in all probability Mommsen did not write a single line of it. As for volume five, which was published in 1885, thirty-two years after the others, it is not a history at all but merely a description of the Empire, province by province. Obviously, the author was consistent throughout. In his intention, the first three volumes were meant to be not a history of Rome but a history of an Italy gradually drawn into the Roman orbit. Likewise, the fifth and last volume, instead of limiting the history of the Empire to the Palatine, where court plots were hatched, aimed at enlivening it with the activities of the populations scattered in the vast and diverse territories that were united in the Pax Romana. But despite this logical design, the book lacks the inner coherence typical of genuine masterworks and, though the edifice may not be wanting in grandeur, it has all the imperfections of a work that is unfinished and insecure.

Thirdly, and this is the most fatal defect of Mommsen's *History of Rome,* it is partly outdated. Considering its age— well over a century—one is surprised that it is not still more so, now that the spread of excavation work, the discovery of new monuments, the multiplication of new inscriptions, the abundant harvest of new-found papyri, have shored up the weakness of Mommsen's successors, who suddenly find themselves in a position to overtake and outstrip their master.

For all its faults and lacunae, Mommsen's *History of Rome* was given a triumphal reception.

Mommsen possessed an incredible general culture, which, in combination with his taste and experience of action, frequently enabled him to shed new light on the people and events of the past by analogy with those closer to our own day. No doubt, some of his comparisons seem farfetched and paradoxical. He was wrong to liken Cicero to a penny-a-liner, Pompey to a sergeant, and Cato to Don Quixote with Marcus Favonius as his Sancho Panza. And, whether through haste, humor, or wavering judgment, he was certainly wide of the mark when he saw Sylla as another Cromwell, an emulator of George Washington, and a replica of Don Juan—all in the space of fifty lines. On the other hand, how many lightning flashes of intuition there were in his unexpected associations of ideas!

But one would belittle his *History of Rome* by believing that it does no more than whet our curiosity. In fact, that curiosity when roused is completely satisfied and, what is more, we are forced to meditate with Mommsen the philosopher— Mommsen the sociologist, I almost said, but that would be anticipating. Listen to

him when he says: "What is won by war can be lost by war; but the conquests of the plow are forever." We should ponder, with the same anxiety with which he wrote them, on the lines where, having admired the "magnificent civilization" built up by the ancient Mediterranean peoples, he records that "their creative force exhausted itself" and new peoples "that had pounded the frontiers of civilization as the sea pounds its shores without breeching them," caused the civilization to shift its center from the Mediterranean to the Atlantic until it was displaced again by later arrivals. More than once his vigorous mind penetrated and elucidated the mystery of the most complex situations. His *History of Rome* may be behind the times in some respects; in others it is so advanced that no scholar can do without it.

But what the average reader finds so fascinating in Mommsen's *History of Rome* is that the author is never indifferent to the events he relates. One looks for the historian and finds the whole man with his infatuations and passions, his exaltation of patriotism and bravery, his uncompromising love of justice.

So long as scholars study the grandiose reality of ancient Rome, they will be indebted to Theodor Mommsen for his *Corpus Inscriptionum Latinarum.* So long as jurists trace back to the mechanism of the institutions of the nation that established the reign of law, founded the Empire, and gave the world two centuries of outward peace, they will borrow freely from his *Roman Public Law.* So long as there are men of letters who consider history not only as a science but also as an art, they will be fascinated by his *History of Rome.*

Jérôme Carcopino is a historian, member of the Académie Française, holder of the Croix de Guerre, and member of the French Legion of Honor.
Translated by Robert Allen.

THE 1902 PRIZE

By GUNNAR AHLSTRÖM

In 1901, the Nobel Committee began its activities with a period of trial and error. The Academy of what was then a small, remote country had awarded a prize of worldwide importance to Sully-Prudhomme. The award was welcomed with respect, for the prestige of France and of the Académie Française compensated for the relative obscurity of the laureate. Official circles took note of a decision w..ich deliberately passed over two giants, Emile Zola and Leo Tolstoy. To the official protest about Tolstoy, the permanent secretary of the Swedish Academy replied that the eminent candidate had not been considered because he had not been proposed by any of the persons or groups who, by the provisions of the bylaws, were entitled to make nominations. A feeble excuse, but invulnerable. The immediate result was that Tolstoy's admirers took up their pens to attack the inanity of such subterfuges. The Swedish critic who was behind the writers' protest, in his capacity as professor of literature in Stockholm, hastened to submit a recommendation, together with a copy of Tolstoy's novel *Resurrection*.

Similar communications were forthcoming from Lichtenberger of the Sorbonne and Michel Bréal of the Collège de France, together with a grave recommendation from the pen of Ludovic Halévy, who in his youth had collaborated with Henri Meilhac in writing the gay librettos of Offenbach's operettas. Since then, Halévy had carried on a steady and diversified literary career, ending up as a kind of elder statesmen of the Parisian literary world. He had been elected to the French Academy in 1884 and was now able to exploit his right to propose candidates in favor of the lord of Yasnaya Polyana.

Tolstoy's candidacy was thus established once and for all and could not be ignored. The Academy was forced to take a position. Traditionally the task of the permanent secretary is to find a formula which crystalizes a decision, even if it may be unpopular. The permanent secretary, Dr. C. D. af Wirsén, dispatched this task *con amore*. He was particularly skillful in framing subjective dislikes in the form of objective arguments. The creator of *War and Peace* was obviously a great writer, but unfortunately he had also behaved in a questionable fashion in the moral realm. Equipped with no professional competence, he had embarked as a dilettante on criticism of the Bible. Now, if the Nobel Prize were to be awarded for his literary merits, the idealism which the Prize was to symbolize would have validated his revolutionary doctrines, thus making them twice as dangerous. Certainly this had not been the intention of the donor, and that is why Tolstoy had declined the Prize with disdain. There was, then, no way to make him accept money which he didn't want.

Tolstoy is in good company. Emile Zola was proposed once again by his faithful supporter Berthelot "for his humanitarian novels"; the names of Gaston Paris and Frédéric Mistral were put forth; George Meredith and William Butler Yeats; Giosuè Carducci and Antonio Fogazzaro, Gerhart Hauptmann, Henryk Sienkiewicz, and Juhani Aho were among the others. Several of these names were to come up again in following years, and some were actually awarded the Prize after various terms of waiting.

The award of the prize to Sully-Prudhomme had been determined by a maneuver of the Académie Française. In those days it was generally considered throughout Europe that a collective proposal had the best chance of succeeding. In 1902, the Swedish Academy had recourse to a name imposed by this method in making its final choice. A candidacy entered as a petition backed up by a roster of influential signatures offered the assurance which had been lacking in the period of initial searching. It was thought that such a procedure would prevent the Prize from being given in answer to caprices of the day or to brilliant but ephemeral talents.

In 1902 Great Britain first appeared in the Nobel competition. A special committee had been set up within the Society of Authors in London to sound out its members with a view to determining who the British candidate should be. The committee sent a list of names to each member, and everything was done in typically British fashion. One day in January, the Swedish Academy received a message from the spokesman for the Society of Authors, Lord Avebury, informing them that the Society had voted overwhelmingly to recommend Mr. Herbert Spencer. Among the forty-eight members who had voted for Spencer were most of the men of letters of the day, including J. M. Barrie and Austin Dobson, together with such popular writers as H. Rider Haggard, Arthur Conan Doyle, and Arthur Wing Pinero. Philology and history were well represented by Edmund Gosse, Frederick Boas, Walter Skeat, and Edward Dowden. Such a team constituted a recommendation of unquestionable power.

The Swedish Academy had little enthusiasm for the rather pedantic, circumspect but rarely brilliant literary style of Mr. Spencer, and they were rescued a few days later by a respectable alternative which was more acceptable. From the Prussian Academy of Sciences in Berlin, which had been created by Frederick II and Leibnitz, there arrived a memorandum announcing that their preferred candidate was the famous historian, Theodor Mommsen, glorified by his masterpiece, *The History of Rome.*

The bylaws of the Academy permitted expanding the concept of "literature" to include humanistic studies and pure poetry. Mommsen's masterpiece would, then, fulfill this definition, particularly since it also was characterized by artistic merit of great distinction. The author had a mastery of style, a skill in portraiture, and a dramatic sense of historical events which completely contradicted the modest remark made by Mommsen in the last part of his history of the Romans: "This book was written with resignation, it must be read with resignation."

The subsequent history of his work, which went through many editions and was widely translated, proved that his readers were not in the least resigned. In all civilized countries readers knew that they were in the presence of one of the great historical books of the century. And so the Prize for 1902 was offered to Theodor Mommsen as "the greatest living master of the art of historical writing, with special reference to his monumental work, *The History of Rome.*"

The citation was immediately published in all German dailies, and two days later Mommsen, in his incomparable style, sent his thanks in these words: "It was as if I had reached the end of my life when suddenly it was remade in its various and, as it were, strangely disparate aspects by the kindness of an alert but charitable criticism; I could not hope for a better commemorative address even if it were really so. However, we haven't quite reached that point; I am, as a matter of fact, just gathering together my juridical works and for that purpose the light takes its rights and, unfortunately, often its struggle. Life is very hard for us Germans right now, but the feeling of not having lived and struggled in vain is greatly revivified by so splendid a honor."

When the money was given to him just before Christmas at the Swedish consulate in Berlin, he welcomed the honor with warmth partly for personal reasons. Mommsen had had sixteen children, of whom six sons and six daughters were still living. Five of the daughters, spinsters, lived with him and kept house for him. The aged professor of Charlottenburg was greatly relieved to be able to assure their security. He died the following year.

Translated by Dale McAdoo.